EX LIBRIS

Georgia Hayes

READER'S DIGEST CONDENSED BOOKS

Volume 4
1981

THE READER'S DIGEST ASSOCIATION
Pleasantville, New York

READER'S DIGEST CONDENSED BOOKS
Editor: John T. Beaudouin
Executive Editor: Joseph W. Hotchkiss
Managing Editor: Anthony Wethered

Senior Staff Editors: Ann Berryman, Noel Rae, John S. Zinsser, Jr.
Senior Editors: Anne H. Atwater, Doris E. Dewey, Tanis H. Erdmann, Olive Farmer,
Fredrica S. Friedman, Sigrid MacRae, Barbara J. Morgan, Marjorie Palmer,
Margery D. Thorndike, Frances C. Travis, Angela Weldon, Angela C. Woods
Associate Editors: Jean E. Aptakin, Barbara Bradshaw, Catherine T. Brown,
Linn Carl, Estelle T. Dashman, Istar H. Dole, Thomas Froncek,
Alice Murtha, Virginia Rice, Patricia Nell Warren
Assistant Editor: Thea R. Crouch
Art Editor: William Gregory
Senior Art Editors: Marion Davis, Soren Noring, Thomas Von Der Linn
Associate Art Editor: Angelo Perrone
Art Research: George Calas, Jr., Katherine Kelleher
Senior Copy Editors: Claire A. Bedolis, Jeane Garment
Associate Copy Editors: Dorothy G. Flynn, Jean S. Friedman
Assistant Copy Editors: Rosalind H. Campbell, Jean G. Cornell,
Ainslie Gilligan, Clara E. Serton

CB PROJECTS
Executive Editor: Herbert H. Lieberman
Senior Editors: Sherwood Harris, Ray Sipherd, Carol D. Tarlow, John E. Walsh
Associate Editors: Dana Adkins, John R. Roberson

Reader's Digest Condensed Books are published every two to three months at Pleasantville, N.Y.

The condensations in this volume have been created by The Reader's Digest
Association, Inc., and are used by permission of and special arrangement with
the publishers and the holders of the respective copyrights.

With the exception of actual personages identified as such, the characters and
incidents in the fictional selections in this volume are entirely the products of the
authors' imaginations and have no relation to any person or event in real life.

The original editions of the books in this volume are published and copyrighted as follows:

The Lord God Made Them All, published at $13.95 by St. Martin's Press, Inc.
© 1981 by James Herriot

Cannibals of the Heart, published at $15.00 by McGraw-Hill Book Company
© 1980 by Jack Shepherd

Texas Dawn, published at $12.95 by Seaview Books
© 1981 by Phillip Finch

Crossing in Berlin, published at $14.95 by Doubleday & Company, Inc.
© 1981 by Fletcher Knebel

© 1981 by The Reader's Digest Association, Inc.
Copyright © 1981 by The Reader's Digest Association (Canada) Ltd.
FIRST EDITION
137
*All rights reserved, including the right to reproduce this book or parts thereof in any form.
Library of Congress Catalog Card Number: 50-12721*

Printed in the United States of America

CONTENTS

7
THE LORD GOD MADE THEM ALL
by James Herriot
PUBLISHED BY ST. MARTIN'S PRESS

125
AN EXCEPTIONAL MARRIAGE
Louisa Catherine and John Quincy Adams
by Jack Shepherd
PUBLISHED AS "CANNIBALS OF THE HEART" BY McGRAW-HILL BOOK COMPANY

275
TEXAS DAWN
by Phillip Finch
PUBLISHED BY SEAVIEW BOOKS

443
CROSSING IN BERLIN
by Fletcher Knebel
PUBLISHED BY DOUBLEDAY & COMPANY

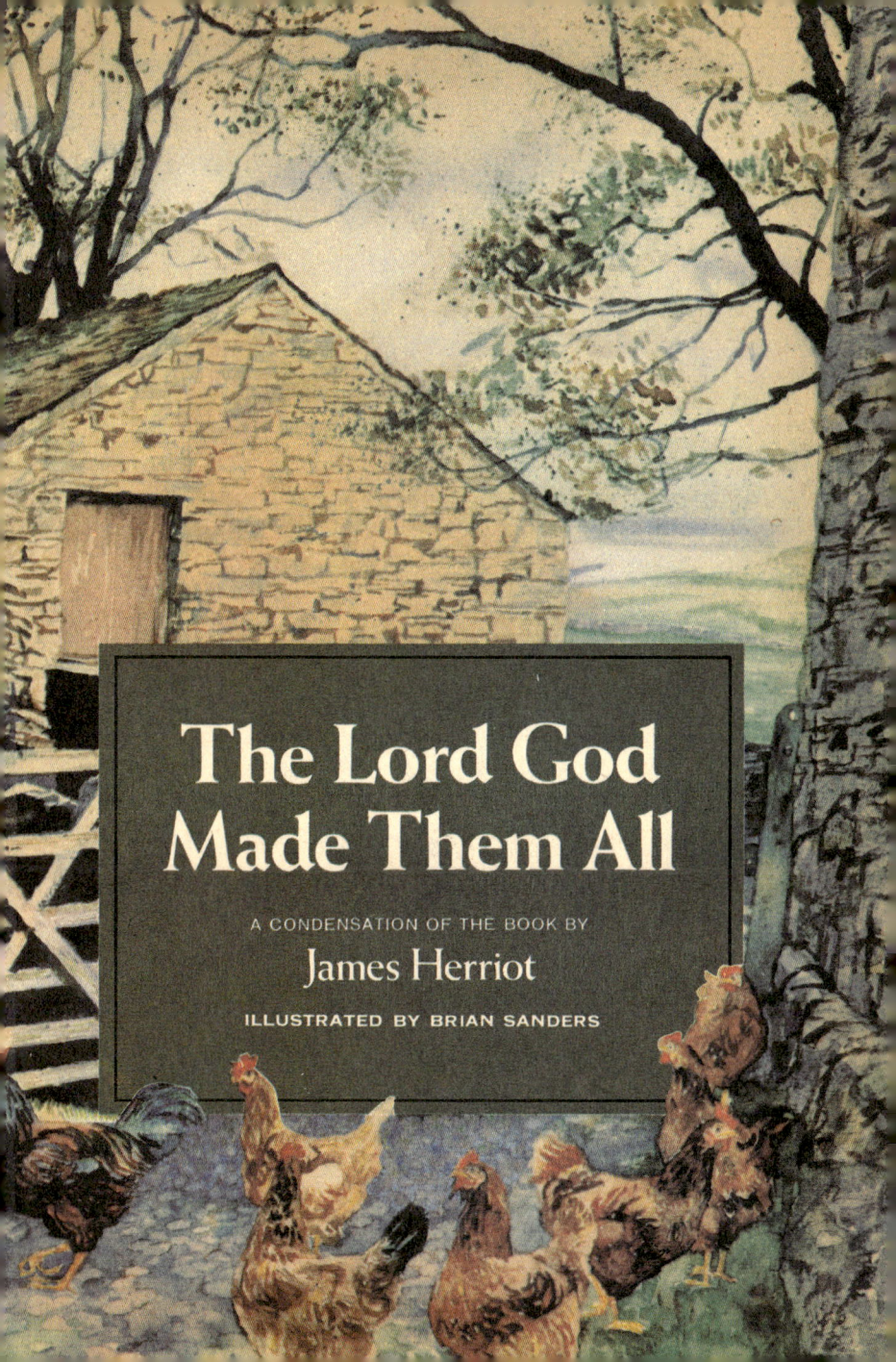

After a stint in the RAF, James Herriot—that engaging veterinary surgeon from the Yorkshire Dales—is home at last. But in the aftermath of World War II, the spirit of change is in the wind. New drugs are revolutionizing animal medicine. And in the Herriot household there is now a roguish young son, Jimmy.

Whether our vet is treating an ailing cow, making a midnight call on a hypochondriacal dog owner, or nervously awaiting the birth of his second child, he never loses the wry humor or the rare sense of joy that have made his *All Creatures Great and Small* and *All Things Bright and Beautiful* favorites the world over.

1

The high moorland road was unfenced, and my car wheels ran easily from the strip of tarmac onto the turf, cropped to a velvet closeness by the sheep. I stopped the engine, got out and looked around me.

The road cut cleanly through the grass and heather before dipping into the valley beyond. This was one of the good places where I could see into two dales. The whole land was spread beneath me: the soft fields in the valley floors, the grazing cattle, the rivers edged with pebbles in places, thickly fringed with trees in others. The brilliant green of the walled pastures pushed up the sides of the fells until the heather and the harsh moor grass began, and only the walls were left, climbing to the mottled summits, disappearing over the bare ridges that marked the beginning of the wild country.

I leaned against the car, and the wind blew the cold sweet air around me. I had been back in civilian life only a few weeks, after a spell in the Royal Air Force. During that spell I had thought constantly of Yorkshire, but I had forgotten how beautiful it was. Just thinking from afar could not evoke the peace, the solitude, the sense of the nearness of the wild that make the Dales both thrilling and comforting. Among the crowds of men and the stale air of the towns it had been hard to conjure up a place where I could be quite alone on the wide green roof of England, where every breath was filled with the scent of grass.

I had had a disturbing morning. Everywhere I had gone I was reminded that I had come back to a world of change, and I did not like change. One old farmer saying, "It's all t'needle now, Mr. Herriot," as I injected his cow, had made me look down at the syringe in my hand and realize suddenly that this was what I was doing most of the time these days.

I knew what he meant. Only a few years before, I would more likely have "drenched" his cow—grabbed it by the nose and poured a pint of medicine down its throat. We still carried a special drenching bottle around with us—an empty wine bottle with no shoulders, which allowed the liquid to run easily. Often we would mix the medicine with black treacle from the barrel that stood in the corner of most cow byres. But all this was disappearing, and the farmer's remark brought it home to me that things were never going to be the same again.

Now, after the war, a revolution was beginning in agriculture and in veterinary practice. Farming was becoming more scientific, and concepts cherished for generations were being abandoned, while in the veterinary world new surgical procedures and drugs such as sulfa and penicillin were slowly sweeping our old treatments into oblivion. There were signs, too, that the small farmers were on the way out. These men, some with only six cows, a few pigs and poultry, still made up most of our practice, but they were beginning to wonder if they could make a living on this scale, and one or two had already sold out to the bigger men. The small farmers—old men doggedly doing what they have always done for the sole reason that they have always done it—were the men I cherished, the truly rich characters living by the ancient values, speaking the old Yorkshire dialect that television and radio have almost swamped.

I took a last long breath and got into my car. As I looked out at the great fells thrusting their bald summits into the clouds, tier upon tier of them, timeless, indestructible, towering over the glories beneath, I felt better immediately. The Dales had not changed at all.

I did one more call, then drove back to our office, the spacious, elegant Skeldale House. The place looked much the same as when I had first seen it years ago, but it had seen change, too. My partner, Siegfried Farnon, had married, as had his younger brother, Tristan. They had both moved out, but Siegfried was living only a few miles outside our town of Darrowby. My wife, Helen, and I and our little son, Jimmy, now had the run of the whole house. Tristan, alas, had left our practice. When the war ended, he was Captain Farnon of the Royal Army veterinary corps, and he went on to join the Ministry of Agriculture as an infertility investigation officer. He left a sad gap in our lives, but fortunately we still saw him and his wife regularly.

I opened the front door, and halfway to the dispensary I almost bumped into Siegfried. He was storming along the passage, and he grabbed my arm in an agitated manner. "Ah, James, just the man I was looking for! I've had the most ghastly time this morning. I knocked the exhaust pipe off my car going up that bloody awful track to High Liston, and now I'm without transport until the repair can be done. It's maddening!"

"That's all right, Siegfried. I'll do your calls."

"No, no, James, it's kind of you, but don't you see, this sort of thing is going to happen again and again. That's what I want to talk to you about. We need a spare car."

"A spare?"

"That's right. Something to fall back upon at a time like this. As a matter of fact, I rang Hammond at the garage to bring round something suitable for us to look at. I think I hear him outside now."

My partner was always one for instant action, and I followed him out the front door. Mr. Hammond was there with a 1933 Morris Oxford, and Siegfried trotted down the steps toward it.

"A hundred pounds, you said, eh, Mr. Hammond?" He walked around the car, picking pieces of rust from the black paintwork and peering at the upholstery. "Ah well, it's seen better days, but the appearance doesn't matter as long as it goes all right."

"It's a sound little job, Mr. Farnon," the garage proprietor said. "New battery, and a good bit o' tread on the tires."

"Mmmm." Siegfried shook the rear bumper with his foot, and the old springs groaned. "How about the brakes? Important in this hilly country."

"They're champion, Mr. Farnon. First-rate."

My colleague nodded slowly. "Good, good. You don't mind if I drive her round the block?"

"Nay, nay, of course not," Mr. Hammond replied. "Give 'er any trial you like." He was a man who prided himself on his imperturbability, and he dropped confidently into the passenger seat as Siegfried took the wheel.

"Hop in, James!" my partner cried. I opened the rear door and took my place behind Mr. Hammond.

Siegfried took off abruptly with a roaring and creaking from the old vehicle, and despite the garage man's outward calm, his shirt collar rose a couple of inches above his jacket as we shot along Trengate Street. The collar subsided a little when Siegfried slowed down to turn left, but reappeared spasmodically as we negotiated a series of sharp and narrow bends at top speed.

When we reached a long, straight lane that runs parallel to Trengate, Siegfried thundered along it. At the end of the lane he came almost to a halt as he turned left again. "I think we'll test the brakes, Mr. Hammond," he said, and suddenly hurled the car ahead. He really meant to carry out a thorough test! The roar of the ancient engine rose to a scream and the Trengate crossing approached with frightening rapidity. When Siegfried braked, the car slued violently to the right, and as we catapulted crabwise into Trengate, Mr. Hammond's head was jammed against the roof and his entire shirt back was exposed. When we came to a halt, he slid slowly back into his seat. At no time had he spoken or, apart from his movements, shown any emotion.

At our front door we got out, and my colleague rubbed his chin doubtfully. "She does pull a little to the right on braking, Mr. Hammond. Perhaps you have another vehicle available?"

The garage man did not answer for a few moments. His spectacles were askew and he was very pale. "Aye . . . aye . . ." he said shakily. "I 'ave another little job might suit you."

"Capital!" Siegfried rubbed his hands. "Perhaps you could

bring it along after lunch, and we can have a spin round to try it."

Mr. Hammond's eyes widened and he swallowed a few times. "I'm goin' to be busy this afternoon, Mr. Farnon. I'll send one of me men."

We bade him good-by, and as we went back into the house my partner put an arm across my shoulders. "Well, James, another step toward increasing the efficiency of the practice. Anyway"—he smiled—"I rather enjoy these little interludes."

Suddenly I began to feel good. So many things were new and different, but the Dales hadn't changed, and Siegfried hadn't changed either.

2

"Hello! Hello!" I bellowed.

"Hello! Hello!" little Jimmy piped just behind me.

I turned and looked at my son. He was four years old now and had been coming on my rounds with me for over a year. Clearly he considered himself a veteran of the farmyards.

This shouting was a common habit of mine. When a vet arrived on a farm, it was often surprisingly difficult to find the farmer. He might be on a tractor half a mile across the fields, or in one of the barns, so I always relied on a few brisk shouts to locate him. Jimmy had caught on to the practice, and there was no doubt he enjoyed the opportunity to exercise his lungs. I watched him as he strutted importantly over the cobbles, giving tongue every few seconds. He was also making an unnecessary amount of noise by clattering on the rough stones with his new boots.

Those boots were his pride, the final recognition of his status as veterinary assistant. When I first began to take him around with me, his reaction was the simple joy of a child at being able to see animals of all kinds, particularly the young ones, and the thrill of discovery when he came upon a huddle of kittens in the straw or found a bitch with pups in a box stall. Before long, however, he wanted to get into the action. The contents of my car trunk were soon as familiar to him as his toy box at home, and he delighted in handing out the tins of stomach powder, the white lotion and the long cartons of Universal Cattle Medicine. Finally he began to forestall me by rushing back to the car for the calcium and the flutter valve as soon as he saw a recumbent cow. He had become a diagnostician as well.

I think the thing he enjoyed most was accompanying me on an evening call, if Helen would allow him to postpone his bedtime. He was in heaven driving into the country in the darkness, training my flashlight on a cow's teat while I stitched it.

The farmers were always kind to him. Even the most uncommunicative would grunt, "Ah see you've got t'apprentice with ye," as we got out of the car.

Those farmers had something Jimmy coveted: their big hobnailed boots. He had a great admiration for farmers in general, strong hardy men who spent their lives in the open and who pushed fearlessly among plunging packs of cattle and slapped the rumps of massive cart horses. I could see he was deeply impressed as he watched them mounting granary steps carrying sacks weighing two hundred pounds on their shoulders, or hanging on casually to the noses of huge bullocks, their boots slithering over the floor.

It was those boots that got under Jimmy's skin most of all. Sturdy and unyielding, they seemed to symbolize for him the character of the men who wore them.

Matters came to a head one day when we were conversing in the car. Or rather, my son was doing the conversing in the form of a barrage of questions, which went on pretty well nonstop every day and followed a well-tried formula. "What is the fastest train—the *Blue Peter* or the *Flying Scotsman?*"

"Well . . . I should say the *Blue Peter.*"

Then, getting into deeper water, "Is a giant train faster than a phantom racing car?"

"That's a difficult one. Maybe the phantom racer is faster."

Jimmy changed his tack suddenly. "That was a big man at the last farm, wasn't he?"

"He certainly was."

"Was he bigger than Mr. Robinson?"

We were launching into his favorite game—"big man"—and I

knew how it would end, but I played my part. "Oh yes, he was."

"Was he bigger than Mr. Kirkley?"

"Without a doubt."

Jimmy gave me a sidelong glance, and I knew he was about to play his two trump cards. "Was he bigger than the gas man?"

The towering gentleman who came to read the gas meters at Skeldale House had always fascinated my son, and I had to reply very carefully. "Well, you know, I really think he was."

"Ah, but . . ." The corner of Jimmy's mouth twitched up craftily. "Was he bigger than Mr. Thackray?"

That was the killer punch. Nobody was bigger than Mr. Thackray, who looked down on the other inhabitants of Darrowby from six feet seven inches.

I shrugged my shoulders in defeat. "No, I have to admit it. He wasn't as big as Mr. Thackray."

Jimmy smiled and nodded, well satisfied. This put him in such high good humor that he broached something that must have been on his mind for some time.

"Daddy," he said. "Can I have some boots?"

"Boots? But you've got some already." I pointed down at the little Wellingtons in which Helen always rigged him before he set out for the farms.

He gazed at his feet sadly before replying. "Yes, I know, but I want proper boots like the farmers."

This was a facer. I didn't know what to say. "But, Jim, little boys don't have boots like that. Maybe when you're bigger . . ."

"Oh, I want them now," he moaned in anguished tones.

At first I thought it was a passing whim, but he kept up his campaign, reinforcing it with disgusted looks as Helen drew on the Wellingtons each morning. His listless slouch conveyed the message that his footwear was entirely unsuitable for a man like him. Finally Helen and I talked it over one night after he had gone to bed.

"They surely don't have farm boots his size, do they?" I asked.

Helen shook her head. "I wouldn't have thought so, but I'll look around, in any case."

And within a week my wife returned from shopping flushed

with success and bearing the smallest pair of farm boots I had ever seen. I couldn't help laughing. They were so tiny, yet so perfect—thick hobnailed soles, chunky uppers and a long row of lace holes with metal loops at the top.

Jimmy didn't laugh when he saw them. He handled them almost with awe, and once he had got them on, his demeanor changed. He was naturally square-set and jaunty, but to see him striding around a farmyard in those boots you would think he owned the place. He clumped and stamped, held himself very upright, and his cries of "Hello! Hello!" took on a new authority.

He was never what I would call naughty, but he had that bit of devil which I suppose all boys need to have. He liked to assert himself, and he was not above taking advantage of me in awkward situations. There was one afternoon when Mr. Garrett brought in his sheep dog. The animal was very lame, and as I hoisted him onto the consulting-room table, a small head appeared outside the window that overlooked the sunlit garden.

I didn't mind that. Jimmy often watched me treat our patients, and I half expected him to come in for a closer look.

It is often difficult to locate the source of a dog's lameness, but in this case I found it immediately. When I gently squeezed the outside pad on one foot he winced, and a tiny bead of serum appeared on the black surface. "Something's in there, Mr. Garrett," I said. "Probably a thorn. I'll have to give him a local anesthetic and open it up."

It was when I was filling the syringe that a knee came into view outside, at the corner of the window. Jimmy surely couldn't be climbing the wisteria! It was dangerous, and I had expressly forbidden it. The branches of the beautiful creeper curled all over the back of the house, and though they were as thick as a man's leg near ground level, they became quite slender as they made their way up to the roof. No, I decided that I'd been mistaken, and I injected the quick-acting anesthetic. I reached for the scalpel. "Hold his leg up and keep it steady," I said.

Serious-faced and obviously deeply concerned about his dog, Mr. Garrett nodded, and pursed his lips in apprehension as I poised my knife.

For me it was an absorbing moment. With the point of my blade I made a careful nick in the pad, and at that moment a shadow crossed the window. I glanced up. It was Jimmy. The little blighter *was* on the wisteria, but there was nothing I could do about it then except to give him a quick glare.

I cut a little deeper and squeezed, but still nothing showed in the wound. I didn't want to make a big hole, but it was clear that I would need a cross-shaped incision to see farther down. I was drawing the scalpel at right angles to my first cut when, from the corner of my eye, I spotted two feet dangling just below the top of the window. I tried to concentrate on my job, but the feet swung and kicked repeatedly, obviously for my benefit. At last they disappeared, which could only mean that their owner was ascending to the dangerous regions.

I dug down a little deeper and swabbed with cotton wool. Ah yes, I could see something now. I reached for forceps, and just then Jimmy's head showed itself again, upside down this time. He was hanging by his feet from the branches, and the face was positively leering. In deference to my client I had been trying to ignore the byplay from outside, but this was too much. I leaped at the glass and shook my fist violently. My fury must have startled the performer, because the face vanished instantly and I could hear faint sounds of feet scrambling upward. That was not much comfort; however, I forced myself back to my task.

"Sorry, Mr. Garrett," I said. "Will you hold the leg up again, please?"

He complied with a thin smile, and I pushed my forceps into the depths. They grated on something hard. I gripped, pulled gently and—oh, lovely—out came the pointed, glistening head of a thorn. It was one of the tiny triumphs that lighten vets' lives. I was beaming at my client and patting his dog when I heard a crack, followed by a howl of terror. Then a small form hurtled past the window and thudded with horrid force into the garden.

I shot outside. Jimmy was already sitting up among the wall-flowers, and I was too relieved to be angry.

"Have you hurt yourself?" I gasped, and he shook his head.

I lifted him to his feet and felt him over carefully. There appeared to be no damage. "Go along and see Mummy," I said, and returned to the consulting room.

"Is he all right?" Mr. Garrett asked.

"Yes, I think so. But I do apologize for rushing out. . . ."

Mr. Garrett laid his hand on my shoulder. "Say no more, Mr. Herriot. I have children of my own." And then he spoke the words that have become engraved on my heart. "You need nerves of steel to be a parent."

Later at tea I watched my son slap plum jam on a slice of bread. Thank heaven he was no worse for his fall, but still I had to remonstrate with him. "Young man," I said, "that was a very naughty thing you did out there. I've told you again and again not to climb the wisteria."

Jimmy bit into his bread and jam and regarded me impassively. I could see that he wasn't taking what I was saying too seriously.

"If you're going to behave like this," I went on, "I'm not going to take you round the farms with me. I'll just have to find another little boy to help me with my cases."

I looked for some reaction in this morsel of humanity who was much later to become a far better veterinary surgeon than I could ever be. "Another little boy?" Jimmy inquired.

"That's right. I can't have naughty boys with me. I'll have to find somebody else."

Jimmy thought this over for a minute or so and appeared to accept the situation philosophically.

Then in a flash his sangfroid evaporated. He looked up at me in wide-eyed alarm and his voice came out in a high quaver. "Would he have my boots?"

3

"It was Hemingway who said that, wasn't it?"

Norman Beaumont shook his head. "No, Scott Fitzgerald."

I didn't argue, because Norman usually knew. In fact, it was one of the attractive things about him.

I enjoyed having veterinary students see practice with us. They helped with fetching and carrying, opened gates, and were company on our lonely rounds. In return they absorbed priceless experience from us in the practical side of their education.

Since the war, however, I found I was learning almost as much from these young men as they were learning from me, because veterinary teaching had taken such a leap forward. The vast new field of small-animal work was opening up dramatically. Advanced surgical procedures were being carried out on farm animals, too, and today's students had the great advantage of being able to see such things done in schools equipped with modern operating theaters.

Norman Beaumont was in his final year and was a deep well of information, at which I drank greedily. But apart from the veterinary side we had a common love of reading. When we weren't talking shop, the conversation was usually on literary lines, and Norman's companionship made the journeys between farms seem short.

He was immensely likable, with a personality that was formal and dignified beyond his twenty-two years and was only just saved from pomposity by a gentle humor. A solid citizen in the making if ever I saw one, and this impression was strengthened by his slightly pear-shaped physique and the fact that he was determinedly trying to cultivate a pipe.

As we drove along, I got onto the topic of the new operations. "And you say they are actually doing cesareans on cows in the college clinics?"

Norman applied a match to his pipe. "Doing them like hotcakes; it's a regular thing." His words would have carried more weight if he had been able to blow a puff of smoke out after them, but he had filled the bowl too tightly, and despite a fierce sucking that hollowed his cheeks and ballooned his eyeballs, he couldn't manage a draw.

"Gosh, you don't know how lucky you are," I said. "The hours I've slaved on byre floors calving cows, knocking my guts out trying to bring heads round or reach feet. And if only I'd known how, I could have saved myself the trouble with a nice straightforward operation. What sort of a job is it, anyway?"

The student gave me a superior smile. "Nothing much to it,

really." He relit his pipe, tamped the tobacco down and winced as he burned his finger. "Takes about an hour, and no hard labor."

"Sounds marvelous," I said wistfully. "It's so much easier to tackle these jobs when you've seen a lot of them done."

"True, true." The student spread his hands. "But of course, most bovine parturitions don't need a cesarean, and I'm always glad to have a calving for my casebook."

I nodded in agreement. Norman's casebook was a heavily bound volume with every scrap of interesting material meticulously entered under headings in red ink. The examiners always wanted to see these books, and this one would be worth a few extra marks to Norman in his finals.

I dropped the student at his digs in late afternoon and went back to Skeldale House for tea. I had just finished when Helen got up to answer the phone. "It's Mr. Bushell of Sycamore House," she told me. "He has a cow calving."

"Oh damn. I thought we'd have the evening to ourselves," I said as I put my cup down. "Tell him I'll be right out, Helen, will you?" I smiled as she put down the receiver. "One thing, Norman will be pleased. He was just saying he always welcomes a calving for his casebook."

I was right. The young man was in excellent humor when I called for him to drive out to the farm.

"I was reading some poetry when you rang the bell," he said. "You can always find something in poetry to apply to your life. How about now, when I'm expecting something interesting— *Hope springs eternal in the human breast.*"

"Alexander Pope's 'Essay on Man,' " I grunted. I wasn't feeling as enthusiastic as Norman. You never knew what was ahead on these occasions.

We drove through the farm gateway into the yard. The farmer led us into the byre, and in a stall opposite the window a small cow looked up at us anxiously from her straw bed. Above her head, her name, Bella, was chalked on a board.

"She isn't very big, Mr. Bushell," I shouted, remembering that he was hard of hearing.

"Aye, she allus was a poor doer. Had a rough time with her first calvin', but she milked well enough after it."

I observed the cow as I stripped off my shirt and soaped my arms. I didn't like the look of that narrow pelvis, and I breathed a silent prayer that there might be a tiny calf inside.

The farmer poked at the rump with his foot and shouted at the animal to make her rise. "She won't budge, Mr. Herriot," he said. "She's been painin' all day."

I didn't like the sound of that either. There was always something wrong when a cow strained so long without result. And the little animal did look utterly spent. Her head hung down and her eyelids drooped wearily.

Ah well, if she wouldn't get up, I had to get down. With my bare chest in contact with the ground, the thought occurred that cobbles didn't get any softer with the passage of the years. But when I slid my hand into the pelvic opening, I forgot my discomfort; it was villainously narrow. And beyond was something that froze my blood: two enormous hoofs, and a huge expanse of muzzle with twitching nostrils. As I withdrew my hand, the rough surface of the calf's tongue flicked briefly against my palm.

I sat back on my heels and raised my voice. "There's an elephant in there, Mr. Bushell. A tremendous calf, and no room for it to come out."

"Can't ye cut it away?"

"Afraid not. The calf's alive."

"Well, that's a beggar," Mr. Bushell said. "She's a good little milker. Ah don't want to send 'er to the butcher."

Neither did I. I hated the very thought of it. Then in a great moment of decision I turned to the student. "This is it, Norman! The ideal indication for a cesarean. What a good job you're with me!" I was slightly breathless with excitement, and I hardly noticed the flicker of anxiety in the young man's eyes.

I got to my feet and seized the farmer's arm. "Mr. Bushell, I'd like to do a cesarean operation on your cow—open her up and remove the calf surgically."

"Like they do sometimes wi' women?"

"That's right."

"Well that's a rum un." The farmer's eyebrows went up. "I never knew you could do that wi' cows."

"Oh, we can now," I said airily. "Things have moved on a bit in the last few years."

He rubbed a hand slowly across his mouth. "Well, ah don't know. I reckon she could die if you made a bloody great 'ole in her like that. Maybe she'd be better goin' for slaughter. I'd get a few quid for her."

I could see my big moment slipping away from me. "But she's only a thin little thing. She wouldn't be worth much for meat, and with a bit of luck we might get a live calf out of her."

I was going against one of my steadfast rules—never to talk a farmer into doing something—but I was seized by a kind of madness. Mr. Bushell looked at me for a long time; then, without changing expression, he nodded. "Awright, what do you need?"

"Two buckets of warm water, soap, towels," I replied. "And I'll bring some instruments into the house to boil, if I may."

When the farmer had departed, I thumped Norman on the shoulder. "This is just right. Plenty of light, a live calf to aim for, and as Mr. Bushell doesn't hear too well, I'll be able to ask you things as we go along."

Norman didn't say anything. I had him set up our equipment and scatter loose straw around the cow while I boiled the instruments in the farm kitchen. Soon syringes, suture materials, scalpels, scissors, local anesthetic and cotton wool were laid in a row on a clean towel draped over one of the bales. I added some antiseptic to the water and addressed the farmer. "We'll roll her over and you can hold the head down, Mr. Bushell."

Norman and I pushed at Bella's shoulder, and she flopped onto her side without resistance. I nudged the student. "Where do I make the incision?" I whispered.

Norman cleared his throat. "Well, er, it's about . . ." He pointed.

I nodded. "Around the rumenotomy site, eh? But a bit lower, I suppose." I clipped away the hair from a foot-long strip. It would need a big opening for that calf to come through. Then I infiltrated the area with local anesthetic and began to cut. Under the peritoneum I was confronted with a protruding pink and white mass of tissue. I poked at it. There was something hard inside. Could it be the calf?

"Is that the rumen or the uterus?" I hissed. "It's pretty low down for the stomach, so I'd suppose it would be the uterus."

"Yes, that's the uterus all right."

"Good." I smiled in relief and made a bold incision. A great gout of impacted grass welled out, followed by a burst of gas and an outflow of dirty brown fluid.

I gasped. "It's the rumen. Look at all that mess!" I groaned as the filthy tide surged from the cow's first stomach into the abdominal cavity. "What the hell are you playing at, Norman?" He was trembling. "Thread me a needle. Quick!"

Norman shakily passed me a length of catgut. Wordlessly, dry-mouthed, I stitched up the gash I had made in the wrong organ. Then the two of us swabbed frantically at the escaped rumenal contents with cotton wool and antiseptic, but much of it had run away beyond our reach. The contamination must be massive.

When we had done what we could, I growled at the student, "I thought you knew all about these operations."

He looked frightened. "They do quite a few of them . . ."

I glared at him. "How many cesareans have you seen?"

"Well . . . er . . . one, actually."

"One! I thought you were an expert! Anyway, even if you'd seen only one, you should know a little bit about it."

"The thing is . . . I was right at the back of the class."

I worked up a sarcastic snarl. "Oh, I understand. So you couldn't see very well?"

"That's about it." The young man hung his head.

"Well, you're a stupid young fool!" I said in a vicious whisper. "Dishing out your confident instructions! You realize you've killed this good cow. With all that contamination she'll certainly develop peritonitis and die. All we can hope for now is to get the calf out alive." With an effort I turned my gaze from his stricken face. "Anyway, let's get on with it."

Apart from my first shout of panic, the entire interchange had been carried out pianissimo, and Mr. Bushell kept shooting inquiring glances at us. I gave him what I hoped was a reassuring smile and returned to the attack. Plunging my arm deep below what I now knew was the rumen, I encountered a smooth and mighty organ containing an enormous bulk with the hardness and immobility of a sack of coal. I felt my way along the surface and came upon the unmistakable contours of a hock pushing against the slippery wall. That was the calf, all right, but it was far, far away.

I withdrew my arm and started on Norman again. "From your position at the back of the class," I inquired bitingly, "did you happen to notice what they did next?"

"Next? Ah yes." He licked his lips. "You are supposed to exteriorize the uterus—bring it up to the wound."

I groaned. "King Kong couldn't lift that uterus! Have a feel."

The student, who was stripped and soaped like myself, introduced his arm for a moment. Then he withdrew it and nodded sheepishly. "You're right. It won't move."

"Only one thing to do. I'll have to cut into the uterus and grab that hock. There's nothing else to get hold of."

It was very nasty, fiddling about in the dark unknown, my arm buried to the shoulder in the cow, my tongue hanging out in anxiety. I was terrified I might slash into something vital, but in fact, it was my own fingers that I cut, several times, before I was able to draw the scalpel across the bulge made by the hock. A second later I had my hand around the hairy leg. Now I was getting somewhere.

Gingerly I enlarged the incision, inch by inch. I hoped fervently I had made it big enough as I seized the leg and tried to lift it. Immediately I knew that it was going to take tremendous strength to bring the calf into the light of day. Nowadays when I do a cesarean, I take care to have a big strong farm lad ready to help me, but that day I had only Norman.

"Come on," I panted. "Give me a hand."

We reached down together and began to pull. Teeth clenched, grunting with effort, we hauled upward till at last I was able to grasp the other hind leg. Even then, with a foot apiece in our hands, nothing wanted to move. As we lay back, pulling with every vestige of our strength, I had the sudden wave of illumination that comes to all members of our profession at times. I wished with all my heart I had never started this ghastly job.

But the calf was gradually coming through. The tail appeared, then an unbelievably massive rib cage and finally, with a rush, the shoulders and head. Norman and I sat down with a bump, the calf rolling over our knees, snorting and shaking his head.

"By gaw, he's a big un!" exclaimed the farmer.

I nodded. "Yes. One of the biggest I've ever seen. He'd never have come out the proper way."

My attention was whisked back to the cow. Where was the uterus? It had vanished. Again I started my frantic groping inside, and after pulling out the placenta, my fingers at last came upon the ragged edge of my incision. I drew as much as possible of the organ up to the light, where I noticed with sinking disquiet that my original opening had been enlarged to such an extent by the passage of that enormous calf that there was a long tear disappearing out of sight toward the cervix.

"Sutures." I held my hand out, and Norman gave me a fresh needle. "Hold the lips of the wound," I said, and began to stitch. I worked quickly until the tear ran out of sight. The rest was a kind of martyrdom. Norman hung on grimly while I stabbed at the invisible tissue far below.

Then to my dismay a further complication arose—the calf was now on his feet, blundering unsteadily around. The speed with which newly born animals get onto their legs has always fascinated me, but at this moment it was an unmitigated nuisance. The calf, looking for the udder with that instinct nobody can explain, kept pushing his nose at the cow's flank and at times went toppling headfirst into the gaping hole in her side.

"Reckon 'e wants back in again," Mr. Bushell said with a grin. "By 'eck, he's a wick un."

"Wick" is Yorkshire for lively, and the word was never more aptly applied. As I worked, I had to keep nudging the wet muzzle away with my elbow, but as fast as I pushed him back, the calf nosed in again, spreading particles of straw and dirt from the floor over the abdominal contents. "Look at that," I moaned. "As if there wasn't enough muck in there."

Norman didn't reply. Sweat ran down his blood-streaked face as he grappled with that unseen wound.

After an eternity I got as far down the uterine tear as I could, then we cleared away a lot of rubbish from the cow's abdomen and covered everything with antiseptic powder. I stitched up the muscle and skin layers, and at last the thing was finished. Norman and I got to our feet slowly, like two old men, and began to scrub and scrape ourselves clean.

Mr. Bushell left his position by the head and looked at the row of stitches. "Nice neat job," he said. "And a grand calf, too."

Yes, that was something. The little creature had dried off now, and he was a beauty, his body swaying on unsteady legs, his wide-set eyes filled with gentle curiosity. But that "neat job" hid things I didn't dare think about. I knew there was no hope for the cow. Still, as a gesture, I left the farmer some sulfa powders to give her three times a day. Then I got off the farm as quickly as I could.

We drove away in silence. I rounded a corner, then stopped the car under a tree and sank my head against the wheel. "Did you ever see such a performance?" I groaned. "All that muck in that poor cow—peritonitis is inevitable. And I'm pretty sure I've left a good-size hole in her uterus."

Norman spoke in a strangled undertone. "It was all my fault."

"No, it wasn't," I replied. "I am supposed to be a qualified veterinary surgeon, and I did nearly everything wrong. On top of it all, I shouted and nagged and behaved abominably toward you, and I owe you an apology."

"You didn't really. I—"

"Anyway, Norman," I broke in. "I want to thank you now. You worked like a Trojan and I'd have got nowhere without you. Let's go and have a pint."

At the village inn, we dropped into a quiet corner and pulled deeply at our beer glasses. We were both hot and weary and there didn't seem to be anything more to say.

I was sure I would never see Bella alive again, but first thing next morning a morbid curiosity made me ring Mr. Bushell.

"Oh, it's Mr. Herriot," he said. "Cow's up and eatin'."

It was several seconds before I was able to absorb his words. "Doesn't she look a bit dull or uncomfortable?" I asked huskily.

"Nay, nay, she's bright as a cricket. Finished off a rackful of hay, and I got a couple o' gallons of milk from 'er."

As if in a dream I heard his next question. "When'll you take them stitches out?"

"Stitches . . . ? Oh yes." I gave myself a shake. "In a fortnight, Mr. Bushell, in a fortnight."

After the horrors of the first visit, I was glad Norman was with me when I removed the sutures. There was no swelling around the wound, and Bella chewed her cud happily as I snipped away. In a pen nearby the calf gamboled and kicked his feet in the air.

"Has Bella shown any symptoms at all?" I couldn't help asking.

"Nay." The farmer shook his head slowly. "You wouldn't know owt had happened to 'er."

That was the way it was at my first cesarean. Over the years Bella went on to have eight more calves normally and unaided, a miracle that I can still hardly believe.

But Norman and I were not to know that. What we felt then was an elation all the sweeter for being unexpected. "Well, Norman," I said. "That's veterinary practice for you. You get a lot of nasty shocks, but some lovely surprises, too. I've often heard of the wonderful resistance of the bovine peritoneum, and thank heaven it's true."

"The whole thing's marvelous, isn't it?" he murmured dreamily. "I can't describe the way I feel. My head seems to be full of quotations like *While there is life there's hope.*"

"Yes, indeed," I said. "John Gay, isn't it? 'The Sick Man and the Angel.'"

Norman clapped his hands. "Oh, well done. Here's another good one: *Out of this nettle, danger, we pluck this flower, safety.*"

"Splendid, splendid," I replied. "Shakespeare, *Henry Fifth.*"

"No, *Henry Fourth.*"

I opened my mouth to argue, but Norman held up a confident hand. "It's no good, I'm right. And this time I *do* know what I'm talking about."

4

"Oooh . . . ooh-hoo-hooo!" The brokenhearted sobbing coming over the telephone jerked me fully awake. It was one a.m.

"Who is this?" I asked. "What on earth is the trouble?"

A man's voice pleaded between sobs. "It's Humphrey Cobb. Please come out and see Myrtle. I think she's dyin'."

"Myrtle?"

"Aye, me poor little dog. She's in a state, pantin' and gaspin'. Come quick! Oooh-hooo!"

"Where do you live?"

"Cedar House. End of Hill Street."

"I know it. I'll be there very soon."

"Oh, thank ye, thank ye. Myrtle hasn't got long. Hurry!"

As I leaped from the bed and pulled on my clothes, Helen sat up. "What is it, Jim?"

"Desperately urgent case. I have to hurry."

I galloped downstairs and out to the garage. I have always envied vets who stay relaxed under pressure. But I wasn't made that way. Cedar House was only a mile away, and I didn't have much time to think about the case before I arrived. In answer to my ring the porch light flashed on, and Humphrey Cobb stood before me. He was a small round man in his sixties with a Humpty-Dumpty appearance accentuated by a gleaming bald head.

"Oh, Mr. Herriot, come in," he cried brokenly as the tears streamed down his cheeks. "Thank ye for gettin' out of your bed to help me poor little Myrtle." As he spoke, the blast of whisky fumes almost made my head spin, and I noticed that as he preceded me into the kitchen he staggered slightly.

My patient was lying in a basket beside the stove in a large, well-appointed kitchen. I felt a warm surge when I saw that she was a beagle, like my own dog, Sam. I knelt down and looked at her closely. Her mouth was open and her tongue lolled, but she did not seem to be in acute distress. In fact, as I patted her head, her tail flapped against the blanket.

A heartrending wail sounded in my ear. "What d'ye make of

her, Mr. Herriot? It's her heart, isn't it?" The little man crouched over his pet, and the tears flowed unchecked.

"You know, Mr. Cobb, she doesn't seem all that bad to me. Don't upset yourself. Just give me a chance to examine her."

I placed my stethoscope over the ribs and listened to the steady thudding of a superbly strong heart. The temperature was normal, and I was palpating the abdomen when Mr. Cobb broke in again. "The trouble is," he gasped, "I neglect this poor animal. Ah've been all day at the races, gamblin' and drinkin', with never a thought for 'er."

"You left her alone all that time in the house?"

"Nay, nay, t'missus has been with her."

"Well, then." I felt I was getting out of my depth. "Wouldn't she feed Myrtle and let her out in the garden?"

"Oh aye," he said, wringing his hands. "But I shouldn't leave 'er. She thinks such a lot about me."

Suddenly I could feel one side of my face tingling with heat. My problem was solved. "You've got her too near the stove. She's panting because she's hot."

He looked at me doubtfully. "We just shifted 'er basket today. We've been gettin' some new tiles put down on the floor."

"Right," I said. "Shift it back again and she'll be fine."

"But, Mr. Herriot." His lips began to tremble again. "It's more than that. She's sufferin'. Look at her eyes."

Myrtle had the lovely big liquid eyes of her breed and she knew how to use them. Many people think the spaniel is number one when it comes to looking soulful, but I personally plump for the beagle. And Myrtle was an expert.

"Oh, I shouldn't worry about that, Mr. Cobb," I said. "Believe me, she'll be all right."

He was still unhappy. "But aren't ye going to do something?"

It was one of the great questions in veterinary practice. If you didn't "do something," people were not satisfied. And in this case Mr. Cobb was in greater need of treatment than his pet. So just to please him I produced a vitamin tablet from my bag and pushed it over the back of the little animal's tongue.

"There you are," I said. "I'm sure that will do her good."

"That's champion. You've set me mind at rest." Mr. Cobb led the way into a luxurious drawing room and tacked unsteadily toward a cocktail cabinet. "You'll 'ave a drink before you go?"

"No, really, thanks," I said. "I'd rather not."

"Well, I'll 'ave a drop. Just to steady me nerves." He tipped some whisky into a glass and waved me to a chair.

My bed was calling me, but I sat down and listened as he drank. He told me that he was a retired bookmaker from West Riding and that he had come to Darrowby only a month ago. Although no longer directly connected with horse racing, he still loved the sport and never missed a meeting in the north of England. "I get a taxi to take me and I have a right good day." His face was radiant as he recalled the happy times; then his woebegone expression returned. "But I neglect me dog. I leave her at home."

"Nonsense," I said. "You give her plenty of exercise?"

"Oh aye, lots of walks every day."

"Well, then, she really has a good life."

He beamed at me and sloshed out some more whisky. "Eee, you're a good lad. Come on, have one before you go."

"Oh, all right, just a small one, then."

As we drank he began gazing at me with something like devotion. "James Herriot," he slurred. "I suppose it'll be Jim, eh?"

"Well, yes."

"I'll call you Jim, then, and you can call me Humphrey."

"Okay, Humphrey," I said, and swallowed the last of my whisky. "But I really must go now."

Outside, he put a hand on my arm, his face serious again. "Thank ye, Jim. Myrtle was right bad tonight and I'm grateful."

Driving away, I realized that I had failed to convince him that I hadn't saved his dog's life. It had been an unusual visit and Humphrey Cobb was a very funny little man. But I liked him.

After that night I saw him frequently, exercising Myrtle in the fields. With his almost spherical build he seemed to bounce over the grass, but his manner was always self-contained and rational, except that he kept thanking me for pulling his dog back from the jaws of death.

Then quite suddenly I was back at the beginning. It was, once again, shortly after midnight when I lifted the bedside phone and heard the distraught weeping. "Oooh . . . oooh . . . Jim. Myrtle's in a bad way. Will ye come?"

"What . . . what is it this time?"

"She's twitchin' summat terrible. Oh, Jim, lad, don't keep me waiting. I'm worried to death. I'm sure she's got distemper." He broke down again.

My head began to reel. "She can't have distemper, Humphrey. Not in a flash, like that."

"I'm beggin' you, Jim," he went on, as though he hadn't heard.

"All right," I said wearily. "I'll be there in a few minutes."

"Oh, you're a good lad, Jim. . . ." The voice trailed away as I replaced the phone. I dressed with none of the panic of the first time. It must be another false alarm—but you never knew.

At Cedar House, the same dizzying wave of whisky fumes enveloped me on the porch. Humphrey, sniffling and moaning, ushered me into the kitchen. "There she is," he said, pointing to her basket. "I've just got back from Ripon and found 'er like this."

"Racing again, eh?"

"Aye, gamblin' and drinkin' and leavin' me poor dog pinin' at home. I'm a rotter, Jim, that's what I am."

"Rubbish, Humphrey! I've told you before. You're not doing her any harm by having a day out. Anyway, how about this twitching? She looks all right now."

"Yes, she's stopped doin' it, but when I came in, her back leg was goin' like this." He made a jerking movement with his hand.

I groaned inwardly. "But she could have been scratching."

"Nay, there's summat more than that. I can tell she's sufferin'. Just look at them eyes."

Myrtle's beagle eyes were pools of emotion, and it was easy to read melting reproach in their depths.

With a feeling of futility I examined her. I knew what I would find—nothing. But when I tried to explain that his pet was normal, Humphrey wouldn't have it.

"Give her a tablet," he pleaded. "It cured her last time."

I felt I had to pacify him, so Myrtle received another vitamin.

Immensely relieved, Humphrey wove his way to the drawing room and the whisky bottle.

"I need a little pick-me-up after that shock," he said. "You'll 'ave one, too, won't you, Jim, lad?"

This melodrama was enacted frequently over the next few months, always after race meetings and always between midnight and one a.m. I had ample opportunity to analyze the situation, and I came to a fairly obvious conclusion: most of the time Humphrey was a normal conscientious pet owner, but after a large intake of alcohol his affectionate feelings degenerated into sentimentality and guilt. I invariably went out when he called me because I knew that he would be deeply distressed if I refused. I was treating Humphrey, not Myrtle. It amused me that not once did he accept my protestations that my visit was unnecessary. Each time he was sure that my magic tablets had saved his dog's life.

Mind you, I did not discount the possibility that Myrtle was deliberately working on him with those eyes. The canine mind is quite capable of disapproval. I took my own dog almost everywhere with me, but if I left him at home and went with Helen to the cinema, he would lie under our bed, sulking.

I quailed when Humphrey told me he had decided to have Myrtle mated, because I knew that the ensuing pregnancy would be laden with harassment for me. And that was how it turned out. The little man flew into a series of unfounded panics, discovering imaginary symptoms in Myrtle regularly throughout the nine weeks. I was vastly relieved when she gave birth to five healthy pups. Now, I thought, I would get some peace. I was just about tired of Humphrey's nocturnal nonsense.

Then late one night soon afterward, the phone exploded in my ear. As I picked up the receiver, the "Oooh . . . oooh . . . ooohl" was only too familiar.

I clenched my teeth. "Humphrey! What is it this time?"

"Oh, Jim, Myrtle's really dyin', I know she is. Come quick!"

"Dying?" I took a couple of rasping breaths. "How do you make that out?"

"Well . . . she's stretched out on 'er side, tremblin'."

"Anything else?"

"Aye, t'missus said Myrtle's been lookin' worried and walkin' stiff when she let her out this afternoon. I'm not long back from Redcar, ye see."

"So you've been to the races, eh?"

"That's right . . . neglectin' me dog. I'm nothing but a scamp."

I closed my eyes. There was no end to the imaginary symptoms. Trembling this time, looking worried, walking stiff. What would it be next? I have always made a point of never refusing to make a call at night, but Humphrey had stretched this principle to the breaking point. This couldn't go on. I had to make a stand.

"Look, Humphrey," I said. "There's nothing wrong with your dog. I've told you again and again. . . ."

"Oh, Jim, lad, don't be long. Oooh-hooo!"

"I'm not coming, Humphrey."

"Nay, don't say that! She's goin' fast, I tell ye!"

"I mean it. It's just wasting my time and your money, so go to bed. Myrtle will be fine."

Tormented by remorse at refusing to go out for the first time in my life, I fell into an uneasy slumber. But it is a good thing that the subconscious mind works on during sleep, because with the alarm clock reading two thirty a.m., I came suddenly wide awake. "Oh no!" I cried. "Myrtle's got eclampsia!" I scrambled from the bed and began to throw on my clothes.

"What is it?" asked Helen. "What's the matter?"

"Humphrey Cobb!" I gasped, tying a shoelace.

"Humphrey . . . but you said there was never any hurry. . . ."

"There is this time. His dog's dying." I glared again at the clock. "In fact, she could be dead now."

I fled out to the car with my brain spelling out the concise case history that Humphrey had given me: small bitch nursing puppies, signs of anxiety and stiff gait this afternoon, and now prostrate and trembling. Classic puerperal eclampsia. Rapidly fatal without treatment. And it was nearly an hour and a half since he had phoned. I couldn't bear to think about it.

Humphrey was still up. He had obviously been consoling himself with the bottle, because he could barely stand.

"You've come, Jim, lad," he mumbled, blinking at me.

"Yes, how is she?"

"Just t'same...."

Clutching my calcium and my intravenous syringe, I rushed past him into the kitchen. Myrtle's sleek body was extended in a tetanic spasm. She was gasping for breath, quivering violently, and bubbles of saliva dripped from her mouth. Those eyes had lost their softness and were fixed in a frantic stare. She looked terrible, but she was alive.... She was alive.

I lifted the squealing pups onto a nearby rug and quickly clipped and swabbed the area over the radial vein. Calcium was the cure for this condition, but a quick blast would surely kill the patient. I inserted a needle into the blood vessel and slowly depressed the plunger. Some of these cases needed narcotics as well as calcium, and I had Nembutal and morphine ready at hand.

But as the time passed, Myrtle's breathing slowed down and the rigid muscles began to relax. When she started to swallow her saliva and look around at me, I knew she would live.

I was waiting for the last tremors to disappear from her limbs when I felt a tap on my shoulder. Humphrey was standing there with the whisky bottle.

"You'll 'ave one, won't you, Jim?"

I didn't need much persuading, knowing that I had almost been responsible for Myrtle's death. I had barely taken the first sip when the little animal got up from the basket and walked over to inspect her pups. Some eclampsias are slow to respond, but others are spectacularly quick, and I was grateful for the sake of my nervous system that this was one of the quick ones. In fact, the recovery was almost uncanny, because, after sniffing her family, Myrtle walked over to greet me, her eyes brimming with friendliness and her tail waving.

I was stroking her ears when Humphrey broke into a giggle. "You know, Jim, I've learned summat tonight," he drawled.

"What's that, Humphrey?"

"I've learned ... hee-hee-hee ... I've learned what a silly feller I've been all these months."

"How do you mean?"

He wagged a forefinger sagely. "Well, you've allus been tellin' me I was imaginin' things when I thought me dog was ill."

"Yes," I said. "That's right."

"And I never believed you, did I? Well, now I know you were right. I've been nobbut a fool." He waved a hand toward his bright-faced, tail-wagging little dog. "Just look at her. Anybody can see there was never anythin' wrong with Myrtle tonight."

5

It was a quiet moment in Skeldale House, and I was thinking back to the old bachelor days when my partner, Siegfried, his student brother, Tristan, and I all lived under that roof.

"You know, Jim," I remember Tristan saying on one of those long-ago mornings, "I often wonder if there is any other household where the mark of a lady's favor is expressed in goat manure."

"Well, isn't that funny," I'd said to Tristan on that occasion. "I've been thinking the same thing. It certainly is rather an odd business."

We had just come from the breakfast table. Mrs. Hall, our housekeeper, had always placed our letters next to our plates, and there, at Siegfried's place, dominating the scene like an emblem of triumph, stood the tin of goat droppings from Miss Grantley. We all knew what it was, despite its wrapping of brown paper, because she always used the same type of container—an empty cocoa tin about six inches high. Either she collected them from friends or she was very fond of cocoa.

One indisputable thing was that she was very fond of goats. They seemed almost to rule her existence, which was strange, because the care of goats was an unlikely hobby for a blond beauty who could have stepped effortlessly into the film world.

Another odd thing about Miss Grantley was that she had never married. Each time I had been at her house I had marveled that anybody like her was able to keep the men away. She would be about thirty, with a nicely rounded figure and elegant legs, and sometimes when I looked at the fine contours of her face I wondered whether that rather firm jaw might have frightened prospective suitors. But no, she was cheerful and charming; I decided that she just didn't want to get married. She had a lovely home and obviously plenty of money. She appeared to be perfectly happy.

There was no doubt at all that the goat droppings were a mark of favor. Miss Grantley took her stockkeeping very seriously and insisted on regular laboratory examination of feces samples for parasites. These samples were always addressed to Siegfried, and I had attached no importance to this until one morning, a few days after I had pleased her immensely by removing an embedded piece of chaff from one of her billies' eyes, the familiar tin appeared by my breakfast plate addressed to me.

That was when I realized it was a gesture of approval. In ancient days a feudal knight would carry a glove at his saddle bow or a scarf on his lance point as a symbol of his lady's esteem. With Miss Grantley it was goat droppings.

On the occasion when I got mine, Siegfried's face showed the slightest flicker of surprise and I suppose I might have shown a trace of smugness, but he needn't have worried. Within a week or two the tin reappeared at his end of the table. And after all, it was the natural thing, because if sheer male attractiveness entered into this situation, there was no doubt that Siegfried was out in front by a street. Tristan pursued the local girls enthusiastically and with considerable success; I had no reason to complain about my share of female company, but Siegfried was in a different class. He seemed to drive women mad.

He didn't have to chase them; they chased him. I hadn't known him long before I realized that the tales I had heard about the irresistible appeal of tall, lean-faced men were true. And when you added his natural charm and commanding personality, it was inevitable that the goat droppings would land regularly by his plate. In fact, that is how it was for a long time, even though Tristan and I paid almost as many visits to Miss Grantley's goats as Siegfried, because she called us out for the slightest ailment.

However, when I heard her voice on the telephone one morning, I knew that this time it wasn't for something trivial.

The Lord God Made Them All

She sounded agitated. "Mr. Herriot, Tina has caught her shoulder on a nail and torn herself badly. Can you come out immediately?"

"Yes, as it happens, I can. I'll leave right away."

A mild glow of satisfaction rippled through me. This would be just another stitching job, and I liked stitching. It was easy and always impressed the client. I would be on happier ground there than when Miss Grantley was quizzing me about goat diseases. They had taught me practically nothing about goats at college, and though I had read up on them, I was no expert.

I was leaving the room when Tristan levered himself slowly from the depths of the armchair where he spent a lot of his time. He yawned and stretched. "Miss Grantley's, eh? Think I'll come, too. Just feel like a ride out."

I smiled. "Okay, come on, then." He was always good company.

Miss Grantley met us in a silky, pale blue coverall that did nothing to diminish her attractions.

"Thank you so much for coming," she said. "Please follow me."

Following her was rewarding. In fact, on entering the goat house Tristan failed to see the step and fell onto his knees. Miss Grantley glanced at him briefly before hurrying to a pen at the far end.

"There she is," she said, and put a hand over her eyes. "I can't bear to look."

Tina was a fine white Saanen, but her beauty was ravaged by a huge laceration that had pulled the skin down from her shoulder in a long V, exposing the muscles down to the bone. It was a mess, but all superficial, and I could easily put it right and look very good in the process. Already I could see myself inserting the last stitch and pointing to the now almost invisible wound. "There now, that looks a lot better, doesn't it?" Miss Grantley would be in raptures.

Now she wrung her hands. "Do you think you can save her?"

"Oh yes." I nodded weightily. "It will be a big stitching job, but I feel sure she will pull through."

"Oh, thank heaven." She sighed, relieved. "I'll fetch hot water."

Soon I was ready for action. Tristan held Tina's head while I cleaned the area thoroughly and began to stitch. Miss Grantley

passed me the scissors to clip each suture. It was a nice smooth start, but it was a large wound and it would take some time. I searched my mind for light conversation.

Tristan chipped in, apparently thinking the same thing. "Wonderful animal, the goat," he said lightly.

"Ah yes." Miss Grantley gave him a bright smile. "I agree."

"When you think about it, they are probably the earliest domestic animals," he went on. "Cave paintings from prehistoric days show that they have been part of the world of man since recorded time. It is a fascinating thought."

From my squatting position I looked up at him in surprise. In my relationship with Tristan I had discovered several things that fascinated him, but goats were not one of them.

"And they have such a marvelous metabolism," he added. "They consume food other animals won't look at, and they produce abundant milk from that food."

"Yes, indeed," breathed Miss Grantley.

Tristan laughed. "They're such characters, too. Tough and hardy under all climatic conditions, absolutely fearless, and they can eat with impunity many poisonous plants that would kill most creatures."

"Oh, they *are* amazing." Miss Grantley gazed at my friend and passed the scissors to me without turning her head.

I felt I ought to make some contribution. "Goats certainly are extremely—" I began.

"But really, you know"—Tristan was in full flow again—"the thing that appeals to me most about them is their affectionate nature. Clearly that is why people become so attached to them."

Miss Grantley nodded gravely. "How true, how true."

My colleague stretched out a hand and fingered the hay in the animal's rack. "I see you feed them properly—thistles, bits of shrubs and coarse plants. Obviously you know that goats prefer rough stuff to grass. No wonder your animals are so healthy."

"Oh, thank you." She blushed faintly. "Of course I give them concentrates, too."

"Whole grain, I hope?"

"Oh yes, always."

"Good, good. Keeps up the pH of the rumen. Goats can get hypertrophy of the rumenal walls and inhibition of cellulose-digesting bacteria with a low pH."

Miss Grantley was staring at him as if he were a prophet.

"Can I have the scissors, please?" I grunted. I was beginning to feel cramped in my bent-over position and also a little piqued at the growing impression that my client had forgotten all about me. But I stitched on doggedly, one half of my mind watching thankfully as the skin gradually covered the denuded area, the other listening in amazement as Tristan pontificated on the construction of goat houses, their dimensions and ventilation.

A long time later I inserted the last suture and straightened up wearily. "Well now, that looks better, doesn't it?" I said, but it didn't have the impact I expected, because Tristan and my client were deeply involved in a discussion of the relative merits of the different breeds of goats.

Miss Grantley suddenly became aware that I had finished. "Oh, thank you," she said absently. "You have taken such pains. Now you must both come in for coffee."

As we balanced our cups on our knees in the elegant sitting room, Tristan carried on unabated, dealing in depth with the feeding of weaned kids and anesthesia for dehorning. Then Miss Grantley turned toward me. She was clearly still under his spell but no doubt felt that it would be only polite to bring me into the conversation.

"Mr. Herriot, one thing worries me. I share a pasture with the farmer next door, and my goats graze with his sheep. Now, I have heard that his animals are troubled with coccidiosis. Is there any chance that my goats could contract it from them?"

I took a long pull at my coffee cup to give myself time to think. "Well . . . er . . . I would say—"

My friend broke in again effortlessly. "Most unlikely. You don't need to worry on that account. Most types of coccidiosis are specific to their individual hosts."

"Thank you." Miss Grantley addressed me again, as though deciding to give me a last chance. "How about worms, Mr. Herriot? Can my goats become infected with worms from the sheep?"

"Ah now, let's see. . . ." I could feel a light perspiration breaking out on my brow. "The thing is—"

"Quite so," murmured Tristan, gliding once more to my aid. "As Mr. Herriot was about to say, there is a very real danger of infection with helminthiasis, since the common nematodes are the same in both species. You must always worm regularly, and if I can give you a brief program . . ."

I sank deeper in my chair and let him get on with it. It came to an end at last, and we went out to the car.

"I'll come back in ten days to remove the stitches," I said to Miss Grantley. It struck me that it was just about the only sensible thing I had said.

I drove a few hundred yards along the road, then I stopped the car and turned to my companion.

"Since when have you been a goat lover?" I demanded bitterly. "And where the hell did you get all that high-powered stuff you were preaching back there?"

Tristan giggled, then threw back his head and laughed immoderately. "Sorry, Jim," he said when he had recovered. "I have exams coming up in a few weeks, as you know, and I heard that one of the examiners is really goat-oriented. Last night I boned up on every bit of goat literature I could find. Uncanny how I had the opportunity to trot it all out so soon after."

"I see," I said. "You'd better let me see those things you read last night. I didn't realize I was so ignorant."

There was an interesting little sequel about a week later. Siegfried and I were going in to breakfast when my partner stopped in mid-stride and stared at the table. The familiar brown-wrapped cocoa tin was there, but this time it was at his brother's place. Slowly he walked over and examined the label. I had a look, too, and there was no mistake. It was addressed to "Mr. Tristan Farnon."

Siegfried said nothing but sat down at the head of the table. Soon the young man himself joined us, examined the tin with interest and started on his meal.

No one said a word, but the undeniable fact hung heavy in the room. Tristan—for the moment at least—was top man.

6

THE farmer moved between the cows and took hold of my patient's tail, and when I saw the man's haircut, I knew immediately that Josh Anderson had been on the job again. It was a Sunday morning, and everything fitted into place.

"Were you in the Hare and Pheasant last night?" I inquired carelessly as I inserted a thermometer in the cow.

The farmer ran a hand ruefully over his head. "Aye. I should've known better, pickin' a Saturday night."

Josh Anderson was one of the local barbers. He liked his job, but he also liked his beer. In fact, he took his scissors and clippers to the pub with him every night. For the price of a pint, he would give anybody a quick trim in the gents' lavatory. With beer at sixpence a pint it was good value, but Josh's clients knew they were taking a chance. If the barber's intake had been moderate, they would escape relatively unscathed—the standard of hairstyling in Darrowby was not fastidious—but if he had imbibed more than his usual eight pints, as he did on Saturday nights, terrible things could happen.

I looked again at the farmer's head. From my experience I judged that Josh could have been around the ten-pint mark when he did that one. The upper hair seemed to have been delved into at random, leaving bare patches in some parts and long, dangling wisps in others. No doubt the back would be interesting, too; there could be a pigtail or anything lurking there.

Yes, I decided, definitely a ten-pinter. After twelve to fourteen pints, Josh was inclined to cast away all caution and simply run over his victim's head with the clippers, leaving a tuft in front— the classic convict's crop that necessitated wearing a cap for several weeks thereafter.

I always played safe; when my hair needed cutting, I went to Josh's shop, where he operated in strict sobriety.

I was sitting there a few days later, waiting my turn with my dog, Sam, under my seat. There was a burly man in the barber chair, and his red face, reflected in the mirror, was contorted every few seconds with spasms of pain. Because the simple fact was that Josh didn't cut hair, he pulled it out. He did this not only because his equipment was antiquated and needed sharpening, but because he had perfected a certain flick of the wrist with his hand clippers, which wrenched the hairs from their follicles at the end of each stroke.

The wonder was that anybody went to Josh for a haircut, because there was another barber close by. Perhaps it was that everybody liked him.

Sitting there in his shop, I looked at him as he worked. He was a tiny man in his fifties with a gentle smile that never seemed to leave his face; that smile and his big, curiously unworldly eyes gave him an unusual attraction. As his client rose from the chair, patently relieved to have his ordeal over, Josh fussed around him, brushing him down and chattering gaily. You could see his obvious love of his fellowmen.

Next to his burly client, Josh looked smaller than ever, and I marveled at how he managed to accommodate all that beer. Even now, after forty years in Yorkshire, I cannot compete. Maybe it is my Glasgow upbringing, but after two or three pints discomfort sets in. The remarkable thing is that throughout the years I can hardly recall seeing a Yorkshireman drunk. They become progressively more jovial as the long cascade goes down their throats, but they seldom fall about or do anything silly. Josh, for instance, would swallow around eight pints every night of the week, except Saturday, when he stepped up his intake to between ten and fourteen, yet he never looked much different. His professional skill suffered, but that was all.

He was turning to me now. "Well, Mr. Herriot, it's good to see you again." He warmed me with his smile and those wide almost mystic eyes as he ushered me to the chair. "Are you well?"

"I'm fine, thank you, Mr. Anderson," I replied. "And you?"

"Nicely, sir, nicely." He began to tuck the sheet under my chin, then laughed delightedly as my little beagle trotted in under the folds. "By gum, Mr. Herriot, Sam's a faithful friend. Never lets you out of 'is sight if he can help it."

"That's right," I said. "And I don't like to go anywhere without him." I swiveled around in my chair. "By the way, didn't I see you with a dog the other day?"

Josh paused, scissors in hand. "You did an' all. A little stray. Got 'er from the Cat and Dog Home at York and she's a grand un. Now that our kids have all left home, t'missus and I fancied gettin' a dog, and we think the world of her."

"What breed is she?"

"Eee, now you're askin'. Nobbut a mongrel, I reckon. I can't see any pedigree about her, but money wouldn't buy 'er. Hang on a minute and I'll bring 'er down."

He clumped upstairs, to where he lived above the shop, and returned with a little bitch in his arms. "There you are, Mr. Herriot. What d'you think of that?" He stood her on the floor for my inspection.

The little animal looked like a miniature Wensleydale sheep, light gray in color, with long, crinkled hair. Definitely a hound of baffling lineage, but the swishing tail bore witness to her good nature.

"I like her," I said. "I think you've picked a winner."

"That's what we think." He stooped and fondled his new pet, picking up the long hairs and rubbing them gently between finger and thumb. It looked a little odd, then it occurred to me that that was what he was used to doing with his human customers. "We've called her Venus," he said.

"Venus?"

"Aye, because she's so beautiful." His tone was serious.

"Ah yes," I said. "I see."

He washed his hands, took up his scissors and grasped a few strands of my hair. Again he went through the procedure of rubbing the hairs between his fingers before cutting them.

I couldn't understand why he did this, but I was too preoccupied to give the matter much thought. I felt an uncomfortable tug as the scissors' blunt edges came together. Still, it wasn't too bad until he reached for the clippers; then I gripped the arms of the chair as though I were at the dentist's. That jerk at the end, plucking the last tuft from its roots, set me grimacing at the mirror. Once or twice an involuntary "Ooh!" or "Aah!" escaped me, but Josh gave no sign of having heard; never had I seen him react to his customers' stifled cries of pain.

Though he was the least arrogant of men, Josh considered himself a gifted hairdresser. Even now, as he gave me a final combing, I could see the pride shining from his face. Head on one side, he made a finicky snip here and there before holding up the hand mirror for my inspection. "All right, Mr. Herriot?"

"Lovely, Mr. Anderson." Relief added warmth to my voice.

"Aye, you know, it's easy to cut hair off. The secret is knowin' what to leave on."

I had heard him say it a hundred times before, but I laughed dutifully as he whisked his brush over the back of my coat.

My hair used to grow pretty fast, but I didn't need to pay another visit to the barber before he arrived at my door one day carrying Venus in his arms. She was a vastly different creature from the placid little animal I had seen in his shop. She was bubbling saliva, retching and pawing frantically at her face.

"Tell me what's happened, Mr. Anderson. Has she swallowed something?"

"Aye, a chicken bone." Josh looked distraught.

"A chicken bone! Don't you know you should never give a dog chicken bones?"

"Aye, ah know, ah know, but we'd had a bird for our dinner and she pinched the frame out of the dustbin. She had a good crunch at it afore I spotted 'er, and now she's goin' to choke!" He was on the verge of tears.

"Now just calm down," I said. "I don't think Venus is choking. By the way she's pawing, I'd say something's stuck in her mouth."

I forced her jaws apart and saw—with a surge of relief—a long bone sliver jammed tightly between the back molars, forming a bar across the roof of the mouth. This was a common occurrence in practice, easily relieved by a flick of the forceps.

I put my hand on the barber's shoulder. "You can stop worrying, Mr. Anderson, it's just a bone stuck in her teeth. Come into the consulting room and I'll have it out in a jiffy."

I could see the man relaxing as we walked to the back of the house. "Oh, thank God for that, Mr. Herriot. I thought she'd had it, honest, I did. And we've grown right fond of the little thing. I couldn't bear to lose 'er."

"No question of that, I assure you." I put the dog on the table and reached for my forceps. "This won't take a minute."

Jimmy, now five, had trailed after us, and he watched with mild interest as I poised the instrument. Even at his age, he had seen this sort of thing many times and it wasn't very exciting. But you never knew in veterinary practice; it was worth hanging around, because funny things could happen. He put his hands in his pockets and rocked back and forth on his heels, whistling softly as he watched me.

Usually it is simply a matter of opening the mouth, clamping the forceps on the bone and removing it. But Venus recoiled in terror from the gleaming metal and so did the barber. I tried to be soothing. "This is nothing, Mr. Anderson. I'm not going to hurt her in the least. Just hold her head firmly for a moment."

He took a deep breath, grasped the dog's neck and shut his eyes. Venus struggled violently, pawing at my hand to the accompaniment of her owner's moans. When I did get the forceps into her mouth, she locked her front teeth on the instrument and hung on fiercely. Finally Mr. Anderson could stand it no longer and let go. The little dog leaped to the floor while Jimmy watched appreciatively.

"Let's have another go," I said to the barber.

Josh bent and extended trembling hands toward his dog, but each time he touched her she slithered away until, with a great shuddering sigh, he flopped face down on the tiles. Jimmy giggled. Things were looking up.

I helped the barber to his feet. "I tell you what, Mr. Anderson. I'll cut out this struggling with a short-acting anesthetic."

Josh paled. "Put her to sleep? Will she be all right?"

"Of course. Just leave her to me and come back for her in an hour. She'll be able to walk then." I began to steer him out. "We'll only upset her if we go on this way."

"Very well, then. I'll go along to me brother's for an hour."

"Splendid." I waited till I heard the front door close behind him, then quickly made up a dose of Pentothal. Dogs do not put on such a tough front when their owners are not present, and I scooped Venus easily from the floor onto the table. I slid the needle into a vein and within seconds she was asleep.

"No trouble now, Jimmy, lad," I said. I pushed the teeth apart effortlessly, gripped the bone with the forceps and lifted it from the mouth. "Lovely. All done."

I dropped the bone into the waste bin. "Yes, my boy. That's the professional way to do it. No undignified scrambling."

My son nodded briefly. Events had gone dull again. He had been hoping for great things when Mr. Anderson draped himself on our floor, but this was tame stuff. He had stopped smiling.

My own satisfied smile had become a little fixed. I was watching Venus carefully, and she wasn't breathing. I tried to ignore the lurch in my stomach, because I have always been a nervous anesthetist. I told myself there was no danger. She had received the correct dose, and you often get this reaction with Pentothal. But just the same I wished to God she would start breathing.

The heart was still going all right. I depressed the ribs a few times—nothing. I touched the unseeing eyeball—no corneal reflex. As I stared closely at Venus, I could tell that Jimmy was watching me keenly, his unerring instinct for the unpredictable aroused.

His hunch was proved right when I suddenly lifted Venus from the table, shook her vainly a few times above my head, then set off at full gallop along the passage. I could hear the eager shuffle of Jimmy's slippers just behind me.

I threw open the side door and shot into the back garden. The little dog's ribs still were not moving and the eyes stared sightlessly ahead. Oh, this just couldn't happen!

I seized Venus by a hind leg in either hand and began to whirl her around my head, attaining a remarkable speed as I put all my strength into the swing. This method of resuscitation seems to have gone out of fashion now, but it was very much in vogue then. It certainly met with the full approval of my son. In his ignorant glee over his father's funny behavior, he laughed so much that he fell down and sprawled on the grass. When I stopped and glared at the still immobile ribs, he cried, "Again, Daddy, again." And he didn't have to wait more than a few seconds before Daddy was in full action once more, with Venus swooping through the air like a bird on the wing.

It exceeded all Jimmy's expectations. How gloriously he had been rewarded. To this day the scene is vivid: my tension and misery lest my patient should die, and in the background the helpless, high-pitched laughter of my son.

I don't know how many times I stopped, then recommenced my whirling; but at last, at one of the intervals, the chest wall gave a heave and the eyes blinked. With a gasp of relief I collapsed face down on the cool turf and peered through the green blades as the breathing became regular and Venus began to lick her lips and look around.

Jimmy was disappointed. "Aren't you going to do any more?"

"No, son, no." I sat up and dragged Venus onto my lap. "It's all over now."

"Well, that was funny. Why did you do it?"

"To make the dog breathe."

"Do you always do that to make them breathe?"

"No, thank heaven, not often." I got slowly to my feet and carried Venus back to the consulting room.

By the time Josh Anderson arrived, his pet was looking almost normal. "She's still a little unsteady from the anesthetic," I said. "But that won't last long."

"Eee, isn't that grand! And that nasty bone, is it . . . ?"

"All gone, Mr. Anderson." I opened her mouth. "You see? Not a thing."

He smiled happily. "Did ye have any bother with her?"

I swallowed. To tell him that his dog had been almost dead for a considerable time would not cheer him, nor would it bolster his faith in me. Out came the whitest of lies: "A quite uneventful operation, Mr. Anderson."

"Wonderful, wonderful. I am grateful, Mr. Herriot." He bent over the dog, and again I noticed the strange rolling of the strands of hair between his fingers.

"Have ye been floatin' through the air, Venus?" he murmured.

The back of my neck prickled. "What . . . makes you ask?"

He turned his eyes up to me, those eyes with their unworldly depths. "Well . . . I reckon she'd think she was floatin' while she was asleep. Just a funny feeling I had."

"Ah yes, well, er . . . right." I had a very funny feeling myself. "You'd better take her home now and keep her quiet for the rest of the day."

When he left I was very thoughtful: floating . . . floating.

A fortnight later I was again seated in Josh's barber chair. Usually he began with the scissors, but today he started straight in with the dread clippers. In an attempt to alleviate the pain, I began to chatter. "How is—ouch—Venus getting on?"

"Oh fine, fine." Josh smiled at me tenderly in the mirror as he whipped out another tuft with that inimitable flick of his. "The thing is, Mr. Herriot, it's grand to 'ave faith in your vet. I knew our little pet was in good 'ands."

"It's—aaah—nice to hear that." Tired of trying to speak while he tugged away, I made an effort to concentrate on something else—a trick I adopt at the dentist's. I thought as hard as I could about my garden at Skeldale House; the lawns really did want mowing, and there were all those weeds to get at when I had a minute to spare. I had got around to considering whether it was time to put some fertilizer on my tomatoes when the barber's voice pulled me back to reality.

"Mr. Herriot." He was twiddling away at a wisp of my hair with his fingers. "I like gardening, too."

I almost jumped from the chair. "That's remarkable! I was just thinking about my garden."

"Aye, ah know." His eyes had a faraway look as he rolled and rolled with finger and thumb. "It comes through the hair, ye know. Your thoughts. They come through to me."

"What!"

"Yes. Well, just think about it, Mr. Herriot. Them hairs go right down into your head, and they catch summat from your brain and send it up to me."

"Oh really, you're kidding me." I gave a loud laugh that nevertheless had a hollow ring.

Josh shook his head. "No, I'm not jokin' nor jestin', Mr. Herriot. I've been at this game for forty years, and it keeps happenin' to me. You'd be flabbergasted if I told ye some of the thoughts that's come up. Couldn't repeat 'em, I tell ye."

I slumped lower in my white sheet. Absolute rubbish and nonsense, of course. But I made a firm resolve never to think of Venus' anesthetic during a haircut.

7

"This is Biggins 'ere."

I gripped the telephone tightly. Mr. Biggins' vacillations always tried me sorely. He regarded calling out the vet as a final desperate measure, and it was sheer torture for him to make up his mind to do it. On top of that, he was extremely pigheaded about taking my advice when I did go to his farm, and I knew beyond doubt that I had never managed to please him.

He had made me suffer during my pre-RAF days, and now, with the war well over, he was still there, a bit older and a bit more pigheaded.

"What's the trouble, Mr. Biggins?" I asked.

"Well . . . I 'ave a heifer badly."

"Right, I'll have a look at her this morning."

"Haud on, just a minute." Mr. Biggins was still not sure he wanted me there. "Are you sure she needs seein'?"

"Well, I don't know. What is she doing?"

"She's been off her grub for a week, and now . . ." There was a long pause. "She's just laid out, like."

"That sounds serious," I said. "I'll be along as soon as possible."

"Ah, but . . . but . . . are ye sure there's any need . . . ?"

I put down the receiver. I knew from hard experience that

this conversation could go on for a long time. I also knew that I was probably visiting a hopeless case, but if I got there immediately, I might be able to do something.

I was on the farm within ten minutes, and Mr. Biggins met me with his typical attitude—hands in pockets, shoulders hunched, eyes regarding me suspiciously from under a thick fringe of graying eyebrows. "Ye're ower late," he grunted.

I stopped with one foot out of the car. "You mean she's dead?"

"Nay, but just about. Ye're too late to do owt now."

I gritted my teeth. This animal had been ill for a week, I had arrived ten minutes after being summoned, but the farmer's tone was unequivocal; if it died it would be my fault.

"Ah well," I said, trying to relax. "If she's dying, there's nothing I can do." I began to get back into the car.

Mr. Biggins lowered his head and kicked at a cobblestone. "Are ye not going to look at 'er while you're 'ere?"

"I will, if that's what you want." I climbed out again.

He hesitated. "Will ye charge me extra?"

"No, I won't. I've made the journey here, and if I can't do anything more, that's all you'll pay for."

The sight in the fold yard was sadly familiar: the skinny young beast lying in a deep coma, eyes glazed and moving every few seconds with the slow nystagmus of approaching death.

"Yes, you're right, Mr. Biggins," I said. "She's dying." I picked up my bag and began to leave.

The farmer gave me a truculent stare. "So you're just goin' to walk away without doin' owt? I've allus heard that where there's life, there's hope."

"Not in this case, I assure you. But if you like, I can try a stimulant injection."

"It's not what ah like. You're t'one that's supposed to know."

"Very well, I'll have a try," I said. But as I slipped the needle in and depressed the plunger, Mr. Biggins gave tongue again.

"Expensive things, injections. How much will this cost me?"

"I honestly don't know." My brain was beginning to reel.

"You'll know awright when you get t'pen in your 'and to send me that big bill, won't ye?"

I didn't answer. As the last drop of fluid trickled into the vein, the heifer extended her forelimbs, stared sightlessly ahead for a second, then stopped breathing. I put my hand over her heart. "I'm afraid she's dead, Mr. Biggins."

The farmer rubbed his chin. "Well, you've wasted me money with that injection. What was t'matter with 'er?"

"I don't know. You would need a postmortem examination to find the cause."

The farmer began to pluck excitedly at his coat. "Well, this is a funny carry-on. I 'ave a dead beast here, and nobody knows what killed her. Could be anything. Could be anthrax!"

"Oh no, Mr. Biggins. Anthrax is very sudden, and you say this heifer was ill for over a week."

"Nay, nay, not right ill. Just a bit off, then she went down like a shot at t'end. That was sudden enough! And Fred Bramley along t'road had a beast wi' anthrax last month, didn't he? The Darrowby and Houlton *Times* was on about it, and they said that all sudden deaths should be examined for anthrax because it was fatal to people." Mr. Biggins stuck his jaw out. "I want ma heifer examined!"

"Okay," I replied wearily. "If you say so. As it happens, I've brought my microscope with me."

"Microscope? That sounds costly. How much will that be?"

"That's all right, the Ministry pays me," I said, and began to walk toward the house.

Mr. Biggins raised his voice. "Where you goin' now?"

"Inside. I've got to use your phone to report to the Ministry. I can't do anything till I get permission."

He stood by me as I spoke to the Ministry clerk, impatiently fidgeting as I asked him for the proper name of the farm and the breed of the heifer. "Didn't know ah'd have to go through all this," he mumbled.

I went out and got my postmortem knife. I made a nick at the root of the heifer's tail, smeared some blood onto a glass slide and took this, along with the microscope, into the farmhouse kitchen. I fixed the film of blood by drawing it through the flames in the hearth, then moved to the sink and poured methylene blue over the slide. In the process a small blue pool formed in the white sink bottom, and the coloration stayed there after I had swilled the slide with water from the tap.

"Look at that!" Mr. Biggins exclaimed. "You've stained t'sink. The missus'll play 'ell when she gets home this afternoon."

I forced a smile. "Don't worry, it will come off easily." But I could see he didn't believe me.

I dried the slide off at the fire, rigged up the microscope and peered through the eyepiece. As I expected, not an anthrax bacillus in sight. "Well, there's nothing there," I said. "You can call the knacker man quite safely."

Mr. Biggins made a long-suffering gesture. "All that fuss for nothin'."

As I drove away I felt, not for the first time, that you couldn't win with Mr. Biggins, and the conviction was strengthened a month later when he came into the surgery. "One of me cows has wooden tongue," he announced. "I want some iodine to paint on."

Siegfried looked up from the daybook, where he was checking the visits. "Oh, you're a bit out of date, Mr. Biggins," he said, smiling. "That treatment went out years ago. We've got far better medicine now—sulfanilamide."

The farmer took his usual stance, head down, glowering under his eyebrows. "Big fancy word, Mr. Farnon. But ah want the stuff I've allus used."

"Mr. Biggins," said Siegfried in his most reasonable tone. "I wouldn't be a competent veterinary surgeon if I prescribed something so totally outdated." He turned to me. "James, would you slip through to the stockroom and bring a pound packet of the sulfanilamide?"

Mr. Biggins was protesting as I hurried out and was still at it when I returned. Siegfried's smile had faded and I could see that his patience was running out. He seized the packet from me and began to write the instructions on it.

"Three tablespoonfuls in a pint of water daily—"

"But ah tell you ah got no faith in them new things—"

"And after you've used the packet, let us know, and we'll give you more if necessary."

The farmer glared at my partner. "That stuff'll do no good."

"Mr. Biggins," Siegfried said with ominous calm. "It will cure your cow."

"It won't!"

"It will!" Siegfried brought his hand down on the desk with a thud. Clearly he had had enough. "Take this, and if it doesn't do the trick, I won't charge you, all right?"

Something for nothing was irresistible. Mr. Biggins took the sulfanilamide.

"Splendid!" Siegfried jumped up and patted the farmer's shoulder. "Now, get in touch with us when you've used it. I bet you anything your cow will soon be better."

About ten days later Siegfried and I were out on a call together, and on our return we passed Mr. Biggins' farm. "Tell you what, James," my colleague murmured. "Let's drop in. We haven't heard from our friend about the sulfanilamide. Doesn't want to lose face, I suspect." He laughed softly. "We'll be able to rub it in a bit."

He drove around to the back of the house. Outside the kitchen door Siegfried raised his hand to knock, then he stopped and said in an urgent whisper, "Look at that, James!"

He pointed to the kitchen window, and there on the sill was our packet, still unopened. My partner clenched his fist. "The old blighter! He wouldn't even try it—out of sheer spite."

At that moment the farmer opened the door and Siegfried greeted him cheerfully. "Ah, good morning, Mr. Biggins. We were just passing and thought we'd check on your cow." He held up a reassuring hand. "No charge. This is just for our own interest."

"But . . . but . . . I've got me slippers on. Was just havin' a cup o' tea. There's no need for ye to—"

Siegfried was already striding toward the cow byre. The patient was easy to pick out. Her skin was stretched tightly over the jutting ribs, saliva drooled from her lips and a long swelling bulged from under her jaw. Siegfried moved to her quickly, opened the mouth and fingered the tongue.

"Feel that, James," he said softly.

I ran my hand over the knobbly hard surface that gave wooden tongue—or actinobacillosis—its name. "This is awful. It's a wonder she can eat at all." I sniffed at my fingers. "And there's iodine here."

Siegfried nodded. "Yes, he's been to the chemist, despite what I said."

At that moment Mr. Biggins hurried in, panting slightly. My partner looked at him sadly. "Well, you were right. Our medicine hasn't done a bit of good. I can't understand it." He rubbed his chin. "And your poor cow is a mess, I'm afraid. Almost starving to death. I do apologize."

The farmer's face was a study. "Aye, well . . . that's right . . . she's done no good. . . ."

Siegfried broke in. "Look here," he said. "I feel responsible for this. My medicine has failed, so it's up to me to get her right. I have an injection here that ought to do it."

"Now then, wait a minute. . . . I don't know . . ."

But the farmer's words went unheeded as my colleague began to fill a syringe from a bottle I couldn't recognize. With the needle ready for entry he glanced at Mr. Biggins. "It's a good job you've been using our medicine; on its own this injection could have serious effects."

"You mean . . . it could kill 'er?"

"Just possible," Siegfried murmured. "But you've nothing to worry about. She's had the sulfanilamide."

He was about to plunge the needle in when the farmer gave tongue. "Hey, haud on. Don't do that!"

"What is it, Mr. Biggins? Something wrong?"

"Nay, nay, but there's maybe been a bit of a misunderstandin'. Ye see, ah don't think she's been gettin' enough of your stuff."

Siegfried lowered his arm. "You mean you've been underdosing? I wrote the instructions on the packet, if you remember."

"That's right. But ah must have got a bit mixed up."

"No matter. As long as you return her to full dosage, all will be well." Siegfried inserted the needle, ignoring Mr. Biggins' yelp of alarm.

As he put the syringe back in its case, he sighed with satisfaction. "Well, I'm sure that will do the trick. But remember, start

again with the full three tablespoons and continue till you've finished the packet. Let us know if you need a further supply."

As we drove away I stared at my colleague. "What the devil was that injection?"

"Oh, mixed vitamins. It'll help the poor thing's condition, but it had nothing to do with the wooden tongue. Just part of my plan." He smiled gleefully. "Now he's *got* to use the sulfanilamide. It will be interesting to see what happens."

It was indeed interesting. Within a week Mr. Biggins was back in the surgery, looking sheepish.

"Can I have some more o' that stuff?" he muttered.

"By all means." Siegfried extended his arm in an expansive gesture. "As much as you like. I suppose the cow is looking better?"

"Aye."

"Stopped slavering? Putting on flesh, is she?"

"Aye." Mr. Biggins lowered his head as though he didn't want to answer more questions. Siegfried gave him another packet.

When he had left, we watched him through the window. My partner thumped me on the shoulder. "Well, James, that was a little victory. At last we've beaten Mr. Biggins."

The victory was very sweet. Still, when I look back over the years, I realize that that was the only time we did beat him.

8

"This is Amber," Sister Rose said. "The one I wanted you to examine."

I looked at the pale, almost honey-colored hair on the dog's ears and flanks. "I can see why you've given her that name. I bet she'd really glow in the sunshine."

The nurse laughed. "Yes, it was sunny when I first saw her, and the name just jumped into my mind." She gave me a sideways glance. "I'm good at names, you know."

"Oh yes, without a doubt," I said, smiling. It was a little joke between us. Sister Rose had to be good at christening the endless stream of unwanted animals passing through the little dog sanctuary that she maintained behind her house. As a nursing sister she already led a full life of service to the human race. I often asked myself how she found time to fight for the animals, too.

"Where did this one come from?" I asked.

Sister Rose shrugged. "Oh, found wandering in the streets of Hebbleton. Obviously abandoned."

Anger tightened in my throat. "How could anyone do this to such a beautiful dog? Just turn it away to fend for itself."

"People have astonishing reasons. In Amber's case, I think it's because of a little skin disease. Perhaps it frightened them."

"They could at least have taken her to a vet," I grunted as I opened the door of the pen. I noticed some bare patches around the toes, and as I knelt to examine them, Amber nuzzled my cheek and wagged her tail. I looked up at her, at the flopping ears, the pronounced jowls and the trusting eyes that had been betrayed.

"It's a hound's face," I said. "But how about the rest of her? What breed would you call her?"

Sister Rose laughed. "It beats me."

I didn't know either. The body, dappled with patches of brown, black and white, was the wrong shape for a hound. She had very large feet, a long, thin tail in constant motion and everywhere on her coat the delicate sheen of gold.

"Well," I said. "Whatever she is, she's a bonny one, and good-natured, too." I opened the mouth and looked at the rows of untainted teeth. "I'd say she's nine or ten months old—she's just a big pup."

"She'll be really large when she reaches full size."

As if to prove the sister's words, the young bitch reared up and planted her forefeet on my chest. I looked again at the laughing mouth and those eyes. "Amber," I said. "I really like you."

"Oh, I'm so glad," Sister Rose said. "We must get this skin trouble cleared up quickly, so I can find her a home. It's just a bit of eczema, isn't it?"

"Probably . . . probably. . . . I see there's some bareness around the eyes and cheeks, too." Skin diseases in dogs, as in humans, are tricky things, often baffling in origin and difficult to cure. I didn't like the combination here of feet and face, but the skin was dry and sound. Maybe it was nothing much. I banished to the back of my mind a specter that appeared for a brief instant. I didn't want to worry Sister Rose.

"Yes, probably eczema," I said briskly. "Rub in this ointment well twice a day." I handed over a mixture of zinc oxide and lanolin. That, together with the nurse's good feeding, I hoped would do the trick.

When two weeks passed without news of Amber, I was relieved. Then Sister Rose phoned one morning. "Mr. Herriot, those bare patches aren't any better. In fact, they're spreading up her legs and on the face."

The specter leaped up again. "I'll come right out, Sister," I said, and on my way to the car I picked up the microscope.

Amber greeted me as before, with dancing eyes and lashing tail, but I felt sick when I saw the ragged denudation of the face and legs. I got hold of the young animal and held her close, sniffing at the hairless areas.

Sister Rose looked at me in surprise. "What are you doing?"

"Trying to detect a mousy smell. And it's there."

"What does that mean?"

"Mange."

"Oh dear." The nurse put a hand to her mouth. "That's rather nasty, isn't it." Then she put back her shoulders in a characteristic gesture. "Well, I've had experience with mange before, and I can tackle it. I've always been able to clear it up with sulfur baths."

I put Amber down and stood up, feeling suddenly weary. "Yes, but you're thinking of sarcoptic mange, Sister. I'm afraid this is something worse. It looks like demodectic mange." I decided to bite the bullet. "Often incurable."

The specter was very large in my mind now. This disease had haunted me ever since I had qualified, and I had seen many fine dogs put to sleep after prolonged attempts to treat them.

I brought my microscope over from the car. "But I may be jumping the gun. I hope I am. This is the only way to find out."

I squeezed and scraped a patch on Amber's left foreleg with a scalpel blade and prepared a glass slide. Then I looked at it under the microscope and there it was—the dread mite, *Demodex canis*. And there wasn't just one. The whole microscope field was teeming with them.

"There's no doubt about it, Sister," I said. "I'm sorry."

The corners of her mouth drooped. "But . . . isn't there anything we can do?"

"Oh yes, we can try. And we're going to try like anything, because I've taken a fancy to Amber. I've cured a few *Demodex* cases in my time with a lotion." I went to the car and fished around in the trunk. "Here it is—Odylen. Rub it on every day. It may just work."

Sister Rose stuck out her jaw with the determination that had saved so many animals. "I'm sure we can succeed. But how about my other dogs? Won't they become infected?"

I shook my head. "Unlike the sarcoptic mange, demodectic is rarely contagious."

"That's something, anyway. But how on earth does a dog get the disease in the first place?"

"We don't know," I said. "The veterinary profession is pretty well convinced that all dogs have some *Demodex* mites in their skins, but why they should cause mange in some and not in others is unclear. Heredity has something to do with it, because it sometimes occurs in several dogs in the same litter. But it's a baffling business."

I left Sister Rose with the can of Odylen. Maybe this would be one of the exceptions to my experiences with the disease. But within a week I heard from her again. Although she had been applying the Odylen faithfully, the condition was spreading.

I hurried out there. Amber's tail-wagging cheerfulness was undiminished, but her face was disfigured by increasing hairlessness, and when I thought of the beauty that had captivated me on my first visit, the sight was like a blow. I had to try something else, so I started her on a course of Fowler's solution of arsenic, which at that time was popular in treating skin conditions.

When ten days passed I had begun to hope, and it was a bitter disappointment when Sister Rose telephoned just after breakfast, her voice trembling. "Mr. Herriot, she really is deteriorating. Nothing seems to do any good. I'm beginning to think that—"

I cut her off in midsentence. "I'll be there within the hour. Don't give up hope yet. These cases sometimes take months."

I knew as I drove to Sister Rose's sanctuary that my words had no real substance. But I had tried to say something helpful because there was nothing she hated more than putting a dog to sleep. Of all the hundreds of animals she had cared for, I could remember only a handful that had defeated her—very old dogs with chronic kidney or heart conditions, or young ones with distemper. With all the others she had battled until they were fit to go to their new homes. And I myself recoiled from the idea of putting Amber down. Something about that dog had taken hold of me.

When I arrived I still had no idea what I was going to do, so when I spoke, my words rather surprised me. "Sister, I've come to take Amber home with me. You've got enough to do here, looking after your other dogs. I know you've done everything possible, but I'd like to take on this job myself."

"But . . . how will you find the time?"

"I can treat her in the evenings, and this way I'll be able to monitor her progress. I'm determined to get her right."

Driving back to the surgery, I was surprised at the depth of my feeling. Throughout my career I have often had this compulsive desire to cure an animal, but never stronger than with Amber. She was delighted to be in the car with me—she capered around, licking my ear, resting her paws on the dash and peering through the windshield. I looked at her happy face, scarred by the disease, and thumped my hand on the wheel. This was one case that was going to get better.

We had no facilities for boarding dogs—few vets did have at that time—but I made up a comfortable pen for her in the old stable in the yard. Despite its age, the building was free from drafts. She would be snug in there.

I made another decision: to keep Helen out of the whole business. I remembered how stricken she had been when we adopted a cat and then lost him to his rightful owner, and I knew she would soon grow too fond of this dog. But I had forgotten about myself. Veterinary surgeons could never last professionally if they became too involved with their patients. But before I knew what was happening, I became involved with Amber.

I fed her myself, changed her bedding and carried out the treatment. It was late November and darkness came early; after my visits at the farms I always drove around to my yard and trained the headlights on the stable. When I threw open the door, Amber was invariably waiting to welcome me, her forefeet resting on the top of her pen, her long yellow ears gleaming in the bright beam. And her tail swished the straw unceasingly even as I did all the uncomfortable procedures: rubbing the tender skin with lotion, injecting her with staph toxoid and taking further skin scrapings to check progress.

As the days and weeks went by and I saw no improvement, I became a little desperate. I gave her sulfur baths, derris baths and a multitude of shampoos and washes then on the market. I hoped there might be a magic cure among them, despite my misgivings. And I think I might have gone on indefinitely with these nightly sessions under the headlights, if it hadn't been for one very dark evening, when I seemed to see the young dog for the first time. The condition had spread over her entire body. The long ears were golden no longer—they were almost bald, as was the rest of her face and head. Everywhere her skin was thickened and wrinkled and had a bluish tinge.

I flopped back and sat down in the straw while Amber leaped around me, licking and wagging. Despite her terrible state, her nature was unchanged.

But this couldn't go on. I knew now that she and I had come to the end of the road. As I tried to think, I stroked her head, and her cheerful eyes were pathetic in the scarecrow face. What was I going to tell Sister Rose after all my brave words?

It took me until the following noon to summon the will to telephone her. In my effort to be matter-of-fact, I was almost brusque. "Sister," I said, "I'm afraid it's all over with Amber. I've tried everything, and she has got worse. I do think it would be the kindest thing to put her to sleep."

Shock was evident in the good lady's voice. "But . . . it seems so awful. Just for a skin disease."

"I know, but this is a dreadful thing. Amber is very uncomfortable now, and she'll soon be in pain. We can't let her go on."

"Oh . . . well, I trust in your judgment, Mr. Herriot. I know you wouldn't do anything that wasn't necessary." There was a long pause, and I knew she was trying to control her voice. Then she spoke calmly. "Very well. I leave everything to you."

A rush of work kept me going all afternoon, so it was, as always, pitch-dark when I drove into the yard and opened the stable doors. And it was like all the other times. Amber was there in the beam, tail wagging with delight, welcoming me. For a long time I made a fuss over her, patting her and talking to her as she leaped up at me. Then I filled the syringe.

"Sit, girl," I said, and she flopped obediently onto her hindquarters. I gripped her right leg to raise the radial vein, and Amber looked at me with interest, wondering what new game this might be as I slipped in the needle. I realized that there was no need to say the comforting things I always said: "She won't know a thing. . . . This is just an overdose of anesthetic," or "It's an easy way out for her." There was no sorrowing owner to hear me. There were just the two of us.

And as I murmured, "Good girl, Amber, good lass," while she sank down on the straw, I had the conviction that if I had said those comforting things, they would have been true. She *didn't* know a thing between her playfulness and oblivion, and it was indeed an easy way out from her suffering, which soon would have become torture. I stepped from the pen and switched off the car lights, and in the cold darkness the yard had never seemed so empty. After the weeks of struggle, the sense of loss and failure was overpowering.

For a long time I carried a weight around with me, and I feel some of it now after all these years, whenever the picture of her comes into my mind: in the picture it is always dark and Amber is always in the headlight's beam.

Today, demodectic mange can often be cured with organophosphates and antibiotics. Neither was available back when Amber needed them. The tragedy of Amber was that she was born too soon.

9

"Just look at that," the farmer said.

"At what?" I was "cleansing" a cow—removing the afterbirth—and my arm was buried deep in the cow's uterus. I turned my head to see him pointing at the animal's udder. Four white jets of milk were spurting out of it onto the floor.

He grinned. "That's a funny thing, isn't it?"

"Not really," I said. "It's a reflex action from the brain caused by my hand twiddling the uterus about. I often see cows letting their milk down like that when I'm cleansing them."

"Well, that's a rum un." The farmer laughed. "Any road, you'd better get finished quick or you'll have a few pints of milk to knock off your bill."

That was in 1947, the year of the great snow. I have never known snow like that before or since. After Christmas it began to get colder and colder. All through January a northeast wind blew; then, borne on the wind, very fine flakes appeared and by February big fat flakes—a steady, relentless descent that went on for weeks, sometimes falling in a lazy curtain that remorselessly obliterated the familiar landmarks, at other times in fierce blizzards. In between, the frost took over and transformed the roads into glassy tracks of flattened snow.

To get to our cases we did a lot of walking, since so many of the farm tracks were blocked. On the very high country there were some farms we couldn't reach at all, and many animals undoubtedly died for lack of veterinary help. It was around mid-March, when helicopters were dropping food on these isolated spots, that Bert Kealey—who ran a small herd of cattle on the high tops of the moors—telephoned me.

"I thought your phone wires would be down, Bert," I said.

"Naw, they've survived. I don't know how." The young man's voice was cheerful, as always. "But ah'm in trouble," he went on. "Polly's just had a litter, and she hasn't a drop of milk."

"Oh, dear, that's unfortunate," I said. Polly was the only pig on the Kealey farm.

"Aye. Bad enough losin' the litter—twelve smashin' little pigs—but it's Tess I'm bothered about."

"Yes . . . yes. . . ." I was thinking of Tess, too. She was Bert's eight-year-old daughter, and she had a thing about little pigs. She had persuaded her father to buy her an in-pig sow for her birthday so that she could have a litter of her own. I could remember Tess's excitement when she had shown me the pig.

"That's Polly," she said, pointing to the sow nuzzling the straw in its pen. "She's mine. My dad gave her to me."

I leaned over the pen. "Yes, I know. You're a lucky girl. She looks a fine pig."

"Oh, she is." The little girl's eyes shone with pleasure. "I feed her every day, and she lets me stroke her. And do you know something else?" Tess's voice took on a conspiratorial tone. "She's going to have babies in March."

"Well, I never!" I said. "Is that so? You'll have a whole lot of little pink pigs to look after." I held my hands a few inches apart. "Just about this size."

She was so thrilled at the thought, she was lost for words.

Now all this came back to me as I listened to Bert Kealey's voice on the phone.

"Do you think Polly's got mastitis, Bert?" I asked him. "Is the udder red and swollen? Is she off her food?"

"No, nowt like that. She's eatin' her head off, and her udder's not a bit inflamed."

"Well, then, it's a straight case of agalactia. She needs a shot of pituitrin to bring down the milk, but how is she going to get it? Your district's been cut off for weeks."

It takes a lot to make a Yorkshire farmer admit that his farm is inaccessible because of the weather, but in these exceptional circumstances, Bert had to agree. "I know," he said. "Ah've tried diggin' me road out, but it fills up as fast as I clear it. Anyway, top road's blocked for two miles, so I'm wastin' me time."

I thought for a moment. "Have you tried getting some cow's milk into the piglets? An egg mixed with a quart of milk and a teaspoonful of glucose isn't a bad substitute."

"I've tried that, but they wouldn't look at it," Bert replied. "If only they could have a good suck at their mother to start them off, then maybe they'd have a go at t'substitute."

He was right. There was nothing to compare with that first suck. And without it, those tiny creatures would soon die.

I tapped my fingers against the receiver. An idea was forming in my mind. "Look, Bert," I said. "I know I can get to the top of Dennor Bank, because the road is open to there. After that it's all flat going to your place. Maybe I could get there on skis."

"Skis?"

"Yes, I've been doing a bit of that lately. But I've not tackled anywhere as far off as your farm. I can't be sure I'll make it, but I'll try."

"By 'eck, I'd be grateful, Mr. Herriot. It's t'little lass ah'm thinkin' of."

"Same here, Bert. Anyway, I'll have a go. I'm leaving now."

On the summit of Dennor Bank, I maneuvered my car as close as possible to the tall white walls the snowplows had thrown up; then I got out and buckled on my skis. I have to admit I was beginning to fancy myself on skis, because one bonus of the long spell of snow was that some nice slopes had become available. With a few other enthusiasts I had found that gliding down the hillsides was most exhilarating. I had even bought a book on the subject and thought I was becoming quite skillful.

All I needed was the bottle of pituitrin and a syringe, and I put them in my pocket.

Normally to get to the Kealey farm you drove a couple of miles along a straight road, turned right and made for the high-lying village of Branderley. Bert's farm lay in an isolated position about halfway between that turn and the village.

But that day, although I had traveled the region a hundred times, I might have been in a strange country; the stone walls had been deeply engulfed, so there were no fields, no roads, nothing but a yawning white expanse with the tops of telegraph poles sticking up here and there. It was uncanny. I felt a twinge of misgiving, but at least I could travel cross-country. It would be like cutting off two sides of a triangle, and I was pretty sure the farm lay in one of the hollows just below the dark skyline.

The Lord God Made Them All

I had slithered amateurishly for about half a mile when the snow started again. A dense white veil obliterated my sense of direction. There is no disguising the fact that I was scared. I stood stock-still in the cold with my eyes half closed, wondering what would happen to me. I could blunder for miles in that empty wilderness without coming upon a house.

Then, just as suddenly as it had begun, the flurry stopped. My heart thumped as I stared around me, and the dark smudge of my car roof in the white distance was a sweet sight. I headed back to it with a speed worthy of an Olympic skier. Upon reaching my link with home, I started the engine and I was well on the way to Darrowby before my pulse rate returned to normal.

"Bert," I said on the phone when I returned. "I'm terribly sorry, but I got caught by a snow shower and had to turn back."

"Well, ah'm glad ye did turn back. I've been a bit worried since ye left. Fellers have got lost and died in the snow up here. I shouldn't have let you try." He paused for a moment, then said wistfully, "If only there was some other way to make Polly let 'er milk down."

As he spoke, the picture flashed into my mind of that cow I was cleansing and the jets of milk striking the byre floor. And there were other memories—when I'd done uterine examinations on sows, the same thing had happened.

"Maybe there is a way," I blurted out. "Have you ever had your hand inside a sow? Examined one internally?"

"In 'er pig bed? Nay, ah leave that to you chaps."

"Well, I want you to start now. Get some warm water and—"

"Hey, hang on, Mr. Herriot. I'm sure there's no more pigs left in 'er."

"I don't suppose there are, Bert, but do as I say. Soap your arm well and use any household antiseptic you have. Then put your hand inside the pig and waggle the uterus around a bit."

"Oh, 'eck, I don't fancy this. What's it all about?"

"It often brings the milk down. So get going."

I hung up and went in to have lunch. While I was eating, the phone rang. It was Bert, breathless but triumphant. "It worked, Mr. Herriot! I 'ad a waggle round like you said, then I tried the

68

udder. I could draw milk out of every tit. It was like magic."

"Are the piglets feeding?"

"Aye, it's lovely to see them."

"Well, that's great," I said. "But we haven't won yet. Polly will probably dry up again by tomorrow. You'll have to get your hand in again."

"Oh, crumbs." A lot of the enthusiasm went out of Bert's voice. "I thought I'd finished wi' that."

The poor man did indeed have to perform his unusual task several times, and Polly never did come fully to her milk, but the piglets were kept going until they were able to drink the milk substitute. The litter was saved.

In late April in the high country the white streaks still lay behind the walls, standing out against the green moorland like the ribs of a great beast. But the roads were clear, and I went to see one of Bert Kealey's heifers. When I had finished my job, young Tess took me to see her beloved Polly and family.

"They're pretty, aren't they?" she said as we watched the twelve chunky little pigs playing around their mother.

"They certainly are, Tess," I replied. "Your first attempt at pig breeding has been a big success, and you have your father to thank for the job he did."

Bert gave a wry smile, then screwed up his face at the memory. "Aye, maybe so, and I reckon it was worth it. It's wonderful what ye can do when you have to."

10

"Are you all right, Helen?"

I looked around anxiously as my wife fidgeted in her seat. We were in La Scala cinema in Brawton, and I had a strong conviction that we had no right to be there.

I had voiced my doubts that morning. "I know it's our half day, Helen, but with the baby due anytime, don't you think it would be safer to stay around Darrowby?"

"No, of course not." Helen had laughed incredulously at the idea of missing our outing, an oasis of relaxation for both of us. For me it was an escape from the telephone and the mud and the Wellington boots, and for my wife it was a rest from her own hard slog, plus the luxury of having meals cooked and served by somebody else.

"It's all right you laughing," I had said. "But what if it comes on quickly? Do we want our second child born in Smith's bookshop or the back of a car?"

There is never much of the yogi in my makeup, but now I just couldn't be calm about this thing. The whole business had me worried. People make jokes about this syndrome, but I didn't find it funny. Something about having babies really got to me, and lately I had spent a lot of time flapping around watching Helen's every move, much to her amusement. Over the last two days the tension had really built up.

This morning Helen had been adamant: she wasn't going to be done out of her half day. And now here we were in La Scala, with Humphrey Bogart competing vainly for my attention while my wife squirmed and from time to time ran a thoughtful hand over her swollen abdomen.

Now, as I scrutinized her keenly from the corner of my eye, she gave a convulsive jerk and a soft moan. Perspiration had already sprung out all over me before she whispered, "I think we'd better go, Jim."

Stumbling over the outstretched legs in the darkness, I guided her up the sloping aisle, past the usherette, to the street and our car. The twenty-five miles to Darrowby seemed to take an eternity, and the rattles and the bumping springs made me wish, for the only time in my life, that I had a Rolls-Royce. Helen sat quietly by my side, occasionally closing her eyes and catching her breath, while my heart beat a tattoo against my ribs. When we reached our town I turned toward the marketplace.

Helen looked at me in surprise. "Where are you going?"

"Well, to Nurse Brown's, of course."

"Oh, don't be so silly. It's not time for that yet."

"But . . . how do you know?"

"I've had a baby before, remember? Come on, let's go home."

Heavy with misgiving, I drove to Skeldale House, and as we mounted the stairs I marveled at Helen's composure. It was the same when we got into bed. She lay there, obviously not comfortable but with a calm acceptance of the inevitable.

I suppose I kept dropping into what is termed a fitful slumber, because it was six a.m. when she nudged my arm.

"Time to go, Jim." Her tone was matter-of-fact.

I shot from the bed like a jack-in-the-box, threw on my clothes and shouted across the landing to Auntie Lucy, who was staying with us for the occasion. "We're off!"

A faint reply came through the door. "All right. I'll see to Jimmy."

Outside, it was a glorious May morning, the air limpid with the new-day freshness that had soothed the irritation of many an early call, but it was all lost on me as I drove to the small dwelling of Nurse Brown. Upstairs there were a couple of bedrooms that for many years had seen the arrival of the local children.

I knocked at the door and pushed it open. Nurse Brown gave me a quick smile and led Helen upstairs. I was left in the kitchen, feeling helpless, when a voice cut in on my jumbled thoughts. "Now then, Jim, it's a grand mornin'."

It was Cliff, Nurse Brown's husband. He was sitting in the corner eating breakfast, his face wreathed in its usual broad grin. I suppose I half expected him to leap up, seize my hand and say, "There, there," or something of the sort. However, he continued to work his way phlegmatically through the stack of bacon, eggs, sausages and tomatoes on his plate, and I realized that over the years he must have seen hundreds of quivering husbands standing in that kitchen. It was old stuff to Cliff.

"Yes, Cliff . . . yes. . . ." I replied. "I think it will turn out hot later." I cringed inwardly at the creaking sounds from the floorboards above. What was happening in that bedroom?

Cliff pushed his plate to one side before turning his attention to bread and marmalade. As he chewed, he seemed to notice that I was perhaps one of the more distraught husbands, because he turned his big, kind smile on me.

"Don't worry, lad," he said gently. "It'll be right."

His words were mildly soothing, and I fled. In those days it was unheard-of for the husband to be present at the birth, and though it is now the "in" thing for the men to observe it all, I marvel at their fortitude; I know beyond all doubt that Herriot would be carried away unconscious from such proceedings.

When Siegfried arrived at Skeldale House, he was thoughtful. "You'd better stick around, James. I'll do the morning rounds on my own. Take it quietly, my boy. All will be well."

It was difficult to take it quietly. I found that expectant fathers really did pace the floor, and I varied this by trying to read the newspaper upside down.

It was around eleven o'clock when the long-awaited telephone call came from my doctor and good friend, Harry Allinson. Harry always spoke in a sort of cheerful shout, and this morning his booming voice was like the sweetest music. "A sister for Jimmy!"

"Oh, great, Harry. Thank you. That's marvelous news." I held the receiver against my chest for a few moments before putting it down. I walked with dragging steps to the sitting room and lay back in a chair until my nerves had stopped vibrating.

Then, on an impulse, I leaped to my feet. Normally I am fairly sensible, but I decided that I had to go to Nurse Brown's immediately. I knew that a husband was not welcome straight after the birth, because I had gone to see Jimmy too soon and had not been well received. But still I went.

When I burst into her establishment, Nurse Brown's usual smile was absent. "You've done it again," she said with some asperity. "I told you with Jimmy that you should have given us time to get the baby washed, but it seems you took no notice."

I hung my head sheepishly, and she relented. "Oh well, now you're here you might as well come upstairs."

Helen had the same tired, flushed look that I remembered from before. I kissed her thankfully. We didn't say anything, just smiled at each other. Then I had a look in the cot by the bed. Last time I had been so aghast at Jimmy's appearance that I had mortally offended Nurse Brown by asking if there was anything wrong with him, and heaven help me, I felt the same way now. My new little daughter's face was red and bloated, and the sense of shock hit me as it had done before.

I looked up at the nurse, whose scowling face made it only too clear that she was waiting for me to say something derogatory.

"Gorgeous," I said weakly. "Really gorgeous."

"All right." She had seen enough of me. "Out you go." She ushered me downstairs, and as she opened the outside door, she fixed me with a piercing eye, speaking slowly and deliberately, as though addressing a person of limited intelligence. "That . . . is . . . a . . . lovely . . . healthy . . . baby." She then closed the door in my face.

And, bless her heart, her words helped me; as I drove away, I knew she must be right.

When I returned to Skeldale House, there was one visit waiting for me, high in the hills, and the journey there was like a happy dream. My worry was over, and it seemed that all nature was rejoicing with me. It was the ninth of May, 1947, the prelude to the most perfect summer I can remember. The sun blazed and soft breezes swirled into the car, carrying their fragrance from the fells: an elusive breath of bluebells, primroses and violets scattered everywhere on the grass.

After I had seen my patient, I took a walk on the high tops, along a favorite path on the hill's edge, with Sam trotting at my heels. I looked away over the rolling patchwork of the plain, sleeping in the sun's haze, and at the young bracken on the hillside, springing straight and green from last year's dead brown stalks. Everywhere new life was calling out its exultant message—

and, for me, aptly so, with my new little daughter down there in Darrowby.

We had decided to call her Rosemary. It is such a pretty name and I still love it, but it became Rosie at a very early stage, and though I did make one or two ineffectual stands, it has remained so to this day.

I would have liked to continue reclining in the sunshine on the springy bed of heather that clusters on these hillsides. But on that May day I had other things to do. I sped back to Skeldale House and began to telephone my glad news all over the country. It was received rapturously by all, but it was Tristan who grasped the essentials of the situation.

"We've got to wet this baby's head, Jim," he said seriously. "I'll be over at seven."

And at seven o'clock there were four of us in the sitting room at Skeldale House—Siegfried, Tristan, Alex Taylor and myself. Alex was my oldest friend—we had started school together in Glasgow at the age of four. It was good that he should be with me tonight.

Tristan was concerned about the venue of the celebration. His fingers drummed on the arm of his chair as he thought aloud, and his expression was fixed and grave. "Let's see, now," he muttered. "We'd normally go to the Drovers, but they've got that big party on tonight. We could go to the George and Dragon for Tetley's beer—splendid stuff, but I've known them a bit careless with their pipes and I've had the odd sour mouthful. And of course we have the Cross Keys. They pull a lovely pint of Cameron's, and the draft Guinness is excellent. And we mustn't forget the Hare and Pheasant—"

"Just a minute, Triss," I broke in. "I went to Nurse Brown's this evening to see Helen, and Cliff asked if he could come with us. Don't you think it would be rather nice to go to his regular pub, since the baby was born in his house?"

Tristan narrowed his eyes. "Which pub is that?"

"The Black Horse."

"Ah yes, ye-es." Tristan looked at me thoughtfully and put his fingertips together. "I've had some first-rate Russell and

Rangham's there, though I've noticed a slight loss of nuttiness under very warm conditions." He looked anxiously out the window. "It's been a hot day today. Perhaps we'd—"

"Oh, for heaven's sake!" Siegfried leaped to his feet. "It's only beer you're talking about; you sound like an analytical chemist! I think the Black Horse is a pleasant idea, James. It's a quiet little place."

And indeed, when we arrived I felt we had chosen the ideal spot. The evening sunshine sent long golden shafts over the pitted oak tables and the high-backed settles, where a few farm men sat with their glasses. There was nothing smart about this little inn, but the furniture, which hadn't been changed for a hundred years, gave it an air of tranquillity.

Reg Wilkey, the diminutive landlord, welcomed us and charged our glasses from his tall white jug, and Siegfried raised his pint. "James, may I be the first to wish a long life, health and happiness to Rosemary."

"Thank you, Siegfried," I said, feeling suddenly very much among friends as the others said, "Hear, hear," and began to drink.

After a few pints, Siegfried patted me on the shoulder. "I'm off, James. Have a good time. Can't tell you how pleased I am."

I watched him go, and I didn't argue. He was right. There was a veterinary practice out there, and somebody had to watch the shop. And this was my night.

It was one of those cozy evenings when everything seemed perfect. Alex and I recalled our childhood in Glasgow, Tristan came up with some splendid memories of Skeldale House in the bachelor days, and over everything, like a beneficent moon, hung the huge smile of Cliff Brown. When Reg Wilkey was obliged by law to announce closing time, we simply adjourned to the pub's cellar, where we stayed, talking and enjoying ourselves, until well after midnight. Then, warmed by the day's events, my anxieties behind me, I went home full of a great love of my fellowmen.

In Skeldale House, I walked up to our big bedroom; it seemed eerily empty without Helen. I opened the door to the long, narrow room that had been the dressing room in the great days of the old house. It was where Tristan had slept when we were all bachelors together, but now it was Jimmy's room, and his bed stood in exactly the same place as had my old friend's.

I looked down on my sleeping son, then glanced at the other end of the room, where a cot stood to receive Rosie. Soon, I thought, I would have two in here. I was becoming rich.

11

I WINCED as the farmer's slender frame was thrown against the cow's ribs, but Jack Scott himself didn't seem troubled. He took a fresh grip on the tail and braced himself for further action.

I was trying to treat the cow for infertility—but it involved the insertion of a long metal catheter through the uterine cervix, and this animal didn't seem to appreciate it. Every time I attempted to work the catheter in, she swung around violently and the farmer was whirled against the neighboring cow.

But this time I had the feeling I was winning. The tube was sliding in nicely. If only she would stand still for a few seconds, the job would be over. "Hang on, Jack," I gasped as I began to pump Lugol's iodine into the catheter. As soon as the cow felt the fluid trickling in, she veered over again and the farmer was squashed once more between the big creatures. I withdrew the catheter and stepped back, thinking that this had been a singularly uncooperative patient.

Jack, however, didn't seem to share my view. He went up to the front of the cow and put his arms around her neck. "Ah, you're a grand lass," he murmured. It was always like this with Jack. He had a deep affection for every creature on his farm, and the feeling always seemed to be returned.

When he had concluded his embrace, he pushed his way out, smiling as usual. Jack did not have the ruddy hue of the typical farmer. His face was pale and haggard, with deep wrinkles that made him look older than his forty years. But his smile was radiant, like an inner light.

"Ah've another job for ye, Mr. Herriot," he said. "There's some lambs ah want ye to look at. I've never seen owt like them."

We walked across the yard with Jack's sheep dog, Rip, gamboling around his master in delight. Often these farm dogs were slinking, furtive creatures, but Rip behaved like a happy pet. The farmer bent and patted him. "Hello, feller, are you comin', too?"

He led me into a Nissen hut, where there were a number of ewes and lambs. Several of the lambs were wobbling on their hind legs as they walked, and two could take only a few faltering steps before collapsing.

Jack turned to me. "What's the matter wi' them, Mr. Herriot?"

"They've got swayback," I replied. "It's caused by a copper deficiency that results in degeneration of the brain. Typically it makes them weak in their hindquarters, but sometimes they become paralyzed or take fits."

"That's strange," the farmer said. "Them ewes have had copper licks to go at all the time."

"I'm afraid that's not enough. If you get many cases, you ought to inject the ewes with copper halfway through pregnancy to prevent it next time."

He sighed. "Ah well, now we know what it is, you'll be able to put these lambs right."

"Sorry, Jack. The ones that are just wobbly have a good chance of making it, but I haven't much hope for those two." I pointed to the pair lying on their sides. "They're already partially paralyzed. I honestly think the kindest thing would be . . ."

That was when the smile left Jack's face. It always did at the merest suggestion of putting an animal down. It is a country vet's duty to advise his clients when treatment is unprofitable; he must always have the farmer's commercial interest in mind. But this system didn't work with Jack. He had animals on the farm that could not possibly be making him money, but they were his friends and he was happy to see them pottering about.

He dug his hands deep in his pockets and looked down at the prostrate lambs. "Are they sufferin', Mr. Herriot?"

"No, Jack, no. It doesn't seem to be a painful disease."

"Awright, I'll keep 'em. If they can't suck, I'll feed 'em meself. Ah like to give things a chance."

As the summer wore on, I was glad to see that his dedication had paid off. The two semiparalyzed lambs were surviving and doing well. They still flopped down after a few steps, but they were able to nibble the fast-growing grass, and the brain degeneration mercifully had not progressed.

It was in October, when the trees were a blaze of color, that Jack hailed me as I drove past his gate. "Will ye stop and see Rip?" His face was anxious.

"Why, is he ill?"

"Naw, naw, just lame, but I can't mek it out."

The dog was, as ever, close to his master; I saw that his right foreleg was trailing uselessly.

"What's happened to him?" I asked.

"He was roundin' up t'cows when one of 'em lashed out and got him on the chest. He's been gettin' lamer ever since. The funny thing is, ah can't find a thing wrong with his leg."

Rip wagged vigorously as I examined him. There was no pain in the limb, no wound or injury, but he winced as I passed my hand over his first rib. Diagnosis was not difficult.

"It's radial paralysis," I said.

"Radial . . . What's that?"

"The radial nerve passes over the first rib, and the kick must have damaged rib and nerve. This has put the extensor muscles out of action so that he can't bring his leg forward."

"Well, that's a rum un." The farmer passed a hand over the shaggy head. "Will he get better?"

"It's usually a long job—weeks or months. Nervous tissue is slow to regenerate, and treatment doesn't seem to help much."

The farmer nodded. "Awright, we'll just have to wait. One thing"—and again the bright smile flooded his face—"he can still round up the cows, lame or not. It 'ud break 'is heart if he couldn't work. Loves 'is job, does Rip."

On the way to the car I tried to say something encouraging. "Don't worry too much, Jack. These cases usually recover in time."

But Rip did not recover. After several months his leg was as useless as ever, and the muscles had wasted greatly. The nerve must have been damaged irreparably, and it was an unhappy thought that this attractive little animal was going to be three-legged for the rest of his life.

Jack was undismayed and maintained stoutly that Rip was still a good working dog.

The real blow fell one Sunday morning as Siegfried and I were arranging the rounds in the office. I answered the doorbell and found Jack carrying his dog. "What's wrong?" I asked. "Is he worse?"

"No, Mr. Herriot." The farmer's voice was husky. "It's summat different. He's been knocked down."

Siegfried and I examined the dog on the surgery table. "Fracture of the tibia," my partner said. "But there's no sign of internal damage. Do you know exactly what happened?"

Jack nodded. "He ran onto the street and a car caught 'im. He dragged 'imself back into t'yard."

"Dragged?" Siegfried was puzzled.

"Aye, the broken leg's on the same side as t'other thing."

My partner blew out his cheeks. "Ah yes, the radial paralysis. I remember you told me about it, James." He looked at me and I knew we were thinking the same thing: a fracture and a paralysis on the same side were a forbidding combination.

We did what we could—we set the leg in plaster. As he was leaving, Jack smiled. "I'm takin' the family to church this mornin', and I'll say a prayer for Rip while I'm there."

Afterward Siegfried was thoughtful. "I just hope that job goes right," he said. "Jack's a truly remarkable chap. He says he's going to pray for his dog and there's nobody better qualified. Remember what Coleridge said? *He prayeth best, who loveth best/All things both great and small.*"

"Yes," I said. "That's Jack, all right."

The farmer brought his dog into the surgery six weeks later for the removal of the plaster. I sawed it off, palpated the limb, and my spirits plummeted. Hardly any healing had taken place. There should have been a healthy callus by now, but I could feel the loose ends of the broken bones moving against each other, almost like a hinge. Siegfried was in the dispensary, and I called to him.

He felt the leg. "Drat!" He looked at the farmer. "We'll have to try again, Jack, but I don't like it."

We applied a fresh plaster, and the farmer grinned confidently. "Just wanted more time, I reckon. He'll be right next time."

But it was not to be. Siegfried and I stripped off the second cast together, but the situation was unchanged. There was little or no healing tissue around the fracture.

"It's just the same, I'm afraid, Jack," I told the farmer.

"You mean it 'asn't joined up?"

"That's right."

Jack rubbed a finger along his upper lip. "Then 'e won't be able to take any weight on that leg?"

"I don't see how."

"Aye . . . well, we'll just have to see how he goes on."

"But, Jack," Siegfried said gently. "Two useless legs on the same side? He can't go on."

I could see the familiar curtain coming down over the farmer's face. He knew what was in our minds, and he wasn't going to have it. I knew what he was going to say next.

"Is he sufferin'?"

"No, he isn't," Siegfried replied. "There's no pain in the fracture now and the paralysis is painless anyway, but he won't be able to walk, don't you see?"

Jack was already gathering his dog in his arms. "We'll give him a chance, any road," he said.

When he had left, Siegfried looked at me wide-eyed. "What do you make of that, James?"

"Same as you," I replied gloomily. "Poor old Jack. He always gives everything a chance, but he's got no hope this time."

But I was wrong. Several weeks later I was called to the Scott farm to look at a sick calf, and the first thing I saw was Rip bringing the cows in for milking. He was darting to and fro around the rear of the herd, guiding them through the gate from the field, and I watched him in amazement. He still could not bear any appreciable weight on his right limbs, yet he was running happily, somehow supporting his body with his two strong left legs and the paws of the stricken limbs merely brushing the turf. Jack didn't say anything about "I told you so," and I wouldn't have cared if he had, because it thrilled me to see the little animal doing the job he loved.

"This calf, Mr. Herriot." The farmer dragged me back to the matter at hand. "Never seen one like it. Goin' round and round as if it was daft."

Depression flowed over me. I had been hoping for something straightforward this time. My recent contacts with Jack's animals could be described as abortive treatment and wrong prognosis, and I did want to pull something out of the bag. This didn't sound good.

It was a bonny little calf about a month old. Dark roan—the Shorthorn farmer's favorite color—and it was lying on its straw bed looking fairly normal, except that its head was inclined slightly to one side. Jack touched the rump with his toe, and the calf rose to its feet.

That was where the normality ended, because the little creature blundered helplessly to the right, as if drawn by a magnet, until it walked into the wall. It picked itself up and recommenced its progress, always to the right.

So that was it. I took the animal's temperature. It was 106 degrees. "This is called listeriosis, Jack," I said. "Circling disease is another name for it, and you can see why. It affects the brain."

The farmer looked glum. "Brain again, just like them lambs? There must be summat in the air about here." He paused, bent over the calf and began to stroke it. "And there'll be nowt you can do for this either, I suppose."

"I hope I can do something, Jack. This is different from the lambs. It's an actual bug affecting the brain, and with a bit of luck I can put this calf right."

I felt like crossing my fingers. In the prewar days these cases had been fatal, but the causal organism was sensitive to antibiotics and now the whole scene had changed. I had seen animals with listeriosis recover completely within a few days.

I injected the calf with a penicillin-streptomycin suspension, a recent acquisition in our profession. Then I turned to Jack.

"I'll be back tomorrow," I said. "I hope to find some improvement by then."

Next day the temperature was down, but the symptoms had not abated. I repeated the injection and said I would call again.

I did call, again and again; but after a week, though the temperature was normal and the appetite excellent, the calf was still circling.

"How d'you feel about t'job, Mr. Herriot?" the farmer asked.

Actually I felt like screaming. Was there a hoodoo on this place? I calmed down and took a deep breath. "I'm sorry, Jack, but we don't seem to be getting anywhere. The antibiotic has saved the calf's life, but there must be some brain damage. I can't see any hope of recovery now."

He didn't seem to have heard me. "It's a grand un, a heifer, too, and out of me best cow. She'll make a smashin' milker—and just look at that color. We've called her Bramble."

"Yes. But, Jack . . ."

He patted me on the shoulder and led me out to the yard. "Well, thank ye, Mr. Herriot. Ah'm sure you've done all you can." Clearly he didn't want to pursue the matter further. He had decided to give Bramble a chance.

IT TURNED out that Jack's faith was rewarded and that my prognosis was wrong again, but I could not blame myself this time, because the sequence of events in Bramble's recovery was not contained in any textbook.

Over the next two years the brain symptoms gradually diminished. The improvement was so slow as to be almost imperceptible, but every time I was on Jack's farm I looked in on her and saw to my astonishment that the animal was a bit better. For many weeks she circled, then this subsided into an occasional staggering toward the right. This in turn faded into an inclination of the head to one side, until one day this, too, disappeared and a fine normal heifer was strolling around. I was delighted.

"Jack," I said. "How marvelous! I'd have bet anything that this was a hopeless case, and there she is, absolutely perfect."

The farmer gave me a slow smile with a hint of mischief in it.

"Aye, ah'm right capped with her, Mr. Herriot, and she's goin' to be one of the best cows in the herd before she's finished. But"—he raised a finger and his smile broadened—"she's not perfect. There's just a little somethin'." He leaned toward me conspiratorially. "Keep watchin' her face."

I stared at the heifer, mystified. "I can't see a— What!"

The farmer laughed. "Did ye see it?"

I certainly had, and it was startling. Just for an instant Bramble's placid expression was transfigured by a faint twitch of the eyes and head to the right. There was something human about the gesture, a come-hither look reminiscent of the film vamps of the 1920s.

Jack was still laughing. "I reckon you've never seen owt like that afore, Mr. Herriot?"

"No, I haven't. Quite extraordinary! How often does she do it?"

"Oh, every now and then. I suppose it'll go away in time like all t'other things?"

"I expect it will," I said. "But how very strange."

"Aye." Jack nodded. "Well, I'm glad we persevered with 'er." (It was nice of him to say we.) "Ah've had 'er served, and she should be calvin' just right for Darrowby show."

"Well, that will be interesting. She's certainly a picture."

It was true. Bramble had developed into a classic Dairy Shorthorn with all the delicacy and grace of that now lost breed—the beautifully straight back, the neat tailhead and the makings of a fine udder.

She was even more of a picture a few months later as she stood in the center of the show-ring with the August sun glinting on her rich dark coat. She had recently produced a calf, and her udder, tight and flat-based, bulged between the back limbs. Surpassing her would take some doing, and it was a pleasant thought that the seemingly doomed creature of two and a half years ago might be just about to win a championship trophy.

However, Bramble was in pretty hot company. The judge, Brigadier Rowan, had narrowed the field down to three, and the other two contestants, a red-and-white and a light roan, were beautiful animals. It was going to be close.

Brigadier Rowan was a distinguished soldier, a gentleman farmer and an unrivaled judge of dairy cattle in the district, and his dress and bearing were fully in keeping with his position. That tall lean figure would have been impressive even without the beautifully cut suit, waistcoat and bowler hat. The fact that he was wearing a monocle added the final touch.

The brigadier strolled down the little row of cattle, occasionally screwing the glass tighter into his eye as he bent to inspect a particular point. Clearly he was having difficulty deciding. His normally pink face was bright red, not, I felt, from the sunshine but from the long succession of whiskies and soda I had seen him consuming in the judge's tent. Finally he pursed his lips and approached Bramble. He leaned forward and peered into the animal's face as though to examine the eyes. Something happened then. I could not see Bramble's face, but my suspicion is that she gave the little twitch that had startled me, because the brigadier's eyebrows shot up and the monocle dropped to the end of its cord, where it dangled for a few seconds before he returned it to his eye.

He studied Bramble fixedly for quite a long time, and even after he had moved away he glanced back at her once or twice. I could read his mind. Had he really seen that, or was it the whisky?

He came slowly back down the row. He had the look of a man who was definitely going to make up his mind. He finished up once more in front of Bramble. As he gave her a final appraising stare he flinched, and I had a strong conviction that she had done her trick again.

The monocle remained in position this time, but the brigadier was obviously shaken. The experience, however, seemed to remove all doubt from his mind; he immediately placed Bramble first. The poor man really had no option.

Later, when he strode to the edge of the ring, he was greeted by a beaming Jack. "A bonny lass, 'ant she, Brigadier? Almost human, ye might say."

"Quite," said the brigadier, adjusting his monocle. "Actually, she reminds me of someone I used to know."

12

IN THE semidarkness of the surgery passage I thought it was a hideous growth dangling from the side of the dog's face, but as he came closer I saw that it was only a condensed-milk can. I was relieved because I knew I was dealing with Brandy again.

I hoisted him onto the table. "Brandy, you've been at the dustbin again." The big golden Labrador gave me an apologetic grin and did his best to lick my face. He couldn't manage it, since his tongue was jammed under the lid, but he made up for it by a furious wagging of his tail.

"Oh, Mr. Herriot, I am sorry to trouble you again." Mrs. Westby, his attractive young mistress, smiled ruefully. "He just won't keep out of that dustbin. Sometimes the children and I can get the cans off by ourselves, but this one is stuck fast."

I eased my finger along the jagged edge of the metal. "It's a bit tricky, isn't it? We don't want to cut him."

As I reached for the forceps, I thought of the many other occasions when I had done something like this for Brandy. He was a huge, lolloping, slightly goofy animal, and this dustbin raiding was becoming an obsession. He liked to fish out a can and lick up the tasty remnants, with such dedication that he often got stuck. Time after time he had been freed by his family or myself from fruit-salad cans, corned-beef cans, baked-bean cans, soup cans—there didn't seem to be anything he didn't like.

I gripped the edge of the lid with my forceps and gently bent it back along its length till I was able to lift it away from the tongue. An instant later that tongue was slobbering all over my cheek as Brandy expressed his delight and thanks.

"Get back, you daft dog!" I said, laughing.

"Yes, come down, Brandy." Mrs. Westby hauled him from the table and spoke sharply. "It's fine making a fuss now, but you're becoming a nuisance with this business. It will have to stop."

The scolding had no effect on the lashing tail, and I saw that his mistress was smiling. You just couldn't help liking Brandy, because he was a great ball of affection and tolerance, without an ounce of malice in him. I had seen the Westby children—three girls and a boy—carrying him around upside down, or pushing him in a pram, dressed in baby clothes. Those youngsters played all sorts of games with him, but he suffered them all with good humor. In fact, I am sure he enjoyed them.

Brandy had other idiosyncrasies, apart from his fondness for dustbins. I was attending the Westby cat at their home one afternoon when I saw the dog acting strangely. Mrs. Westby was knitting in an armchair, while the oldest girl squatted on the hearthrug with me and held the cat's head.

It was when I was searching my pockets for my thermometer that I noticed Brandy slinking into the room. He wore a furtive air as he moved across the carpet and sat down with studied carelessness in front of his mistress. After a few moments he began to work his rear gradually up the front of the chair toward her knees. Absently she pushed him down, but he immediately restarted his backward ascent, his hips moving in a slow rumba rhythm as he elevated them inch by inch, and all the time the golden face was blank and innocent, as though nothing at all were happening.

Fascinated, I stopped hunting for my thermometer and watched. Mrs. Westby was absorbed in her knitting and didn't seem to notice that Brandy's bottom was now firmly parked on her shapely knees, which were clad in blue jeans. The dog paused, as though acknowledging that phase one had been successfully completed; then ever so gently he began to consolidate his position, pushing his way up the front of the chair with his forelimbs. Just when one final backward heave would have seen the great dog ensconced on her lap, Mrs. Westby looked up.

"Oh really, Brandy, you are silly!" She put a hand on his rump and sent him slithering to the carpet, where he lay disconsolately, looking at her with liquid eyes.

"What was all that about?" I asked.

Mrs. Westby laughed. "Oh, it's these old jeans. When Brandy first came here as a tiny puppy, I spent hours holding him on my knee, and I used to wear the jeans a lot then. Ever since, the very sight of them makes him try to get on my knee, even though he knows perfectly well I can't have a huge Labrador in my lap."

"So now it's the stealthy approach, eh?"

She giggled. "That's right. Sometimes it works, when I'm preoccupied—knitting or reading. If he's been playing in the mud, he makes an awful mess and I have to go and change. That's when he really gets a scolding!"

This patient of mine, Brandy, added color to my daily rounds. When I was walking my own dog, I often saw him playing in the fields by the river. One particularly hot day many of the dogs were taking to the water to cool off, but whereas they all glided in and swam off sedately, Brandy's approach was unique; he ran up to the riverbank, launched himself outward, legs splayed in a sort of swallow dive, and hung for a moment in the air rather like a flying fox before splashing thunderously into the depths. To me it was the action of a completely happy extrovert.

On the following day in those same fields I witnessed something even more extraordinary. There in a little playground Brandy was disporting himself on the slide. For this activity he had assumed an uncharacteristically grave expression and stood calmly in the queue of children. When his turn came he mounted the steps, slid down— all dignity and importance—then took a staid walk around to rejoin the queue.

The boys and girls who were his companions seemed to take him for granted, but I found it difficult to tear myself away. I could have watched him all day.

I often smiled to myself when I thought of Brandy's antics, but I didn't smile when Mrs. Westby brought him into the surgery a few months later. His bounding ebullience had disappeared, and he dragged himself along the passage to the consulting room.

As I lifted him onto the table, I noticed that he had

lost a lot of weight. "What's the trouble, Mrs. Westby?" I asked.

She looked at me worriedly. "He's been listless and coughing for a few days and not eating very well, but this morning he seems quite ill, and you can see he's starting to pant."

"Yes . . . yes. . . ." As I inserted the thermometer I watched the rapid rise and fall of the rib cage and noted the gaping mouth and anxious eyes. "He does look very sorry for himself."

His temperature was 104. I applied my stethoscope. I have heard of an old Scottish doctor describing a seriously ill patient's chest as sounding like a "kist o' whustles," and that just about described Brandy's. Rales, wheezes, squeaks and bubblings were all there against a background of labored respiration.

I put the stethoscope back in my pocket. "He's got pneumonia."

"Oh dear." Mrs. Westby reached out and touched the heaving chest. "That's bad, isn't it?"

"Yes, I'm afraid so."

"But . . ." She gave me an appealing glance. "I understand it isn't so fatal since the new drugs came out."

I hesitated. "In humans and most animals the sulfa drugs, and now penicillin, have changed the picture completely, but dogs are still very difficult to cure."

"You don't think it's hopeless?" Mrs. Westby asked.

"No, not at all. I'm just warning you that many dogs don't respond to treatment. But Brandy is young and strong and stands a fair chance. I wonder what started this off."

"I think I know, Mr. Herriot. He had a swim in the river about a week ago. I try to keep him out of the water in this cold weather, but if he sees a stick floating, he dives right in. You've seen him—it's one of the funny little things he does."

"Yes, I know. And was he shivery afterward?"

"He was. I walked him straight home, but it was such a freezing cold day. I could feel him trembling as I dried him down."

I nodded. "That would be the cause, all right. Anyway, let's start his treatment. I'm going to give him a penicillin injection, and I'll call at your house tomorrow to repeat it. He's not well enough to come to the surgery."

"Very well, Mr. Herriot. Is there anything else?"

"Yes. I want you to make him what we call a pneumonia jacket. Cut two holes in an old blanket for his forelegs and stitch him into it along his back—he must have his chest warmly covered."

I called and repeated the injection on the following day. There wasn't much change. I injected him for four more days, but Brandy wasn't responding. His temperature did drop a little; however, he ate hardly anything and gradually grew thinner. I put him on sulfapyridine tablets, but they didn't seem to help. As the days passed and he sank deeper into lethargy, I was forced to a conclusion that a few weeks before would have seemed impossible—this happy, bounding animal was going to die.

But Brandy didn't die. He survived, although you couldn't put it any higher than that. His temperature came down and his appetite improved, and he climbed onto a plateau of twilight existence where he seemed content to stay.

"He isn't Brandy anymore," Mrs. Westby said a few weeks later when I stopped by. Her eyes filled with tears as she spoke.

I shook my head. "No, I'm afraid he isn't. He has recovered from a really virulent pneumonia, but it's left him with a chronic pleurisy, adhesions and probably other lung damage."

She dabbed at her eyes. "It breaks my heart to see him like this. He's only five, but he's like an old, old dog. He was so full of life, too." She sniffed and blew her nose. "When I think of how I used to scold him for getting into the dustbin and muddying up my jeans. How I wish he would do some of his funny tricks now."

I thrust my hands deep into my pockets. "Never does anything like that anymore, eh?"

"No, he just hangs about the house. Doesn't even want to go for a walk."

As I watched, Brandy rose from his place in the corner and pottered over to the fire. He stood there a moment, gaunt and dead-eyed, before he coughed, groaned and flopped down on the hearthrug. Mrs. Westby was right; he *was* like a very old dog.

"Do you think he'll always be like this?" she asked.

I shrugged. "We can only hope not."

But as I got into my car and drove away, I really didn't have much hope. I had seen calves with lung damage after bad pneumonias. They recovered but were called "bad doers," because they remained thin and listless for the rest of their lives. Doctors, too, had plenty of "chesty" people on their books who were, more or less, in the same predicament.

Months went by, and the only time I saw the Labrador was when Mrs. Westby was walking him on his lead. I always had the impression that he was reluctant to move, and his mistress had to stroll along very slowly so that he could keep up with her. I sadly thought of the lolloping Brandy of old, but I told myself that at least I had saved his life. I could do no more for him now, and I made a determined effort to push him out of my mind.

I managed to do so fairly well until one afternoon in February. On the previous night I had treated a colicky horse until four a.m. and had just crawled into bed when I'd been called to a difficult calving. I'd got home too late to return to bed. Plowing through the morning rounds, I was so tired that I felt disembodied, and at lunch Helen watched me anxiously as my head nodded over my food.

There were a few dogs in the waiting room at two o'clock, and I peered at them through half-closed eyelids. By the time I reached my last patient, I was almost asleep on my feet. "Next, please," I mumbled as I pushed open the waiting-room door and stood back, expecting the usual sight of a dog being led out to the passage.

But this time there was a difference. There was a little poodle and a man in the doorway all right, but the thing that made my eyes snap wide open was that the dog was walking upright on his hind limbs.

Surely I wasn't seeing things? I stared down at the dog; the small creature strutted through the doorway, chest out, head up, as erect as a soldier.

His master must have seen my bewilderment, because he burst into laughter. "Don't worry, Mr. Herriot," he said. "This little dog was circus trained before I got him as a pet. I like to show off his little tricks. This one really startles people."

"You can say that again," I said.

The poodle wasn't ill; he just wanted his nails clipped. I smiled as I hoisted him onto the table and began to ply the clippers, but by the time I had finished, the lassitude had taken over again, and I felt ready to fall down as I showed man and dog out.

I watched the little animal trotting away down the street—in the orthodox manner this time—and it came to me suddenly that it had been a long time since I had seen a dog doing something unusual and amusing. Like the things Brandy used to do.

A wave of gentle memories flowed through me as I leaned wearily against the doorpost and closed my eyes. When I opened them, I saw Brandy coming around the corner with Mrs. Westby. His nose was entirely obscured by a large red tomato-soup can, and he strained madly at the leash and whipped his tail when he saw me.

It was certainly a hallucination this time. . . . I was looking into the past. . . . I really ought to go to bed immediately. But I was still rooted to the doorpost when the Labrador bounded up the steps and made an attempt, aborted by the soup can, to lick my face.

I stared into Mrs. Westby's radiant face. "What . . . what . . . ?"

With her sparkling eyes and wide smile she looked more attractive than ever. "Look, Mr. Herriot, he's better!"

In an instant I was wide-awake. "And I suppose you'll want me to get that can off him?"

"Oh yes, please!"

It took all my strength to lift him onto the table. He was heavier now than before his illness. I reached for the forceps and began to turn the jagged edges of the can outward from the nose and mouth. Tomato soup must have been one of his favorites, because he was really deeply embedded, and it took some time before I was able to slide the can from his face.

I fought off his slobbering attack. "He's back in the dustbin, I see."

"Yes, quite regularly. And he goes sliding with the children, too." She smiled happily.

I listened to his lungs; they were wonderfully clear. A slight roughness here and there, but the old cacophony had gone. I leaned on the table and looked at the great dog with a mixture of thankfulness and incredulity. He was as before, boisterous and full of the joy of living.

"But, Mr. Herriot." Mrs. Westby's eyes were wide. "How on earth has this happened? How has he got better?"

"*Vis medicatrix naturae*," I replied in tones of deep respect. "The healing power of nature. Something no veterinary surgeon can compete with when it decides to act."

"I see. And you can never tell when this is going to happen?"

"No."

For a few seconds we were silent as we stroked the dog.

"Oh, by the way," I said. "Has he shown any renewed interest in the blue jeans?"

"Oh, my word, yes! They're in the washing machine at this very moment. Absolutely covered in mud. Isn't it marvelous!"

13

"*I let my heart fall into careless hands.*" Little Rosie's voice piped in my ear as I drove. I was on my way to dress a wound on a cow's back, and it was nice to hear the singing. When Jimmy had entered school, I missed his company on my rounds, the childish chatter that never palled, and the intense pleasure of seeing his growing wonder at the things of the countryside. Now it was all beginning anew with Rosie.

The singing had originated in the purchase of a radio phonograph. Music has always meant a lot to me and I already owned a record player, but I wanted better sound, and at that time there were no hi-fis or stereos—the best a music lover could do was to get a good phonograph. After much agonizing, reading of pamphlets and listening to advice, I decided to buy a Murphy—a handsome piece of furniture with a louvered front, which bellowed out the full volume of the Philharmonia Orchestra without a trace of muzziness. There was only one snag. It cost more than ninety pounds, and that was a lot of money in 1950.

"Helen," I said when it was installed, "the kids can use my old player, but we must keep them away from the Murphy."

Foolish words. The very next day as I came home, the passage was echoing with *"Yippee ay ooooh, yippee ay aaaay, ghost riders in the sky!"* It was the other side of Bing Crosby's "Careless Hands"—Rosie's favorite—and the Murphy was giving it full value.

I peeped into the sitting room as "Ghost Riders" came to an end. With her chubby little hands Rosie removed the record, placed it in its cover and marched, pigtails swinging, to the record cabinet. She had just selected another disc when I waylaid her.

"Which one is that?" I asked.

" 'The Little Gingerbread Man,' " she replied.

I looked at the label. It was, too, and how did she know? I had a whole array of these children's records—many of which looked exactly alike—and Rosie, now three, could not read.

She fitted the disc expertly on the turntable and set it going. When it was over, she picked out another record.

I looked over her shoulder. "What is it this time?"

" 'Tubby the Tuba.' " And indeed it was.

In the end I decided that it was fruitless to try to keep Rosie and the Murphy apart. Whenever she was not out with me, she played with the phonograph. It was her toy. It all turned out for the best, too, because she did my precious acquisition no harm, and during my rounds she sang, word perfect, the songs she had played so often. "Careless Hands" soon became my favorite, too.

There was a gate on the road to the farm we were visiting, and we came bumping up to it now. The singing stopped abruptly. This was one of my daughter's big moments. When I drew up, she jumped from the car, strutted proudly to the gate and opened it. She took this duty very seriously, and her small face was grave as I drove through. When she returned to take her place by my dog, Sam, on the seat, I patted her knee. "Thank you, sweetheart," I said. "You're a big help to me."

She blushed and swelled with importance. She knew I meant what I said, because opening gates is a chore.

We drove into the farmyard. The farmer, Mr. Binns, had shut the cow up in a ramshackle pen with a passage that stretched from a dead end to the outside. The animal in the pen was a Galloway—black and shaggy, with mean eyes—and I saw with some apprehension that her tail whipped perpetually, a sure sign of ill nature in a bovine.

"Couldn't you have got her tied up, Mr. Binns?" I asked.

The farmer shook his head. "Nay, I'm short o' room, and this un spends most of 'er time on the moors."

I could believe it. There was nothing domesticated about this animal. Usually I lifted my daughter into hayracks or onto the tops of walls while I worked, but I didn't want her anywhere near this beast. "It's no place for you in there, Rosie," I said. "Stand at the end of the passage, well out of the way."

Mr. Binns and I went into the pen, and I was pleasantly surprised when the farmer managed to drop a halter over the cow's head. He backed into a corner and held tightly to the shank.

I looked at him doubtfully. "Can you hold her?"

"I think so," Mr. Binns replied a little breathlessly. "You'll find t'place at the end of her back, there."

As I gently passed my fingers over the big abscess near the root of the animal's tail, the hind foot lashed out, catching me a glancing blow on the thigh. I had expected this, and I got on with my exploration. "How long has she had this?"

The farmer dug his heels in and leaned back on the rope. "Oh, 'bout two months. It keeps bustin' and fillin' up. Every time I thought it'd be the last, but it looks like it's never goin' to get right. What's t'cause of it?"

"I don't know, Mr. Binns. She must have had a wound there that became infected. On the back, drainage is poor. There's a lot of dead tissue I'll have to clear away before it can heal."

I leaned from the pen. "Rosie, will you bring my scissors, some cotton wool and that bottle of peroxide?"

The farmer watched wonderingly as the tiny figure trotted to the car and came back with the three things. "By gaw, t'little lass knows 'er way around."

"Oh yes," I said, smiling. "She's an expert on the things I use regularly." I reached over the door for the items, then Rosie retreated to her place at the end of the passage.

I began to work on the abscess. Since the tissue was dead, the cow couldn't feel a thing as I snipped and swabbed, but that didn't stop the hind leg from pistoning out every few seconds; this was one of those animals that just cannot tolerate any interference. I finished at last, then trickled some hydrogen peroxide over the area. I had a lot of faith in this old remedy as a penetrative antiseptic, and I watched contentedly as it bubbled on the skin. The cow, however, did not seem to enjoy the sensation, because she made a sudden leap into the air, tore the rope from the farmer's hands, brushed me to one side and made for the door. She crashed through it and into the passage. I desperately willed her to turn left, into the yard, but to my horror she thundered right, down toward the dead end where my daughter was standing.

It was one of the worst moments of my life. I heard a small voice say, "Mama." No scream, just that one word, said very quietly. Rosie was standing against the wall, and the cow, stationary now, was looking at her from a distance of two feet.

The animal turned when she heard my footsteps, then galloped past me into the yard. Overwhelmed with thankfulness, I lifted Rosie into my arms. She could easily have been killed.

As we started to drive away, I remembered that something very like this had happened when Jimmy was out with me. It had not been so horrific because he had been playing in a passage with an open end leading into a field, and he was not trapped when the cow I was working on broke loose and hurtled toward him. I could see nothing, but I heard a piercing yell of *"Aaaagh!"* before I rounded the corner. To my intense relief, Jimmy was streaking across the field to where my car was standing and the cow was trotting away in another direction.

This reaction had been typical because Jimmy was the noisy one of the family. Under stress he believed in making his feelings known in the form of loud cries. When Dr. Allinson came to give him his routine inoculations, for example, Jimmy heralded the appearance of the syringe with yells of *"Ow! This is going to hurt!"* And he had a kindred spirit in our good doctor, who bawled back at him, *"Aye. You're right, it is! Oooh! Aaah!"*

Now, as Rosie and I left the farm, she solemnly opened and closed the gate for me, then looked up at me expectantly. I knew why—she wanted to play one of her games. She loved being quizzed, just as Jimmy had loved to quiz me.

I took my cue and began. "Name six blue flowers."

She blushed quickly in satisfaction, because of course she knew. "Field scabiosa, harebell, forget-me-not, bluebell, speedwell, meadow cranesbill."

"Clever girl," I said. "Now—how about six birds?"

Again the blush and the quick reply. "Magpie, curlew, thrush, plover, yellowhammer, rook."

The game went on daily, with infinite variations. I only half realized then how lucky I was. I had my job and the company of my children at the same time. So many men work so hard to keep the home going that they lose touch with their families. But both Jimmy and Rosie, until they went to school, spent most of their time with me on the farms.

As Rosie's school days approached, her attitude, always solicitous, became distinctly maternal. "Daddy," she would say seriously, "how are you going to manage when I'm at school—all those gates to open and having to get everything out of the car yourself? It's going to be awful for you."

Patting her head, I used to try to reassure her. "I'm going to miss you, Rosie, but I'll get along somehow."

Her response was always the same: a relieved smile, and then the comforting words, "Never mind, Daddy. I'll be with you on Saturdays and Sundays. You'll be all right then."

I suppose it was natural that my children, seeing veterinary practice from early childhood and witnessing my pleasure in it, never thought of being anything but veterinary surgeons.

There was no problem with Jimmy; he was a tough little fellow, well able to stand the buffets of our job, but somehow I couldn't bear the idea of my daughter being kicked and knocked about and covered with muck. Practice was so much rougher in those days; there were no metal crushes to hold the big struggling beasts that regularly put vets in hospital with broken legs and ribs. I have always believed that children should follow their own inclinations, but as Rosie entered her teens, I dropped broad hints, and perhaps played unfairly by showing her as many grisly jobs as possible. She did finally decide to be a doctor on humans, and today she is "Dr. Rosie" in our community.

Now, when I see the high percentage of girls in veterinary schools and observe the excellent work done by the two women assistants in our own practice, I sometimes wonder if I did the right thing. But Rosie is happy and successful, and parents can only do what they think is right at the time.

However, all that was far in the future as I drove home from Mr. Binns's with my three-year-old daughter by my side. She had started to sing again and was just finishing the last verse of her great favorite: *"Careless hands don't care when dreams slip through."*

14

WAS there no peace in a vet's life? I wondered fretfully as I hurried my car along the road to Gilthorpe village. Eight o'clock on a Sunday evening and here I was, trailing off to visit a dog ten miles away; according to Helen, who had taken the message, the animal had been ailing for more than a week.

When I left Darrowby, the streets of the little town were empty in the gathering dusk and the houses had that tight-shut, comfortable look that raised images of armchairs and pipes and firesides; and now, as I saw the lights of the farms winking on the fells, I could picture the stockmen dozing contentedly with their feet up. I had not passed a single car on the darkening road. There was nobody out but Herriot.

I was sloshing around in a trough of self-pity by the time I drew up outside a row of gray stone cottages in Gilthorpe. "Mrs. Cundall, number 4, Chestnut Row," Helen had written on the slip of paper, and as I opened the gate and stepped through the tiny strip of garden, my mind was busy with half-formed ideas of what I was going to say. No need to be rude, just a firm statement of my position, that vets liked to relax on Sunday evenings just like other people, and though we did not mind coming out for emergencies, we did object to visiting animals that had been ill for a week.

The Lord God Made Them All

I had my speech fairly well prepared when a little middle-aged woman opened the door.

"Good evening, Mrs. Cundall," I said, slightly tight-lipped.

"Oh, it's Mr. Herriot." She smiled shyly. "We've never met, but I've seen you walkin' round Darrowby. Come in."

The door opened straight into the tiny low-beamed living room, and I took in at a glance the shabby furniture and a curtained-off area at the end. Mrs. Cundall pulled the curtain aside. In a narrow bed lay a skeleton-thin man with sunken eyes in a yellowed face.

"This is my husband, Ron," she said cheerfully. The man smiled and raised a bony arm in greeting.

"And here is your patient, Hermann," she went on, pointing to a dachshund who sat by the side of the bed.

"Hermann?"

"Yes, we thought it was a good name for a German sausage dog." They both laughed.

"An excellent name," I said. "He looks like a Hermann."

The little animal gazed up at me, bright-eyed and welcoming. I bent down and stroked his glossy coat. "He looks healthy. What's the trouble?"

"Over the last week he's been goin' funny on 'is legs," Mrs. Cundall replied. "We weren't all that worried, but tonight he sort of flopped down and couldn't get up again."

"I see. I noticed he didn't seem keen to rise when I patted him." I put my hand under the dog's body and gently lifted him to his feet. "Come on, lad, let's see you walk."

As I encouraged him, he took a few hesitant steps, but his hind end swayed progressively and he soon sat down again. I did not like the look of this at all.

"It's his back, isn't it?" Mrs. Cundall said. "He's strong enough on 'is forelegs."

"That's ma trouble, too," Ron said in a soft husky voice, but he was smiling, and his wife fondly patted his arm.

I lifted the dog onto my knee. "Yes, the weakness is certainly in the back." I began to palpate the lumbar vertebrae, watching for any sign of pain.

"Has he hurt 'imself?" Mrs. Cundall asked. "Has somebody hit 'im? We don't usually let him out alone, but sometimes he sneaks through the garden gate."

"There's always the possibility of an injury," I said. "But more likely it's his disks."

"Disks?"

"Yes, little pads of cartilage and fibrous tissue between the vertebrae. In long-bodied dogs like Hermann, they sometimes protrude into the spinal canal and press on the cord."

Ron's husky voice came again from the bed. "What's 'is prospects, Mr. Herriot?"

That was the question with this syndrome—anything from complete recovery to incurable paralysis. "Very difficult to say," I replied. "I'll give him an injection and some tablets, and we'll see how it goes."

I injected an analgesic and some antibiotic and counted out some salicylate tablets—the best treatment of the day.

"Now then, Mr. Herriot." Mrs. Cundall smiled at me eagerly. "Ron has a bottle o' beer every night about this time. Would you like to join 'im?"

"Well, it's very kind of you, but I don't want to intrude. . . ."

"Oh, you're not. We're glad to see you."

She poured two glasses of brown ale, propped her husband up with pillows and sat down by the bed.

"We're from South Yorkshire, Mr. Herriot," she said.

I nodded. I had noticed the difference from the local accent.

"Aye, we came up here eight years ago, after Ron's accident."

"What was that?"

"I were a miner," Ron said. "Roof fell in on me. I got a broken back, crushed liver and a lot o' other internal injuries, but two of me mates were killed in the same fall, so ah'm lucky to be 'ere." He sipped his beer. "I've survived, but Doctor says I'll never walk no more."

"I'm terribly sorry."

"Nay, nay," the husky voice went on. "I count me blessings, and I've a lot to be thankful for. Ah suffer very little, and I've got t'best wife in the world."

Mrs. Cundall laughed. "Oh, listen to 'im. But I'm right glad we came to Gilthorpe. We used to spend all our holidays here in the Dales; we were great walkers, and it was lovely to get away from the smoke and the chimneys. The bedroom in our old house just looked out on a lot o' brick walls, but here Ron has this big window right by 'im and he can see for miles."

"Yes," I said. "This is a lovely situation." The village was perched on a high ridge and that window would command a view of the green slopes running down to the river and climbing high to the wildness of the moor on the other side. This sight had often beguiled me on my rounds. The grassy paths climbing among the airy tops beckoned to me. But they would beckon in vain to Ron Cundall.

"Gettin' Hermann was a good idea, too," he said. "Ah used to feel lonely when t'missus went out, but the little feller's made all the difference. You're never alone when you've got a dog."

I smiled. "How right you are. What is his age now?"

"He's six," Ron replied. "Right in the prime o' life, aren't you, old lad?" He let his arm fall by the bedside, and his hand fondled the sleek ears.

"That seems to be his favorite place—nearby you."

"Aye, it's a funny thing. T'missus walks and feeds 'im, but he's very faithful to me. I only have to reach down and he's there."

I had often seen this with disabled people: their pets stayed close by, as if to comfort and befriend them.

I finished my beer and got to my feet. Ron looked up at me. "Reckon I'll spin mine out a bit longer." He glanced at his half-full glass. "Ah used to shift more some nights when I went out wi' the lads, but you know, I enjoy this one bottle just as much. Strange how things turn out."

His wife bent over him, mock-scolding. "Yes, you've had to right your ways, haven't you?" and they both laughed.

I moved toward the door. "Well, thank you for the drink, Mrs. Cundall. I'll look in to see Hermann on Tuesday."

As I left I waved to the man in the bed, and his wife put her hand on my arm. "We're grateful to you for comin' on a Sunday night, Mr. Herriot. We felt awful about callin' you, but you un-

derstand it was only today that the little chap started going off his legs."

"Of course, please don't worry. I didn't mind in the least."

And as I drove through the darkness I knew that I didn't mind—now. My petty irritation had evaporated within minutes of entering that house, and I was left only with a feeling of humility. If that man back there had a lot to be thankful for, how about me? I had everything. I only wished I could dispel the foreboding I felt about his dog. There was a hint of doom about those symptoms of Hermann's, and yet I knew I just had to get him right. . . .

On Tuesday he looked a little worse.

"I think I'd better take him to the surgery for X ray," I said to Mrs. Cundall. "He doesn't seem to be improving."

In the car, Hermann curled up happily on Rosie's knee, submitting with good grace to her petting. And I had no need to anesthetize him when I placed him on our newly acquired X-ray machine. Those hindquarters stayed still all by themselves—too still for my liking.

In the pictures I thought I could detect a narrowing of the space between a couple of the vertebrae, which would confirm my suspicion of a disk protrusion. Today we can correct this condition with steroids or surgery, but in those days I could only continue my treatment, and hope.

By the end of the week hope had grown dim. I had supplemented the salicylates with other stimulant drugs, but Hermann was still unable to rise. I tweaked the toes of his hind limbs and was rewarded by a faint reflex movement, but I knew with a sick certainty that complete posterior paralysis was not far away.

By the next Saturday I had the unhappy experience of seeing my prognosis confirmed. When I entered the Cundalls' cottage, Hermann came to meet me, happy and welcoming in his front end but dragging his hind limbs helplessly.

"Hello, Mr. Herriot." Mrs. Cundall gave me a wan smile and looked down at the little creature stretched froglike on the carpet. "What d'you think of him now?"

I bent and tried the reflexes. Nothing. I shrugged my shoulders, unable to think of anything to reply. I looked at the gaunt figure in the bed. "Good morning, Ron," I said as cheerfully as I could, but his face was averted, looking out the window. It was as though he did not know I was there.

"Is he annoyed with me?" I whispered to his wife.

"No, no, it's this." She held out a newspaper. "It's upset him something awful." I looked at the printed page. On it was a large picture of a dachshund exactly like Hermann. This dog, too, was paralyzed, but its hind end was supported by a little four-wheeled trolley. The animal appeared to be sporting with its mistress and looked happy and normal, except for those wheels.

At the rustle of the newspaper Ron's head came around quickly. "What d'ye think of that, Mr. Herriot? D'ye agree with it?"

"Well . . . I don't know, Ron. I don't like the look of it, but I suppose that lady thought it was the only thing to do."

"Aye, maybe." The husky voice trembled. "But ah don't want Hermann to finish up like that." The arm dropped by the side of the bed and his fingers felt around on the carpet, but the little dog was still splayed out near the door. "It's 'opeless now, Mr. Herriot, isn't it?"

"Well, it was a black lookout from the beginning," I said. "These cases are so difficult. I'm sorry."

"Nay, I'm not blamin' you," he said. "You've done what ye could. What do we do now—put 'im down?"

"No, Ron, forget about that just now. Sometimes paralysis cases recover on their own after many weeks. We must carry on, for I honestly cannot say there is no hope."

On the way back to the surgery, the thought hammered in my brain. The hope I had extended was slight. Spontaneous recovery did sometimes occur, but Hermann's condition was extreme.

However, I kept going back every few days. Sometimes I took a couple of bottles of brown ale along in the evening and drank them with Ron. He and his wife were always cheerful, but the little dog never showed the slightest improvement. It was on one of these visits that I noticed an unpleasant smell as I entered the house. There was something familiar about it.

I sniffed, and the Cundalls looked at each other guiltily. Then

Ron spoke, his fingers twitching on the bedclothes. "It's some medicine ah've been givin' Hermann. Stinks like 'ell, but it's supposed to be good for dogs. Bill Noakes, an old mate o' mine—we used to work down t'pit together—put me on to it when he came to visit last weekend. Keeps a few whippets, does Bill. Knows a lot about dogs, and 'e sent me this stuff for Hermann."

Mrs. Cundall went to the cupboard and sheepishly presented me with a plain bottle. I removed the cork, and as the horrid stench rose up to me, my memory became suddenly clear. Asafetida, a common constituent of quack medicines before the war and still lingering on the shelves of occasional pharmacies. Its popularity was probably based on the assumption that anything that stank so badly must have magical properties. I knew it could not possibly do anything for Hermann.

I replaced the cork. "So you're giving him this, eh?"

Ron nodded. "Aye, three times a day. He doesn't like it much, but Bill says it's cured lots o' dogs with Hermann's problem." The deep-sunk eyes looked at me in silent appeal.

"Fine, Ron," I said. "Carry on. Let's hope it works." I knew the asafetida couldn't do any harm, and since my treatment had proved useless, I was in no position to turn haughty.

Mrs. Cundall smiled and Ron's expression relaxed. "That's grand, Mr. Herriot," he said. "Ah'm glad ye don't mind. I can dose the little feller myself. It's summat for me to do."

About a week later I called in at the Cundalls. "How are you today, Ron?" I asked.

"Champion, Mr. Herriot, champion." He always said that, but today there was a new eagerness in his face. He reached down and lifted his dog onto the bed. "Look 'ere." He pinched one hind foot, and there was a faint but definite retraction of the leg. I almost fell over in my haste to grab at the other foot. The result was the same.

"Look at that," I gasped. "The reflexes are coming back."

Ron laughed. "Bill Noakes's stuff's working, isn't it?"

A gush of emotions, mainly professional shame and wounded pride, welled in me, but it was only for a moment. "Yes, Ron," I replied. "No doubt about it."

He stared up at me. "Then Hermann's going to be all right?"

"Well, it's early yet, but that's the way it looks."

It was several weeks more before the dachshund was back to normal, and it was a fairly typical case of spontaneous recovery, with nothing whatever to do with the asafetida or, indeed, with my own efforts.

My final call at the cottage happened around the same time as my first visit—eight o'clock in the evening—and when Mrs. Cundall ushered me in, the little dog bounded joyously up to me before returning to his post by the bed.

"Well, that's a lovely sight," I said. "He can gallop like a race-horse now."

Ron dropped his hand down and stroked the sleek head. "Aye, isn't it grand? By heck, it's been a worryin' time."

"I just looked in to make sure all was well." I gave Hermann a farewell pat. "Well, I'll be going."

"Nay, nay," Ron said. "Don't rush off. Have a bottle o' beer before ye go."

I sat down by the bed and sipped my beer, and their faces glowed with friendliness. I marveled because my part in Hermann's salvation had been anything but heroic. In their eyes everything I had done must have seemed bumbling and ineffectual, and they must have been convinced that all would have been lost if Ron's old chum Bill Noakes had not stepped in and put things right. But though my ego had been bruised, I did not really care; I was witnessing a happy ending instead of a tragedy.

15

"Parents need nerves of steel"—those words that I heard years ago came to mind many times while Jimmy and Rosie were growing up. One notable occasion was a recital given by Miss Livingstone's piano class.

A soft-voiced, charming lady in her fifties, Miss Livingstone started many of the local children in piano lessons, and once a year she held a concert in the Methodist Hall for her pupils to show their paces. They ranged from six-year-olds to teenagers, and the room was packed with their proud parents. Jimmy was nine at the time and had been practicing without much enthusiasm for the big day.

Everybody knows everybody else in a small town like Darrowby, and as the place filled up, there was much nodding and smiling when people recognized each other. I found myself on the center aisle, with Helen on my right, and just across the way I saw Jeff Ward, old Willie Richardson's cowman, sitting very upright, dressed in his Sunday best.

"Hello, Jeff," I said. "One of your youngsters performing?"

He turned and grinned. "Aye, it's our Margaret. She's been comin' on right well at t'piano, and I just hope she does herself justice this afternoon."

"She will, Jeff. Miss Livingstone is an excellent teacher."

He nodded and turned to the front as the concert commenced. The first few performers who mounted the platform were very small boys in shorts and socks, or tiny girls in frilly dresses, and their feet dangled far above the pedals as they sat at the keyboard. Miss Livingstone hovered nearby to prompt them, but their little mistakes were greeted with indulgent smiles from the assembly, and the conclusion of each piece was greeted with thunderous applause.

I noticed, however, that as the children grew bigger and the pieces became more difficult, a certain tension began to build in the hall. The errors weren't so funny now, and when little Jenny Newcombe, the fruiterer's daughter, halted a couple of times, the silence in the room was absolute and charged with anxiety. When Jenny successfully restarted and I relaxed with all the others, the realization burst upon me that we were not just a roomful of parents watching our children perform; we were a band of brothers and sisters suffering together.

When little Margaret Ward climbed to the platform, her father stiffened perceptibly in his seat, his big, work-roughened fingers clutching tightly at his knees. However, Margaret went on very nicely till she came to a rather complicated chord that jarred with harsh dissonance. She knew she had got the notes wrong and tried again . . . and again . . . and again.

"No, C and E, dear," murmured Miss Livingstone, and Margaret crashed her fingers down once more, violently and wrongly.

She's not going to make it, I breathed to myself, aware that my pulse was racing and my muscles were rigid.

I glanced over at Jeff. His face had assumed a hideously mottled appearance and his legs were twitching convulsively. Just beyond him, his wife was leaning forward. Her mouth hung slightly open and her lips trembled.

It seemed an eternity before Margaret got the right notes and galloped through the rest of the piece, and although everybody applauded at the finish, the episode had taken its toll on all of us. I certainly didn't feel so good and watched in a half trance as a succession of children went up and played their pieces without incident. Then it was Jimmy's turn.

There was no doubt that most of the performers—as well as their parents—were suffering from nerves, but this couldn't be said of my son. He almost whistled as he trotted up the steps, and there was a hint of swagger in his walk over to the piano. In marked contrast, I found I was breathing with difficulty. My palms broke out in instant sweat.

Jimmy's piece was called "The Miller's Dance," a title burned on my brain till the day I die. It was a rollicking little melody, which of course I knew down to the last semiquaver, and Jimmy started off in great style, throwing his hands about and tossing his head like Artur Rubinstein in full flow.

Around the middle of "The Miller's Dance" there is a pause in the quick tempo where the music goes from a brisk ta-rum-tum-tiddle-iddle-om-pom-pom to a lingering taa-rum, taa-rum, before starting off again at top speed. It was a clever little ploy of the composer's and gave a touch of variety to the piece.

Jimmy dashed up to this point with flailing arms till he slowed down at the familiar taa-rum, taa-rum. I waited for him to take off again, but nothing happened. He stopped and looked down fixedly at the keys for a few seconds; then he played the slow bit again and halted once more.

My heart gave a great thud. Come on, lad, you know the next

part—I've heard you play it a hundred times. But Jimmy didn't seem troubled. He looked down with mild puzzlement and rubbed his chin.

Miss Livingstone's gentle voice came over the quivering silence. "Perhaps you'd better start at the beginning, Jimmy."

"Okay." My son's tone was perky as he plunged confidently into the melody again, and I closed my eyes as he approached the fateful bars. Ta-rum-tum-tiddle-iddle-om-pom-pom, taa-rum, taa-rum—then nothing. This time he put his hands on his knees and bent closely over the keyboard as though the strips of ivory were trying to hide something from him. He showed no panic, only a faint curiosity.

In the almost palpable hush of that room, I was sure the hammering of my heart must be audible. I could feel Helen's leg trembling against mine. I knew we couldn't take much more of this.

Miss Livingstone's voice was soft as a zephyr. "Jimmy, dear, shall we try it once more from the beginning?"

"Yes, yes, right." Away he went again like a hurricane, all fire and fury. It was unbelievable that there could ever be a flaw in such virtuosity.

By now the other parents had come to know "The Miller's Dance" almost as well as I did, and we waited in agony for the dread passage. Jimmy came up to it at breakneck speed. Ta-rum-tum-tiddle-iddle-om-pom-pom, then taa-rum, taa-rum . . . and silence. Helen's knees were definitely knocking now, and she was very pale.

As Jimmy sat motionless except for a thoughtful drumming of his fingers against the woodwork of the piano, I felt I was going to choke. I glared around me desperately, and I saw that Jeff Ward was also in a bad way. His face had gone all blotchy again and perspiration covered his forehead. Something had to break soon, and once more it was Miss Livingstone's voice that cut into the terrible atmosphere.

"All right, Jimmy, dear," she said. "Never mind. Perhaps you'd better go and sit down now."

My son rose from the stool and marched across the platform to rejoin his fellow pupils in the first few rows.

I slumped back in my seat. Ah well, that was it. The final indignity. The poor little lad had blown it. And though he didn't seem troubled, I was sure he must feel a sense of shame.

A wave of misery enveloped me, and though many of the other parents turned and directed sickly smiles of sympathy at Helen and me, it didn't help. I hardly heard the rest of the concert, which was a pity, because as the bigger boys and girls began to perform, the musical standard rose to remarkable heights, from Chopin nocturnes to Mozart sonatas. It was a truly splendid show—by everybody but poor old Jimmy, the only one who hadn't managed to finish.

At the end, Miss Livingstone came to the front of the platform. "Well, thank you, ladies and gentlemen, for your kind reception. I do hope you have enjoyed it as much as we have."

There was more clapping and the pushing back of chairs. But Miss Livingstone wasn't through. "Just one thing more, ladies and gentlemen." She raised a hand. "There is a young man here who, I know, can do much better. I wouldn't be happy going home now without giving him another opportunity. Jimmy." She beckoned toward the second row. "Jimmy, I wonder if you would like to have one more try."

As Helen and I exchanged horrified glances, our son's voice rang out, chirpy and confident. "Aye, I'll have a go!"

I couldn't believe it. The martyrdom was surely not about to start all over. But it was true. The small familiar figure was already striding to the piano. From a great distance I heard Miss Livingstone again. "Jimmy will play 'The Miller's Dance.'" She didn't have to tell us—we all knew.

A few seconds earlier I had been conscious only of a great weariness, but now I was gripped by a fiercer tension than I had known all afternoon. As Jimmy poised his hands over the keys, a vibrant sense of strain lapped around the silent room. The little lad started off as he always did, as though he hadn't a care in the world, and I began a series of long, shuddering breaths designed to carry me past the moment that was fast approaching. Because I knew that he would stop again. And I knew just as surely that when he did, I would topple senseless to the floor.

When he reached the crucial bars I closed my eyes tightly. But I could still hear the music—so very clearly. Ta-rum-tum-tiddle-iddle-om-pom-pom, taa-rum, taa-rum . . . There was a pause of unbearable length, then, tiddle-iddle-om-pom, tiddle-iddle-om-pom, Jimmy was blissfully on his way again.

He raced through the second half of the piece, but I kept my eyes closed as relief flooded through me, opening them only when he came to the finale. Jimmy was making a real meal of it, head down, fingers thumping, and at the last crashing chord he held up one hand in a flourish a foot above the keyboard before letting it fall by his side, like a true concert pianist.

I doubt if the Methodist Hall has ever heard a noise like the great cheer that followed. The place erupted in a storm of clapping and shouting, and Jimmy was not the man to ignore such an accolade. All the other children had walked impassively from the stage at the end of their efforts, but not so my son. To my astonishment, he strode to the front of the platform, placed one arm across his abdomen and the other behind his back, extended one foot and bowed, first to one side of the audience then to the other, with the grace of an eighteenth-century courtier.

The cheering changed to a great roar of laughter, which continued as he left the platform, and everybody was still giggling as we made our way out. In the doorway we bumped into Miss Mullion, who ran the little school that our son attended. "Oh dear," she said, dabbing at her eyes. "You can always depend on Jimmy to provide the light relief."

I drove back to Skeldale House slowly. I was still in a weakened condition, and I felt it dangerous to exceed twenty-five miles an hour. The color had returned to Helen's face, but there were lines of exhaustion around her mouth and eyes as she stared ahead through the windshield.

Jimmy, in the back, was lying full length along the seat, whistling some of the tunes that had been played that afternoon.

"Mum! Dad!" he exclaimed in the staccato manner so typical of him. "I like music."

I glanced at him in the driving mirror. "That's good, son. So do we."

Suddenly he rolled off the back seat and thrust his head between us. "Do you know why I like music so much?"

I shook my head.

"Because it's"—he groped rapturously for the phrase—"because it's so soothing."

16

When Walt Barnett asked me to see his cat, I was surprised. He had always employed other veterinary surgeons, ever since Siegfried had mortally offended him by charging him ten pounds for castrating a horse, and that had been a long time ago. I was surprised, too, that a man like him should concern himself with the ailments of a cat.

Walt Barnett was reputed to be the richest man in Darrowby. He was mainly a scrap merchant, but he had a haulage business, too. In fact, he did anything that came his way, if there was money in it—for money was the ruling passion of his life. There was no profit in cat keeping.

Another thing that puzzled me as I drove to his office was that owning a pet indicated some warmth of character, a vein of sentiment, however small. It just didn't fit into his nature.

I picked my way through the scrapyard to the shed from which the empire was run. Walt Barnett was sitting behind a cheap desk exactly as I remembered him, the massive body stretching the seams of the shiny navy-blue suit, and the brown trilby hat perched on the back of his head. Unchanged, too, was the beefy red face with its arrogant expression and hostile eyes.

"Over there," he said, glowering at me and poking a finger at a black and white cat sitting among the papers on the desk.

It was a typical greeting. I hadn't expected him to say good morning, and he never smiled. I reached across the desk to tickle the animal's cheek and was rewarded by a rich purring. He was a big tom, long-haired and attractively marked, with a white breast and white paws, and I took an immediate liking to him.

"Nice cat," I said. "What's the trouble?"

"It's 'is leg there. Must've cut 'isself."

I felt among the fluffy hair, and the little creature flinched as I reached a point halfway up the limb. I took out my scissors and clipped a clear area. I could see a deep transverse wound with a thin serous discharge. "Yes . . . this could be a cut. But there's something unusual about it. I can't see how he's done it. Does he go out in the yard much?"

The big man nodded. "Aye, wanders around a bit."

"Ah well, he may have caught it on some sharp object. I'll give him a penicillin injection and leave you a tube of ointment to squeeze into the wound morning and night."

Some cats object strongly to hypodermics, and since their armory includes claws as well as teeth, they can be difficult, but this one never moved as I inserted the needle. In fact, the purring increased.

"He really is good-natured," I said. "What do you call him?"

"Fred." Walt Barnett looked at me expressionlessly, discouraging further comment.

I produced the ointment from my bag and placed it on the desk. "Right, let me know if he doesn't improve."

I received no reply and took my leave, feeling the prickle of resentment that had heretofore characterized my dealings with this man. But as I walked across the yard, I soon forgot my annoyance in my preoccupation with the case. There was something peculiar about that wound. It didn't look accidental; it was neat and deep, as though somebody had drawn a razor blade across the flesh.

A touch on my arm brought me out of my musings. One of the men who had been working amid the scrap was looking at me conspiratorially. "You've been in to see t'big boss?"

"Yes."

"Funny thing, t'awd sourface botherin' about a cat, eh?"

"I suppose so. How long has he had it?"

"Oh, about two years now. It was a stray. Ran into 'is office one day, and, knowin' him, I thought he'd 'ave booted it straight out, but 'e didn't. Adopted it instead. Ah can't reckon it up. It sits there all day on 'is desk."

"He must like it," I said.

"Him? He doesn't like anythin' or anybody. He's a—"

A bellow from the office doorway cut him short. "Hey, you! Get on with your work!" Walt Barnett, huge and menacing, brandished a fist, and the man, terrified, scuttled away.

As I got into my car, the thought stayed with me that this was how Walt Barnett lived—surrounded by hate. His ruthlessness was a byword in the town, and though no doubt it had made him rich, I didn't envy him.

Two days later he telephoned. "Get out 'ere sharpish and see that cat."

"Isn't the wound any better?"

"Naw, it's wuss, so don't be long."

Fred was in his usual place on the desk, and he purred as I went up and stroked him, but the leg was certainly more painful. Even more baffling, the wound had lengthened; it was as though it were trying to creep its way around the leg.

I passed a metal probe gently into the depths of the cut. I could feel something there, something that caught the end of the probe and sprang away. I gripped the unknown object with forceps, and when I brought it to the surface and saw the narrow brown strand, all became suddenly clear.

"He's got an elastic band round his leg," I said. I snipped the thing off and dropped it on the desk. "There it is. He'll be all right now."

Walt Barnett jerked himself upright in his chair. "Elastic band! Why the 'ell didn't you find it fust time?"

"I'm sorry, Mr. Barnett," I said. "It was embedded in the flesh, out of sight."

"Well, 'ow did it get there?"

"Somebody put it on his leg, without a doubt."

"Put it on . . . Wot for?"

"Oh, there are some cruel folk around."

"One o' them fellers in the yard, ah'll wager."

"Not necessarily. Fred goes out in the street, doesn't he?"

"Oh aye, often."

"Well, it could have been anybody."

The big man scowled, eyes half closed. I wondered if he were going over the list of his enemies. That would take some time.

"Anyway," I said. "The leg will heal quickly now. That's the main thing."

Walt Barnett reached across the desk and slowly rubbed the cat's side with a sausagelike forefinger. I had seen him do this several times during my previous visit. It was an odd gesture but probably the nearest he could get to a caress.

On my way back to the surgery I slumped low in the car seat, hardly daring to think of what would have happened if I hadn't found that elastic. Arrest of circulation, gangrene, loss of the foot or even death. I broke into a sweat at the thought.

Walt Barnett was on the phone three weeks later, and I felt a twinge of apprehension at the sound of his voice.

"Is Fred's leg still troubling him?" I asked.

"Naw, that's 'ealed. There's summat matter with 'is head."

"His head?"

"Aye, keeps cockin' it from side to side. Come and see 'im."

The symptoms sounded like canker, and when I saw the cat, twisting his head around uneasily, I was sure that was it; but the ears were clean and painless. This amiable cat seemed to like being examined, and the purring rose to a crescendo as I inspected his teeth, mouth, eyes and nostrils. Nothing. Yet something up there was causing a lot of discomfort.

I began to work my way through the black hair on his neck, and suddenly the purring was interrupted by a sharp meow as my fingers came upon a painful spot.

"Something here," I murmured. I took out my scissors and began to clip. And as the hair fell away and the skin showed through, a wave of disbelief swept through me. I was looking down at a neat little transverse slit, a twin of the one I had seen before. But surely not on the neck!

I went into the wound with probe and forceps, and within seconds I had brought the familiar brown band to the surface and snipped it off. "Another elastic band," I said. "Somebody really meant business this time."

Walt Barnett drew his forefinger along the cat's furry flank. "Who could be doin' this?" he asked.

I shrugged. "No way of telling. The police are always on the lookout for cruelty, but they would have to catch a person actually in the act."

I knew he was wondering when the next attempt would come, and so was I, but there were no more elastic bands for Fred. The neck healed rapidly, and I didn't see the cat for nearly a year. Then Helen met me one morning as I was coming in from my rounds. "Mr. Barnett's just been on the phone, Jim. Would you please go at once? He thinks his cat has been poisoned."

I found a vastly different Fred this time. The cat was not on the desk but rather was crouched on the floor among a litter of newspapers. He retched and vomited a yellow fluid as I went over to him. More vomit lay around among pools of diarrhea with the same yellowish hue.

Walt Barnett spoke up. "He's poisoned, isn't 'e? Somebody's given 'im summat."

"It's possible. . . ." I watched the cat move slowly to a saucer of milk and sit over it in the same crouching attitude. He did not drink but sat looking down with a curious immobility. There was a sad familiarity in the little animal's appearance. This could be something worse even than poison.

"Well, it is, isn't it?" the big man went on. "Somebody's tried to kill 'im again."

"I'm not sure." As I took the cat's temperature, there was none of the purring of before. He was sunk in a profound lethargy. The temperature was 105 degrees. Palpating the abdomen, I felt a doughy consistency in the bowels, a lack of muscular tone.

"Well, if it's not that, what is it?"

"It's feline enteritis," I said. "Some people call it cat distemper. There's an outbreak in Darrowby just now. I've seen several cases lately, and Fred's symptoms are typical."

The big man heaved his bulk from behind the desk, went over to the cat and rubbed his forefinger along the unheeding back. "Can you cure 'im?"

"I'll do my best, but the mortality rate is very high."

"You mean, most of 'em die?"

"I'm afraid so."

"How can that be? I thought you fellers had all them wonderful new medicines now."

"This is a virus, and viruses are resistant to antibiotics."

"Awright, then. What are you goin' to do?"

"I'm going to start right now," I said. I injected electrolytic fluid to combat the dehydration. I gave antibiotics against the secondary bacteria and finished with a sedative to control the vomiting. But I knew that everything I had done was merely supportive. I had never had much luck with feline enteritis.

I visited Fred each morning, and the very sight of him made me unhappy. He was either hunched over the saucer or curled up on the desk in a little basket. He had no interest in the world around him. When I gave him his injections it was like pushing a needle into a lifeless animal, and on the fourth morning I could see that he was sinking rapidly.

"I'll come by tomorrow," I said, and Walt Barnett nodded silently. He had shown no emotion throughout the cat's illness.

Next day, when I entered the office, I found the usual scene—Mr. Barnett in his chair, the cat in the basket on the desk.

Fred was very still, and as I approached I saw with a dull feeling of inevitability that he was not breathing. I put my stethoscope over his heart, then looked up.

"I'm afraid he's dead, Mr. Barnett."

The big man did not change expression. He reached slowly across and rubbed his forefinger against the dark fur in that familiar gesture. Then he put his elbows on the desk and covered his face with his hands. I watched helplessly as his shoulders began to shake and tears welled between the thick fingers. He stayed like that for some time, then he spoke. "He was my friend."

I could find no words, and the silence was heavy in the room until he suddenly pulled his hands from his face and glared at me defiantly. "Aye, ah know what you're thinkin'. This is that big tough Walt Barnett, cryin' his eyes out over a cat. What a joke. I reckon you'll have a bloody good laugh later on."

He was sure that what he considered a display of weakness would lower my opinion of him, and yet he was so wrong. I have liked him better ever since.

17

It was a Sunday morning in June, and I was washing my hands in the sink in Matt Clarke's kitchen. The sun was bright, and there was a brisk wind scouring the fellsides; through the window I could see every cleft and gully lying sharp and clear on the green flanks as the cloud shadows drove across them.

I glanced at the white head of Grandma Clarke bent over her knitting. The radio on the dresser was tuned to the morning service, and as I watched, the old lady looked up from her work and listened intently to some words of the sermon before starting her needles clicking again.

In that brief time I had a profound impression of serenity and unquestioning faith that has remained with me to this day. Whenever I have heard discussions and arguments on the varying religious beliefs and doctrines, there still rise before me the seamed old face and calm eyes of Grandma Clarke. She knew and was secure. Goodness seemed to flow from her.

She was in her late eighties and always dressed in black with a little black neckband. She had come through the hard times of farming and could look back on a long life of toil, in the fields as well as in the home.

As I reached for the towel, Matt led Rosie into the kitchen. "Mr. Clarke has been showing me some baby chicks, Daddy," Rosie said.

Grandma looked up. "Is that your lass, Mr. Herriot?"

"Yes, Mrs. Clarke," I replied. "This is Rosie."

"Aye, of course. I've seen her before, many a time." The old lady put down her knitting and rose stiffly from her chair. She shuffled over to a cupboard, brought out a gaily colored tin and extracted a bar of chocolate. "How old are ye now, Rosie?" she asked as she presented the sweet.

"Thank you. I'm six," my daughter replied.

Grandma looked down at the smiling face, at the sturdy, tanned legs in their blue shorts and sandals. "Well, you're a grand little lass." For a moment she rested her work-roughened hand against the little girl's cheek, then she returned to her chair. They didn't make much of a fuss, those old Yorkshire folk, but to me the gesture was like a benediction.

The old lady picked up her knitting again. "And how's that lad o' yours? How's Jimmy?"

"Oh, he's fine, thank you. Ten years old now. He's out with some of his pals this morning."

"Ten, eh? Ten and six . . ." For a few seconds her thoughts seemed far away as she plied her needles, then she looked at me again. "Maybe ye don't know it, Mr. Herriot, but this is the best time of your life. When your children are young and growin' up around ye—that's when it's best. It's the same for everybody, only a lot o' folk don't know it and a lot find out when it's too late. It doesn't last long, you know."

"I believe I've always realized that, Mrs. Clarke, without thinking about it very much."

"Reckon you have, young man." She gave me a sideways smile. "You allus seem to have one or t'other of your bairns with you on your calls."

As I drove away from the farm, the old lady's words stayed in my mind; and they are still in my mind, all these years later, when Helen and I are about to celebrate forty years of marriage. Life has been and is still good to us—we have had so many wonderful times—but I think we both agree that Grandma Clarke was right about the very best time of all.

When I got back to Skeldale House that summer morning, I found Siegfried replenishing the store of drugs in his car trunk. His children, Alan and Janet, were helping. Like me, he usually took his family around with him.

He banged down the lid of the trunk. "Right, that's that for another few days." He glanced at me and smiled. "There are no more calls at the moment, James. Let's have a walk down the back."

With the children running happily ahead of us, we went through the passage and out into the long garden behind the house. Here the sunshine was imprisoned between the high old walls, with the wind banished to the upper air and ruffling the top leaves of the apple trees. When we reached the big lawn, Siegfried flopped on the turf and rested on his elbow. I sat down by his side.

My partner pulled a piece of grass and chewed it contemplatively. "Pity about the acacia," he murmured.

I looked at him in surprise. It was many years since the beautiful tree, which had once soared from the middle of the lawn, had blown down in a gale.

"Yes, it is," I said. "It was magnificent." I paused for a moment. "Remember, I fell asleep against it the day I came here to apply for a job? We first met right on this spot."

Siegfried laughed. "I do remember." He looked around him at the mellow brick and stone copings of the walls, at the rockery and rose bed, at the children playing in the old hen house at the far end. "My word, James, when you think about it, we've come through a few things together since then. A lot of water, as they say, has flowed under the bridge."

We were both silent for a while, and my thoughts went back over the struggles and the laughter of those years. I lay back on the grass and closed my eyes, feeling the sun warm on my face, hearing the hum of the bees among the flowers, the croaking of the rooks in the great elms that overhung the yard.

My colleague's voice seemed to come from afar. "Hey, you're not going to do the same trick again, are you? Going to sleep in front of me?"

I sat up, blinking. "Gosh, I'm sorry, Siegfried, I nearly did. I was out at a farrowing at five o'clock this morning and it's just catching up with me."

"Ah well. You won't need to read yourself to sleep tonight."

Siegfried and I each had favorite books to which we sometimes resorted when sleep would not come—books that never failed to start us nodding. I laughed. "No," I said, rubbing my eyes. "I won't need any encouragement tonight." I rolled onto my side. "By the way, I was at Matt Clarke's this morning." I told him what Grandma had said.

Siegfried selected a fresh piece of grass and resumed his chewing. "Well, she's a wise old lady and she's seen it all." My partner startled me then by sitting up abruptly. "Do you know, James," he said, "I'm convinced that the same thing applies to our job. We're going through the best time there, too."

"Do you think so?"

"Sure of it. Look at all the new advances since the war—drugs and procedures we never dreamed of. We can look after our animals in a way that would have been impossible a few years ago, and the farmers realize this. You've seen them crowding into the surgery on market day to ask advice—they've gained respect for the profession and they know it pays to call in the vet now."

"That's true," I said. "We're certainly busier than ever."

"In fact, James, I'd like to bet that these present years are the high noon of country practice."

I thought for a moment. "You could be right. But if we are on the top now, does it mean that our lives will decline later?"

"No, no, of course not. They'll be different, that's all. I sometimes think we've only touched the fringe of so many things. . . ." Siegfried brandished his gnawed piece of grass at me, and his eyes shone with the enthusiasm that always uplifted me.

"I tell you this, James. There are great days ahead!"

Still "Our Vet"

"Mr. Herriot," said a Yorkshire taxi driver to a visiting journalist, "he tends my dog. A nice man, a bit quiet."

In spite of the fame that James Herriot's books have brought him, his life remains essentially unchanged. First and foremost he is still a country vet, absorbed in his practice. Although he has always taken pains to disguise the true identity of his fictional town of Darrowby, forty to fifty fans turn up every day on his doorstep; but the animals in the surgery are always tended first. Only then does Herriot go out to meet his reading public, to pose for their clicking cameras and to autograph his books.

James and Helen now live in a village outside "Darrowby." The practice has increased in size. Siegfried and James have been joined by James's son, Jimmy, and in addition to three veterinary assistants, they also have the help of Jimmy's own four-year-old son, Nicholas. In true Herriot tradition, he loves to accompany his father on his rounds, but whether Nicholas' baby sister, Zoe, will also join the practice is still in doubt. Herriot's daughter, Rosie, meanwhile, is a people doctor in a nearby group practice; her six-year-old daughter, Emma, is the third of James and Helen's grandchildren.

James Herriot

In the past, James traveled widely in connection with veterinary work and to publicize his books, but these days he prefers to stay at home. When a new book comes out, he tours the British Isles for signing sessions and much enjoys meeting his readers. But the Herriots' idea of a perfect holiday is to tuck themselves away in a remote little cottage they have in the Dales.

Although James Herriot has been in practice since before World War II, he has not begun to think of retirement. "I just can't imagine what it would be like never to go through that surgery door again," he says. "I'm too fond of animals."

AN EXCEPTIONAL MARRIAGE

Louisa Catherine and John Quincy Adams

A CONDENSATION OF THE BOOK
Cannibals of the Heart
BY
JACK SHEPHERD

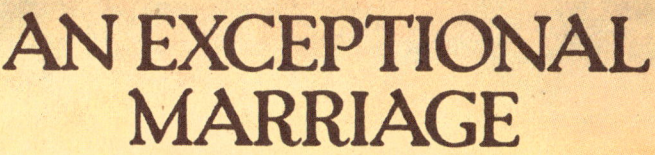

ILLUSTRATED BY

When sprightly Louisa Johnson married John Quincy Adams, she little guessed what change her life was about to undergo. Young Mr. Adams was a man driven by ambition and by a vision of his and his nation's destiny.

The couple would be swept away from their native shores to the glittering courts of Europe, and on to the White House itself. Their public lives demanded private sacrifices so painful that more than once rebellion surged in Louisa's heart. Yet she emerged triumphant, the unsung heroine of one of history's most remarkable partnerships.

"With the fine touch of a novelist, Shepherd builds his story . . . a detailed study of the wife and children of the sixth President of the United States."
—Washington *Post*

PART I
London, 1797

CHAPTER ONE

LOUISA Johnson loved spring best of all the seasons. It was a time of promise and a season of insistence, when all that had been dead was born again. Throughout her life, Louisa measured the passing of winter, and welcomed the clouds of wild pigeons filling the spring sky, the flowering of the earth, the singing of birds, the rich smells of tree and vine. Louisa, with her inherited Maryland blood, loved the heat, and spring carried with it the never failing promise of warmer weather.

Like her favorite season, Louisa was a velvet-budding spirit who grew up carefree and spoiled. She filled the air with music, and played the pianoforte and the harp; she wrote and recited poetry, and sang and danced with great enthusiasm. She loved the excitement of her impulses, and indulged herself.

John Quincy Adams liked the snow and cold; heat troubled him. He was born in New England and was as hard, cold, and purposeful as a stone wall. He was the firstborn son of John Adams, who had been a Founding Father, the nation's first Vice-President, and its second President. The Adams family was the first American political dynasty, and JQA, as he was often designated, was nurtured by a father and mother who carefully planned his political life.

John Quincy Adams made it his duty to be precise. He measured, timed, and recorded everything. He started a diary at

An Exceptional Marriage

fourteen and kept it faithfully each day for almost sixty-seven years. He deprived himself of pleasure and welcomed misfortune as a means of improving character. Throughout his life, he would rise every day at four or five, build his own fire, read his Bible, then work a full day and lament the social events of evening that interfered with his privacy. He never lost sight of history: he viewed his diary and the many portraits he sat for as permanent national records. He exercised with intensity: fast walks, horseback rides, skinny-dips in the Potomac River. He always maintained that there were three rules for living correctly: (1) Regularity, (2) Regularity, and (3) Regularity.

In London, safely three thousand miles from his domineering mother, John Quincy Adams, at the age of thirty, had decided to get married. On Wednesday, July 26, 1797, he and Louisa Catherine Johnson walked with her parents from the Johnson home on Tower Hill to the Church of All Hallows Barking. Of his family, only his brother Thomas, serving as best man, was with him. Beyond the thick oak doors of the church and the rows of empty pews, the small wedding party gathered around the Reverend John Hewlett. There was no one else in the church.

Louisa, at twenty-two, appeared delicate and small, with soft brown eyes and curly light brown hair. She was wearing a blue bonnet. John Quincy Adams was short, slightly plump, and balding. He wore a powdered wig that made his deep black eyes seem even darker. Their low voices echoed among the ancient shadows as he vowed to love and cherish, she to honor and obey; both would struggle to keep those promises.

The union was incongruous. Where she was kind, loving, and gentle, he was stern, gruff, and sometimes nasty. Where her love was spontaneous and wide, his was parceled out narrowly: first to God, then to Country, then to Duty, then to Family, and finally to individuals. Louisa had lived her childhood in Europe uninhibited by the claims of a New England conscience. She cherished the "Johnson wit" and could buckle the stiffest guest with her humor. Adams had difficulty appearing cheerful. "Gravity is natural to him," said a contemporary. While Louisa read history, poetry, and the novels of the day, JQA gloried in his Bible and solid classical fare. Cicero, Louisa said ruefully, was his "passion." She, evidently, was not. He loved her most when they were apart.

John Quincy Adams, later in life, admitted their many differences "of sentiment, tastes, and opinions in regard to domestic economy and to the education of children. There are frailties in our tempers—both being quick and irascible, and mine being sometimes harsh." But, he concluded, marriage was better than celibacy. Louisa, after fifty years with her husband, thought with gloom "that hanging and marriage were strongly assimilated."

On July 26, 1797, Louisa Johnson Adams entered her womanhood full of promise. But hers was a marriage out of season: of light to shadow, of springtime to winter, of heart to cannibal.

Louisa Catherine Johnson was born in London on February 12, 1775. She was the second child of Joshua and Catherine Nuth Johnson, in a family of one son and seven daughters, every one of them "remarkable for beauty." From the start, life was serene and comfortable, and the distant rumbling of the American Revolution scarcely intruded upon the Johnsons.

An enterprising man from a large Maryland family of merchants, Joshua Johnson had been sent to England by his Annapolis trading partnership to manage the firm's transatlantic affairs. He proved clever at this and seemed to take no sides in the emerging conflict between British crown and American colonies. For although he had been born in Maryland of an old and established family, his grandfather had been born an Englishman, and Joshua himself showed a willingness to cope with, and join, the British colonial system of trade.

Soon after arriving in London in 1771, Joshua met a lovely young Englishwoman named Catherine Nuth; little is known of her family, but she was one of twenty-two children. The couple were married, and Nancy, their firstborn, arrived in December 1773. Louisa followed in 1775, and then Carolina Virginia Marylanda in July 1776, named to mark the vote of those colonies for independence. One son, Thomas, and four more daughters followed.

An Exceptional Marriage

Louisa Johnson's childhood was well ordered, unthreatened. Her father stood at the head of the family: protector, master, unquestioned power. She loved him more than she had ever loved any other person and thought him "the handsomest man" she ever beheld. He was, she said, honest, kind, and affectionate, but he could lose his temper, and when he did he showed "a dazzling fixed severity."

Louisa's mother was small and delicate, exquisitely beautiful, and so spoiled that whenever she fell ill, Joshua warmed the handles of her knives and forks before she used them.

Childhood for Louisa was one of those times when "sorrows are like rainbow clouds dispersed ere they are seen." The Johnsons lived richly and on the edge of their resources: a precarious position from which the fall would be swift and hard.

In early 1778, when the Revolutionary War made life uncomfortable for Americans in England, the Johnsons sailed to France and settled in Nantes. There Joshua undertook various commercial missions, and, as Louisa remembered, the family continued to live "in a handsome style" for the duration of the war.

The Johnson girls spoke only French, and Louisa remained fluent in the language for the rest of her life. When she reached school age, she went to the nearby Catholic convent school. Since her parents emphasized no religion over another, Louisa embraced the Roman Catholic faith. Later she would recall the strong influence the church had upon her, "the heartfelt humility with which I knelt before the image of the tortured Jesus and the horror at the thought of mixing with hereticks."

JOHN Quincy Adams was born on July 11, 1767, in a small upstairs bedchamber in the family's farmhouse in Braintree—later called Quincy—a farming area south and east of the village of Boston, in Massachusetts Bay Colony. His ancestors had lived among these hills near the sea for more than one hundred years before his birth. His father, John Adams, had been born on this same farm in 1735.

As John Quincy Adams drew first breath, the life was ebbing out of his seventy-eight-year-old maternal great-grandfather—

John Quincy. A venerated man of the colonial legislature, he would die on July 13, and the newborn child would be named for him, the great departing patriarch. So for three days, as one life entered and another departed this world, the treasured family heritage stretched back in the heart of the old man to the colony's earliest days, and rested in his infant great-grandson, who would carry it almost halfway into the nineteenth century.

John Quincy Adams was a son of the American Revolution. His father, a circuit lawyer, attended meetings of the Sons of Liberty, organized by his cousin Samuel Adams. The family moved between the Braintree farm and houses in Boston, where JQA and his older sister, Abigail, called Nabby, heard the Sons of Liberty play violins and flutes under their bedroom windows. Toddling one day with Samuel Adams around Boston Common, little Johnny, as his parents called him, made the mistake of admiring the British redcoats at drill. His uncle, JQA recalled, gave him an early political lesson by shouting, "Haughty redcoats! Wicked redcoats! They must *go away!*"

John Quincy's mother, the former Abigail Smith, had married John Adams when she was not yet twenty. She bore two daughters, one of whom died before age two, and three sons: John Quincy, Charles, and Thomas Boylston Adams.

Abigail took charge of the Adams farm when her husband was in Philadelphia for sessions of the Continental Congress. She gave the orders, hired and fired the workers, paid the wages, made clothing, and directed everything from meal preparation to planting.

Even though he was gone much of the time—Abigail complained that they were apart for more than half of their first twelve years of marriage—John Adams took a deep interest in the education of his children. "Let Frugality, And Industry, be our Virtues," he wrote Abigail. "Train our Children to Virtue. Make them consider every Vice as shameful and unmanly; fire them with Ambition to be useful."

John and Abigail Adams taught their children that life was serious, that they must excel in all they did. And John Quincy reflected his parents' expectations in a letter to his father: "I hope I grow a better Boy and that you will have no occasion to be ashamed of me when you return. I read my Books to Mama. We all long to see you; I am Sir your Dutiful Son."

Before turning ten, this dutiful son knew Shakespeare and Milton, and the King James Version of the Bible. Although his parents' favorite poem, *Paradise Lost*, proved difficult for him, he read it twice. He copied out in his own hand the preceptor's *Elements of Logic*, and Abigail read him Dr. Watts's *Divine and Moral Songs for Children*.

Young John Quincy drove himself to fulfill his parents' ambition for him. In June 1777, age nine, he wrote to his father: "I love to receive Letters much better than I love to write them, I make but a poor figure at Composition. My head is much too fickle, my Thoughts are running after birds eggs, play and trifles, till I get vexed with my Self." He asked his father to give him instruction on the proper use of time—how to apportion it for study and play—and he promised to follow his father's advice.

That same June, John wrote Abigail concerning their firstborn son: "Let him be sure that he possess the great Virtues of Temperance, Justice, Magnanimity, Honour and Generosity, and with these he cannot fail to become a wise and great man." This, too, was what they wished for him: that he be wise and great. The Adamses considered themselves America's aristocracy; it was up to them to train their children to be leaders.

Long before there was a presidency, John and Abigail directed their son toward leadership, toward highest office. John Adams wrote his son suggesting that he study the Revolutionary War— which was then thundering around his home—read the newspapers, read history, make observations. This war, he said, may lead to future wars, as well as councils and negotiations. The father told the son to turn early to those studies that would give "solid Instruction and Improvement for the Part which may be allotted you to act on the Stage of Life."

To the Adams family, the war was a daily reality. In the spring of 1775 the battles of Lexington and Concord had brought the war to within reach of the Braintree farm. John Quincy Adams gave passing soldiers water from the well, and his sister, Nabby,

An Exceptional Marriage

served them slices of salt meat. One day a raggedy band of minutemen stopped and asked if Abigail had any metal to spare to make bullets. Elihu Adams, John Adams' brother, helped her gather her pewter dishes. They put them into a large kettle to be melted down over the kitchen fire. When young John Quincy squeezed through the cluster of minutemen, he asked, "Why, Uncle, what are you doing? What strange soup!"

"Bullet soup," Uncle Elihu replied.

"Do you wonder," JQA wrote sixty-eight years later, "that a boy of seven who witnessed this scene should be a patriot?"

Abigail and her children lived in constant fear. As JQA recalled: "My mother with her infant children dwelt, liable every hour of the day and of the night to be butchered in cold blood, or taken and carried into Boston as hostages." John Adams—as a delegate to the Continental Congress, which was funding arms against England—was considered a traitor by the British and would be hanged if caught.

On Saturday morning, June 17, 1775, at about three o'clock, Abigail and her children were awakened by what they first thought was a thunderstorm but soon realized was the sound of distant cannons. Like a mother of ancient Rome, Abigail deemed it wise that her son witness war and see for himself what others would only read about in history books. She led John Quincy up Penn's Hill behind their farm, hurrying through meadow grass and over rock walls until they reached the top, where, looking toward Boston, they could see the flashes of cannons and puffs of explosions.

Charlestown, Abigail later wrote to her husband, "is laid in ashes." The British attack upon entrenchments at Breed's Hill—known as the Battle of Bunker Hill—brought cannonades that went on all Saturday and into Sunday. "The constant roar of the cannon," she wrote, "is so distressing that we cannot eat, drink or sleep." John Quincy thought the battle was like those he had read about in the Bible, "the sword of the Lord and of Gideon," and he never forgot it.

In early March, 1776, Abigail and her children watched the local militia march toward Boston, every man carrying three days' rations and a blanket on his back. In Boston, General Washington's troops were bombarding the British ships to divert them from the American fortifications on nearby Dorchester Heights. Abigail Adams went to bed at midnight, but slept only an hour. The farmhouse shook and the windows rattled as bursting shells brightened the sky. The cannonades were renewed nightly for a week, and the house shuddered with every burst. "I sometimes think I cannot stand it," Abigail wrote John. "I wish myself with you, out of hearing, as I cannot assist them."

Bad weather and rough water prevented the British from assaulting the American fortifications, which were strengthened and enlarged every day. After a second week of shelling, Abigail and Johnny again climbed up Penn's Hill. What a sight they found. John Quincy counted one hundred and seventy ships, which Abigail called "the largest fleet ever seen in America." Within a day the ships were filled with fleeing British soldiers and American Loyalists. Boston was free, and the town that Abigail had feared might "cost a river of blood" had been regained.

But the war was far from over, and cannonading only part of the Adamses' fears. Disease cut through their family as no cannon ever had. Uncle Elihu died of dysentery, and Abigail herself took violently sick with the disease; then Tommy and Nabby fell ill. The house was washed with vinegar to halt the sickness, but when Abigail's mother arrived to help care for the ill, she, too, got dysentery, and died within six days.

In 1776 the American medical profession—a cluster of barbers, magicians, charlatans, and dedicated physicians—was helpless before disease. Measles killed three hundred children in Boston in one month.

Little could be done; physicians had only meager knowledge of causes, symptoms, or treatments. The standard remedy for any complaint was cleansing the body of evil "humours" through bloodletting, induced vomiting, and enemas. To cure apoplexy, vomiting was induced by giving the patient a glass of urine mixed with salt. For gout, earthworms were applied to the affected area until they began to swell. Physicians understood only three diseases and their remedies: fever, treated by quinine; dysentery,

An Exceptional Marriage

treated with ipecac; and smallpox, treated by inoculation. Such treatments, tentative and still experimental, did not prevent these diseases from killing many people.

One of the most terrifying illnesses was smallpox. It killed quickly and mysteriously. It rendered the beautiful hideous; fathers did not recognize their children after smallpox finished with them. In the summer of 1776, after the British evacuation, Abigail took her four children to Boston to be inoculated; she clearly understood that the procedure was dangerous, lengthy, and painful, but it might prevent death or disfigurement. That year alone, some 5292 people in and around Boston got smallpox. Of these, 304 cases were caused naturally and 29 were fatal; but 4988 cases were caused by the inoculation, and of that large number only 28 people died. Abigail knew that the odds were on her side.

On July 12 she and the children began their smallpox inoculations. Special hospitals had been established for a massive immunization program. Patients were first sent to a "cleansing house," where "cleansers" washed them in a solution of rum and vinegar and fumigated their clothes. Next, purging was begun: the usual treatment was thirty to forty grains of mercury, twice or three times every day for six or seven days, sufficient to remove "old obstructions" in the patient's system. However, Dr. Cotton Tufts, Abigail's uncle, was a bit more gentle in his treatment of Abigail and her children. His purging method included a light diet and "purging powders" of antimony and mercury, and the regimen lasted only two days.

The next step was inoculation. The physician made incisions about one-eighth inch long, and inserted a small piece of lint moistened with infectious material obtained from a person suffering with a mild case of smallpox. Each patient got two incisions, on either the arm or the leg, and the punctures were covered with a plaster dressing. Patients then either caught the disease in a mild form, or they died.

Dr. Tufts inoculated the Adamses, as well as himself, his son, and Mary Cranch, Abigail's sister. Then they all retired to a special house and waited for the disease to erupt. Here, too, a regimen had to be followed. Air was thought beneficial, so they took walks or rode horseback, and slept on the floor with the windows open. A special diet included puddings, gruel, milk, fruits, and vegetables.

Since the first inoculations did not take, Abigail had herself and her children treated a second time to be certain. Nabby became "cold and shivery"; that was followed by a "violent Heat" and then "small pox in plenty." John Quincy took the inoculation well and had the disease "exactly as one would wish, enough to be well satisfied and yet it was not troublesome."

All the Adamses came through the inoculations safely, and by August 7 they were ready to leave Boston. They were washed with soap and rubbed with vinegar and brandy. After putting on clean clothing, they were fumigated with sulfur in a smokehouse and then released.

During their inoculation period, the newly written Declaration of Independence had arrived in Boston from Philadelphia. On July 18 Abigail had walked to King Street to hear it read from a balcony of the State House, and she was much pleased with the work. Troops appeared, bells rang, warships in Boston Harbor fired salutes.

Liberated from George III and smallpox, the Adamses rode home to Braintree, fit and ready to serve their young nation.

CHAPTER TWO

IN APRIL 1783 Joshua Johnson and his family left France and returned to England. Although his business fluctuated violently due to postwar economic stresses, Joshua remained foolishly extravagant. He purchased a large house on Tower Hill, overlooking the Thames, and staffed it with eleven servants. He prided himself on running the entire operation—staff, children, wife—"like clockwork," and when he was at home, Louisa said, the place felt like a ship at sea, with all hands moving smartly.

Louisa's parents spoiled her. She was, she admitted, "the first object of attention at home, every fault pardoned, every virtue loved." Her mother and father filled her room with playthings,

An Exceptional Marriage

which she tried to keep from her brother and sisters. The spoiling and the toys resulted from Louisa's recurring childhood illnesses, which always brought special attentions. She grew so skilled at interspersing feigned illnesses with real ones that soon even she could not tell the difference.

After the years in France, Louisa spoke no English but "yes" and "no." To ease her adjustment, Joshua placed her and her sisters Nancy and Carolina in an English boarding school. But here the "pure and unadulterated French" that the Johnson girls spoke was laughed at and corrected, and their fine French clothes made them the focus of teasing.

Eight-year-old Louisa also had to resolve painful conflicts about her religious upbringing. She had loved the music and ritual of the Catholic Church in France. Now, entering the Episcopal Church in England, she was forced to kneel down among what she had been taught in France to call the "hereticks." This so shocked her that she fainted. Led on other occasions to the Episcopal services, Louisa fainted again—and again. Finally Joshua placed her with a kind clergyman named John Hewlett, who undertook the process of withdrawing the child from the Catholic faith and educating her to the Episcopal. She was not baptized in the Episcopal Church until she was sixty-three, after decades of struggle.

The faintings at chapel and the teasings by her classmates made her melancholy and gloomy, and her playmates cruelly nicknamed her Miss Proud. "I fear my character was stamped from that moment," she said later. She had reacted with "haughtiness and pride," which had been impossible for her to subdue.

There occurred during these years a series of small events that together created a major impact upon Louisa. Although she was bright, alert, and well traveled, she was naïve about social conditions. While in London, for example, she received as a houseguest a family friend, Kitty Carroll, from Maryland. Miss Carroll was accompanied by a black slave girl about Louisa's age, and for the first time Louisa considered how a slave was treated. The cruel language spoken to her, her subservience, the suppression of her *spirit* shocked Louisa. At about the same time, in school, Louisa became friends with a dark-skinned young girl her own age, from India. They roomed together, read the same books, discussed ideas, and "were almost inseparable." Her own inner pain at this time in her life, and the comparison of slave to roommate, made Louisa aware of the social differences and parallels between herself and others.

At school, Louisa admired a teacher, Miss Young, who was, she said, "a most extraordinary woman." Unlike most women of her day, Miss Young had acquired the classical education usually reserved for men. She knew Greek and Latin, and her intellect was exciting. Louisa was fascinated. Here was a woman who dared reveal her intelligence and who demanded that her favorite students follow her example. Miss Young made Louisa question things and converse openly about books and ideas. This was radical stuff.

Louisa was quick and from her travels she knew a little of what life held. But she also knew that it did not hold, for women, any opportunities. Was she, in fact, much different from the slave girl? Most women of this period were not taught to think and question. Their education centered upon the arts of housekeeping and conversation. Louisa's curriculum consisted of reading, writing, enough math for running a house, dancing, French, drawing, singing with piano—just enough music to entertain men in a parlor. Her days were filled with paper cutting, painting on glass, patchwork, shellwork, featherwork, embroidery, stitchery, beadwork, and other time-devouring trivia. Louisa received training in proper manners and conduct in company, because for a woman the skills of school and home had one purpose: to entice a man to marry her.

Louisa, exposed to a teacher like Miss Young, was soon trapped by her own intellect. Women, and men, feared what they called the "learned ladies," and a young woman like Louisa Johnson had to conceal whatever learning she attained. She soon lamented being a victim of "a happy but alas visionary education" that did not prepare her for "the disgusting realities of a heartless political life, a source of perpetual disappointment." She read *Paradise Lost* and understood it far better than John

An Exceptional Marriage

Quincy Adams did, although she never let him know it; more than that, Louisa grew to feel the words of the majestic work. She was discovering a serious and contemplative world within herself, which was already in conflict with the boundaries placed around her, and she later wondered: "How often since that time have I thought my reading injured me, by teaching me to scrutinize motives too closely, and look too closely at the truth. Much, much depends upon the reading of our early life."

To Louisa's regret, when she was twelve, Miss Young left her school. Two years later, Louisa's father removed his daughters from the boarding school, since the expense was too great. Louisa's formal education ended. A few years later, her only brother, Thomas, was sent to America for his education, which included instruction at Harvard, but Louisa, Nancy, and Carolina had to be content with a governess who taught them trivialities.

THE education of John Quincy Adams took an entirely different path. As the firstborn son, he stood at the forefront of his family; he was their hope. In 1777 Congress appointed John Adams a joint commissioner to represent the United States in France, and in February 1778 John Quincy, age ten, sailed with him to Europe. They returned to Boston a year later, and in a few months sailed again to a second appointment in Paris.

In all, John Quincy Adams spent eight years in Europe with his father. He put the time to excellent purpose. While at sea, he learned the names of the sails and the use of the mariner's compass. At school in Passy, then a suburb of Paris, he rose at six and studied until eight thirty in the evening. When his father went to the Netherlands to negotiate a Dutch loan for the United States, JQA went to school at the University of Leiden.

Abigail wrote to her son urging him to "govern and control" his temper, to observe, listen, report, and use the "superior advantages" of traveling with his father. Her ambition for him was boundless, and her letters sounded a litany of expectations. It was not enough to enjoy the travel, she warned; he must prepare himself. "Justice, humanity and benevolence are the duties you owe to society in general." To his country, he should pay a price, "sacrificing ease, pleasure, wealth, and life itself for its defence and security." To his parents, he owed "love, reverence, and obedience to all just and equitable demands."

In July 1781 John Quincy, then just fourteen, left his studies in the Netherlands and traveled as secretary to Francis Dana on a diplomatic mission to Saint Petersburg, Russia. Again JQA's parents wanted him to use the experience to enrich his mind and develop his powers of observation. His father wrote the boy and urged him to report on the state of education in Russia, the religions, the construction of the houses, and the styles of the people and the public buildings.

John Quincy reported in detail. His desire to please his parents was excessive. Their ideas, their dreams, their morality took shape in him. Unlike Louisa, John Quincy from childhood carried a sense of purpose, of destiny.

On September 3, 1783, the Americans and the British concluded the Treaty of Paris, ending the Revolutionary War. John Quincy had returned to the Netherlands, and now he and his father toured England together.

From 1783 to 1785 JQA served as his father's private secretary in Paris, where John Adams was a member of a diplomatic commission set up to negotiate treaties of friendship and commerce with European nations. In July 1784 JQA's mother and sister joined them—having left Charles and Thomas behind with relatives.

At this time John Quincy Adams and his parents made a decision about his education. He had savored the delicacies of Europe, both diplomatic and social, and found them to his taste. He had studied German, Latin, Greek, Dutch, and French. He had traveled to the major European cities and had met and dined with many of the leading men of the day. His diary was filled with such names as Franklin, Pitt, Lafayette, Jay. One entry recorded: "Spent the evening with Mr. Jefferson whom I love to be with." In 1825 his father would write to Thomas Jefferson that in those days in Paris, John Quincy had "appeared to me to be almost as much your boy as mine."

But his parents wished to have JQA educated at home, and in

the fall of 1784 John Adams wrote President Joseph Willard of Harvard to ask that John Quincy be admitted. Willard replied that the young man could join whatever class an examination showed him qualified to enter. In languages and literature, John Quincy was admirably prepared for Harvard, but he needed more tutoring and preparation in mathematics. So it was arranged that he would return to America and stay with Aunt Elizabeth and Uncle John Shaw in Haverhill. His parents and his sister would be in London, where John Adams was to serve as the first U.S. minister to Great Britain.

While preparing for his examination, JQA never left the Shaws' house, or his books, for more than four hours a week. In March 1786 he was admitted to Harvard as a junior. His father crowed at his admission: "You are now among Magistrates and Ministers, Legislators and Heroes, Ambassadors and Generals, Persons who will live to Act in all these Characters"—which was exactly what his parents wished him to do.

Adams arrived at Harvard sporting European manners, which made him a bit of a fop. Although he resembled his mother, he enjoyed striking poses like his father: head cocked, one eye half closed, his right hand in his pocket. His hair was fashionably groomed, and he carried a sword like a European gentleman. JQA soon shed all of this, however. He did little but study. When two of his cousins, the Cranch girls, visited his room in Hollis Hall, they found it filthy and smelling of stale tobacco smoke. Adams, pale and drawn, was wearing a soiled dressing gown. He complained of headaches, and Aunt Mary Cranch urgently sent Dr. Tufts, the family physician, to the young man's room. The doctor advised more exercise and a better diet.

John Quincy was graduated from Harvard on July 16, 1787. Aunt Mary Cranch prepared the graduation feast, and all available Adams relatives were invited to help devour two shoulders of beef, four boiled hams, six tongues, and a plum cake that took twenty-four pounds of sugar, plus an ample supply of porter, hard cider, punch, and wine.

They had much to celebrate. John Quincy ranked second in his class of fifty-one and joined the recently founded Phi Beta

Kappa Society. Throughout the family, there was pride over the young scion's achievement. John Quincy himself said that attending the college was the "most judicious choice I ever made. My short discipline of fifteen months at Harvard University was the introduction to all the prosperity that has ever befallen me."

Abigail Adams was equally pleased. Writing from London, she told her son:

> We may become a great and powerful nation. But it will require industry and frugality, wisdom and virtue to make it so. I hope you will never lose sight of her interests; but make her welfare your study, and spend those hours, which others devote to cards and folly, in investigating the great principles by which nations have risen to glory; for your country will one day call for your services, either in the cabinet or field. Qualify yourself to do honor to her.
>
> Your affectionate mother, AA

AFTER leaving boarding school, Louisa Johnson and her sister Nancy became the belles of their parents' evening entertainments.

At sixteen, two years older than Louisa, Nancy "gave promise of great beauty." Louisa herself was growing into a lovely young woman, but she was envious of her sister. Although Louisa was a good student, she never considered herself as spectacular as Nancy, who had, Louisa thought, "a sort of intuitive genius." It wasn't only Nancy's brains that Louisa coveted. It was also her social ease; Louisa felt painfully shy, and ill equipped emotionally for her social role.

The Johnsons entertained a great deal, especially after Joshua was appointed by George Washington in 1790 to fill the post of U.S. consul in London. They gave "little unceremonious dinners," after which sometimes the carpet was rolled up and everyone would dance, including Joshua and Catherine. Louisa, Nancy, and Carolina were pushed forward to entertain the company; each played a musical instrument or sang. Carolina presented a danger, however, for her true talent was not music, but mimicry. She brought her sisters to tears of laughter with her imitations of guests—including a stuffy young diplomat named John Quincy

Adams. Her father, wisely, did not push Carolina too hard to perform before the guests, lest she allow her real aptitude to emerge in public.

The London social season lasted from New Year's until June. The Johnsons spent their summers in the country town of Highberry. There Louisa, Nancy, and Carolina were free from the restrictions of society and, best of all, from the restraints of fashion. Relieved of laces and stays, they swam and fished and exercised in a most unladylike manner.

When she was eighteen, in 1793, Louisa stood five feet tall. She had a fair complexion, hazel eyes flecked with green, curly auburn hair, and graceful hands. If she had a flaw in her beauty, it was her mouth, which appears straight and narrow in her portraits. She may have been concealing her teeth, however, for she always had trouble with them, perhaps as the result of her love of sweets. She had teeth pulled early in her adolescence, and fortunately for her appearance, the extractions were made from the back of her mouth. Not wishing to show too much of her teeth, she developed a mysterious, quick smile that gave the impression of sparkle and enigma.

Despite the dazzling sisters, the Johnson house did not swarm with suitors. Joshua Johnson was the problem. When his oldest daughters entered society, he received a letter from his brother, Governor Thomas Johnson, whom he admired to excess. Thomas wrote that he had heard, all the way back in Maryland, of the beauty of the Johnson girls, and was worried about their marital prospects. He implored Joshua to have his daughters "form connections with none but men of note and distinction from his own Country." In no hurry to lose his parlor full of song and dance, Joshua concluded that Thomas was right. Calling his family together, he announced that henceforth his daughters would be prohibited from meeting with eligible Englishmen.

Thus restricted, Louisa and her sisters had to fall back upon visitors from the United States. But Louisa soon had "a number of ardent admirers," and her favorite was young David Sterrett, who worked in her father's office. He wrote verses to her and she to him. David called Louisa his "little Wife," and years later she remembered that "everybody delighted to tease me about him until a sentiment formed in my heart, which no one doubted, least of all myself." But when David returned to the United States, the romance faded. She would long recall his voice and good looks and manners that had captured her heart.

AFTER graduating from Harvard, John Quincy Adams went to study with a lawyer named Theophilus Parsons. With several other law students he became a clerk in Parsons' office, which was located in Newburyport, a seaport forty miles north of Boston.

The study of law never excited Adams, but he felt pushed to it by his father and mother. Yet if he disliked law, found it tedious and boring, how could he meet his parents' wishes? He wrote in his diary: "The question, what am I to do in this world, recurs to me frequently and never without causing great anxiety, and a depression of spirits. My prospects appear darker to me every day." He began to suffer from headaches, dizzy spells, colds, a sour stomach, sore eyes, insomnia, and, when he could sleep, troubled dreams. He visited a doctor and got a prescription for "the bark" (quinine) for his "nervous system." He also wrote to Dr. Tufts, who again suggested exercise.

But what troubled John Quincy lay at the very soul of his being, unreachable by medicine or physical activity. He was rebelling against his parents' control of his life. They had allowed him little self-examination and expected him to follow the path they had selected. His studies were making him unhappy and ill; his parents' dreams for him were becoming nightmares.

Adams found relief from his torment in the temptations of Newburyport. The town was isolated, separated from Newbury by Old Town Bridge and from Boston by the Lynn marshes. When John Quincy and the other young law clerks became restless, they clustered for company at the local taverns, where Adams soon discovered a passion for drink, ladies, and serenading. He and his friends concocted a short route to intoxication called a Stonewall, which combined cider and rum and rendered its imbiber as horizontal and silent as the New England boundary walls for which it was named. Some days Adams' drinking and

An Exceptional Marriage

roistering left him so shaky that he could neither read nor write.

More agreeably, Adams discovered that he was a young man among young women. He disliked the law and his chosen profession, but he loved the "frolicks" and the young ladies of Newburyport. In winter there were sleighing parties, which prompted JQA to recall with fondness when in his late sixties: "The art of making love, muffled up in furs, in the open air, with the thermometer at Zero, is a Yankee invention, which requires a Yankee poet to describe." And he and his friends "paraded round town till four in the morning" serenading the ladies, or spent snug evenings before the great fire at Sawyer's Tavern, where Adams drank and danced and, in January of 1788, fell in love.

In his diary he noted only that he "danced with the oldest Miss Frazier." On another occasion he and his friends spent an evening at Mary Frazier's home playing pawns, a kissing game. "Ah!" Adams wrote. "What kissing!"

But in his ecstasy there was pain. Mary Frazier offered a temptation he could not satisfy; he knew he was headed down a path without hope. In those days a young man married only when he could afford a family, and JQA was still dependent upon his father for funds. His complaints to his parents that his advancement in a career had been delayed by service in Europe met with little sympathy. Four days after dancing with Mary at Sawyer's, JQA confided in his diary: "I feel dull and low spirited. I have neither that insatiable ambition, nor that ardor for pursuing the means to gratify it." In February his "low spirits" continued, and "not even dissipation has been able to support me."

By May, Adams' dissipations and love were causing depression that was giving way to "terror" as he contemplated two more years of study for a profession unpromising of personal fortune. On July 11 he woefully noted his twenty-first birthday. The occasion, he said, "emancipates me from the yoke of parental authority and places me upon my own feet, which have not strength enough to support me. I continue therefore still in a state of dependence." As long as his parents had to provide for him, he could never live and love as he wished.

Yet his love for Mary Frazier also gave him reason to study

and complete his law work. She was, according to a friend of JQA's, "exquisitely beautiful, faultless in feature, complexion, expression." Mary's plump cheeks and full lips, her gentle blue eyes captivated Adams. Together they went to melon parties, picnics, snow parties, dances, and sometimes walked home side by side from church. Adams visited the Fraziers so often that rumors circulated of his and Mary's engagement.

THE year 1790 was a fateful one for John Quincy Adams. He regained his health, his love for Mary increased, and his law studies finally ended. In July he was admitted as an attorney in the Court of Common Pleas for the county of Essex. A week after his admission to the bar, Adams opened his office in Boston in the front parlor of one of his father's houses, at 10 Court Street. He was in a race with his heart. Could he get his law practice under way fast enough to marry? This was a period when a man's "declaration" must soon be followed by marriage; long engagements risked the woman's reputation.

Now began an exchange of letters with his mother and father in which the parents reasserted their control over their son. In August, Adams wrote to his father of the circumstances that delayed his career—and that denied his dream. Unfortunately this was not the time to speak to John Adams of finances; as the nation's first Vice-President, he was complaining of his miserly salary of five thousand dollars and the meager returns on his investments. He was also helping Nabby, who had married a man who appeared unwilling to work, although she had just given birth to their third child. "I only ask you to recollect that my Circumstances are not affluent," John Adams replied to John Quincy; he could not increase his financial assistance.

Abigail warned John Quincy about falling in love before he could support a family, and she playfully—but pointedly—hinted that he search for a wealthy woman. It had been made clear to JQA that he must support his lady or not have her.

John Quincy assured his parents that he would never marry a woman for wealth, nor join a woman to poverty. During this correspondence, however, he continued seeing Mary. He visited

An Exceptional Marriage

her in Newburyport in August, and in September returned for evenings at the Fraziers'. On October 29 he wrote in his diary: "M.F. came to town." Mary also made several visits to friends in nearby Medford, and JQA met her there. The conflict between his love for her and the exchange of letters with his parents made JQA "perplexed." He would either have to announce his intentions soon or break off his love.

On November 13 Adams wrote and underlined in his diary: "Letter from my mother." The letter he had dreaded had arrived. His mother insisted that he end his romance. Abigail wrote from her sickbed—and she made the most of that fact—that she felt she had to act, however sick she might be. Since her son had no financial means to enter into an engagement, and since he had promised never to join a woman to his poverty, he was now in danger of breaking his word to her and hurting the young lady.

John Quincy replied within a week, first expressing concern for his mother's health, then telling her that his love affair had ended. "The Lady will henceforth be at the distance of 40 miles from me and I shall have no further opportunities to indulge a weakness, which you may perhaps censure," but which, he added in a defiant tone, "if you knew the object, I am sure you would excuse." He had done as his mother instructed; he had quickly, almost surgically, broken off with Mary.

In saying farewell to Mary Frazier, John Quincy was also saying farewell to much within himself. He was putting aside the things of youth; he was placing duty before the woman of his life. He was, as well, suppressing his spontaneity.

But he did not simply toss Mary Frazier aside. The letters to his mother suggesting that the breakup had been accomplished with ease concealed the hurt and anger he would feel for the rest of his life. Mary Frazier was his heart; he had confided to one friend that "all my hopes of happiness in this life center in the possession of that girl."

John Quincy would later complain of his "blunted sensations" and of the painful lesson, coming when it did in his life, that certainly contributed to his later icy and stern character.

ADAMS SPENT THE NEXT FOUR years trying to earn a living as a lawyer in Boston. But attorneys' fees were low: seventy-five cents to two dollars for drawing up indictments for courts and sessions. Not until the fourth year did he earn a profit.

Central to his life at this time was the Crackbrain Club, eight to ten young men who met to drink wine and dance with the Boston ladies. His life took on a regularity: work at his office most days, drinking and dining with his friends most evenings, and a bath twice a month.

But Adams found that his depression returned. To overcome it, he took walks on Boston Common almost daily after work or late at night. Sometimes he danced until two a.m., wandered home around three, and then spent the morning "much fatigued" in his office.

However, his life was about to change. On June 3, 1794, he received letters from Philadelphia, which was then the nation's capital, informing him that President Washington had appointed him minister resident to the Netherlands. He was to sail for The Hague as soon as possible. The appointment, ending his idleness and tiny law business, made John Quincy sick. His parents considered the appointment the splendid start "in the cabinet or field" that they had raised him to accept. But John Quincy found "the idea of leaving all my friends very painful." He was still unwell on June 30, when, once more the dutiful son, he left the pleasures of Boston to enter the arena of public life.

He rode the stage to Providence, Rhode Island, where he caught the packet *Clemantine* for Newport and then the packet *Romero* to New York. He went by stage over the jarring clay roads of New Jersey—all of them like plowed fields with furrows two feet deep—and arrived in Philadelphia at sunset, July 9, to be briefed on the responsibilities of his new position. From that hour, with only two short intervals until he died, John Quincy Adams devoted himself to public service.

His family could scarcely contain their excitement. His father was ecstatic. Martha Washington had written to Abigail consoling her on losing a son to diplomatic service, but extolling that son's prospects. Aunt Elizabeth of Haverhill said that she

An Exceptional Marriage

knew John Quincy had obtained "the palm" by following the path of virtue. But while the palm was his, JQA was never asked whether he wished to accept it. No one considered that young Adams might want to choose what he wished to do with his own life. The parental dream was overwhelming. "I have long known," said JQA, "that my father is far more ambitious for my advancement than I ever have been or ever shall be."

On September 15 he sailed from Boston for London and the Netherlands with his brother Thomas as his secretary. Before departing, John Quincy received a gift from his father: an order on Dutch bankers for five thousand guilders, a large sum. The money, which would have meant so much to him four years earlier, now meant little. He arranged to have some of it paid to Aunt Elizabeth for the education of her son. The rest he turned over to his brother Charles to invest, for a handsome commission. Then John Quincy sailed toward a new life, where he was more sure of himself, where the control of emotion, the suppression of passion, were rewarded with the only thing that men value more than sex or money—power.

CHAPTER THREE

AT THIS moment in John Quincy Adams' life, the appointment to the Netherlands proved fortunate. The Hague was the least significant of the five U.S. diplomatic posts overseas. France, England, Spain, and Portugal ranked above it. Adams was single and had much free time. His instructions were only to tend to the Treasury loans that the United States had obtained from the Dutch during the war, and to keep a watchful eye on European affairs, especially the French Revolution. Adams was an ocean distant from his parents, and he wrote to his friend John Gardner that he was his "own man again." His salary of forty-five hundred dollars a year allowed little extravagance but made him independent. Given the position, the leisure, the income, and freedom, Adams was ready to whirl the ladies, and he wasted no time. On their stopover in England, JQA and Thomas spent two weeks sporting "around in the fling of London."

John Quincy returned to London from The Hague in November 1795 on a diplomatic errand. John Jay had been negotiating a treaty with Britain in which the United States gave up freedom of the seas in exchange for Great Britain's surrender of its remaining frontier posts in the New World. Since Jay had gone back to America, Adams was to complete the exchange of ratifications necessary to conclude the treaty. Such diplomacy, then as now, dragged. Adams found himself with little to do but receive invitations to balls and dinners; among these was a request that he dine with the Joshua Johnsons of Tower Hill.

This came at a time when the Johnson home was well known among American young men as a place of fine wines and dinners, and excellent parlor entertainments performed by three daughters of marriageable age, heirs to Joshua's fortune. John Quincy Adams passed through the immense front doors of the Johnson home for the first time, a bachelor willingly shopping in London's richest bazaar. He had dressed for the occasion in his new, heavy Dutch clothing, which featured a thick white overcoat. He spent the evening in "high spirits" visiting with Joshua and Catherine and being entertained by their daughters. When he left, the family collected, as they did on such occasions, to evaluate the young man. All agreed that Adams was a solid prospect but a shoddy dresser. JQA returned frequently, and soon became a favorite of Louisa's mother's.

When Adams visited, Louisa and Nancy were put forward to play the piano and sing. He liked some kinds of music, but female singing was not one of them. If Louisa or Nancy began a song Adams found "disagreeable," he immediately put on his hat and bid them all good-by.

But he always returned. This was the marketplace, and JQA needed a wife. He was lonely, almost twenty-nine, and thought this might be his last chance. Everything came together at once: profession, income, leisure, age, his freedom to choose. Marriage was the business at hand, and he knew what he wanted. He was determined to marry a short woman; he worried that a tall one might appear superior to him. He wanted an intelligent woman, a good conversationalist. The Johnson ladies were doubly attrac-

An Exceptional Marriage

tive: they were small and they conversed with a rare intelligence.

At first the Johnsons believed JQA fancied Nancy; this made Louisa feel more relaxed around him. He gently teased her about her music. She teased him about his poetry and asked him to prove he was indeed a poet by writing a poem to her. He did, and one evening at dinner he passed it to her across the table. Louisa started reading it aloud, embarrassing Adams and Nancy, and stopped only when her governess whispered that it was impolite to read at the table.

On February 12, 1796, Louisa celebrated her twenty-first birthday with a ball, and John Quincy spent the evening dancing with her and escorting her about on his arm. His "decidedly publick" attentions "brought much trouble on my head," Louisa later wrote, especially from Nancy, who sulked and pouted.

But Louisa was uncertain. Wasn't love supposed to laugh, to sing, to make her heart run fast? Instead, she found herself having to be "coaxed into an affection." Although she was twenty-one, "in knowledge of the world I was not fifteen." Louisa had always been chaperoned. John Quincy was the first man with whom she had ever been alone, and the first she had ever kissed.

Instead of passion, however, JQA's courtship created doubt. "Love seem'd to chill all the natural hilarity of my disposition," she said, "and those hours which had been spent in cheerful mirth were passed in gloom and anxiety." Louisa sensed, she later wrote, "something wrong without knowing how to find the error." They walked in the parks and took rides together, but the two squabbled almost from the start. Adams was quiet, slovenly, and clumsy at dancing. Any efforts at reform by her met with harshness from him. When Louisa invited him to a family picnic, she jokingly suggested "that if he went with us, he must dress himself handsomely and look as dashing as possible." Her demand made Adams angry. He did dress handsomely, in an elegant blue suit and a large tricorne hat, but when she complimented him on his appearance, "he immediately took fire" and told her that *his wife* must "never take the liberty" of interfering in his dress. Louisa, offended, told him that she rejected his marriage offer. Both made apologies on the way home, but lessons had been learned. John Quincy now understood Louisa's strong "fixedness of opinion," and she, for her part, felt the "sting" of his temper.

After asking Joshua for his daughter's hand and getting a quick approval, John Quincy departed in May for The Hague. He thought he had frittered away too much time in London. He told Louisa to ready herself for marriage. He laid out a course of study for her with the hope of improving her mind. He promised to return for her—perhaps in a year.

Abigail wrote John Quincy: she approved the decision to return to The Hague without marrying, "to accumulate some solid property before you take upon you the charge of a Family." JQA replied defiantly that he was "old enough to get married." His mother responded: "You are certainly old enough. Your father was married nine days younger than you are now." But Abigail continued to raise doubts. She worried that Louisa was too English; anti-British feeling still ran high in the United States. Would Louisa survive "at so early an Age, without any knowledge or experience of the World, the manners, luxuries, dissipations and amusements of a foreign Court?" Would she find the continental style of living incompatible with their later prospects in America? Abigail suggested that JQA place country before "contentment and delight." But John Quincy had made this sacrifice once; never again. He replied sharply to his mother that "if upon the whole I have done wrong, I shall be the principle sufferer." If he waited until everyone approved of his choice, "I should have been certainly doomed to perpetual celibacy."

During the summer of 1796, Louisa lived with her governess at Clapham Common in a small house that her father had rented for her. Here she had privacy to devote her time "to such studies," she wrote, "as I hoped would lessen the immense distance which existed in point of mind and talents between myself and my future husband." She was so isolated that her sisters called her "the Nun." John Quincy asked that she send him "a detail of everything interesting to yourself in your situation. Your progress upon the Harp, I am persuaded is great." And he hoped that her reading equaled it. He wanted her attentive to her studies and her music, for they would make her a valuable asset to a public man.

An Exceptional Marriage

LOUISA AND JOHN QUINCY conducted their courtship almost entirely by mail, although sometimes Louisa didn't receive a word for almost a month. The contrast with the passionate courtship enjoyed by JQA's parents is revealing, not only of their different personalities but of the different social periods.

That this was a time of social transition is apparent in the disparate lives of Abigail and Louisa. During the colonial period, when Abigail was raising her family, women were considered the equals of men. Women ran businesses, worked as shopkeepers, teachers, blacksmiths, innkeepers, silversmiths, shipwrights, barbers. A few women taxpayers appeared on the colonies' records, and some even cast ballots. In short, colonial women were people of unquestioned value, and Abigail was the quintessential colonial woman: purposeful, frugal, independent, courageous, and passionate.

During their courtship, John and Abigail could hardly keep their hands off each other. After one meeting, John wrote Abigail that his ardor was aboil, and that he suffered "Itches, Aches, Agues, and Repentance" as a consequence. He showed up on Abigail's doorstep one day with a letter demanding that she "give the bearer as many kisses, and as many Hours of your Company after 9 O'Clock as he shall please to Demand and charge them to my Account."

No such demands for Louisa slipped from John Quincy's pen. He called her "my amiable friend," and saw himself, he told her, as "a faithful and anxious though not a romantic lover." Louisa, in turn, called him "my beloved and most esteemed friend."

During John Adams' years serving in Philadelphia, Abigail had run the farm, educated her children, and still melted pewter plates for bullets. She told her husband that, in time, she hoped "to have the reputation of being as good a *farmeress* as my partner has of being a good statesman." The essential word was "partner."

The American Revolution, though it freed men, caused the gradual imprisonment of women. Louisa, born on the eve of the Declaration of Independence, grew up at a time when women were becoming less the equals of men and more the ornaments of home and marriage. Her life spanned an era of transition, when the comparative equality of the colonial period was giving way to the confinement and suppression of women that characterized the Victorian era. After the Revolution, as men left the farms to work at industrial jobs, women's lives narrowed and their importance beyond the home diminished. Women who had shared the work of farming and the perils of the frontier now presided gracefully over the drawing room. Calling cards came into vogue, as did family conversation, letter writing, indoor games, reading aloud, and musical instruments. By 1800 Abigail Adams, the "farmeress," would become a fussy hostess.

There was great preoccupation with good manners and social graces. Women now conformed to elaborate rituals of behavior that included increased modesty about their bodies; the wearing of nightclothes; dexterity with rows of knives and forks, and separate plates for every course; the introduction of washbasins, portable bathtubs, and soap. The upkeep of appearances was essential. Diaries became popular, and the common theme of leisure ran through them: "At home with company," "Dined out," "Attended ball."

Women had one purpose: to become "stewards and guardians of their husbands' property." Louisa's education was directed toward controlling servants, raising children, creating intelligent conversation, and soothing "the cares of domestic life." Like other women, she had been instructed to make her home a refuge where she would dispense comfort to her husband, whose major concerns would take place away from her, outside the boundaries of her life. "Sweetness is to woman what sugar is to fruit," said one authority. "It is her first business to be happy—a sunbeam in the house, making others happy."

Louisa was taught the lesson contained in a treatise called "A Father's Legacy to His Daughter," printed the year she was born: "If you happen to have any learning, keep it a profound secret, especially from the men, who generally look with a jealous and malignant eye on a woman of cultivated understanding." All her life, however, Louisa would rebel against this instruction; she would refuse to be a mere bright ornament, a decorative sunbeam in a man's house.

An Exceptional Marriage

JOHN QUINCY PROVED A RELUCTANT fiancé. Writing to Louisa, he told her that their separation would teach them control, fortitude, duty. He wanted her to be happy, but said that this was achieved only by controlling "our wishes and passions." Her desire to be with him matched his to be with her, he said, but she must learn, as he had, "to acquire the faculty of cheerful conformity to things which must be endured." Louisa, however, was not interested in learning how to endure. To her dismay, she discovered that John Quincy actually welcomed their separation. He used deprivation, even misfortune, to test and improve himself. He told her to "reconcile" herself to a long separation, and advised her that "a large portion of all human merit consists in *suffering* with dignity and composure."

Louisa found this philosophy a *"dreadful* thing," she told him. "You have very little knowledge of my disposition and I hope in time to convince you that I possess both fortitude and dignity, sufficient at least to conceal any unbecoming emotion." True, she agreed, we are unfit for life's path if we think "our way strewn with flowers, yet I did not expect that *you* would have been the person to have strewn my path with needless thorns."

Testing his character or not, Adams was in no hurry to be married. In May 1796 President Washington had appointed him minister plenipotentiary to the Court of Lisbon. His salary would double from forty-five hundred to nine thousand dollars a year. Adams could afford a wife, and he wrote Louisa that he planned, at a time still unspecified, to sail from Holland to Portugal by way of London, "taking you as the companion for the remainder of the Journey or Voyage, and of my Life."

Joshua Johnson, with his daughter's gentle urging, wrote JQA that he was considering outfitting a ship to carry the Johnson family to America and that they might stop first in the Netherlands to visit Adams. John Quincy recoiled at the suggestion. He wrote Louisa that the plan contained too many "obstacles," and that he saw behind it a scheme for her to disembark in Holland and remain with him. Louisa denied this and said her father's suggestion was an impulsive act "of the most honourable feelings," intended to promote "the happiness of a child so dear to him." She regretted most sincerely ever having expressed a wish to meet him in Holland, she told John Quincy, "since it appears to have given you so much uneasiness."

Louisa's feelings and her pride were hurt. She found John Quincy's letter "so severe, so cold and so peremptory" that it made her furious.

JQA, in fact, thought so little of this match that he closed 1796 by writing in his diary his concerns for that year: "The situation of two objects the nearest to my heart, my country and my father, press continually upon my reflections. They engross every thought and almost every power, every faculty." He did not mention a young woman and her heart.

That autumn, meanwhile, Joshua Johnson had learned some bad news. His partnership was being dissolved, and there were rumors of a possible embezzlement of the company's profits by a partner in Maryland. Johnson's lawyers had urged him to sail for the United States to settle the matter. But Catherine Johnson had refused to let her husband go; care of the family, she said, would be "too great for her nerves." Joshua, however, kept a ship standing by, just in case.

Therefore, when in the spring of 1797 he offered Adams a ship—either to carry him from Holland to England, and then to his appointment in Portugal, or to bring Louisa to him in the Netherlands—it is unclear whether Johnson was merely making the kind gesture of a loving father or whether he had another motive in mind. In retrospect, the facts appear suspicious. With his daughter married, Johnson could sail to the United States with his family; but as long as Adams remained stubborn, Johnson had to remain in London.

Still John Quincy delayed. Before proceeding to Portugal, he told Louisa, he should await his replacement in The Hague. He saw no prospect of peace between France and Portugal, nor any means of passage from England through the French privateers. Perhaps she should not accompany him "into so dangerous a situation." Perhaps he should wait a month or two. But even JQA's mother thought the time had come: "I advise you to marry the lady before you go to Portugal," she wrote.

An Exceptional Marriage

Adams could feel the trap closing. To Joshua's offer of a ship he made a weak rebuttal. The ship, he wrote, "would suit *me* very well," but at this time of year, for a lady unused to the sea, "I feel it would be too unpleasant." This, of course, was nonsense: Louisa had also been at sea enough to know what to expect. She had written in 1796 that she sometimes thought of the severity of their life together and concluded, "With you at hand I find every idea of danger vanished." She was ready to be courageous; he was not.

John Quincy now played his final card, and offered Louisa a chance to say no. He told her that in his manners toward her and his letters he had disguised none of his true character. She knew the man she was to marry. Adams told her, speaking of himself in the third person:

> You know the chances for hardship, inconvenience and danger, which you may be called to share with him. You know his inviolable attachment to his Country, and his resolute determination not to continue long his absence from it. — You know that upon his retirement, the state of his fortune will require privations. Choose, Louisa, choose for yourself, and be assured that his Heart will ratify your choice.

Louisa replied immediately:

> Why my beloved friend did you tell me to choose? What I have always declared required not a moments hesitation to determine. No my Adams, I have long ardently wished you might be enabled to return. Your return would make me happy and I only fear my friend that you will find *me* a troublesome companion.

Before leaving bachelorhood, Adams made a final scold. He did not like the term "my Adams." "It is a stile of address that looks too much like that of novels. A bare proper Name does not sound or look well for a Man in real life." Adams added that he worried that Louisa might not be dignified enough for a public man. Perhaps she had been indulging in novels, instead of the more serious matter detailed by him for her studying.

Nevertheless, John Quincy, having arranged his own passage, sailed from The Hague on July 9. He arrived at his hotel in London at five o'clock in the afternoon on July 12. He had time to stroll over to the Johnsons', but he delayed one more day. When he finally saw Louisa on the thirteenth, Adams asked her to set a wedding date, and she named July 26, two weeks hence. John Quincy was shocked at so early a date, but the bride held firm and finally he agreed.

In the midst of wedding preparations, Adams learned that the Senate on May 30 had confirmed his appointment as minister plenipotentiary to Berlin. He had been nominated by the new President—his father—who wrote that he hoped his son's plans were not upset "by the Alteration I have made in your destination." The mission to Portugal was "less important" than that to Prussia; the north of Europe was "more interesting" to the United States.

John Quincy was hurt and furious. Again his parents had not considered his plans or feelings. He had already bought passage and shipped personal effects to Lisbon, rented a house there, and committed twenty-five hundred dollars in expenses that he would never recover. He wrote to his mother that the appointment tainted the "satisfaction" he had enjoyed so far in being a public servant. Yet, after the bluster, he agreed to go. Berlin was the more challenging post.

AND SO, on July 26, at the parish church of All Hallows Barking, two of America's leading families were joined together: the Johnsons of Maryland and the Adamses of Massachusetts; the daughter of a prominent merchant and the son of the President of the United States. After the brief ceremony, the wedding register was brought out. Under number 202, John Quincy signed his name, and Louisa, her handwriting strikingly like his, signed hers.

The idea of a honeymoon as a time of leisurely travel—but not a time of privacy for the newly married couple—was now popular. Chaperons accompanied every bride and groom. It was not remarkable, therefore, that Louisa and John Quincy set out to tour England accompanied by Louisa's maidservant and John Quincy's brother Thomas. The honeymoon, like the wedding, was somber and quiet. The only reference to anything that occurred during

An Exceptional Marriage

the entire trip came from JQA, who noted in his diary, after visiting Tilney House, that it was "one of the splendid country seats for which this country is distinguished." Nothing else.

Two days after the wedding, John Quincy wrote his parents, "I have the happiness of presenting to you another daughter." Louisa attached a note "to solicit your parental affection," and promised to fulfill her "duties as wife and daughter."

Thomas was unreservedly taken with his new sister-in-law. He wrote home that she was beautiful and intelligent, and "has much sweetness of Temper and seems to Love *as she ought*." She had "with apparent Cheerfulness renounced father and Mother, kindred and Country to unite her destinies" with her husband's.

Thomas could only sense Louisa's sacrifice. When she married John Quincy, her father was a prosperous merchant who had promised each of his children a small fortune. But after two "happy weeks" of marriage, Louisa learned that her father had suffered a major financial collapse.

Johnson's departure from London just a few months after his daughter's marriage gave the impression that he was fleeing his creditors. Worse, events suggested that with Louisa's compliance the Johnsons had lured an eligible bachelor into marrying a daughter who would soon be left penniless. Louisa was filled with shame and guilt. In her troubled words, it appeared that her father was "palming his daughter off" upon the Adamses.

John Quincy was unsympathetic. He found the situation embarrassing, and worried about "disgrace" at just the moment when his career seemed so promising. He was also not oblivious to the loss of a handsome dowry.

Joshua Johnson wrote his new son-in-law soon after boarding ship at Gravesend. Rough seas caused sickness and alarm, but they were nothing, he said, compared to the humiliation and "sufferings on this occasion of leaving England."

Joshua was beaten and doomed. Within three years, bankrupt, he would turn desperately to President Adams for help; he was appointed Superintendent of Stamps in Washington, which enabled him to survive. But two weeks before Johnson died in 1802, his post would be stripped from him by President Thomas Jeffer-

son, and Johnson would leave this world, Louisa said, "destitute, with the horrible conviction that he left his widow and family penniless."

Her father's financial collapse and flight parted Louisa from her family for the first time in her life; she wrote, "The separation almost broke my heart." She withdrew into a depression, and suffered "anguish of mind and deep feeling of wounded sensibility," which, in turn, created "a total loss of sleep." The thought of traveling in winter to Berlin over churning seas and rock-hard roads was not comforting, nor was her realization that she had married a man who would spoil no one, not even himself.

"Such," Louisa said, "was my honeymoon."

PART II
Berlin–Washington, 1797–1809

CHAPTER ONE

IN NOVEMBER 1797 the newlyweds and Thomas Adams sailed from Gravesend for Hamburg on their journey to Berlin. Louisa was seasick for eight days, while John Quincy enjoyed the excellent food that was served aboard their Danish ship. He approved even more of the sailors' economy in the use of sugar: a piece tied to a string was passed among them, and each then dipped it into his tea. Adams admired frugality.

The Adamses rested ten days in Hamburg. Louisa remembered the air as smelling of peat, the winter fuel, the fumes of which hung in thick clouds over narrow, dreary streets.

She felt desolate, alone. She had broken from parents, sisters, freedom, innocence. Moreover, she had not been prepared for what marriage held. Having been taught that the "normal" woman had no sexual drive, only the generosity to submit to her husband, she entered the marriage bed in the spirit of self-sacrifice. Her obligation to John Quincy was to produce children, after which sex might be avoided. Louisa's journey to Berlin, therefore, was not only a voyage away from her treasured past but also a venture into a threatening future, and womanhood.

From Hamburg the Adamses continued their journey in a heavy English carriage that swayed and jolted across two hundred miles of land washed into bogs by the rains. When they reached Berlin, Louisa was "seized with a violent and dangerous illness," which was in fact the first of her seven miscarriages.

In Berlin, she spent eleven days of anguish huddled in her room at a public inn. Ailing and homesick, Louisa became a recluse. Rumors spread among the wives of the diplomatic corps that Mrs. Adams was ugly, horse-faced, ashamed to be seen at court. Louisa thought that John Quincy did not wish to appear in public with her "owing to his mortification at his marriage." And in effect, Adams abandoned his wife in Berlin; he paid far more attention to his diplomatic duties than to her.

Eventually she was befriended by Countess Pauline Neale, a member of the royal court, who was astonished to find the wife of a minister at home alone. Countess Neale took Louisa to the theater, so she would be noticed, and the rumors about her appearance quickly dissipated: "They found me pretty," Louisa wrote. Six weeks after her arrival, she was finally presented to the Prussian king and queen, and for the next four years she took part in "the giddy round of fashionable life" in Berlin, "a world altogether new" to her.

But it was not John Quincy Adams who escorted his wife and made her popular in society. It was his brother Thomas, now the secretary of legation. Unlike the somber John Quincy, Thomas loved to joke and dance. One evening at a ball, Louisa boldly asked Thomas to dance, "and he danced so well I was quite delighted." Louisa attracted a succession of partners that evening, and from that time on, she declared, "I became a Belle." Thomas' kindness and humor gave her confidence. More important, until he returned to America in 1798, Thomas protected her from the coldness of John Quincy and the harsh realities of her marriage.

Once launched, Louisa went everywhere. While the court in Saint Petersburg displayed more wealth and ceremony, and a court ball in London or Paris brought out more silks and jewels, Berlin was unique because of its sheer madness. When a young officer dropped dead during a lively quadrille at a ball, for example, his wife donned his uniform and paraded about the city for days. Nothing stopped the fun. When the Prince of Orange died just before the annual carnival, the celebrations continued; mourning was postponed. Even young King Frederick William III was a bit daffy, and insisted that the royal family and any foreign prince who might be in Berlin take time to play one of his favorite diversions—blindman's buff.

Berlin dazzled. "Every night," Louisa wrote, "was engaged for Courts, Parties, or Dancing Teas. Operas twice a week in full dress. A masked ball on Thursday. Dance and supper at one of the Ministers and Sunday ball at Court."

John Quincy was offended by this "sea of dissipation" and ostentation, and complained that life in Berlin was boring and unprofitable for an ambitious man. But he kept busy. He renegotiated America's treaty with Prussia, to bring it into agreement with Jay's Treaty with England, which had become the new standard of American neutrality. He sent his father detailed reports of the current diplomatic affairs of Europe. These were the convulsive years of the French Revolution, and information gathered by John Quincy helped President Adams pursue peace instead of war with France between 1798 and 1800.

However, the slow pace of diplomacy was not enough for the younger Adams, and he undertook extra work, including the study of German. He struggled several hours a day to learn the language. Louisa, on the other hand, picked it up readily at the balls and dinners; languages, like laughter, came easily to her.

At social gatherings, John Quincy often left Louisa to wander by herself while he played cards. Sometimes when he retired early, Louisa stayed late for supper and would give her dance card to the hostess, who always made sure it was full. Louisa loved the attention and flattery, and as the daughter-in-law of the American President and the wife of America's minister to Berlin, she was addressed as "Your Excellency" and "Princess Royal." She danced frequently with the king, and it was not unusual for her to stay out until two. Although she sent a disclaimer to her mother—"I do not think I am calculated for a Court"—Louisa was, indeed, the belle of Berlin.

For Louisa, Berlin was both a last childhood fling and a shocking awakening. She constantly tested her relationship with John Quincy, always searching for a way of asserting her rights, or at least defining their limits. Louisa's and John Quincy's contrasting attitudes toward their respective roles in marriage are best exemplified by three problems that emerged in Berlin: pregnancy, money, and, of all things, the use of rouge.

Louisa had twice been offered a box of rouge by the queen, who thought she looked pale. Both times John Quincy ordered Louisa to refuse the gift, and she complied. During the carnival ball in the winter of 1800, however, Louisa had second thoughts. She admired, even envied, the effect of rouge on the women in their black costume dresses, and wrote with some petulance that "those who were pale look cadaverous, particularly when not relieved by the brilliancy of diamonds." Louisa thought she "looked a fright in the midst of Splendour." When the queen offered her rouge for the third time, therefore, Louisa accepted it.

Now Louisa undertook her first open defiance of her husband. While the issue appears petty, the confrontation was not. One evening as Louisa dressed to attend the opera, she applied some rouge to her cheeks. She thought it "made me look quite beautiful." John Quincy, however, was furious. He took a wet towel and washed her face clean. On a later occasion, Louisa applied the rouge as she dressed for court, then walked boldly up to John Quincy. He ordered her to remove it, and Louisa refused "with some temper." Here was a major effrontery: few women of this time ever challenged their husbands on any issue. Without a word John Quincy turned and ran down the stairs, out the door, and into his carriage. He attended the court alone. Louisa felt a rush of triumph. She had asserted a small right, and underscored her refusal to be a compliant, docile wife.

About money Louisa and John Quincy fought repeatedly. Adams had always felt poor and would until his death; when the promise of Louisa's large dowry evaporated, he felt he had been cheated. In Berlin, although his salary came to nine thousand dollars a year, his life contained pinching expenses: housing, carriages, entertainments, clothing, servants. With some bitterness

An Exceptional Marriage

Louisa noted that "the Salaries of an American minister are too mean to place you on a level with your Colleagues." She sewed almost all of her court dresses and furnished the family's small apartment with the "very plainest and cheapest" furniture. Their carriage was secondhand, and they kept few servants.

In addition to this, there was a major money problem. It concerned the large sum that JQA had received from his father in 1794 before he sailed for the Netherlands, and which he had turned over, in part, to his brother Charles for investment. In the crash of 1797 Charles had lost every penny.

In many ways Charles represented the side of the Adams family that it wished to hide. There were flaws in this dynasty, embarrassing, deep weaknesses that ran like fissures through the generations. They had to do with money, mental depression, and alcoholism. In Charles Adams these three flaws connected.

Charles, the middle of three sons, was frail and shaky. At Harvard he had enjoyed what his parents and older brother deemed "bad company." He had played too much and had drunk too hard. By 1798 he was sliding into alcoholism. Married and the father of two girls, he was broke and in debt. Unable to handle the dishonor of losing his older brother's funds, he stopped functioning and drank heavily. Abigail Adams became frantic with foreboding for her son. She wrote John Quincy: "Charles's habits are so rooted, the temper so soured, the whole man so changed that ruin and destruction have swallowed him up."

In November 1800 Abigail—on her way to Washington to be with her husband, who had lost to Thomas Jefferson in his bid for reelection—stopped by Charles's small chambers in New York City. She found her son in squalor, alone, drunk, and in the last stages of his alcoholic sickness. "All is lost," she wrote, "poor, poor unhappy wretched man." But though her heart went out to Charles, she could not stay long. Dutifully Abigail continued her journey southward to the new federal city, Washington, now under construction in the swampland along the Potomac River. The President's House contained a sense of tragedy. Humiliated by his electoral defeat, John Adams remained at home, never visiting Charles and refusing to acknowledge his son's

illness. On November 30 Charles Adams died alone in New York.
The Adamses viewed Charles's frailties as a threat that weakened the family; they would unsuccessfully try to ignore alcoholism and depression in future generations. Thomas spoke for them all when he wrote of Charles: "Let silence reign forever over his tomb." However, for John Quincy, Charles's loss of that money went noisily onward.

MORE than problems with money or rouge, childbearing defined Louisa Adams' role; it made clear who she was and what she could do. Louisa was pregnant eleven times in her first thirteen years of marriage. Although she was terrified of childbirth, she endured pregnancies as God-given, and her husband referred to the ordeal as "the pleasing punishment that women bear."

Louisa's pregnancies and miscarriages drained her health. When she miscarried the fourth time, early in 1799, her doctor recommended a health-restoring journey to the fashionable spa at Teplitz-Schönau. This was the first of two such journeys that the Adamses made during their Berlin years to help Louisa recover.

The village of Teplitz nestles deep in a valley through which courses a stream that swirls into rock-lined pools, where both hot mineral water and cold mountain snow-runoff collect. At intervals along the stream, a series of baths had been constructed; physicians assigned their patients to the baths according to the varying temperatures and mineral properties of the water. Louisa bathed three times a week and drank a bottle of mineral water daily. Soon she and John Quincy had settled into an idyllic routine. Music from the nearby cathedral filled their chambers, and their windows overlooked a park where deer gamboled across meadows of wild flowers. Louisa walked four and a half miles each day, hiked up the nearby mountains with John Quincy, and felt a new and surprising strength and vitality.

After eight weeks at the spa, the Adamses returned to Berlin. The following year, when her fifth miscarriage occurred, they again left Berlin society, this time to explore the mountains of Silesia. In October 1800 Louisa discovered that she "was once

An Exceptional Marriage

more as 'Ladies wish to be who love their Lord.'" This, her sixth pregnancy, created such alarm because of her previous miscarriages that the Adamses kept it a secret from their families in America. But Louisa enjoyed better health than at any other time since her marriage, and, for the first time, she carried successfully to term. On April 12, 1801, she was "blessed" with a son.

Louisa, however, had been handled so roughly by a drunken midwife that she almost died, and for five weeks her left leg was paralyzed. The king and queen of Prussia, almost as excited as the parents, inquired daily about Louisa, and to assure quiet in her home they ordered the streets around the Adamses' house closed. For all the pain and fuss, Louisa was joyful: "I was a *Mother*. God had heard my prayer."

John Quincy wrote with equal fervor in his diary of the "long expected, ardently desired, painfully born and only child." He was cooler about the birth when writing to his parents. After four pages of news, quotes from Cicero, speculations upon his term at Berlin, JQA finally noted in the last paragraph that two days earlier Louisa "gave me a Son."

Louisa wanted the baby's name to be from both families. John Quincy, however, had been saddened a year earlier by the death of George Washington, who had appointed him to his first diplomatic post. When JQA's son was born, the choice was clear. Adams named him George Washington Adams. He wrote to his brother, Thomas:

> President Washington was, next to my own father, the man to whom I was indebted for the greatest personal obligations. I knew not whether upon rigorous philosophical principles it be wise to give a great and venerable name to such a lottery-ticket as a new-born infant—but my logical scruples have in this case been over-powered by my instinctive sentiments.

In June 1801 John Quincy, having been recalled, prepared to leave Berlin. The family's departure was delayed because of Louisa's health. Still unable to walk, she was carried to the coach. But the "change of air" during the stage ride, the spring flowers, and the prospect of seeing her family made Louisa stronger. By the time she reached Hamburg, she could walk leaning on John Quincy's arm. On July 8 she climbed the gangplank of the *America* without help.

The ship docked in Philadelphia on September 4. Thomas met it, happily embracing brother, nephew, and sister-in-law. Louisa's recent pregnancy and delivery had left her so thin and weak that Thomas, she said, was "shocked when he saw me."

Louisa was in no hurry to confront her formidable parents-in-law. She knew that the Adamses called her "an *English* bride" and openly asked whether she was bright enough or tough enough to be the lifetime partner of New England's favored son. Could she measure up? For her part, Louisa considered the Adamses—members of America's small aristocracy—coarse replicas of Europe's real thing.

Instead of going north to Massachusetts with her husband, Louisa took George and, escorted by servants, rode the stagecoaches to Washington, to her own parents' home. Joshua Johnson did not recognize his favorite daughter when she climbed down from the carriage, and Louisa found her father "fearfully changed" after their four years of separation. During her stay, Joshua complained of an undefined illness, and held his grandson on his lap all the time as though trying to assure himself of a future.

Louisa wrote frequently to John Quincy, who was enjoying "the inexpressible delight" of seeing his parents after seven years of absence. Louisa tried to coax him to come to Washington to fetch her, but Adams was in no hurry to make a trip of more than six hundred miles.

The journey, in truth, was dangerous. The roadways were nothing more than cleared paths angling down from Boston to Providence and on to Newport. There one caught the packet for New York, then crossed New Jersey to Philadelphia, and went on to Baltimore. Only in the last three years had the route south to Washington been cleared through the wilderness. On the terrifyingly rutted log roadbeds, stagecoaches underwent terrible strain, plunging into deep mudholes or jarring over rocks and stumps. There were few bridges, and swollen streams occasionally swept the coaches away. Another hazard was overloading; when fully loaded, with nine passengers inside, four more holding on outside, and trunks piled on top, the stage's center of gravity would sometimes shift, and the coach rolled over.

Despite these dangers, however, John Quincy eventually gave in to Louisa's demands and journeyed to Washington. Trying to cut his travel time, he rode all night—which also saved hotel costs. He arrived in Washington on October 24, having covered the distance from Philadelphia in thirty-four hours.

After a week in Washington, Louisa and John Quincy set out, together with little George, on the return trip to Boston. George became very sick with dysentery, but John Quincy insisted they hurry home. They rode stagecoaches, the ferry, and then the stage again, departing at two in the morning. Louisa protested that the pace was "too violent" and took sick. They slept jammed together in the stage or in crowded hotel rooms, and banged along the log roads, crossed the Hudson in an open boat in pouring rain, and sailed in subfreezing weather to Newport, Rhode Island. They arrived in Boston tired and ill and, fortunately, too late for that day's stage on to the family homestead in Quincy, as that part of Braintree was now called. For Louisa, the trip had meant sickness, cold, wet, exhaustion. "These," she said, "were my first impressions of America."

The older Adamses received Louisa "very kindly" and were "much pleased" with baby George. Dozens of Adams relatives, arriving in carriages or on horseback, filled the house. But to Louisa, the clothes, the food, the nasal Yankee accents, all seemed strange and separated her from her husband's family.

The Adamses treated her with care, prepared special delicacies, opened special preserves. Yet every treat made her feel more separate, more "stamped with unfitness."

Louisa felt especially unsuited to the standards of her mother-in-law; Abigail Adams, she said, "was in every point of view a superior Woman." But Abigail found Louisa wanting. She believed JQA had married a weakling, and remarked on her daughter-in-law's frailty and inability to please her paragon son.

John Adams, on the other hand, immediately liked Louisa, and she him. "The old gentleman took a fancy to me," she said, "and he was the only one." Louisa found her father-in-law a warm, approachable man. After her own father died, on April 17, 1802, John Adams would become, slowly, over the years, a willing and loving replacement.

These were pivotal times for Louisa. Her father's death had left her mother destitute, and in Catherine Johnson's widowhood Louisa saw the injustice of being a sacrificial woman. Her mother had done her duty to husband and children, "with no possibility of entering on any useful career" for herself. She had given her life to a man whose death left her impoverished.

Her mother's destitution, her own self-questioning, and her continuing admiration for educated and strong-minded women made Louisa increasingly sensitive to the narrow role that society and her husband were directing her to assume. She began asking: Did not God create man and woman equal? And she also began examining her fear of living a life without purpose, overshadowed by her husband.

John Quincy, meantime, was worried about his own future. He had, of course, greater choices and assurances than Louisa had. Restless, uninterested in practicing law in Boston, where he and Louisa and their child were now living, he wrote in his diary: "I feel strong temptation to plunge into political controversy." He decided that if he entered politics, it would be on his own terms. "A politician in this country," he continued, "must be the man of a party. I would fain be the man of my whole country." In April 1802 John Quincy was elected to the Massachusetts legislature, and a year later the Federalists asked him to fill the vacant U.S. Senate seat for Massachusetts. He was elected, and at thirty-five became a U.S. senator.

As John Quincy prepared for the Senate, Louisa, pregnant for the seventh time, prepared to give birth. On July 4, 1803, while John Quincy was visiting his parents in Quincy, Louisa went into labor just after midnight. Her groans awakened Carolina, her younger sister, who jumped out of bed and ran into the room to assist. At three a.m., as the first cannons fired salutes for the Fourth of July, Louisa gave birth to another baby boy.

An Exceptional Marriage

As soon as she was well enough, she and the baby rode out to Quincy, where the little boy was named—with everyone's approval—after his grandfather: John Adams 2d.

WHEN the Adamses arrived in Washington for the Senate session in the fall of 1803, the city was an unfinished wilderness. It contained no more than six hundred buildings, most made of wood, and two large stone structures, the Capitol and the President's House. Streets were pitted pathways, and bridges a mere layering of planks. Because of the expense, few congressmen brought their wives with them, and most members roomed together in boardinghouses. The Adamses moved in with Louisa's sister and brother-in-law, Nancy and Walter Hellen, who lived in a "lonely and dreary" house in the country. John Quincy walked five miles every day to and from the Capitol, even in driving rain or snow. His health was sometimes poor, his clothes frazzled, his appetite erratic, but he found politics to be his real passion, and he gave it his full attention.

Washington, a meager backwater capital, had few diversions. Attention to dress, much less to soap and water, had not yet achieved popularity; water had to be hauled by buckets from wells in the public squares. Chewing tobacco took the place of snuff, and walls and fireplaces were streaked with the juices. There were occasional social functions at the President's House, but Thomas Jefferson was cheap with fuel, and often the Adamses huddled around his coal grate, shaking with cold.

Louisa Adams disliked Jefferson. "His person was ungainly, ugly and common." She abhorred his "awkward" manners, his "peering restlessness." He had obtained his office, she said, by "mere good fortune attained in a lucky hour."

She complained when Jefferson declared that European court rules of precedence had no place in his republic, and that henceforth all official functions would be *"pêle-mêle."* Guests scrambled for the best seats at table, jostled the President, and spoke to anyone they wished. The traditional New Year's Day at the President's House became a horror to Louisa. She was shocked by the "unruly crowd of indiscriminate persons from every class" who bumped the diplomats and stared at their carriages and clothing.

Nevertheless, the Adamses were frequent guests at the President's House, and John Quincy retained his admiration for this older statesman, begun in Paris more than twenty years earlier, when he had been almost as much Jefferson's boy as John Adams'.

In contrast to the official functions, Jefferson's private dinners pleased both John Quincy and Louisa. The President spent fifty dollars a day to feed and wine his guests, and even Louisa thought the French cuisine "and plate" very handsome.

During his five years in the Senate, JQA often went home to Quincy to be with his mother and father, usually traveling without Louisa in order to cut expenses. Abigail complained that her son arrived looking shabby, pale, and thin, and she sent instructions to her daughter-in-law that upon his return to Washington, she was to make him attend to his appearance. She fussed over the cut of his coat, his wig, the color of his neckcloth.

Abigail nagged John Quincy about his eating and wrote to Louisa: "I wish you would not let him go to Congress without a cracker in his pocket. The space between breakfast and dinner is so long that his Stomach grows sour and his food when he takes it neither digests nor nourishes him."

John Quincy, however, remained indifferent to everything except his career. Louisa's life apart from her husband grew harsh. "My health and spirits were sadly depressed," she said. George, she wrote to JQA in the spring of 1804, talked of his father "incessantly, though he has never forgiven you for your desertion. John calls every body papa; poor little fellow he was too young when you left us to remember you."

Louisa was alone again in June 1806 when, pregnant for the eighth time, she went into "a very bad" labor and gave birth to a stillborn boy. This was the second birth without her husband at home, and for years Louisa remained resentful at having "to endure such heavy personal trials" on her own.

JOHN Quincy knew that his political future in the Senate was dubious, since he was only nominally a member of the party that had placed him in office. Foreseeing an end to his public life and

An Exceptional Marriage

wishing to settle his family, he purchased a house in Boston and accepted a position as the first Boylston professor of rhetoric and oratory at Harvard. He started his lectures in the summer of 1806, in the interim between Senate sessions.

Late that autumn Louisa found herself in her ninth pregnancy. On August 18, 1807, she gave birth to her third son, as John Quincy listened from the next room. The baby was born after six hours of "extremely severe" labor and was apparently dead; the midwife left Louisa's room in tears. But Louisa, determined to save him, struggled with the baby, and within five minutes he took several deep breaths and appeared to breathe on his own. For two days this newborn tentatively grasped life, and by the third day, as he started nursing and thriving, Louisa wrote: "Thanks be to God!" The infant was baptized Charles Francis. Louisa proudly reported to her mother that she was doing well, and "the little Gentleman is likely to do so too."

In the fall of 1807, and again in 1808, Louisa and John Quincy left George with Aunt Mary Cranch and John with his grandparents, taking Charles with them to Washington for the Senate sessions. The family, Louisa wrote, was "scattered to the winds."

Politics soon "were growing very hot." The Whigs, Louisa said, were "jealous" of Adams, and the Federalists "hated him" because he had split with his party on several important issues. In 1808 he was repudiated by the New England Federalists, who dumped him for disloyalty. Stung, he resigned from the Senate in June and moved with Charles and Louisa back to Massachusetts, where once again Louisa noted with pleasure "we were a family." But not for long.

In March 1809, while alone in Washington to argue a case before the U.S. Supreme Court, John Quincy was called to the President's House, where the newly elected James Madison offered him the post of first U.S. minister plenipotentiary to Russia. John Quincy later wrote: "I could see no significant reason for refusing the nomination."

He would have had reason enough had he asked his wife. In Boston, Louisa had heard rumors of a foreign post, "a thing perfectly abhorrent to me." When news of the confirmation reached her, Louisa was "stunned." She said, "I had been so grossly deceived, every apprehension lulled." When she complained to John Quincy, he laughed and called her suffering "affectation." He also made another fateful decision: that of her three sons Louisa could take only Charles with her to Russia, along with her sister Catherine; George and John must remain behind with relatives in Massachusetts. Louisa later wrote: "The disposal of my Children was fixed without my knowledge until it was too late to Change." John Quincy sent his brother, Thomas, who had been so kind to Louisa in Berlin, to be kind once more. He was to take her out to the Adamses' in Quincy to visit her two older sons for the last time before leaving for Russia. They would be young men when she saw them again.

"In this agony of agonies," Louisa wrote, "can ambition repay such sacrifices? Never!!!"

PART III
Saint Petersburg–London, 1809–1817

CHAPTER ONE

AT NOON on August 5, 1809, Louisa, John Quincy, and Charles climbed into the carriage waiting outside their house. They made room for Catherine Johnson and for William Steuben Smith, John Quincy's young nephew and private secretary. Outside the carriage rode two servants. The vehicle, piled high with trunks and baggage, lurched through the narrow streets before pulling up to a wharf on the Charlestown waterfront. There the entourage boarded the *Horace*, bound for Saint Petersburg.

The ship was without other passengers, and the Adamses had to purchase their own bedding and food, all in addition to the six-hundred-dollar fare. Because so few Americans went overseas, those who did took on special obligations, such as delivering mail or packages, or taking along the sons of friends for the exposure and education of travel. Two such young men had been placed in JQA's care: Alexander H. Everett and Francis C. Gray, who would work as secretaries to the legation, under Adams' scrutiny.

John Quincy himself had first seen Saint Petersburg as the secretary to diplomat Francis Dana.

The *Horace* cast off at precisely one o'clock. As it hoisted sail and pulled away from Boston Harbor, carrying America's first minister plenipotentiary to Russia, the ship was bidden farewell with salutes from the navy yard, then from Fort Independence on Castle Island. Later, as evening descended and "a tolerably fresh Breeze" came up, the *Horace* ran briskly toward the open Atlantic, while its passengers lingered on deck until the hills of Boston were lost from their view.

In the night, beyond the smell of land, with the sea cool and foggy, Louisa and John Quincy sat apart in private thought. Separation from parents and children carried with it a sense of foreboding. Louisa knew that she would never share the childhoods of her two older boys. She was, she wrote, "broken hearted, miserable, alone in every feeling."

John Quincy worried not about his sons, but about his parents; their old age meant that he might never see them again. When five hundred miles at sea, John Quincy wrote to his mother that no other parting in his life had been "so painful."

Louisa's recollection of the crossing was of spending one dreadful night after another with the seas running "mountains high"; or, when the ship edged through fog, of dampness penetrating the blankets. John Quincy, however, could "scarcely perceive that we are at sea." He rose at six, and after reading the Bible and breakfasting, he walked the deck for exercise and made observations of the ship's position by quadrant. He spent most afternoons reading and writing and, after dinner, read or played cards until eleven or twelve.

John Quincy considered the assignment to Russia extremely important. He prayed that the result would prove "beneficial to my country, prosperous to my family, and advantageous to all who are concerned in the voyage." He entered the world stage at a dramatic moment. Since 1801, when the Adamses had left Berlin, Napoleon had conquered vast areas of Europe. New puppet states, ruled by the Bonaparte family, took their places on a ruined continent. After his plans for an invasion of England were halted by Lord Nelson at Trafalgar in 1805, Napoleon had pivoted his Grand Army to the east, and advanced to the Danube. Austria, Prussia, and eastern Russia fell. The emperor paused at Russia's Baltic border. Peace with Russia would allow him to consolidate his Continental System—his plan was to shut off British commerce with Europe and thereby force Britain to come to terms.

Although America remained neutral in the war between France and England, in 1809 the ports of Europe were still dangerous for United States ships. British ships halted American ships and American seamen were impressed to help man Britain's navy. The Danes, allies of Napoleon, seized several hundred American ships between 1807 and 1812, on the assumption that they were actually British vessels in disguise or were carrying British cargoes. This was one of the issues on John Quincy Adams' agenda as he and his family sailed toward Saint Petersburg.

The Adamses' Atlantic crossing progressed without event. But as the *Horace* entered the North Sea and then the Baltic, it was repeatedly stopped, first by an armed brig, which refused to identify itself, then by a British brig, which sent over an officer to inspect the ship's papers. Two hours later, a Danish brig hailed them and asked where they came from and where they were bound. Delayed by the continual haltings and by gales, the *Horace* finally reached Saint Petersburg on the afternoon of October 23 after eighty days "of tedious and dangerous navigation."

SAINT Petersburg, built on the Neva River delta, was, with Paris, the jewel of Europe. Its wide boulevards, open squares, palaces, and cathedrals went beyond the dream of Peter the Great, who started building the city in 1703. Peter had planned the capital to be Russia's western seaport and had built a fortress to protect it. By 1809, with its active sea trade, Saint Petersburg filled the left bank of the Neva. Its palaces, fortresses, and ornate gardens spilled across the surrounding canals to the countryside beyond. The old city itself, where the Adamses now lived, was on a large almond-shaped island near the left bank. Narrow canals and streets looped through the city, and the Nevsky Prospekt, its one-hundred-and-thirty-foot-wide major thoroughfare, stretched four miles in a straight line from the countryside into the very heart of the city.

Two great squares formed the focal point of Saint Petersburg: the magnificent Senate Square—also called Saint Isaac's, after the Church of Saint Isaac in its center—and to the north an equally magnificent expanse, called Palace Square. Along the latter sprawled the Winter Palace, the largest royal palace in the world, with three hundred rooms decorated with paintings and sculpture, and a maze of apartments that could accommodate sixty-five hundred overnight guests. The Winter Palace connected with the imperial palace called the Hermitage, which contained, in John Quincy's words, "one of the most magnificent collections of masterpieces of the arts that the world can furnish."

Every Sunday morning as many as forty thousand men filled the two squares as Czar Alexander I reviewed his soldiers. Here, too, the czar and the nobility celebrated, promenaded, rode their carriages to luxurious dinners and balls. And here, as well, the common people gathered in veneration of their czar.

Saint Petersburg was a city of palaces, such as the opulent Marble Palace, with its large rooms and enclosed garden with an aviary and "trees of full growth." The Anichkov Palace contained bronzes and ornamentals, gilded sofas and chairs, and steam and water baths. The czar lacked nothing: his greenhouses produced fresh pears through the Russian winter, so that he might present them to his mother on her birthday.

Saint Petersburg was also a city of cathedrals, and John Quincy Adams would worship during the next five years in almost every one of them, returning so often to the Roman Catholic church to hear the music, that in 1812 the Father General of the Jesuits would make an effort to convert the New England Protestant.

Only twenty-four hours after his arrival, John Quincy was told that the chancellor of the Russian Empire, Count Nikolai Petrovich Rumiantsev, wished to see him immediately. Adams was caught by surprise. He was, after all, only the minister from a third-rate nation, entering a country ruled by one of the most powerful men in the world. The invitation was an unusual honor.

Adams left for his appointment attired in his best court clothing, "dressed from top to toe, much to his discomfiture, in a superb style," said Louisa, "wig and all."

John Quincy Adams, in fact, had arrived in Saint Petersburg with far more political muscle than he had estimated. Napoleon wanted Russia to halt all trade with the United States, since American ships sometimes carried British goods. But the czar needed American trade. Ships and trade thus placed the American minister between two large powers, and in a position of considerable importance.

CZAR Alexander received John Quincy Adams at the Winter Palace a week after the new minister arrived in Saint Petersburg. This formal ceremony was necessary for presenting credentials and for entering the court and diplomatic society. The court employed a Monsieur le Commandeur de Maisonneuve, who instructed John Quincy on the ceremonial procedures for his presentation. Adams considered court formalities "so trifling and so insignificant," but he went through with the preparations.

Louisa, too, had to be presented, and one Countess Litta, "very handsome and very fat," visited her to rehearse the ceremony. For the formal presentation, Louisa wore a silver hoop skirt, heavy crimson robe, and long train lined with white. At the Winter Palace, she stood in the center of a vast empty room, facing tall double doors. Two large black men dressed like Turks took positions by the doors and drew sabers with gold handles. When the doors opened, Louisa saw a corridor lined with identically dressed black men, their swords drawn. Down the long corridor marched the grand marshal, followed by the czar and czarina, walking side by side, followed by a long train of ladies and gentlemen. As they entered the room, Louisa slowly curtsied, trembling with nervousness.

When Louisa finished her curtsy, Czar Alexander walked up to her and made small talk in French, while the czarina said nothing. Then their imperial majesties withdrew.

John Quincy's audience with the czar was less formal. When Adams stepped into his private cabinet, Alexander walked forward and said in French, "I am so glad to see you here." The czar was thirty-one, tall, fair-haired, strong, and cordial. After presenting his credentials, John Quincy told Alexander that he should consider the American mission as proof of President Madison's desire to strengthen relations between their two countries. Alexander replied that he, in turn, sought friendly relations with the United States. The czar spoke about the political alignments of Europe, and of United States neutrality, which he thought "wise and just." Adams also emphasized his nation's wish to remain free from political ties to Europe, and its interest in open commerce. When John Quincy left this first meeting, he felt that his mission to Russia was off to an excellent start.

Alexander at this moment was nearing the apogee of his power. He would govern Russia for almost twenty-five years, and under his rule that nation would reach a pinnacle of influence in Europe unequaled in the century. Alexander would match Napoleon, and their decisions would shape the destiny of Europe.

Alexander, however, was a man divided against himself, a man who personified the contradictions of his own empire. Beneath his handsome appearance lay disease, and emotional imbalance marked by explosions of rage that were soothed only by séances with a religious mystic. His sexual indulgence may have contributed to his instability, for syphilis was slowly driving him mad. The seeds of true madness, however, had been implanted in Alexander in boyhood. His father, Czar Paul I, ruled his empire and his family with cruelty and violence. He excluded foreigners from Russia, censored free thought, and burned books. When Alexander was twenty-three, he learned of a coup against his father and did nothing to prevent it. In March 1801 Paul was strangled in his bedroom, and Alexander became czar.

This new czar was young and open-faced, and the peasants loved him. He was thought to be the man who would restore the glories of Russia, who would free the serfs, reorganize the bureaucracy, and keep the country at peace. But Alexander did none of these. The Russian army marched, and met defeat. The serfs remained oppressed, the bureaucracy huge and unresponsive. Bribery was a way of life, and corruption was so extensive that the French ambassador complained that "there was perhaps no government employee who did not have his price."

Adams had to work with an impenetrable Russian foreign ministry, the largest in all Europe, with some three hundred employees. The bloated staff was inefficient, and for Adams to accomplish anything, he had to read, spy, and cultivate the czar. The Adamses read the *St. Petersburgischer Zeitung*, a German-language edition of the local Russian paper, for news, though its political section was controlled by the foreign ministry.

The czar not only controlled the press, he also intercepted the mails, including all the private letters and diplomatic dispatches sent by Louisa and John Quincy Adams. There was little that diplomats could do. Some tried writing in invisible ink. Adams sent dispatches to the State Department written in a code that, by modern-day standards of espionage, appears childlike.

The social festivities of Saint Petersburg offered the best source of gossip and news, and therefore among diplomats social skills were highly valued. The idea was to meet other members of the diplomatic corps, the nobility, the czar himself, and gather what one could. A casual remark, or an oversight, could have special meaning. Too shallow a bow could cause speculation that nations were at odds. Louisa Adams watched, amused, another aspect of this game: Russian officers employed at the court balls to dance with any woman, however ugly, for political purposes. Louisa called them "waltzing machines," these windup soldiers who charmed women for information.

The corruption, the inefficiency, the gossip, all took on an almost charming aspect in this most unreal capital. The czar alone decided the really essential things. The best way, the only way to know Russia's intentions was to know Alexander—and even then one couldn't be sure. Friendly but suspicious, brilliant yet erratic, Alexander was called, for good reason, "the enigmatic czar."

LOUISA and John Quincy Adams were soon socializing until four every morning, rising at eleven, dining at five, taking tea at ten, and going out once more. No capital anywhere maintained such an exhausting round of ceremony and banqueting. The nobility kept perpetual open house, where the Adamses found card parties and gaming tables piled with large amounts of international currencies. John Quincy prayed that he and his family would "come out of this violent whirl still in possession of our Senses."

Saint Petersburg turned raw and dark in October, and the Adamses then dined by candlelight at four in the afternoon. As though to hold back the time of cold and darkness, the November ball for the czar's mother was illuminated by fifteen thousand candles and concluded with a magnificent supper for two hundred and fifty guests, who wore a profusion of diamonds and sashes and ribbons. This was followed by thunderous fireworks high above the frozen Neva River. By the czar's birthday fete in December, the capital was dark at three in the afternoon. During the shortest day, John Quincy measured sunrise at nine fourteen and sunset at two twenty-six. He recorded nightly temperatures of minus thirty and minus forty degrees Fahrenheit. Louisa wrote that her body "was almost congealed by the intense cold." Horses' hoofs made musical notes striking the hard snow, leather boots cracked, and metal adhered to the fingers of those foolish enough to touch it.

With the canals and rivers sealed by ice six feet thick, food had to be hauled in on sleds. The last vessel sailed in early November, and the Adamses received no letters from America until May. To ward off the terrors of such isolation and darkness, the Russians concocted pageants and entertainments. In January the imperial family, wrapped in luxurious furs and followed by shivering diplomats, joined the archbishop in blessing the frozen Neva River. The New Year's celebration featured an enormous masquerade ball, with sixteen hundred guests swarming through the Winter Palace in ornate costumes.

No one in the Adams family escaped these rituals. Every year Louisa took Charles to the children's ball, where elegantly attired mothers sparkling with diamonds watched their youngsters dance the polonaise and the Polish promenades. For his first ball, Louisa dressed three-year-old Charles as an Indian chief, and prolonged applause greeted him as he entered the dance floor. Following the dance, the children ate an elegant supper with "oceans of Champagne," while their mothers stood behind their chairs. Afterward there was a lottery for expensive toys, but John Quincy would not allow Charles to accept gifts, and he was taken home empty-handed at two in the morning.

Winter ended with great rejoicing when the ice blocking the Neva River broke open. Church bells rang, and as the first boats crossed, the governor of Saint Petersburg brought the czar a glass of water from the river to drink.

Soon summer began, and Louisa happily noted: "Letters from America now come more frequently God be thanked." On the summer solstice John Quincy noted that the sun rose at two forty-six and never really set at all.

The highlight of the summer was the annual carriage procession into the countryside to the palace at Peterhof, where Czar Alexander gave a ball, and guests rode about the gardens in carriages and watched the illumination of three thousand lamps ignited at once by sixteen hundred servants. As John Quincy rode back to the city, he passed perhaps fifty thousand of the common people, who had walked out to the palace to share this midsummer night with the rich.

John Quincy's salary was just nine thousand dollars a year, plus an equal amount as "outfit" for traveling and establishing a residence. To the American people this appeared extravagant, but in Saint Petersburg, JQA felt pinched and embarrassed. Members of other diplomatic missions received high salaries, and the French ambassador spent more than a million rubles a year—which was $350,000 at that time—on entertainment. Adams was faced with spending beyond his means, which would put him in debt and reduce his meager property in America, or incurring a reputation for parsimony. He accomplished both.

"What mortifications attend an American Mission!!!" Louisa said. She refused to go to the czar's birthday ball, because she had only one dress, in which she had already appeared several times. Her absence brought the Adamses' poverty to royal attention, and the czar's mother warned her that if she refused again, she would not be invited to any future court functions. Louisa wrote Abigail that "the manners, customs and expenses of the Country are insurmountable."

When the Adamses first reached Saint Petersburg, they had moved into small chambers, where Louisa's room, she said, "was a stone hole so full of rats that they would drag the braid from the table by my bedside." The Adamses moved almost every year, as landlords raised their rents or sold houses out from under them. They never found a comfortable residence they could afford.

In addition, the number of servants who "must" be retained, John Quincy said with dismay, was three times more than elsewhere. The Adamses kept fourteen. "The expense is intolerable and the trouble ten times worse," he said. The cook and the steward stole so much food that John Quincy fired them both and hired a caterer to furnish the family dinners. "You will readily conceive the embarrassment in which I find myself," he wrote his parents, "and the desire which I feel to get out of a situation, irksome beyond expression."

Yet not one member of the diplomatic corps ever raised questions about the Adamses' poverty or snubbed them for it. Perhaps they found parsimony charming, as though the Adamses were the poor that the rich always had with them. Czar Alexander, wealthy as he was, seemed to understand this unusual economic situation. One May morning Alexander and John Quincy met while walking near the Neva. As the czar approached, he greeted Adams warmly and asked him if he intended to take a house in the country for the summer. Adams replied no; "I had for some time had such an intention, but have given it up."

"And why so?" Alexander asked. "Financial considerations, perhaps?"

"Well yes, sire, in large part," Adams replied, trying to make the phrase sound lighter than it felt.

"You are quite right," the czar continued. "One must always balance income and outgo."

A maxim worthy of emperors, Adams thought to himself, but one few practice.

JOHN QUINCY ADAMS AND Czar Alexander both walked for exercise, and they met often along the Neva or in the Summer Gardens. Their walks together brought a closeness and admiration for one another that helped Adams in his conduct of foreign policy.

Louisa and her sister Catherine, too, were assets to John Quincy's diplomacy.

Alexander found both women enticing, especially the unmarried Catherine. At a ball in May 1810, the czar danced the opening polonaise with Louisa and, when the music ended, asked where her sister might be. "I don't know," Louisa replied, "but I will go immediately to seek her."

"No," said the czar, "I will do that myself."

Alexander located Catherine and led her out to dance. Catherine, not aware that etiquette called for her to be silent and stiff, laughed and talked with the czar as they danced. Alexander was delighted with this impudent, vivacious lady.

Louisa found herself acting as a chaperon. She and her sister walked regularly along the Nevsky Prospekt, and Alexander often stopped and spoke with them, charming them equally.

With her smile and laughter Catherine Johnson had broken into the most etiquette-conscious court in Europe. The czar ordered that she, as well as Louisa and John Quincy, be invited to all royal functions. This startled society, and Louisa herself called the invitation "one of the greatest honors ever conferred upon a foreign young Lady"—as well as, of course, upon a minister of the second rank. Indeed, the czar gave the Adamses privileges accorded only to the higher-ranking French ambassador. Most particularly, he also allowed them all to use the private entrance at the Hermitage. Catherine played her role of special favor coolly; she gave her hand and smile to Alexander, but she gave her heart to William Steuben Smith, JQA's private secretary. Catherine and William would marry in 1813 in Saint Petersburg, with the czar's blessing.

These social encounters had political effects. By October 1809 the Danes had seized and were holding in their ports fifty-two American ships. Adams pressed Chancellor Rumiantsev to ask

Czar Alexander to use his influence with Denmark for the release of the captured ships. Alexander moved with surprising speed, and in 1810 the ships were released.

A year later, again thanks to his contacts with Alexander, Adams also won the release of twenty-three American ships that were being detained in Russian ports on suspicion of carrying false colors or cargoes of British goods. John Quincy thus had the satisfaction of knowing that hours of socializing had been worth millions of dollars to his countrymen. By the end of 1811, American merchant ships were sailing freely in and out of Russian ports, much to Napoleon's growing anger.

To the French, there was no doubt about the value of the friendship between the Adamses and Alexander. Armand de Caulaincourt, Napoleon's ambassador to Saint Petersburg from 1807 to 1811, and John Quincy's chief rival for the czar's attentions, himself confided to Adams, "It seems you are great favorites here. You have found powerful protection." Not a little of his importance Adams owed to his wife and sister-in-law.

THE Adamses spent the summer of 1811 in a rented house on Apothecary Island in the Nevka River, a tributary of the Neva. The location was idyllic—near Saint Petersburg's Botanic Garden with its large public walks, and across the river from the czar's Summer Palace. Louisa, now burdened with her eleventh pregnancy, walked in the garden, listened to the concerts given by the czar's military bands, sat with Charles on the riverbank and fished, and watched the boats go by. One afternoon she and John Quincy boarded a small boat and were rowed up the river by muscular boatmen in plumed hats, who softly sang Russian songs while the Adamses momentarily let their cares ripple away.

At seven in the evening on August 11 Louisa gave birth to a baby girl. "God was very merciful to me for I had been in great danger ever since morning." A daughter made the perfect blessing for their summer, which was one of the most serene of their lives. The Adamses christened the baby Louisa Catherine Adams 2d.

But as one life began, others ended. They had received letters telling them of the death of Louisa's sister Nancy, in childbirth, and of her mother. Louisa wrote in her diary, "My Poor Mother! After ten years of poverty, dependence and suffering, which at this great distance it was so utterly out of my power to mitigate or assuage." The Adamses learned also that John Quincy's beloved sister, Nabby, was hopelessly ill with cancer. John Quincy tried to place these events within the framework of his religious beliefs. We will learn, he wrote, by meditating upon death, "to be better prepared for our own."

Louisa found contentment as she tended her baby daughter. "O she grows lovely," Louisa rejoiced in a letter. "I fear I love her too well." When she walked her daughter along the Neva embankment, Russian *babushkas* stopped to tell her how beautiful the baby was, with her huge dark eyes. "Born for heaven— an angel," they told her.

CHAPTER TWO

THE threat of war cast a shadow over the splendor of Saint Petersburg. Napoleon was sending arms and men to Danzig and Warsaw, and Alexander was countering with two hundred thousand Russian soldiers on the frontier from Riga to Kiev. By the end of February, 1812, eight regiments of Russian soldiers had paraded across Palace Square on their way to the front, and by mid-March three regiments were leaving every week. The sight caused Alexander anguish. He told John Quincy, "And so it is that war is coming, in spite of all I have done to prevent it. Napoleon keeps on advancing. He has just occupied Prussia. He can't advance much further without attacking us."

By the end of Easter week, 1812, fifteen Russian regiments had left for the frontier. John Quincy estimated that Alexander now had more than six hundred thousand young men under arms, facing an equal number of French, Prussians, Poles, and Germans.

In Saint Petersburg, everyone awaited the shock of two immense powers colliding. Most of the diplomats packed and left. On June 28 French troops crossed the Neman River and drove back the Russians. The two empires were at war.

While soldiers died, the Adamses' daughter, not yet a year

old, became sick with "a violent Dysentery." Louisa was helpless, frantic, as for eight weeks she watched her beloved child slowly waste away. John Quincy said that his daughter's sufferings were "so severe that the sight would have wrung a heart of marble." On September 15, 1812, Louisa Adams ended her diary with one sad sentence: "My Child gone to Heaven." Part of her had died as well.

For more than a year Louisa mourned her daughter, the little angel born for heaven, who was, said John Quincy, "the darling of her Heart." No matter what she did, the pain did not diminish. "I read. I work, I endeavor to occupy myself usefully but it is all in vain. My heart is buried in my Louisa's grave and my greatest longing is to be laid beside her." Louisa read fifty-three books during the winter of 1812 to 1813, many on religion and the promise of a better life to come. She sensed in herself "a great change in character" since her daughter's death. "My heart is almost broken and my temper, which was never good, suffers in proportion to my grief."

John Quincy forced Louisa to attend dinners and court functions, and when she sought "affection and gentleness," she said, she was rejected with "harshness or contempt." JQA had no time for his grieving wife. Paralleling his diplomatic duties was his responsibility for the upbringing of his sons. In 1809 Adams had begun a system of instruction by letter for the boys, especially George, whom he invested with the burden of being the leading Adams of the next generation. This correspondence continued into the 1820s, and it documents the kind of parents Louisa and John Quincy Adams were, and the tragedy that resulted.

John Quincy was a proud and determined father. Since the births of his sons, he had studied many works on education. He understood a father's duty to oversee, guide, and control the conduct of his children. He applied intense pressure on his sons to shape them. There were no beatings, but the repetition of stern demands, the withholding of love and approval, struck as hard upon the Adams children as hickory rods. "He ruled his children," Louisa wrote of her husband years later, "and I quietly acquiesced to his right of control."

"You should each of you," John Quincy wrote to his sons in America, "consider yourself as placed here to accomplish some single great end or object." He sent directions for "steady and continual improvement in piety and virtue." He went on for four pages discussing deficiencies in George's education. He told him to study Greek and Latin until he could read "Homer, Demosthenes, and Thucydides, Lucretius, Horace, Livy, Tacitus and *all* Cicero with *almost* as much ease and readiness as if they were written in English. Learning is but the *food* of the mind." He also directed his son to prepare to be "most beneficial to your country and most *useful to mankind.*"

To young George the list of demands seemed endless. When he wrote to his father in September 1810, in a letter obviously dictated to Cousin Susanna Adams, John Quincy responded in disgust with a series of stern directions. The next time you write to me, he told George, do so in your own hand. Tell me that you have been a good Latin scholar, "and that you will before long be a good Greek one." Improve your handwriting, your grammar; treat classmates kindly; make only good boys your friends; and remember above all to worship God, piety, and virtue.

Who could fulfill such expectations? George was not cast in his father's image. Unlike JQA at the same age, George preferred chasing after birds' nests to reading and ciphering. He eased the pains of separation from his family, and the realities of his father's unmeetable standards, by drowning himself in fiction—what his father considered the trash novels of the day. When his Quincy school was closed, George was sent to Atkinson, New Hampshire, to live with his grandaunt Elizabeth Smith Peabody, Abigail Adams' sister. George, now twelve, began searching and reaching, but not always in directions his father approved of. He loved poetry, and he wrote five plays. He studied Virgil and Cicero, and then Shakespeare's plays, which he read "with utter astonishment" at their strength and beauty.

George liked to escape into the distant archipelagoes of his mind. He might have become a writer, poet, or actor, had it not been for his father's relentless expectations.

John Quincy was easier with Charles, who was with him in Russia. During his first four years in Saint Petersburg, Adams instructed Charles himself. The boy read the Bible in French and English every day. He also learned Russian and German and, at five, started arithmetic. Although he was sometimes stubborn and perverse, Charles was the beloved son. When her daughter died, Louisa said that Charles "seemed to read my heart," and showed his mother a tenderness and affection beyond his age. While his brothers hardly knew their parents at all, Charles grew up with their care and attention.

IN SEPTEMBER 1812, as Louisa Adams' daughter lay dying, Napoleon's troops entered Moscow and began burning it to the ground. The war blazed in the Russian countryside only three days' horseback ride from Saint Petersburg. Meanwhile, war had also begun between Great Britain and the United States. The causes were complex: the impressment of American seamen, infringement of the shipping rights of neutral nations, American expansion into Canada and Florida. One of the ironies of this other war of 1812 was that negotiations for peace began almost as soon as the war started.

Here again Adams' friendship with Alexander aided the United States. The czar, seeking to balance France against England, offered to mediate an end to the war in America. The United States armies had been beaten in Canada and in Florida, and the country was now eager for peace. When word of the czar's offer reached President Madison, he quickly sent two special envoys to serve with Adams as a negotiating team: Albert Gallatin, Secretary of the Treasury, and Senator James A. Bayard of Delaware. But the British rejected the czar's offer, and Bayard and Gallatin lingered six months in Saint Petersburg before heading for home by way of London. There, by a stroke of luck, they found the British agreeable to direct negotiations. Alexander's overture had opened the dialogue, and after some haggling over where to hold the meetings, everyone agreed on a compromise location: Ghent, in East Flanders—part of present-day Belgium.

In Russia, meanwhile, Alexander had reversed his defeat.

Napoleon, two thousand miles from his supplies, had lost half his men to a tenacious Russian army and to the Russian winter, and had retreated toward Paris "in disguise," the papers reported. Russians spoke thankfully of their two generals who had defeated Napoleon: General Frost and General Famine.

IN 1814, APPOINTED a member of the peace commission at Ghent, JQA sensed that his moment was approaching. The war in Europe had ended when the victorious allies, led by Alexander, entered Paris on March 31, and Napoleon abdicated soon after. "With this prospect of a general peace in Europe," Adams said, "I commenced my journey to contribute, if possible, to the restoration of peace to my own country."

The news from home, however, was bad. The American army had fewer than twenty-four regiments, and by the second year of war the Americans had been cleared from Canada. With the end of war in Europe, Britain was able to concentrate her navy off the American coast and force peace on her own terms. The British planned to invade at Niagara, Lake Champlain, Chesapeake Bay, and New Orleans. Now, even as John Quincy was preparing to leave Saint Petersburg for Ghent, the land and sea forces of Britain and America were moving toward a final confrontation.

On April 28, 1814, John Quincy said good-by to Louisa and Charles and boarded the carriage he had specially outfitted for the journey to Ghent. He had installed a reclining couch, as well as a small lamp for reading, and provisions that included a tin kettle, a knife, forks, a corkscrew, and five bottles of wine. He had also taken a bath for good health, and purchased two pistols for protection.

He spent fifty-seven days on the road, and arrived in Ghent on June 24. There he joined Bayard, Gallatin, and two new members of the peace commission: Jonathan Russell, the American minister to Sweden, and the irreverent Henry Clay, Speaker of the House of Representatives, who would have preferred being in Kentucky, smoking cigars, drinking bourbon and branch water, and playing poker. The five commissioners settled into bachelor quarters on the rue des Champs, where they waited almost six weeks for the British to arrive. Adams, whose constitution drove him to rise early and write by candlelight, kept himself busy. His colleagues, meanwhile, hung about the coffeehouses, played billiards, smoked, and drank.

When the British commissioners finally did appear, in August, they were a cut below the Americans in diplomatic ability. Britain's first-string negotiators remained in London, preparing for the opening of the peace conference in Vienna that would settle the European situation. Knowing they had regiments of crack troops sailing for the United States, the British at Ghent took a hard line: they insisted on an Indian buffer territory north of the Ohio River, abandonment of U.S. rights to fisheries off Newfoundland and Labrador, and revision of the boundary line between Canada and the United States in order to give British Canada access to the upper Mississippi. For four months, however, the American commissioners held their ground, and the British slowly shifted theirs. Negotiations took the form of memorandums exchanged between the two sides, with long delays while the British sent everything to London for consideration.

The British diplomats seemed to follow the fortunes of their forces in America. In July they were defeated at Niagara, New York; negotiations then started at Ghent. But in August the British army took Washington, D.C., and burned the President's House and the Capitol. With the war looking good to them, negotiations dragged on.

Despite the bad news from home, the American commissioners stood firm. In December 1814, just as the final battle of the War of 1812 was taking shape, a treaty of peace was agreed upon. The British negotiators withdrew their territorial claims, and the Americans dropped their demands for seamen's rights. The Treaty of Ghent, signed on Christmas Eve, stated simply that the two nations, presently at war, wished to be at peace.

The war, meanwhile, continued; the news of the treaty did not reach America until February. On January 8 General Andrew Jackson, fortified on the left bank of the Mississippi at New Orleans, between the levee and the swamps, took on a frontal assault

An Exceptional Marriage

by British troops under Sir Edward Pakenham. In the attack, the British general was killed and his troops suffered two thousand casualties. Only thirteen Americans fell.

The Battle of New Orleans and the Treaty of Ghent would in the years ahead bring two men to the forefront as candidates for the U.S. presidency: Andrew Jackson, general, and John Quincy Adams, negotiator.

In Ghent, the American delegation broke up after more than a week of celebrations. The parties and banquets and too little exercise caused John Quincy to write Louisa: "I am grown so fat you will hardly know me. My health is good, but I cannot wear my clothes." And Louisa kindly replied: "I think at our time of life fat is very becoming."

The American commissioners decided to go to Paris to await word of American ratification of the treaty. Before leaving Ghent, Adams showed the city to Catherine Johnson and her husband, who were on their way home to the United States. John Quincy also sent Louisa instructions: "I invite you to break up altogether our establishment at Saint Petersburg, to dispose of all the furniture which you do not incline to keep, and come with Charles to me at Paris, where I shall be impatiently waiting for you."

Louisa had expected her husband to return to Russia, and when his letter arrived, she was shocked. John Quincy's charge to her was extraordinary. Most women of Louisa's class were transported with care from place to place. But Adams had instructed his wife to sell or ship all of his European possessions, including his lawbooks and papers, to dismiss and hire servants, to outfit a carriage, and to ride more than eighteen hundred miles from Saint Petersburg to Paris across the winter wastelands of Russia and eastern Europe. Adams' charge, therefore, contained a marvelous contradiction: he often treated Louisa as a frail underling, a woman; now he asked that she act with the skill, courage, and toughness of a man.

Louisa herself was uncertain that she could do what he asked, but was soon packing, crating, selling furniture, hiring servants, and keeping records. "I am turned into a woman of business," she wrote. She purchased "an excellent Carriage" and outfitted the vehicle with provisions that included rum, butter, cheese, chocolate, and the family medicine chest.

On February 12, 1815, the day she turned forty years old, Louisa Adams set out across the frozen wastes of Russia for Paris. Because of the snow, Louisa and Charles and Madame Babet, their French maid, traveled in a carriage with runners. Behind them was another, carrying two armed menservants. It was so cold that all their provisions, including the Madeira wine, soon froze solid. The carriage sank so deeply into the snow that on occasion they had to stop and awaken peasants to dig them out with shovels and pickaxes. The road was at best a cleared way through a vast wilderness, rutted, torn by gullies, cut by frozen rivers that, with sudden spring thaws, could sweep them away without a trace. To cross the frozen Vistula into Poland, Louisa hired men to walk ahead with poles to test the ice. The men pounded the ice with the heavy prods to find the firmest path. With a resounding boom the ice would crack, and they would all halt, holding the horses steady, watching for signs of water. They had just reached the other side when the ice gave way, and only the driver's violent whipping of the horses pulled Louisa's carriage out of the water in time.

In Poland, Louisa, Charles, and the servants traveled in wheeled carriages through "the most filthy and beggardly Villages." Late one night a front wheel of her carriage tore off. Two or three "surly ill-looking men" from a nearby farmhouse said they would fix the wheel, but it would take time. Louisa reluctantly prepared to spend the night. She brought in Charles's bed, ordered one servant to guard the carriage, and posted the other outside the door to the room where she and her maid sat awake all night, "neither of us feeling very secure." The next morning a clumsy wheel was fitted onto her carriage, and it worked well enough for them to proceed to Berlin along "the most beautiful road in the world," constructed by Napoleon's troops. Now, for the first time, Louisa heard praise for the French emperor and fear of the Russian cossacks.

Louisa spent a week in Berlin while her carriage was being repaired and outfitted. She felt nostalgic for the time fourteen years earlier, and visited her old friends. But while the bridges and palaces remained grand, Berlin felt "cold and flat," and Louisa's friends had all suffered greatly from the invasion.

Upon leaving Berlin, Louisa proceeded "quietly," her party occasionally meeting straggling groups of disbanded soldiers. Her two servants rode with their pistols displayed. In one village, an innkeeper told Louisa that Napoleon was rumored to have returned to France from Elba, where he had been living since his abdication. From then on, wherever she stopped to change horses, Louisa heard of Napoleon's return, and in Hanover, she found troops being called up. Her two menservants, fearful of having to join the French army, refused to continue to Paris, and she had to engage a "Prussian lad of fourteen" as a servant and escort. They hurried on to the town of Nancy, where "the square was full of French troops, who were mustering in preparation for joining the Emperor."

In Paris, meanwhile, John Quincy Adams followed the news of Napoleon's approach calmly. On the first of March Napoleon had landed at Cannes with 1140 men and four cannons. In ten days he had marched into Lyons at the head of an army of twelve thousand, and by the end of March had reached the outskirts of Paris, causing the king to flee. On March 20 Adams watched a detachment of Napoleon's advance guard enter the capital to the acclamation of the people, who only a fortnight earlier had been screaming *"Vive le Roi!"* As Napoleon approached, masses of royalists were fleeing north, directly toward Louisa Adams.

On the road, wagons filled with soldiers rushed past Louisa's carriage toward the frontier. Louisa was questioned at every village, her baggage inspected and their passports examined. Then, only a mile outside Épernay, she suddenly found herself in the midst of drunken imperial guards on their way to meet Napoleon. The soldiers, seeing that her carriage was Russian, seized her horses and threatened her and her manservant. "Tear them out of the carriage," they shouted. "Kill them, they are Russians!" An officer rode up and, after formally addressing Louisa, read her passport; then he called out to the troops, "This is an American lady going to meet her husband in Paris." Now the soldiers shouted, *"Vive les Américains!"* The officer warned her that her situation was precarious: "The army is totally undisciplined." Whenever they shouted *"Vive les Américains,"* she must reply *"Vive Napoléon."* Louisa behaved coolly, and cheered and waved her handkerchief continuously.

With the officer and his men escorting her, Louisa reached a posthouse at midnight. The landlady admitted her only on the condition that she stay in a darkened room and conceal her party and her coach. The officer continued on with the troops, but all night other soldiers crowded into the roadside house, drinking and shouting. Louisa, however, slept until nine and, after an "excellent breakfast," took her carriage out of hiding and continued on the long route to Paris.

The rumor that she was Napoleon's sister swept before her, and Louisa encouraged this with smiles and waves of her handkerchief. On March 23 she safely entered the French capital, "happy to find myself once more under the protection of a husband, who was perfectly astonished at my adventures, as everything in Paris was quiet."

Louisa had kept careful accounts of her expenses. Including the cost of her carriage and provisions, she had spent $1606.38. She worried that the amount would shock her husband. It was not her fault, she said. "Perhaps the government will be in good humor with the Peace and will make it up to you."

CHAPTER THREE

ON MAY 7, 1815, John Quincy Adams received word that he had been named minister plenipotentiary to Great Britain, a post first held by his father. The Adamses sailed for London, where they were soon joined by their sons George and John, who had been sent from Quincy.

The next two years in England were the best the Adamses ever had. Louisa found a little country house at Ealing, eight miles from Hyde Park Corner in London. The house, with its laurel-bordered garden and bucolic setting, bound the family together, and they fondly nicknamed it their "little Boston home." Louisa and John Quincy played the pianoforte and flute. Adams hired a fencing master for his sons, and bought a pair of pistols for target practice. The boys performed scenes from plays, and they all spent long hours at cards, walking, or riding. John Quincy also bought a telescope; at night he gathered his sons and their friends around him in the backyard and taught them the names of the major constellations.

Adams had little official business to do in England. The British Foreign Office's attention was diverted to the Continent, where the Hundred Days of Napoleon's return ended with his defeat at Waterloo and the restoration of Louis XVIII in June 1815. Adams largely occupied himself by preaching peace and improving relations between Britain and the United States. He had plenty of time for visitors, one of whom was a young American painter, Charles Robert Leslie. Both John Quincy and Louisa sat for their portraits, and Louisa thought her husband "never looked so well or so handsome as he does now." Adams was forty-nine, plump, almost bald, and had a double chin. Louisa's portrait shows a woman with tight brown curls and a small double chin to match her husband's.

The Adamses' house in Ealing was a mile from an excellent school, which all three of the boys attended. In addition, George was tutored by his father in preparation for Harvard. He wrote elaborate letters to his grandparents, as well as poems and plays, and often rode to London to the theater, his "very favorite amusement." George found it difficult, however, to keep up with his class, and Charles, too, made slow academic progress.

For the first time John Quincy got a hint that his children might not reach his expectations. He had wanted to inspire them with "the sublime Platonic idea of aiming at ideal excellence." But they disappointed him, and he took it hard. He might have to content himself, he wrote his mother, with seeing his sons grow up to be "like other men."

After two restful years in England, Adams was appointed Secretary of State by President James Monroe. The position would mean a cut in pay, but it was known as the stepping-stone to the presidency. Abigail wrote to her son that people back home already spoke of him as "worthy to preside over the Counsels of a great Nation." On June 15, 1817, the Adamses embarked on the *Washington* for New York.

As they sailed, the old order was changing. Following the War of 1812, the United States started upon its separate and independent path. The young nation was small and rural, but its population would increase to almost ten million by 1820, and it was filled with expansion fever and sectional rivalry. The clouds were gathering over what would become the central issue of John Quincy's and Louisa's later years: slavery. In politics, the days of the Founding Fathers were ending; only six signers of the Declaration of Independence lived on, including Thomas Jefferson and John Adams. Power was passing to young men in Congress, such as Henry Clay, thirty-nine, and John C. Calhoun, thirty-five. John Quincy Adams, the new Secretary of State, turned fifty during this sea voyage.

JQA found life on shipboard dull and uneventful, except that at this time Louisa suffered "a bad miscarriage" and was extremely ill. It was her twelfth and last pregnancy.

PART IV

Washington, 1817–1825

CHAPTER ONE

AFTER fifty-three days at sea, their ship docked at the southern tip of Manhattan. When word reached John and Abigail in Quincy that the Adamses had landed safely, old John Adams wrote with the trembling hand of age: "Yesterday was one of the most uniformly happy days of my long life." He added, in wobbling capital letters, "ALL WELL."

On August 18, at the Old House, John Adams' clapboard farmhouse in Quincy, the family waited impatiently for the arrival of JQA and his family. At about ten o'clock there was a whoop of excitement as a coach-and-four was seen coming down Penn's Hill. Abigail Adams ran to the door. In a few minutes the stagecoach rolled to a stop before the house, and Adamses filled the

yard. First from the stage was young John, who rushed up to his grandmother and threw his arms around her neck. Then came George, joyfully calling out, "Oh, Grandmother! Oh, Grandmother!" Only Charles hesitated—having been away eight years, he was unable to remember his grandparents; he walked up to them and shook hands. Louisa and John Quincy climbed out and began embracing the relatives. "I had the inexpressible happiness," JQA wrote rather stiffly in his diary, "of finding my venerable father and mother in perfect health."

Aunts and uncles, nieces and nephews soon filled the old farmhouse. Thomas and his wife and five children walked over to

share dinner. The neighbors rode up on horseback and in carriages. Hard cider and wine and Abigail's fine food started a slam-bang good time; everyone ate and celebrated.

For the next twenty-two days the Adamses luxuriated in the welcome and love at the Old House. They put the place in turmoil, Abigail wrote good-naturedly, and her rooms were "covered with trunks, Bookes and papers."

For John Quincy, coming home meant touching once more the verities of his life: his parents, the farm, and the Old House. He swam at Black's Wharf, where he had gone swimming as a youth, and walked the fields and hills of his boyhood. He and Louisa also

An Exceptional Marriage

rode into Boston, which had grown to 32,250 people. There were new shops, and some houses were five stories high and darkened the narrow streets. Bostonians didn't forget: two hundred of them gave a party for John Quincy to wish him well.

Louisa spent her days fishing with her sons and getting to know her husband's parents better. Abigail, now seventy-two, was content at last with home, family, and Louisa. The two women shared a friendly, respectful but wary time talking together, sorting out their differences. "She herself told me she was worried she had not better understood my character," Louisa said, "and she proved herself on every occasion a kind and affectionate Mother." Abigail, in turn, saw in her daughter-in-law a stronger woman than she had first suspected. The pregnancies, the fatiguing court life, the sea voyages, and the journey across Europe impressed Abigail. The two women found they shared much in common, including their mutual ambitions for John Quincy and admiration for each other's inner strengths. Their reconciliation came just in time. Abigail Adams would die in fourteen months from typhoid fever.

The Old Gentleman, as Louisa fondly called John Adams, was almost eighty-two, and blissfully happy planting, pruning, farming. Louisa loved John Adams, and thought him as kind and gentle as a New England Indian summer, a warm exception among the cold Adams men. He never spoke a harsh word to her. He "treated me with the utmost tenderness," she said.

On September 9, 1817, Louisa and John Quincy said good-by to his aged parents and left for Washington. Once again they parted from their sons. John and Charles were enrolled in Mr. Gould's Boston Latin School, and boarded in the city with Dr. and Mrs. Thomas Welsh, who were friends of the family. Ten-year-old Charles briefly rebelled at this first separation from his parents. He tried to remain at Quincy with his grandparents by feigning dysentery, but when Grandmother Abigail brought forth the home remedy of medicine and emetics, Charles's symptoms suddenly disappeared and he went on to Boston. There John drifted into sports—shooting and fishing—while Charles struggled to remain faithful to his books.

George moved into the Cambridge home of Samuel Gilman, a mathematics tutor at Harvard, and he was, at age sixteen, "generally speaking happily situated," he said. Preparing for Harvard's entrance examination would make his life "regular even to monotony." He worked hard, and in February 1818 he took the Harvard examination and was accepted.

So the family had split apart. The young Adams men visited their parents in Washington during school holidays, but they had relied on their grandparents to be their loving family, and the aged John and Abigail were feeble substitutes for parents. The boys' feelings of abandonment were to persist.

In the service of his country, John Quincy Adams thought no sacrifice too great, for himself or for others. This time the separations would exact their price. John Quincy would become an outstanding Secretary of State. But as his political career approached the goal he and his parents had so ardently sought, beneath the strong foundation of service and duty and sacrifice, the Adams dynasty began to show cracks.

LOUISA and John Quincy's trip to Washington took eleven days and cost $237.44, which included porters, hackneys, carriages, six steamboats, and six stagecoaches. At four o'clock in the afternoon of September 20—precisely when Adams had promised President Monroe he would arrive—their stage reached the broad expanse of mud that was Pennsylvania Avenue. John Quincy reported to the President and, two days later, took the oath of office as Secretary of State.

The State Department was located in a large brick building at Seventeenth and G streets, N.W. Nearby were the President's House, War Office, Treasury Department, City Hall, the poorhouse, and the prison. Adams' entire staff consisted of Daniel Brent, his chief clerk, and seven assistant clerks. State Department expenditures totaled just $123,062, which was less than the British Foreign Office spent for its secret service alone. And while Adams earned $3500, his British counterpart, Lord Castlereagh, received about $72,000 a year.

Adams found the State Department in disarray. James Monroe,

his predecessor, had been a bit of a scatterbrain, disliking details. Accounts were in arrears. Correspondence and diplomatic dispatches lay about the office, and important letters had been misplaced. Adams ordered an index prepared of all diplomatic correspondence, and directed that every dispatch from America's ministers abroad be entered, numbered, and summarized—much as he had always directed his family to do with their own private letters. He organized another register for consular correspondence and one for notes from foreign ministers.

Adams was everywhere. He established the State Department library, put together the Secretary's instructions for newly appointed ministers to foreign nations, redesigned the agency's accounting, supervised office routine. He read all dispatches to and from U.S. ministers and consuls abroad, and the notes from foreign representatives in Washington. He drafted and redrafted replies in his own hand.

At home, Louisa copied all of John Quincy's private letters into his letter books, "to save his hand and Eyes," his mother said, "his Eyes being very weak, and his right hand much upon the tremble." This was no small task. Adams replied to every letter and petition from private citizens. He also superintended the census and managed the printing and distribution of all congressional acts and resolutions. He collected the laws of the states and handled extradition warrants and pardons of criminals.

During his seven and a half years as Secretary of State, Adams negotiated several major treaties with the Spanish and British settling the western boundaries and those of Florida and Canada. He also stood firm against Spain and Great Britain at a time when, as Lord Castlereagh later said, "war might have been produced by holding up a finger."

In America, this was a time of nationalism, growth, and energy. The nation's expansion was beginning. Adams himself was a nationalist and a continentalist. On February 22, 1819, he signed the Transcontinental Treaty with Spain. Under the terms of the treaty, Spain ceded to the United States all lands east of the Mississippi; in return, the United States assumed all outstanding claims brought against Spain by American citizens, up to a total of five million dollars. West of the Mississippi, the treaty also fixed the boundary line between the United States and Mexico. So essential were these gains that Adams called the day of the treaty signing "the most important day of my life."

During his years as Secretary, John Quincy Adams also formulated the foreign policy that became the backbone of the Monroe Doctrine—the policy that declared that the United States would not interfere in European affairs and that "the American Continents are not to be considered as subjects for future colonization by any European power."

To perform his many functions, Adams regulated his life. He rose before daybreak, read his Bible, and then exercised, either by walking or, on warm days, swimming. From the house he and Louisa rented for six hundred and fifty dollars a year, Adams strode briskly the mile to an old sycamore and a large rock where Tiber Creek flowed into the Potomac. He would start peeling off his clothes as he approached the tree, then fling them on the riverbank before plunging headfirst into the water. He came up noisily and stroked out about fifteen yards as the sun's first rays played through the wooded shoreline. For almost three decades John Quincy would swim at this spot. Occasionally he was surprised by early-rising residents, such as Stratford Canning, the British ambassador, who reported seeing JQA out for a swim wearing a black cap and a pair of green goggles—and nothing else. After returning home and breakfasting, Adams would walk a mile to the State Department.

As he entered Pennsylvania Avenue, Adams could see the Capitol, with its dome towering eighty feet above the Potomac—held safely above the tidewater, Louisa liked to joke, by the hot air of its inhabitants. John Quincy often stopped in the shops on the avenue. He was not above a wager and sometimes played the horses at the Washington Race Track or paused at Davis & Force to play the lotteries. He was frugal, however, and always bought the cheapest lottery ticket possible, which cost five dollars. The lottery probably attracted him because he was always broke. Although Congress raised his salary to six thousand dollars in 1819, his family expenses exceeded income by at least four thousand dollars every year that he served as Secretary of State. Fortunately Thomas Adams had invested his brother's money wisely during JQA's second European stay, and by 1817 John Quincy showed a personal estate worth one hundred thousand dollars, much of it in land and buildings, a little of it in stocks. He and his family lived off the income from this, plus his meager salary during the rest of his public service. Adams never won a lottery, but he bought his tickets and hoped.

BEFORE James Monroe's first term as President ended in 1820, members of his Cabinet were jostling each other for position in the presidential campaign of 1824 and using Cabinet meetings as a platform. The three leading contenders were Adams; John C. Calhoun of South Carolina, the Secretary of War; and William H. Crawford of Georgia, the Secretary of the Treasury. A fourth candidate was Henry Clay, John Quincy's negotiating partner at Ghent, who now used his position as Speaker of the House to oppose Adams and Monroe. A fifth aspirant, depicted at the time as a dark horse coming up fast, was General Andrew Jackson, the hero of New Orleans, who would win a seat as U.S. senator from Tennessee in 1823.

Adams himself would not campaign for the presidency, although it was the goal of his life and his parents' dream. He wanted the office to come to him, seemingly unsolicited, as a reward for service to his country. There was only one person who could gain for him his coveted place: Louisa. During the elaborate six-year ritual of social activities that marked a campaign without election speeches, Louisa was John Quincy's best asset, filling the position that today would be called campaign manager.

Appropriately, she started her diary in 1818 with this idea from Shakespeare: "All the world's a stage, and all the men and women in it players." She was a major player on the political stage. She paid strategic visits to the wives of congressmen and members of the Cabinet and she spent whole days at home receiving them. At night she and John Quincy maneuvered through dinners, drawing rooms, and balls, always "Smiling." For the next six years there was hardly a single day when Louisa did not campaign for her husband. She often got up from her sickbed, even went out on Christmas Eve and during a driving snowstorm to make these political visits. John Quincy clearly understood the value of her social calls. Every morning he prepared a set of visiting cards, Louisa said, "with as much formality as if he was drawing up some very important article to negotiate in a Commercial Treaty."

What necessitated Adams' interest was the complex process of nominating presidential candidates. No countrywide system prevailed, and anyone could recommend a man for the presidency. In election years, congressmen met in caucus as a nominating convention and in practice virtually selected the President. The system was, however, increasingly unpopular. As John Quincy wrote: "The only chance for a head of Department to attend the Presidency is by ingratiating himself personally with the members of Congress. As many of them have objects of their own to obtain, the temptation to form corrupt coalitions is immense."

The caucus system, in fact, would end after the election of 1824, to be replaced by the national convention. But for as long as the system prevailed, the courting of congressmen was essential to a presidential candidate's aspirations. By 1820 no ball or dinner given by a member of the President's Cabinet could omit its cluster of gentlemen, and their ladies, from Capitol Hill. In 1824 Louisa and John Quincy would boast of having sixty-eight congressmen as steady guests.

Rival social formations created salons loyal to one or another candidate, and there were elaborate formats for attracting followers: games, sideboards heaped with food, an enticing variety of drinks. Wives and daughters read poetry and sang or played instruments. Louisa's drawing rooms mixed American hospitality and European sophistication; she played the harp and pianoforte, and sometimes recited her plays or poems. In a city without much entertainment this was high-class fare. Notables passing through Washington were grabbed by eager hostesses, and such celebrated writers as James Fenimore Cooper and Washington Irving became major salon attractions.

Louisa opened her home every Tuesday evening during the social season, and the wine and entertainment attracted promi-

An Exceptional Marriage

nent members of Congress and the Cabinet. Among the men, mustaches, muttonchop whiskers, epaulets, and high starched collars were the fashion. "Greek fever" was sweeping America, and women wore adaptations of Greek costumes, with turbans of spangled muslin or drooping ostrich plumes in their hair, and low-cut gowns with trailing skirts.

To entertain their guests and to attend social engagements, the Adamses spared little expense. Musicians cost twenty dollars a party, and members of the marine corps band received five dollars apiece. The Adamses had the piano tuned regularly ($1.50), replaced the carpeting every year ($120), paid grocer's, baker's, miller's, and butcher's bills, and maintained horses, coachmen, and carriages for transporting themselves about Washington on visits and to parties. The cost of tailoring the coachman's uniform ($34.17) almost equaled his yearly salary ($36). The Adamses bought hogsheads of wine (at $29 each), and coal twice a winter ($56 each time). They bought calling cards ($8) and a new door knocker ($2.50) to announce the guests' arrival.

Just how valuable were their Tuesday entertainments and Louisa's visits? It is safe to say that John Quincy Adams would not have been elected President without them. Louisa carefully planned each evening, and with her charm, wit, and beauty she compensated for her socially backward husband. John Quincy Adams' social manner was as dull as granite. He greeted everyone solemnly with an old pump-handle shake of the hand. He disliked changing his conduct or clothes to suit the fashion; intellectually he was fastidious and arrogant, and often offended guests. He was self-righteous, dogmatic, filled with wrath, forgetful of small courtesies. At least one visitor wondered whether he ever laughed. Understanding well his own weaknesses, John Quincy relied upon Louisa's gracious manners to offset his own stony silences.

But Louisa was uncomfortable in this role. She did not like large gatherings and struggled always to overcome her lifelong shyness. She hated the visits, the attention, the loss of privacy, the gossip. Why, then, did she do it? First, because of an obligation to her husband: as a man, his life came before hers, and Louisa's place in the family was behind those of her husband

and her children. Second, she was as ambitious for John Quincy as he was for himself. Third, achieving JQA's goal also gave Louisa a new identity: if he became President, she became First Lady. And finally, Louisa's role in her husband's campaign gave her definition, a purpose. She was no longer merely wife, mother, household supervisor, or ornament. So completely did John Quincy depend upon her that for a few years, in the center of her crowded rooms, playing for the high political stakes that always fascinated her, Louisa Adams was an important person in her own right. Campaigning for her husband, she could travel about Washington freely, and her opinions were observed and sought. She clearly understood the boundary lines of her life, but she constantly sought to extend them a little farther.

CHAPTER TWO

DURING these years, John Quincy continued writing to his children, detailing their studies, habits, duties. He fumed over their defects, real or imaginary, and preached at his sons constantly to rise early, be punctual, attend church, keep diaries. But they almost always failed him.

Each son went to Harvard, but only George did well. He won the Boylston Prize in his junior year—defeating Ralph Waldo Emerson—and, significantly, it was his grandfather who praised him, not his father. "Our George," John Adams wrote proudly to JQA, "has gained the first prize, and bears his honour meekly. He is a dutiful son." After graduation, George went on to study law in Boston under Daniel Webster.

John entered Harvard in 1819, and underwent a four-year struggle; he complained often of having to study hard and of not receiving a large enough allowance. John Quincy accused him of taking "dissipation and extravagance" as his twin companions. When Adams learned that John stood forty-fifth in a class of eighty-five, he refused to allow his son to come home during Christmas. He must stay in Cambridge and study. "I could take no satisfaction in seeing you," he wrote. "I could feel nothing but sorrow and shame in your presence." Even when John rose to sixteenth in his class, his father was not satisfied; if he stood lower than fifth, the boy was told, his father would not attend his commencement. John Quincy never got to carry out his threat. John was expelled from Harvard in 1823 for participating in a student riot, after which he returned to Washington to his parents.

Charles entered Harvard at age fourteen. By the end of his freshman term he was fifty-first out of fifty-nine students. He pleaded to be allowed to quit college, confessing that he was "addicted to depraved habits," such as smoking cigars, playing billiards, and drinking wine. Had John or George confessed to drinking and billiards, and languished at the bottom of their classes, John Quincy's wrath would have seared them. Instead, Charles was told that whatever his standing, if he would only employ his time at his studies, his father would be satisfied. Charles graduated in 1825, within hailing distance of the upper ranks of his class. He then moved to Washington to study law under his father.

Throughout these years, Louisa and John Quincy also raised nieces and nephews, and endured daily turmoil in their home. In 1818 the three orphaned children of Louisa's sister Nancy Hellen—Johnson, Thomas, and Mary—moved into the Adamses' house, giving them two additional rebellious young men to raise. The flirtatious Mary romantically entangled each of JQA's sons before finally marrying John.

Adams as well as Johnson children joined the family. Abigail Adams Smith, Nabby's oldest, stayed with the Adamses for long periods. And when Thomas Adams started drinking heavily and became violent, his daughters, Elizabeth and Abigail 2d, and his sons, Isaac Hull and John Quincy 2d, also took shelter with Louisa and John Quincy. The Adamses fed, clothed, educated, and cared for them all, treating each child like their own, perhaps better. Their doors were always open, and each guest remained as long as he or she wished.

BY THE winter of 1821 to 1822, when Louisa turned forty-seven, the rounds of society, the turbulence of the household, and the burdens of public life were making her physically and emo tionally ill. She suffered from several painful ailments. Hemorrhoids troubled her greatly, and she complained of erysipelas, a disease whose symptoms included rapidly rising fever, a "nervous irritability," and severe swelling of a hard ridge across the forehead. Louisa's face puffed until her eyelids closed; the disease so inflamed her hands and feet that she could not write or walk comfortably for several days after an attack, or meet her political obligations. She worried that many new members of Congress did not know her or her husband.

This was a time when diseases of every description scourged the United States. Doctors understood little about illness, and the medicines they dispensed were of dubious help and often harmful. Pulmonary consumption was regarded as incurable, and dyspepsia was thought to be caused by "ardent spirits" in salt meat and by spoiled cooking. Doctors said that gout followed gluttony, drunkenness, and debauchery. Physicians and clergy together assured people that cholera was divine punishment for sin.

The great medicine of the day was mercury; Louisa sometimes worried that she would be killed by an overdose. Doctors also gave opium freely, and patient-addicts were common. Some diseases were thought to be caused by bad humors and bile, and doctors thought that bloodletting lessened "the morbid and excessive action in the blood vessels," eased pain, induced sleep, and prevented hemorrhages.

Louisa often served as doctor in her home. She kept a well-stocked medicine chest, which contained six shelves displaying labeled bottles and vials. Included were castor oil, medicinal wines, tincture of rhubarb, paregoric, Peruvian bark, epsom salts, niter, spirits of hartshorn, spirits of turpentine, camphor, laudanum—tincture of opium—ether, tincture of steel, arsenic, oil of wormseed, essence of peppermint.

In the spring of 1822 Louisa's brother, Thomas Baker Johnson, who was postmaster of New Orleans, arrived in Washington to seek Louisa's medical advice. Like her, he was suffering from hemorrhoids. Louisa, he knew, was not only a good physician, but she and John Quincy were also acquainted with some of the best doctors in America. Thus, when Louisa was unable to remedy

An Exceptional Marriage

either her brother's poor health or her own, the two of them agreed to see a surgeon. The decision was difficult in those times of no sterile instruments and no anesthesia. The patient lay conscious upon a table, often in excruciating pain, held down by attendants. The best surgeon, therefore, was the one who could cut most rapidly.

In 1822 that person was a Philadelphia doctor with the felicitous name of Philip Syng Physick. He had a precise knowledge of anatomy and the "feel" of human tissue. He was decisive, quick, and accurate. It was to see Dr. Physick that Louisa, with her niece Mary Hellen and her brother, Thomas, left for Philadelphia on June 21.

Louisa called Dr. Physick "one of the great men of our age"—wisely leaving room for her husband. And a fellow surgeon proclaimed that the doctor "could even talk away disease."

Dr. Physick had won an international reputation for his surgical technique. He had performed his first lithotomy, cutting for stones in the bladder, in 1797. He had improved on the instruments of his profession, developing new methods of traction for dislocations and new treatments for hip-joint disease. He designed wood splints for major fractures of the femur and ankle, as well as pewter syringes and flexible catheters. Dr. Physick also designed the guillotine tonsillotome for the removal of tonsils, and a form of wire snare, a double cannula, to slough tumors—an instrument that would soon greatly interest Louisa Adams and Thomas Johnson.

But Philip Physick was also a man of eccentricities. He insisted upon strict diets: he ordered a woman with breast cancer to eat only a piece of dry bread with a little salt and to drink a glass of cold water three times a day. No one was certain whether the cancer or starvation got her first. Dr. Physick permitted no discussion of his treatments. When one patient complained of innumerable bleedings, the doctor reached for his coat. "Sir," he said, "I must have my own way, or none at all. I bid you good day." Dr. Physick knew the human body, but he little understood the human heart. In 1800 he had married Elizabeth Emlen, and they produced two daughters, two sons, and one of the earliest divorces in America. Philip Physick had insisted upon keeping the windows of their home closed, even in summer, and he always slept with gloves on to improve his surgical feel. His behavior drove his wife to drink, and they separated in 1818.

As soon as Louisa and Thomas arrived in Philadelphia, they went to Dr. Physick's office on Mulberry Street, where the doctor greeted them stiffly. Physick was then fifty-four, of medium build with a high forehead. He wore his hair "powdered and clubbed" in a queue that concealed enormous ears. He had a large nose, penetrating hazel eyes, and a wide mouth.

Dr. Physick diagnosed Thomas Johnson's case as "a dreadful one," Louisa wrote. The question of "a painful operation" was postponed until Thomas could gain the strength to bear it. But "the Dr. says he looks at Thomas with astonishment, for his sufferings are beyond description. He assures me that nothing will do but the Knife." Dr. Physick also assured Louisa that he had never lost a patient in such an operation.

Louisa liked and trusted Philip Physick, and she asked him to examine her hemorrhoids, too. Dr. Physick did, and concluded that sooner or later she must have the same operation as Thomas. But Louisa feared the knife. "I am not in a hurry to do anything in so unpleasant a business," she wrote John Quincy, "and shall certainly take time to think about it."

Louisa and Thomas were well aware that surgery carried great risks. The basic surgical tools consisted of several large amputation knives, chisels, hammers, and scalpels. Doctors operated in street clothes, in homes or boardinghouses, on conscious patients. The best Thomas and Louisa might hope for in the way of anesthesia was thirty drops of laudanum and a glass of cherry bounce. Sterilization was unknown, and infection a great killer. The certainty of fatal infection precluded major operations, and almost all surgery performed was limited to the surface of the body, superficial orifices, and the extremities.

Dr. Physick ordered Louisa, Mary, and Thomas into Miss Pardon's boardinghouse in the heart of Philadelphia, where he lodged his patients. There they lived comfortably, said Louisa, "at five dollars a week a head, and we propose to stay here as quietly as possible until he decides when the dreadful business can be done." Physick had selected the location of their living quarters, Louisa learned, because he "never knew it to be unhealthy in this part of the city." They could not leave Philadelphia without his permission, for Dr. Physick believed that the countryside contained bad air and fevers. When one patient, a Mrs. Weston, disobeyed and slipped out of Philadelphia, she got as far as Trenton, New Jersey, before suddenly dropping dead. The lesson impressed those people left behind in the Sixth Street boardinghouse.

A heavy "overpowering" summer heat settled upon the city, and Dr. Physick postponed the operation until the temperature went down. In the interim, he prescribed a "rigid diet." For two weeks Thomas could eat nothing but Iceland moss, a lichen, "which is a powerful stomachice," Louisa wrote to John Quincy, "and which appears to agree with him, although it is very nauseous to the taste." The diet required so much preparation, including cooking for eight to ten hours, that Louisa and Mary became prisoners to the cookpot.

While they waited for the heat to lift, Louisa read the newspapers and Dr. Benjamin Rush's *Medical Inquiries and Observations upon Diseases of the Mind.* If her family was driving her "raving mad," as she said, she wanted to know why. Louisa reached the comforting conclusion "that we all have a Crack."

She also procured an old piano "to strum on." Soon the boardinghouse resounded with "By the Side of the Weeping Willow," "The Hunters of the Alps," and "Ah! Why Did I Gather this Delicate Flower?"

During the first week of August, rains washed the heat from Philadelphia, and Dr. Physick deemed it cool enough to operate on Thomas Johnson. The surgery was performed on August 7 "with the utmost success," Louisa wrote, "and giving great hopes of recovery of our poor patient." Thomas suffered a few hours "of great anguish" and passed "a wretched night," but was soon cheerful.

There were still four or five tumors remaining, and on the seventeenth Dr. Physick cut again. This time Thomas suffered "great anguish" for two hours, and Louisa gave him a dose of laudanum, which calmed "the irritation of his nerves."

She, however, was soon bored by the endless nursing of Thomas, who, she said, fancied himself "afflicted with every disease under the Sun." So she left with her young niece, Mary, by steamboat for a short holiday up the Delaware River to visit friends in Bordentown, a quaint New Jersey spa.

Louisa filled her days with exercise and fun. She rowed, fished, and walked; it was as though she were young again, unencumbered by social dress or conformities. She strolled to the spring for healthful drinks, read in the evenings, or played whist. She gained strength, and put her physical troubles aside. About her holiday Louisa wrote to John Quincy: "Nearly ten weeks of my time since I left home have been spent in pain and anxiety, but this week has been one in which I have lived a year."

Louisa needed her renewed strength. Immediately after she returned to Philadelphia, Dr. Physick operated on her at Miss Pardon's boardinghouse. To extract Louisa's tumors, Dr. Physick employed the soft-wire snare he had invented. The procedure worked "marvelously well," he reported. Louisa suffered extreme pain, but neither she nor the doctor recorded that she cried out or fainted.

She recovered quickly, and on October 2 she wrote John Quincy: "Dr. Physick is unwilling to part with me, as he does not think the operation completed. As however I am very well, I did not think it worth while to suffer again, as it really reduced me to a shadow." Her brother, Thomas, she said, was "a new man." Louisa, Mary, and Thomas left Philadelphia in early October and made their way back to Washington as the leaves on the trees were turning.

CHAPTER THREE

DURING the final months of the presidential campaign, Louisa renewed her efforts for her husband's success. In January 1823 she proclaimed, "My health is uncommonly good this winter and my spirits are proportionately high." At one party that month,

An Exceptional Marriage

she enjoyed "as complete a frolick as you ever witnessed, singing, dancing, playing and laughing. I doubt if the youngest of that party enjoyed it more."

The Adamses had bought a three-story house at 244 F Street. They hired carpenters and built an addition that included a coach house, a stable, and a large area that served as drawing room and ballroom, where six sets of guests could dance cotillions at the same time. This allowed for entertainment on a grand scale, and the new house, said Louisa, was often "crowded to overflowing."

The Adamses decided to give a ball for General Andrew Jackson, who was JQA's rival for the presidency, but whom Adams revered as a patriot. The Jackson Ball was to be held on January 8, 1824, the ninth anniversary of the Battle of New Orleans. The Adamses ordered five hundred invitations; theirs would be the largest party of the season, and it marked a major step in the campaign; it was a recognition of the fact that with Crawford suffering from a stroke, and Calhoun and Clay trailing, Jackson and Adams were the leading presidential candidates.

Immediately after the first of the year, Louisa began preparations for the ball. Charles bemoaned his mother's turning the house "topsy turvey." She had twelve pillars hammered into place under the lower floor to support the weight of the guests. She set her sons and the other young people to work weaving laurel wreaths. By the sixth of January the house was "all in disorder," and the Adamses had to dine in Louisa's dressing room. They had planned to open only four rooms to the party, but Louisa was besieged for invitations, and as the guest list increased, they soon needed eight. A pantry was temporarily removed, and Louisa shifted her own chambers to the third floor.

The day before the ball everyone except John Quincy was busily constructing wreaths. Louisa directed the last-minute preparations and got so excited that Charles thought she might faint. On the morning of the eighth the wreath making went on in a frenzy; Louisa oversaw all the work, the placing of the wreaths, the arranging of the dinner table. There would be so many guests, they would eat standing up. Doors were removed from the four lower rooms, and when the house was finally ready in the late afternoon, it was filled with flowers and greenery and had a feeling of space and light. The Adamses ate dinner at four, and by six were ready.

The Jackson Ball was perhaps the largest of the decade. Louisa had eventually sent out more than nine hundred invitations. Andrew Jackson, said Louisa, was "a magnet so powerful as to attract not only all the Strangers but even the old residents of the City who never thought of coming to see us before." Only President and Mrs. Monroe, whose custom it was not to visit private homes, and the indisposed Crawford stayed away. Clay and Calhoun, and their ladies, arrived early. At about nine o'clock General Jackson pulled up in his carriage. The eight large rooms were already overflowing. The upper floors were packed "to suffocation," and the newcomers found the house filled with "at least a thousand people."

The four lower rooms were hung with the laurel wreaths entwined with roses. Garlands of evergreens had been wrapped around the pillars, and even the bookcases in John Quincy's study were camouflaged with pots of flowers. The rooms were filled with the pungent smell of candles, oil lamps, roses, and ladies' perfume. The drawing room was festooned with evergreen garlands, which cascaded from the chandelier to the pillars. On the floor beneath the chandelier, an artist had created a chalk painting of eagles, flags, and military emblems, with the words "Welcome to the Hero of New Orleans" intertwined. The women were brilliantly gowned and jeweled, and all the men except John Quincy Adams "wore full dress attire—blue coats, gilt buttons, white or buff waistcoats, white neckties, high chokers, white trousers, silk stockings, and pumps."

Louisa Adams met General Jackson at the front door, where she had stationed herself to watch for him, and she took him around the rooms, introducing him to the guests. Jackson was visibly impressed with the ornate decor, and flattered; and Louisa shared the center of attraction with him. *Harper's Bazaar* later reported she was wearing "a suit of steel. The dress was composed of steel lamé; her ornaments for head, throat and arms were

An Exceptional Marriage

all of cut steel, producing a dazzling effect. General Jackson was her devoted attendant during the evening, and caused much comment." The supper tables, opened at nine thirty, were laden with "natural and candied fruits, pies, sweetmeats, tongues, game, etc. prepared in French style, and arranged with most exquisite taste." The general managed to shout a toast to Louisa above the din, and most of the guests found space to raise their glasses. After the supper, Jackson did not stay long; there were also bonfires and fireworks in his honor that evening: Americans still thought Jackson's victory in New Orleans, and not Adams' treaty at Ghent, had ended the War of 1812.

"The dancing continued until one in the morning," John Quincy wrote in his diary. "The crowd was great and the house could scarcely contain the company." The last guest left at two, "all in good humour," said Louisa. She felt satisfied. The Jackson Ball had been a smashing success.

PART V

Washington, 1825–1830

CHAPTER ONE

IN THE presidential election of 1824, Jackson won ninety-nine votes in the Electoral College, Adams eighty-four, Crawford forty-one, and Clay thirty-seven. Calhoun, who had dropped out of the presidential race in March to run for Vice-President, won that office. Since no presidential contender had the required majority of electoral votes, the top three men turned to the House of Representatives for a decision, and the weeks preceding it were marked by backstairs wheeling and dealing. Realizing that the presidency might not come to him unless he actively sought it, John Quincy Adams glad-handed those who might help him and dropped in on congressmen at their boardinghouses and hotels to solicit their support.

On January 9 the maneuvering for House votes got under way. That evening JQA and Henry Clay met at Adams' house and what took place swung the election. Although Clay could no longer win the presidency for himself, he was in a powerful position as House Speaker to help someone else. But in exchange for what? Clay, John Quincy recorded in his diary, assured Adams that among "General Jackson, Mr. Crawford and myself, his preference would be for me." Clay also mentioned, with some apparent disgust, that certain friends, without Adams' authority of course, approached him with suggestions of impropriety. From John Quincy's brief account it is clear that such "personal considerations" also entered that evening's conversation. Historians have concluded that the two men reached an understanding: that for his support of Adams in the House election, Clay would be appointed Secretary of State. Such an agreement was essential to John Quincy Adams' victory. Clay controlled the Kentucky, Missouri, Illinois, and Ohio delegations.

Meantime, word also went out to Daniel Webster that if the Federalists of Delaware and Maryland marched into the Adams camp, the post of minister to Great Britain, which Webster shamelessly coveted, might be his. Adams was playing politics the way Clay, that "gamester," played.

The balloting took place in the House on February 9, 1825. Everything that could be done had been done. Webster had lined up the Federalists for Adams. Clay delivered the votes of Ohio, Kentucky, even Louisiana. But the burden of the election fell finally upon Stephen Van Rensselaer of New York, "a kindly, upright, simple old Federalist gentleman." Van Rensselaer was thought to be a Crawford man, and indeed had said that nothing could persuade him to vote for Adams. But when he arrived at the Capitol on the ninth, he was grabbed by Clay and taken to the Speaker's room. There Webster awaited them, and those two, Van Rensselaer later wrote, "could not be resisted."

The first ballot, with Van Rensselaer's help, gave Adams the votes of thirteen states; Jackson, seven; and Crawford, four. The Speaker of the House, Henry Clay, rose from his seat and intoned, "John Quincy Adams, having a majority of the votes of these United States, is duly elected President of the United States." Light clapping in the gallery dissolved to loud hissing by Crawford supporters. Disappointed by Van Rensselaer's vote, they yelled "treachery and cowardice," and later one said, "It's enough to make a saint swear!"

Two days after the election, John Quincy Adams told President Monroe that Henry Clay would be his choice for Secretary of State. It was a suspicious capstone to this precarious election, for every President since John Adams had first served as Secretary of State. Monroe, however, remained polite and silent.

In his diary, John Quincy admitted that he had not been elected in "a manner satisfactory to pride or just desire, but with perhaps two thirds of the whole people adverse to the actual result." Adams and Clay would spend their lives refuting the accusation that "bargain and corruption" had won for them the presidency and the State Department.

JOHN Quincy Adams, the sixth President of the United States, had achieved his dream. He now set forth to bind up sectional differences and to establish a national program of internal improvements. But his plans proved too bold and required of him skills he never had, and they came too early in America's history. Instead of triumph, Adams' four years as President were marked by political miscalculation and personal sadness.

In his first annual message to Congress, on December 6, 1825, Adams called for the founding of a national university, the establishment of a uniform standard of weights and measures, the building of a national astronomical observatory, the creation of a Department of the Interior, and the undertaking of a large-scale development program that included canals and highways. The speech was met with hostility, for it came at a time when most Americans wanted less government, not more. Adams' proposals recalled Patrick Henry's warning of a "great magnificent government" overwhelming the rights of the states, and it raised this specter just as men of the South were realizing that their "peculiar institution" of slavery might be in peril. Vice-President Calhoun, in fact, suspected that Adams' inner desire was to abolish slavery.

The President compounded his misreading of American sentiments by citing the example of "the nations of Europe and their rulers," an unfortunate echo of his father, who had long ago been labeled a monarchist by some of the men now listening to JQA. The American people accused Adams of seeking power for himself, and greeted his ideas with mockery. Far worse, Congress rejected every one of his proposals.

John Quincy Adams had not the talent or patience to be, as he wished, "a Man of the Whole Country." From the outset, he aroused sectionalism by stumbling over such obstacles as the disposal of public lands in the West, the removal of Indians from Georgia, and the passage of a tariff so loaded with favors to the North and so damaging to the South that it became known as the Tariff of Abominations.

Life in the White House, as it was now called, quickly degenerated to a lonely existence. The building itself stood upon bare open land and had neither running water nor indoor plumbing. Monroe had taken much of the furniture with him, and the rooms were almost empty when the Adamses arrived. But Congress had appropriated fourteen thousand dollars to furnish the mansion, and Adams moved in some of his old furniture, bought a set of silver plate from Crawford, and, unwisely as it turned out, added a secondhand billiard table.

Louisa and John Quincy lived quietly. Often their evenings were marked by loneliness or the President's dozing off while reading. They seldom went out socially, and during the season, they gave dinners once a week, fortnightly receptions, and an occasional ball, plus the traditional New Year's open house.

On some occasions, when Adams let himself relax, he enjoyed discussing literature, science, painting, classical poetry—even the vintages of wines. But too often he remained his usual dull self. One guest, after encountering a bored and sleepy President, wrote this doggerel, which found its way into Louisa's notebook, perhaps because it caught a response in her as well:

> *Asked by the Nation's chief to take my tea,*
> *I hastened to him in surprising glee,*
> *But when I got there, all my treat, by God,*
> *Is just to watch His Excellency's Nod.*

An Exceptional Marriage

John Quincy continued to analyze his own shortcomings. "I was not satisfied with myself this day," he wrote in his diary, "having talked too much at dinner. Nor can I always—I did not this day—altogether avoid a dogmatic tone and manner, always offensive in persons to whose age or situation others consider some deference due."

From his diary we learn that President Adams allowed himself an hour for breakfast, skipped lunch, and took two hours for dinner. He spent two hours in the morning exercising, then from ten to five tended to business. The Secretary of the Treasury might confer with him on questions of revenue law. The Secretary of War might place before him lists of promotions in the army, courts-martial proceedings, Indian treaties. The Secretary of the Navy might come by with dispatches from commanders at sea. Adams also read dispatches from U.S. ministers overseas, State Department instructions, and other correspondence. There were twelve to fifteen newspapers to read, letters to be answered, and state papers flowing by so fast he complained of having only time to sign his name and move on. Intruding on all this was a steady stream of visitors soliciting favors or office.

The four evening hours John Quincy thought "the least effective of the day," when he was "usually weary and heavy laden." He disliked dinner parties and receptions, as he always had. He never had enough time to catch up on his letter writing or diary or reading, before going to bed promptly at eleven.

Halfway through his presidency John Quincy faced a hostile Congress. With the elections in 1826, his opponents captured a majority in Congress. In effect, Adams became a minority President, and to put together his programs he would need the cooperation of his rivals. He never had it. "I fell," he wrote with sadness, "and with me fell, I fear never to rise again in my day, the system of international improvement by means of national energies."

For the first time in the nation's history both houses of Congress contained a majority of members opposed to the President. One fourth of the congressmen even refused to pay courtesy calls on President and Mrs. Adams. John Quincy confided to his diary: "My own career is closed." He grew depressed and lost weight. He looked forward only to his annual trips to Quincy, between August and October. He traveled quietly and made only two public speeches in his entire four years in office. Increasingly bitter, he awaited an inevitable second-term defeat. Adams would be the second President in U.S. history not to win reelection. His father had been the first.

LOUISA Adams' dream—of becoming her own person—ended with her husband's election. Once the campaign was over, so was her unique moment, her special status. As First Lady she had little to do, other than meaningless entertainments, and her four years in the White House were years of psychological imprisonment. Charles thought his mother more sad and depressed after 1825, and said that she lost her "elasticity of character."

Small and physically frail, Louisa now exemplified a self-fulfilling prophecy about American women, who were depicted as weak, sickly, needing protection. Widespread illness began to appear among them at this time. Catharine Beecher, a woman who herself suffered from "extreme prostration of the overworked brain and nerves," undertook a study. After visiting women in many towns, she concluded: "There is a terrible decay of Female health all over the land." The principal causes were women's confinement, lack of exercise, and isolation. Men controlled how women lived, where they went, what they said in public; even a woman's clothing—sharp whalebone stays and pinching corsets—restricted her.

Like other American women, Louisa Adams spent days, sometimes weeks, in her chambers. Shut up in the White House, which she hated, she complained that "I am now always cross and unpleasant, to myself and to everybody else." Each winter she developed coughs and pain in her chest. Enclosed in her unventilated rooms, she breathed the fumes of coal stoves and fireplaces for several months of every year, and sometimes joked about having the "Lehigh Coal Catarrh." She was certain that she regained her strength with spring, when she could walk outside. Since women were confined far more than men, they

An Exceptional Marriage

suffered far more the ravages of poorly ventilated quarters.

Louisa, and other women whose activities were restricted, suffered from excessive sentimentality and melancholia. Their preoccupation with death and illness filled diaries and seeped into newsprint. "Nervous exhaustion" and "nervous prostration" became terms to cover a woman's inability to deal with her own life. The symptoms—nausea, dizziness, fainting spells, backaches, and partial paralysis—are well known today as manifestations of neurosis, hysteria, anger, and anxiety.

In a desperate episode during her White House years, Louisa turned to her son Charles for help. She complained of having nothing to do, no one to "break the dreadful tedium of an almost entire solitude." She begged Charles for "some French book to translate by way of occupation, as I cannot bear the loneliness of my life." But Charles, like the other Adams men, offered Louisa nothing in the way of understanding or comfort. He knew of no French book for her, and replied that hers "was the lot of every woman after she has attained a certain age."

Louisa continued bored, isolated, and angry. She played with skill the role of a sickly woman who could faint when she thought it appropriate. Her husband and sons considered her a hypochondriac given to melancholia and "fits," but they never bothered to ask why. Louisa, once so strong and resilient, became a self-pitying recluse. Alone in her chambers, she sometimes wrote plays and poems, and wallowed in outrageous descriptions of her own ill health, ending with her glorious, widely bewailed, always untimely death.

In the White House, Louisa Adams went on a chocolate-eating binge. She spoiled herself with it. Devouring it occupied time and comforted her by recalling a childhood when she got what she wanted. Never gaining weight, she surrendered nothing of her physical beauty to chocolate, except perhaps her teeth. She had started eating chocolate in her teens; by adulthood she had few teeth left and carried dentures around with her in a bottle. False teeth, however, did not discourage her from eating more chocolate. She demanded its deliciousness, gorged on it. She ended many of her letters to Charles and George and John

Quincy with a postscript requesting that they send her chocolate from Boston immediately. And they almost always complied.

One can picture Louisa in the White House, chocolates at hand, writing her poems, essays, and letters. In 1825 she started writing her autobiographical *Record of a Life, or My Story,* which formed a basic source for the present book. She also wrote melodramas that opposed passion and glorified female purity and blissful domesticity.

A theme that began emerging in Louisa's writings at this time was the right of women to be free from domination by men. Her sensitivity to "rights" was never far from the surface, and in September 1825 she boiled over when she read a newspaper account about a poor servant girl who had been seduced by her master. Louisa wrote her son George a long letter detailing the case. This girl had lived "in the constant hope that her master would marry her." But when, "to the poor girl's utter horror and consternation," he married a prettier maiden, she drank quicksilver and "died in dreadful agony."

The event truly angered Louisa. Newspapers portrayed the girl as dying for love. Louisa saw it differently: the woman had died without love, seduced and discarded by a man now "revelling in all the enjoyments of life" while the servant girl was "borne to the grave without a friend."

Women's right to freedom was not a new concern of Louisa's. Constant acquiescence to her husband's demands had long forced her to ponder the question, How can a woman control her own life? Was she, Louisa asked, any different from the servant girl?

IN BOSTON, meanwhile, George had started a process of unraveling that was to last four years. It was marked by a series of small failures that left his parents increasingly frustrated and angry. Gentle, never loved enough or needed at all, George lived in a fantasy world. He shared his mother's interest in fiction, and developed a taste for narratives of crime and mystery that summoned fully his imagination.

George loved his grandfather Adams, and wanted so much to be a hero like him and to make the old man proud that in his

An Exceptional Marriage

third year at Harvard he had joined the student rioting, convinced that he was gloriously resisting tyranny as his grandfather had done in 1776. But as much as he loved his grandfather, George feared his father. This feeling permeated every moment of his life. When George was attracted to a young woman during his freshman year, for example, he quickly ended the romance after having a dream in which, as he kissed his love, his father suddenly appeared and scolded him, "Remember, George, who you are, and what you are doing."

By 1825 George had finished reading law for Daniel Webster. He opened an office at 10 Court Street in Boston, and boarded with the same Dr. Welsh that John and Charles had stayed with earlier. To get him started, John Quincy placed George in charge of the family's financial accounts. But George soon fell behind in this work, and JQA wrote him nasty letters.

The father tried unceasingly to improve his son. He instructed George to study harder, rise early, attend church, be temperate. He demanded that George keep a diary, and in 1825 the young lawyer dutifully took up his pen. But where John Quincy Adams' diary would stretch over sixty-seven years, George kept at his for only twenty-three days.

George began with strong resolution. He divided his day into two parts: the morning for law and his father's accounts; the afternoon for reading. It was all in vain. George rose late, idled with his grandfather in Quincy, and napped in the hot August afternoons. His indifference to his law practice deteriorated into incompetence. Even a simple trip to the bank took on aspects of a comic routine: George forgot the order form, returned to his office, and on the way back to the bank got a speck of brick dust in his eye. He found the eye so troublesome that, he said, "I determined to humour it and try to escape from the suffering by sleep. I slept two hours and for this do not feel any dissatisfaction or self reproach."

There was something wonderfully human about George Adams. His brief diary reveals a gentle, delicate, lost soul open to his inner feelings. In one entry, for instance, he describes reading Dante's "Inferno" to a group of ladies, and becoming so upset with the passages of "intense suffering" that he had to stop and step outside to breathe the evening air.

Fantasizing about women, George soared to romantic heights. During visits to Washington between 1820 and 1823, he had awkwardly courted his cousin Mary Hellen, and in the summer of 1823 he had asked his father's permission to become engaged. George assured JQA that the marriage would wait until his law practice was established, "in perhaps four or five years."

John Quincy had reluctantly consented, but during the next three years, George seldom traveled to Washington to see Mary and wrote to her infrequently. Worse, Mary proved to be, as Charles described her, "one of the most capricious women that was ever formed." She openly flirted with Charles and then with John. The best-looking of the three Adams sons, John was a self-centered young man who treated Mary's engagement to George as "an utter absurdity." Mary, in turn, thought John magnetic; with George in Boston and Charles now at Harvard, John was also conveniently handy.

Charles and George took long walks in the gardens at Quincy, discussing Mary, and Charles foresaw "a good deal of trouble" in his brother's intended match. So did Louisa, and when the family gathered in Quincy in September 1824 for a dinner with old John Adams, she pulled Charles aside and told him she could not keep John and Mary apart much longer. She urged him to cause George to "terminate" the union. Owing to Louisa's conspiracy with Charles, George's engagement to Mary ended, although George was never actually told so by Mary nor she by him. The whole thing simply melted away.

George's diary now contained the words "dejection" and "much depressed." He made a final entry on December 31, 1825. He regretted that keeping a regular diary was beyond his ability or desire, and lamented the distractions that diverted him and the past irresolution that "has recently alarmed me by its gradual expansion." George prayed to be delivered—from his tyrannical father.

Instead of easing pressure on George, however, John Quincy increased it. In the spring of 1826 George won election to the

An Exceptional Marriage

Massachusetts state legislature, a brave step into what Charles called "the ocean of political life." John Quincy, after congratulating George, began issuing a list of warnings and advice that continued into the autumn. "Arm yourself with fortitude," the President told his son. "Prepare and discipline your mind for disappointment." The list went on and on. Read Plutarch, acquire knowledge of politics, know the laws of your state, cultivate the governor; employ "all the Stoic virtues—Prudence, Temperance, Fortitude, Justice." John Quincy never let up. No one could have satisfied his requests: he sent forms from the family insurance company, inquiries about stock for sale, demands for a list of deeds or vouchers, questions concerning the operation of the farm in Quincy.

But George, who liked to nap and smoke cigars and visit, slipped behind in his accounts. He sent neither list nor answers. To John Quincy's repeated inquiries about their business interests, George replied with silence.

CHAPTER TWO

THE death of John Adams set off a sequence of events that tore his son's family apart. In his last days the old patriot wished nothing more than to survive to July 4, 1826, the fiftieth anniversary of the signing of the Declaration of Independence. On the morning of the Fourth, after his granddaughter bent to his pillow and told him the date, Adams rested peacefully. At about one o'clock in the afternoon he whispered, "Jefferson still survives." Those were his last words.

When George had learned that his beloved grandfather was dying, he had hurried from Boston to Quincy to be with him. The old man recognized his favorite grandson. George stayed with Grandpapa, the man who had raised him and loved him, until the old gentleman died at six thirty that day, "as calmly," George wrote his father, "as an infant sleeps."

In Washington, the second President Adams spent the day listening to the July 4 commemorative ceremonies. Unknown to him then, his father lay dying in Quincy and Thomas Jefferson

was slipping into death at Monticello in Virginia. At one o'clock, as John Adams spoke his final words, Jefferson died. The details of the deaths of these two men—on the fiftieth anniversary of the Declaration of Independence—enthralled the nation. That each in his final hours had the great day in mind made the event more dramatic.

In Massachusetts a week later, as John Quincy entered his father's empty bedchamber, the loss struck him a blow. "That moment was inexpressively painful," JQA wrote in his diary. In this room the two men had shared opinions, political news, and strategy; here they had said good-by for the last time. The wisdom, the counsel, the sage advice would be heard no more.

The disposition of John Adams' will set off a snapping, summerlong feud between Louisa and John Quincy. The old gentleman had left JQA the family homestead and one hundred and three acres of land surrounding it. But John Quincy would have to pay the estate twelve thousand dollars to possess the property. Further, he would have to pay his brother, Thomas, half the value of their father's books, papers, and portraits. Meeting the conditions of the will meant that JQA would have to go "heavily into debt," he wrote to Louisa, but he decided to do it.

Louisa vehemently opposed this. "That you should be desirous of owning the House that was your Fathers is natural," she wrote him, "but that you should waste your property and burthen yourself with a large unprofitable landed estate is scarcely prudent." John Quincy reacted in anger: he planned to survey the lands and to inventory the estate, he told Louisa, and to do it with the help of George and John. She could do what she wished.

Louisa, embittered by this rebuke, quickly left Washington—not for Quincy, but for the spas. A few weeks later, she received a letter from her husband that terrified her. John Quincy, George, and John had started surveying the land. It rained, and they trudged through waves of mosquitoes, "over tangled brakes and Rattlesnakes," and felt "everything of heroic fatigue but the glory," JQA wrote. John had quickly announced his displeasure, and quit. George lasted but half a day. In this small exchange of news Louisa read great peril. John and Charles were able to rebel against their father; they were strong. But George was weak, and if he had quit after only half a day's work, the vituperation must have been severe. Louisa rushed to her son.

She found him huddled alone in his chamber in Boston, curled against the late August chill like a fallen leaf. Louisa reported that George was "in very bad health. The state of his mind is by no means what I would have it." As she suspected, John Quincy's frustration with his son and with his own life had reached its worst moment during the land survey. Unable to keep up, slapping at mosquitoes, complaining about the rain, George had been "lashed and sneered at" by his father.

George could not shoulder the demands, the cutting humiliations. He could not handle the weight of being the firstborn son of a firstborn son. Emptied by the death of his beloved grandfather, he had been devoured by his unquenchable father. His spirit died.

Louisa comforted George as best she could, but neither she nor John Quincy had the tools or special knowledge for dealing with his complaints. Vague discomforts, lethargy, procrastination, "moments of despondency"—as George called them—had no medical treatments. Louisa urged the benefits of sea air and a Washington visit. She also suggested optimism. John Quincy instructed his son to rise early, make his own fire, read the Bible, and "not indulge mere melancholy humours."

WHILE George was sliding downhill, Charles was rising into prominence within the family. The favored son, he was all George wished to be but wasn't. He had learned how to handle his parents, and best of all, he knew how to take care of himself.

For about eighteen months Charles lived in the White House, trying to read law. A handsome, fair young man, he shared Louisa's romantic blood and devotedly read poetry and novels. He also loved wine, champagne, and billiards. Wearing his royal-blue coat with a high silk choker and jeweled stickpin, he enjoyed strolling Pennsylvania Avenue, appreciating the ladies who were out in large numbers during sunny weather. Unlike George, he kept his wit and a clear perception of his family.

An Exceptional Marriage

Charles well understood the dissension that political life caused between his mother and father. He wished to avoid it, and had written his grandfather in 1826: "A political life is after all a very disagreeable one. In quiet times there is little room for distinction, and in violent times, all the rest of life is sacrificed. And what's all this for? A name." Charles was unwilling to sacrifice himself for the Adams name, or tradition.

In love Charles proved to be both calculating and prescient. At the French ambassador's ball, he had met a beautiful young woman named Abigail Brooks who lived in Medford, Massachusetts, but traveled to Washington during the winter for the social season. Charles had decided that Abby Brooks was the girl he would marry. In February 1827, at another ball, Charles made the accepted social signal of continually dancing with Abby, and she reciprocated by taking his arm and walking the room—the same signals John Quincy and Louisa had exchanged in 1795. Charles formally asked if she would permit his attentions in the future, and Abby replied that she would have to ask her father.

At first her father, Peter Chardon Brooks, refused to give his consent to his daughter's engagement. He wished to keep his "pet" child at home a little longer. Abby was just nineteen, and Charles not yet twenty. Charles had only started law studies and had no prospects for employment. In a series of letters between the Adamses and Peter Brooks, John Quincy suggested that the two young people contract an engagement but postpone marriage until Charles reached the age of twenty-one. John Quincy wrote a flattering endorsement of his son: he was "sedate and considerate—his disposition studious and somewhat reserved—his sense of honour high and delicate; his habits domestic and regular, and his temper generous and benevolent." Brooks gave in and granted his consent.

The Adamses reacted with enthusiasm. Why were they so pleased? Louisa told George that "Miss Brooks is a great belle here and a wonderful favorite with the family." Abby was indeed young and lovely, but more than that, her father was the wealthiest man in New England. Unlike his parents, Charles would never worry about money.

BY JUNE 1827 THE FISSURES in the Adams family had widened substantially. After his party's defeat in the autumn elections, President Adams himself came under attack. Not surprisingly, he complained of nervous symptoms, and his spirits drooped.

Meanwhile, defeat piled upon defeat for George. In May he had run for reelection to the Massachusetts legislature, and lost. He promptly took sick, and his mother again rushed northward.

When Louisa reached Boston, she found her son on the mend, and during the month she nursed him back to health, she wrote John Quincy trying to make him see George as she did. His personality, she wrote, went through "twenty changes in a day," and it was "of the utmost importance that he should not be harassed with business or care." He was "an uncommonly fine young man," who needed "kindness blended with firmness to prevent his taking some rash step." JQA replied that George's illness was an excuse to avoid work. He merely needed "bolstering."

In late July Louisa and George headed south, and John Quincy, John, and Charles started north; on August 2 the entire family met at the City Hotel in New York. Husband and wife hardly spoke to each other. "My mother," Charles wrote in his diary, "does not appear either in good health or spirits. My own feelings inclined to great melancholy on seeing what I think to be the future prospects of our family. My father seemed excessively depressed. George's manners struck me in a very strange way at first, and it has taken some time to become familiarized with them." The Adamses parted the next day, with all the men going to Boston, and Louisa visiting Saratoga Springs and a New Jersey beach spa.

For the remainder of the summer Louisa and John Quincy wrote infrequently and briefly. He addressed her as "Mrs. Louisa C. Adams" or "Mrs. Louisa Catherine Adams" and sometimes used no greeting at all. JQA was frustrated with George, who kept avoiding him, and angry with Louisa, who was convinced that his pressures on George were harmful. When Louisa wrote John Quincy, she addressed her letter to "The President," and signed it "Love to John and Charles from your Wife, L. C. Adams." She, too, remained angry.

An Exceptional Marriage

PRESIDENT ADAMS SPENT THE late summer and part of the fall of 1827 in "idleness" in Quincy. He got Charles settled in Boston, where he was to study law under Daniel Webster. He attended chowder picnics and fishing parties, and went sea bathing. And he began the slow and painful process within himself of putting aside his oldest son and placing his hope in the youngest.

Adams left for Washington in October, and on his way stopped for several days at the farm of an old friend, Ward Boylston. He slept in the room he and George had shared during a visit in 1825, and the memory moved him greatly. He understood that George's failure was his failure, too, and he wrote him a letter of lost hope and missed opportunity:

> I am writing by morning candlelight in the little room where just two years since, I gave you a pair of sleeve buttons and a copy of verses, as tokens of my affection and hopes for you. This room contains as you remember a singular picture, which as you pass before it changes its aspect and character so as to present the portraiture of three different persons. Can you imagine the feelings which this combination of trivial incidents has excited in my bosom? In the first letter you write me, let me know whether you still possess the sleeve buttons and the verses and whether they ever excite any reflections in your mind.

George's reply, if he wrote one, has been lost. But his father's touching inquiry remains, with its haunting symbolism. Verses and sleeve buttons: one gift was poetical, the other useful; one was Johnson, the other Adams. John Quincy had prayed that George would live up to the best of both families. But now his image had changed, like the portrait; George was no longer the person he had once seemed to be, but had shifted slowly with the passage of time from one character to another, finally being neither Johnson nor Adams.

John Quincy was deep in thought as he rode southward from the Boylston farm to Hartford. There he wrote to Charles, suggesting that they start a regular correspondence. Charles replied with enthusiasm to this idea, and they began a lengthy exchange JQA was cautiously reaching out to his youngest son.

John Quincy intended these letters to be guides for success. He believed that Charles would follow in the Adams footsteps and seek a public career. He urged him to improve himself, to budget his time by rising at five o'clock in the morning, to write regularly, and to read newspapers as well as American history and the works of Cicero, Voltaire, Pascal, and Bacon.

Charles was nimble enough not to take his father too seriously. He frequently disagreed with him. He could never, he wrote, rise early no matter how much time it might save him, and he pointed out with some glee that when his father rose at five, exercised, and conducted business for twelve hours, he frequently fell asleep at the dinner table. John Quincy, in turn, challenged Charles to name anyone, anywhere, who had risen at five for the last five years and was now unsure of his prospects. Charles immediately indicated a friend named Kimball, who "seems not a bit more advanced in reputation or standing than when he first started" rising early. John Quincy fell silent on the subject.

Charles also disagreed with his father's recommended reading list. He said that Cicero, "the individual whom you have pronounced your favorite," lacked "firmness of character." He went on to mock John Quincy's definition of office holding as a "call to duty," when the true motive, as Charles saw it, was raw political ambition disguised as patriotism.

The exchange became testy, but both father and son seemed to enjoy it. Charles felt closer to his father, and thought he saw through his iron mask. John Quincy found his son's combative letters a welcome contrast to the gloomy political view outside his windows in the capital.

The collapse of this closeness came over love and money. When Charles turned twenty-one, he still had not been admitted to the bar. Without steady income he could not marry, and he asked his father to fill the financial gap by increasing his allowance. John Quincy, foreseeing his retirement from public life, refused, and added a heated warning against extravagance. Charles thought his father cruel. The least he expected was "an active kindness. Not in deeds if he was unable to assist me, but in words and manner." He got neither.

An Exceptional Marriage

Charles unwisely took his case to Peter Brooks, who had promised his daughter a twenty-thousand-dollar dowry. Charles wrote Brooks that the thousand-dollar-a-year allowance he received from John Quincy, together with the dowry, might "barely suffice to support us." He argued that it would be years before he earned anything practicing law. Brooks wasn't impressed. He told Charles that he wished his marriage to Abby deferred a year. It was an "unexpected blow," and Charles, hedged in by the two older men, felt his spirits "prostrated."

One reason John Quincy had said no to Charles was that George had plunged himself into debt. This was a time when indebtedness led to imprisonment, and angry as he was, Adams devised an offer that would save George, but one that made Charles's plea impossible to heed. John Quincy proposed to buy George's books for two thousand dollars. All his son had to do was make a list of the titles, draw up a bill of sale, and write his father's name in each volume. George could retain possession of the books until John Quincy called for them, which both men understood the father would never do. This was simply a bail-out for George, a disguised gift. John Quincy implored his son "nevermore to burden yourself with shameless expenses and senseless debts." He sent George the money, and he prayed, "May a merciful God redeem you from the very verge of ruin." But George never compiled the list of books, or wrote up a bill of sale, or entered his father's name in any volume.

It is not difficult to understand John Quincy Adams' despair. His presidency had diminished him to "toil and distemper." His mental and physical ailments persisted. His sons seemed determined to embarrass the family.

Desperate for continuity and with little else to do, Adams turned to horticulture. With the White House gardener he planted vegetables, flowers, and trees. He placed oaks and walnut trees around the mansion, hoping that they would survive into the next century. Within a year he had seven hundred trees in the White House grounds. He believed in the symbolism of his planting: that a man should raise a son and grow a tree, both giving regeneration and continuity. While his sons might fail, his trees would not. Or so he thought. In actuality, all his seedlings would be abandoned and trampled upon when Andrew Jackson moved into the White House. "A planter," Adams said, with possible reference to both his presidency and his fatherhood, "must make up his mind to endure many disappointments."

CHAPTER THREE

THE contest between John Quincy Adams and Andrew Jackson for the presidential election of 1828 was developing into what historians would describe as the "dirtiest" political race in the nation's history. And while Charles and George continued to create private anguish at the White House, John caused a public embarrassment during the campaign.

Shortly after becoming President, Adams had installed the secondhand billiard table in the White House for his "exercise and amusement." In March 1826 John, who served as his father's private secretary, had forwarded to a House committee an inventory of furnishings purchased with congressional appropriations. He had carelessly included the billiard table. When the report was published, it appeared that the President had used public funds for private pleasure. President Adams immediately notified the House that the "inventory so far as it related to the billiard table, &c. was entirely erroneous; and that no part of the public appropriation had been, or would be applied to any such purpose." But the damage was done.

John's mistake brought the opposition press into full howl. Among most Americans the term "billiards" evoked images of dark rooms, cigar smoke, wagering, and liquor. One editor warned that young men enticed by the click of billiard balls and smell of cigars would now tell their frowning elders, "Why, the President plays, too!"

The outcry set the tone of the campaign. The protests about "gambling furniture" encouraged other charges: that the Adamses lived in "regal magnificence" and that throughout his career, John Quincy had waxed fat on public funds. The pro-Adams press replied by calling Jackson "adept at billiards, cards, dice, horse-

An Exceptional Marriage

racing, cock-fighting, and tavern brawls," and went on to imply that an adulterous relationship had preceded his marriage to his wife, Rachel.

Sometime after the billiards incident, John Adams, much against his parents' wishes, became the first President's son to be married in the White House. In November 1827 Louisa had asked John Quincy to consider the engagement of John to Mary Hellen, but the President had refused. As a result, a strange charade got under way, and for the next ten weeks the President silently ignored a romance that noisily filled the White House.

On February 1 John told his mother that his marriage to Mary Hellen would take place in twenty-four days. The preparations for the wedding then proceeded so quietly that, as Louisa wrote to Charles, "you could never imagine that any thing of the sort was dreamt of. Neither by word or look has your father intimated the idea of such an event taking place."

On Monday evening, February 25, twenty-three guests gathered in the Blue Room of the White House; Charles and George remained in Boston. The candlelight ceremony went forward heavily, but after supper President Adams, perhaps loosened by the many champagne toasts, danced a Virginia reel "with great spirit," to the surprise of his wife.

Mary and John settled into the White House, where they lived until 1829, when the entire Adams family moved out. Their first baby, Mary Louisa Adams, was born in the White House on December 2, 1828, and fondly nicknamed Looly. Within two years Mary would again give birth, this time in Quincy, to Georgiana Francis Adams—Fanny—named after her two rejected uncles.

IN THE presidential election Adams carried the New England states, New Jersey, Delaware, and Maryland. The rest of the nation went overwhelmingly for Andrew Jackson. Louisa tried to cheer the family. "It has never been possible to make me believe that defeat is disgrace," she wrote Charles. "We are all in good spirits."

But at the start of 1829 President Adams wrote: "The year begins in gloom. My wife had a sleepless and painful night. The dawn was overcast, and, as I began to write, my lamp went out, self-extinguished." Was it an omen? In John Quincy's troubled mind such a trivial event took on meaning. He had tried to lead the nation along the path that he believed manifested God's will. But the people elected Jackson, whom Adams considered less than God-fearing. Had Adams failed his Creator?

The Adamses moved out of the White House on March 3, and the next day, after the inaugural ceremony, President Jackson and his followers marched down Pennsylvania Avenue to the mansion. They burst into the White House, bounced upon the beds, looked in the closets, and turned the furniture over. "Orange punch by barrels full was made," Henry Clay later reported, "but as the waiters opened the door to bring it out, a rush would be made, the glasses broken, pails of liquor upset. It was difficult to keep any thing like order, and it was mortifying to see men, with boots heavy with mud, standing on the damask satin chairs, to get a sight of the President." Like Jefferson, Jackson represented a change toward a broader democracy. And as had happened with Jefferson, the President he succeeded refused to attend the inauguration. Instead, John Quincy Adams went horseback riding.

Since their F Street house had been leased out, the Adamses rented a farm, called Meridian Hill, about a mile and a half from the White House. The farmhouse formed two separate residences, with room for Mary and John—who was employed by his father—and their baby daughter. Here JQA entertained a steady flow of visitors, and read and wrote, and, with a daily walk or horseback ride, soon declared that he was more occupied than in the White House.

While the Adamses rested comfortably, Charles, in Boston, wrote that his brother George complained of "dejection, low spirits, and an inability to occupy himself. And this acts upon melancholy reflections in regard to Father and himself." Charles's report was cool, objective. Like his father, he attributed George's difficulties to a lack of discipline.

But Louisa was alarmed. She still thought sea travel and being home would help, and in early April she wrote George suggesting

An Exceptional Marriage

that he come to Washington "to escort your father and myself on our way home to Quincy." Louisa wrapped her request in an obvious fib: "You know that we are neither of us famous travelers," wrote the woman who had crossed Europe in a carriage in winter. George would live with them in Quincy, she said, and his father would keep a horse and a gig "and you will always command the use of it." As a final inducement to her son, Louisa promised that she would keep his father from persisting in his demands upon him. She portrayed John Quincy as mellowing, and added a final enticement: "P.S. If you come you will see our pretty Baby."

What chaos filled George's life. He had a pretty baby of his own, born to Eliza Dolph, a young chambermaid at Dr. Welsh's, whom he had seduced. He was still seeing her. The fact must have been known to Charles. He and the Welshes were close friends, and Charles even alluded to such a liaison in his diary in April. Therefore, Charles's reports to his parents on George's failing health may have been designed to elicit letters from Louisa urging George to come to Washington—away from the chambermaid.

In January George had moved Eliza from the Welshes' to live with another family elsewhere in Boston. He had previously addressed to Charles—but not posted—a confidential letter detailing his entanglement with Eliza, stating that if he should die within the year 1828, he wished his debts to be paid and the balance of his estate given to her. He had placed the letter in his trunk, and told Charles to search for it should anything happen to him.

On April 20, 1829, George received a direct appeal from his father: "I wish you to return to us immediately upon receiving this Letter." George dreaded seeing John Quincy. He had broken every rule his father ever made and was now frozen into inaction by fear of his retribution. Facing a journey that could have immense consequences, George began hallucinating. He heard birds speaking to him, and two nights before taking the stage to Providence, he thought someone tried to break into his chamber. He scrambled out of bed and searched his room. He found no one, but remained convinced that someone lurked nearby.

In Providence on April 29, George Washington Adams boarded the *Benjamin Franklin*, a luxurious new steamboat bound for New York under Captain E. S. Bunker. That afternoon, as the steamboat headed down Long Island Sound, George appeared cheerful and gave a donation to a missionary on board. But as evening came on, he complained of a headache to a passenger named Keep, who struck up an acquaintance. Later George became more troubled. He thought he heard voices in the steamboat's engines: "Let it be, let it be." When he retired to his berth, the sound followed him, pounding the side of the ship: "Let it be, let it be." He went to bed but got up almost immediately. He awakened another passenger and accused him of spreading rumors against him. When the gentleman denied the charges, George backed away and returned to his berth.

He slept fitfully, and at about three o'clock the next morning rose once more, dressed, and climbed to the bridge, where he confronted Captain Bunker. He demanded to be put ashore. The *Benjamin Franklin* was then cutting through the lower reaches of the Sound in good time, and Captain Bunker would not be delayed. He asked George, "Why do you wish to be set ashore?" "There is a combination among the passengers against me," the young man replied. "I heard them talking and laughing at me."

Captain Bunker waved George away, and a few minutes later, George encountered John Stevens, a Jackson partisan who was hurrying to Washington in search of a job. The two men held a brief conversation and then Stevens continued his walk upon the upper deck. Ten minutes after that, he happened to look over the rail and saw George's hat lying on the deck near the stern. He shouted for the captain, and the ship was immediately searched, but in the predawn darkness all they found was George's cloak, near his hat. He had jumped or fallen overboard.

Two days later, Louisa Adams' brother-in-law Nathaniel Frye walked solemnly into the house at Meridian Hill. In the parlor, he showed Louisa and John Quincy that morning's *Baltimore American*, which carried a small notice of George's disappearance. The news, Louisa wrote, wrung John Quincy's heart "almost to madness." Both he and Louisa feared that they had urged George

An Exceptional Marriage

beyond his strength "to exertion foreign to his nature." They reviewed their errors and suffered great feelings of guilt. Louisa wept, remembering the joy of her first son during those bleak days in Berlin twenty-eight years earlier. If only she had insisted that George and John come with them to Russia instead of leaving them in the care of others during their youth, perhaps their days together would have been more like the early ones at Ealing, when George was full of promise.

John Quincy, too, recalled that "lottery ticket" of a lad "as he was, all goodness and affection." He remembered George's last visit and their walks in Washington.

In death George did something he could not do in life: because of him, his parents reached toward each other; in George's death they began their own lives together. They prayed for each other and asked Heaven's mercy upon their errors as parents. John Quincy, who had been so harsh, was tender to Louisa, "a ministering angel always at my side," she said. He read to her from the Bible, and she to him. They drew strength, one from the other, and within a few days JQA could write that Louisa was "composed and exhibiting that fortitude that comes only from on high."

Three weeks after George's death, the *National Journal* of Washington published one of his poems, titled "The Spark at Sea," and Louisa Adams read it for the first time.

> *There is a little spark at sea*
> *Which grows 'mid darkness brilliantly,*
> *But when the moon looks clear and bright,*
>   *Emits a pale and feeble light,*
> *And when the tempest shakes the wave*
>   *It glimmers o'er the seaman's grave....*
>
> *Such friendship's beaming light appears*
> *Through the long line of coming years*
> *In sorrow's cloud it shines afar,*
>   *A feeble but a constant star.*
> *And like that little spark at sea*
>   *Burns brightest in adversity.*

Here was George's message to Louisa. She embraced it as a sign that his love was eternal, like the little star-spark at sea marking his grave. Each year after her son's death, Louisa paused on his birthday to remember him with a poem.

The Adamses delayed their journey to Quincy for a month. Louisa was reluctant to leave Washington and her precious new granddaughter for the emptiness of New England, now bereft of her oldest son. In sorrow, John Quincy and John left for Massachusetts on June 10, and from Baltimore John Quincy wrote a loving letter to his wife, "my dearest friend," telling her of his trip and closing: "May the blessing of God rest upon you till we meet again. Love to Mary and a kiss to Baby. From your affectionate J. Q. Adams."

On June 13 on the steamboat to New York City, Adams read in the *New York Herald* that his son's body had been found three days earlier. It had drifted in with the tide on City Island. "May it soothe you to learn," he wrote Louisa upon landing in New York, "that the person was entire, without mark of violence or contusion. My most beloved friend, may you receive this as a dispensation of Mercy of Heaven in its severity."

In New York, Adams' friends told him the details. A coroner's inquest had been held—death due to drowning—and the body placed in a tomb in East Chester, about sixteen miles northeast of the city. The next day John Quincy and John rode to East Chester and dined at the home of a physician, who gave George's personal things to his father. Afterward John Quincy saw his son's coffin and, with an Episcopalian minister, said a brief service. Then, when he had made arrangements to have the body sent on to Quincy in the autumn, he and John returned to New York City.

Alone in his hotel room, John Quincy spread George's belongings upon the bed: bank bills, receipts and notes of accounts, a purse, a penknife, a watch, a cipher seal, a silver pencil, George's snuffbox, a comb. And there, too, were the sleeve buttons that John Quincy had given George four years before as tokens of his love and hope. He had demanded that George write an explanation of what he had done with them. Now he knew that

An Exceptional Marriage

George had carried them in his pocket. Tears welled in the father's eyes. At last the buttons were fully accounted for.

In Boston, Charles's mourning for George took a more practical turn. While saddened by his brother's death, Charles was also determined that the family name not be further tarnished and that all debts be settled. As he went through his brother's papers, there was one item that he sought immediately, as, he wrote in his diary, "it might pain my father." The letter that George had addressed to him turned out to be a will of sorts, settling George's debts and providing for Eliza. Charles was not surprised by it— he had probably known its outline. Since George's death had occurred in 1829, not 1828 as the will assumed, Charles felt no legal obligation to follow its instructions. Nevertheless, he decided to do what he could in the spirit of his brother's request to "preserve Eliza, if possible, from destruction," although George's debts to his father would wipe out any balance for her.

After sifting through George's papers, he burned most of them. The tangled family accounts, the jumble of books and letters, all led Charles to a harsh judgment: "George's fate was melancholy but on the whole, I have been forced to the unpleasant conclusion that it was not untimely." Had he lived, Charles thought, George probably would have caused more misery to himself and to his family.

PART VI

Washington, 1830–1852

CHAPTER ONE

JOHN Quincy spent the summer alone in the Old House trying to gain strength from the simple repetitions of life. He rose at five, and before breakfast read from the Bible—for comfort and as "a guide through the darksome journey of life." He would need the strength: in November George's coffin would arrive in Quincy, and John Quincy would place it in the family tomb. These were months of taking measure: Adams was sixty-two years old, alone, beaten, and saddened. He had no way of knowing that the most important work of his life lay ahead of him.

Louisa remained in Washington. To mitigate her sadness, she wrote dozens of poems about George's death. The writing helped her relieve some of her anguish and understand much of her loss. But she could not journey to Quincy. To do so would mean riding the steamboat that had carried George to his death, which Louisa was then unable, or unwilling, to do.

She was still in Washington when Charles married Abby Brooks on September 3, 1829, at the Brooks home in Medford, but John Quincy attended. After the wedding, his bride and his future secure, Charles rode with Abby to the house on Hancock Avenue in Boston that Peter Brooks had purchased for his precious daughter.

Abby was to prove a docile, obedient, and fecund wife. In 1831 she would give birth to Louisa Catherine Adams 2d, "as bright eyed and sprightly," John Quincy would proclaim, as his other little granddaughters, "of whom we are so foolishly proud." John Quincy Adams 2d would arrive in 1833, to be followed by four brothers and one more sister.

IN THE fall of 1830 the National Republicans from the Plymouth district sounded out old John Quincy about running for the House of Representatives. For a time Adams remained firm in his belief that public office should seek the man. He told his supporters that his acceptance would wait until the people had voted.

Finally, however, as the people of his district rallied to him, Adams declared to his family his willingness to accept election. Charles tried to dissuade him. John Quincy had already devoted too much time to public service, and he was too old and too poor. Louisa simply exploded in anger. She had planned a quiet retirement for her husband, and was even willing to remain in New England herself for a winter or two. Adams had once again placed personal ambition above her wishes.

Louisa announced that she would not return to Washington. John wrote his mother a mild letter approving his father's choice and requesting her return to Washington. When she received it,

An Exceptional Marriage

Louisa turned all her anger upon her son. Hadn't she suffered enough for her husband's career? she asked. Where was her reward for this? Was it in George's grave, or in the grave of her daughter in Russia? Was it in the closeness of their family after years of political turmoil? She was being asked once again to sacrifice herself for her husband's "grasping ambition." But such was not her interpretation of marriage. "In the marriage contract," she told John, "there are *two parties*, each of which have rights strictly defined by law and by the usages of society. The parties *agree* to promote as far as in their power the welfare and happiness of *each other*." But where was this mutual cooperation in her marriage? she asked. More importantly, she believed that the marriage contract gave her a right to disobey her husband and a right to express her opinion.

The congressional election took place November 1, 1830. John Quincy received 1817 votes, his nearest opponent, 373. He had won by a landslide. "I am a member-elect of the Twenty-second Congress," he wrote elatedly in his diary. "My election as President was not half so gratifying to my inmost soul."

John Quincy had reasons for welcoming his election. He was obviously very flattered. He also missed politics. And accepting election would set an example for future American Presidents to continue in service to their nation. Finally, he needed the income; he was, perhaps, at the very edge of financial ruin.

Louisa, aware of her husband's reasons, gave in. After Thanksgiving, she set off overland for Washington. In Connecticut, her carriage was "buried" in snow; she had to walk a quarter of a mile "clinging to the bushes for support. It is strange," she wrote, "that I should have suffered so much to avoid Steam Boats in the night."

John Quincy preferred the steamboats. Although he left Quincy five days after Louisa, he arrived in Washington only an hour behind his wife.

FROM 1807 to 1857 the House of Representatives held its sessions in a beautiful semicircular room in the Capitol. The focal point of the chamber—now known as Statuary Hall—was the

Speaker's chair, elevated well above the floor, with its canopy of rich crimson silk trimmed with a bright fringe. The members sat around this throne. Each enjoyed a plush mahogany easy chair and a mahogany desk with drawers—an excessively comfortable and injudicious arrangement, some thought, which encouraged long sitting and windy speeches.

Into this rich chamber marched John Quincy Adams, a bald little old man with a high-pitched voice that did not carry well. Nevertheless, he would make his fellow congressmen hear him very clearly.

In 1831, when Louisa and John Quincy returned to Washington, the coming struggle between the Union and the slaveholders was taking shape. Adams, who as a boy had watched the nation battle for its independence, would now as an old man fight to ensure its survival. The issues surrounding slavery were complex, but the human tragedy was all too clear. The rising world demand for cotton had made slave labor widespread in the South. Slaveowners dominated the House, where representation was based on the "federal ratio." This provision of the Constitution said that the slaveholding states could count five slaves as being equal to three free white men, and the number of representatives in the House was based upon this confected population scheme. Slaveholders, therefore, enjoyed immense power.

John Quincy Adams did not abhor slavery with all his soul as the abolitionists did. For him, preserving the Union was the heart of the issue. He thought the situation had been best articulated by Daniel Webster: "Liberty and Union, now and forever, one and inseparable." On July 4, 1831, while speaking before a large gathering in Quincy, JQA set forth his own rallying cry with the stirring words, "Independence and Union Forever!" That was what he was fighting for.

The Adamses, as residents of Washington, saw slaves around them all the time. The business of buying and selling black men and women thrived in the District of Columbia. Yet some Washingtonians were troubled by the sight of long lines of slaves, in chains, shuffling through the capital on their way to market. Petitions to rid the District of slavery started trickling into Con-

An Exceptional Marriage

gress; the first carried only a few hundred signatures. But the flood was coming.

It would be an error to say that Louisa, any more than John Quincy, was eager for emancipation. If he saw the issue of slavery primarily in terms of saving the nation, she saw it largely in personal terms.

As a resident of Washington with relatives in Maryland, she feared the retribution of the slaves and the surliness of the free blacks. She also now harbored shameful prejudices. In February 1831, for example, she reported that President Jackson had closed the social season in Washington "with a grand Negro Ball." To Louisa, it was offensive to have these guests present in the drawing rooms, using the President's china. This attitude would gradually change. In time she would remember her feelings toward her dark-skinned roommate at boarding school in England and the slave girl in London. Her interest in the role of women in society, and her contacts with abolitionists, would slowly enlarge her vision; she would come to see that slavery and women's rights had similar roots. John Quincy, in turn, would become one of the first, and loudest, voices in the House of Representatives to cry out against the institution of slavery.

As THE Adamses embarked on this great cause, personal tragedy visited them again. In 1832 John Quincy's brother, Thomas, died, at age sixty. A lawyer and judge, Thomas had started his adult life with such promise, but he had also suffered as a young man from depression. Like other Adamses, he had sought relief in the bottle. He could not break the vice—the "affliction" old John Adams thought was visited upon his family to check its pride—and by 1831 he had degenerated into a frail man, his body jarred by nervous spasms. Thomas Adams died—as his brother Charles had years earlier—from alcoholism.

John Quincy and Louisa's middle son, John, also had difficulty with drinking. He worked hard at the Columbian Mills, which JQA had purchased in 1823. The mills, which stood along Rock Creek in Washington, ground wheat and corn into flour and meal, and John knew that their success was important to his father's financial security. Put in charge of the mills in 1829, John went at the job with dedication, but the task was overwhelming. He could not control drought on the farmlands, or an abundance of wheat one year and a dearth the next, or the fluctuation of flour prices in Europe. Still John had enthusiasm. He rose at five, worked for several hours, then went home for breakfast; after that, he returned to the mills, worked until dinner, and after dinner went back to the mills until eight at night.

Soon his health deteriorated, and he began drinking. He suffered from stiff joints and limbs, fevers, loss of memory. He periodically lost his eyesight. For two years he lingered in pain and sickness, growing weaker and weaker, and by 1834 Louisa was convinced that his illness was owing to "the dreadfully debilitating" climate and "the evening damps" around the mills. She exhorted her husband to find "some lucrative and advantageous scheme of business" in Quincy for John. In a touching series of letters, JQA, who was on one of his annual visits to the Old House, tried to persuade his son to move to Massachusetts. There was plenty of work at the Old House, Adams promised, where John could "be useful to me." But Adams' loving offers could not help his son. In early autumn, 1834, a letter arrived in Quincy saying that John was gravely ill. Adams quickly left for Washington, but when he arrived on October 22, his son lay in a coma. He died the next morning, with his father at his side.

Both John Quincy and Louisa were shocked into collapse by their second son's death. John's wife, Mary Hellen, and her two young daughters moved in with the Adamses, who turned all their love to their grandchildren, and all their commitment to the issues ahead.

CHAPTER TWO

THE abolitionist movement was part of the great humanitarian awakening overflowing the land. Education, temperance, penal reform, social responsibility for the poor were measures that increasingly concerned many Americans. The abolitionists were the radicals of their day. They advocated nonviolence, integrated

An Exceptional Marriage

their meetings with free black men and women, faced threats and stonings from hostile mobs. Within the heart of their movement arose the most radical thought of all: the liberation of women. Members of the all-male American Anti-Slavery Society petitioned Congress for the abolition of slavery. The process of circulating petitions and collecting signatures had a surprising effect: it organized northern communities, educated large numbers of Americans to the plight of the slaves, and created a focal point around which women could rally.

By mid-decade petitions were pouring into John Quincy Adams' office. Angry southerners sought to halt all discussion of slavery in Congress by blocking the presentation of the petitions. Member after member rose in vitriolic wrath. After several days of listening to the southerners' views, Adams wrote Charles: "The voice of Freedom has not yet been heard, and I am earnestly urged to speak in her name. She will be trampled under foot if I do not, and I shall be trampled under foot if I do."

By January 1836 Adams was rising from his desk every day to debate slavery and to read petitions calling for its abolition. In joining the battle, he discovered new purpose. He loved the rules, the language, the verbal rolls and thunders that trapped an opponent. Each day now seemed worthwhile. "A skirmishing day," he wrote with glee. He had read three petitions to the squirming House members; the presentation was followed by "a sharp debate." Nothing stopped him—not his age, health, weaknesses, and certainly not the opposition. Nearing seventy, Adams was hardly the heroic figure the abolitionists might have chosen. He feared speaking in public and labored arduously to prepare each speech. He was also long-winded and tended to flourishes. More than once Louisa had to warn him to control "the winged griffins" of his imagination.

In May 1836 the slaveholders and their northern sympathizers sought to cut off all debate on slavery and to end all presentation of the troublesome petitions. In effect, they wished to limit the right of some members of the House to speak freely, and worse, they determined to halt the right of Americans to petition their government. What they did, however, was to stir old John Quincy

Adams to long battle and awaken the American people to the very issue the proslavery spokesmen sought to suppress.

A committee headed by Henry Laurens Pinckney of South Carolina presented three resolutions to the House. The first two stated that Congress had no constitutional power to interfere with slavery in any state or in the District of Columbia. But the third resolution was more dangerous. "All petitions, memorials, resolutions, or papers," it said, "relating in any way, or to any extent whatsoever, to the subject of slavery or the abolition of slavery, shall, without being either printed or referred, be laid on the table, and no further action whatever shall be had thereon."

The resolutions were clearly a violation of the Constitution, but the Speaker of the House, James K. Polk, a Tennessee slaveholder, shut off any argument against them. During the next two days, the irascible Adams spoke against slavery and warned that the nation was being led to a war that threatened the Union. His duty, Adams wrote a friend, was to speak out and delay the coming conflict. His goal was always firm: preservation of the Union.

On May 26 the House took the final step against the petitioners. The clerk called the roll on the third question—that of silencing all discussion of slavery in the House. When John Quincy Adams' name was called, the old man rose and shouted above the cries of the opposition, "I hold the resolution to be in direct violation of the Constitution of the United States, of the rules of this House, and of the rights of my constituents." But he went unheeded, and the resolution passed, 117 to 68. Pinckney's third resolution became known as the gag rule, and the House renewed it in more and more stringent form with each session.

The gag rule became a rallying point for an ever-widening cause. It nullified the right to petition but could not destroy it. Abolitionists attacked the House with petitions; in the next two years the American Anti-Slavery Society alone sent 196,720 petitions opposing slavery and another 32,000 against new versions of the gag rule. Not a single one was heard by the House. The controversy spread beyond the radical abolitionists. Other Americans joined the struggle. Where at first the issue had been the abolition of slavery, it soon became the right to petition, then

An Exceptional Marriage

the cause of freedom of speech. More and more white men and women became concerned about their constitutional rights. For the first time white and free Americans saw their freedom interwoven with that of the black slaves. For the first time they asked, If any among us is enslaved, are we free?

IN 1837 AND 1838 American women became political activists. Not since the Revolution had women in such numbers spoken out in public and never before had they argued so strongly for their rights and those of slaves.

Pulpit and press had long advocated that women be pious, pure, domestic, and submissive. The courts had declared that a woman could not vote or stand for public office. Women were excluded from institutions of higher learning. A married woman had no legal rights to inherited property or to her earnings; she could make no contracts, could neither sue nor be sued, nor claim her own children in case of marital separation. The concept was firm in the law and in the public mind: women were secondary creatures.

Early in the century a few women had met in home parlors for charitable, religious, or educational work. Gradually these gatherings grew into such organizations as the Washington Orphans' Society, to which Louisa Adams belonged. Raising money for the poor, collecting food for the indigent, gave women skills in working together toward a goal, fund raising, and speaking—among themselves at first—about their lives, politics, and the barriers they encountered.

These were precisely the skills the antislavery movement needed. Women who could organize meetings, debate issues, collect money, could also gather signatures and distribute petitions for the enslaved. The antislavery petitions, therefore, helped to focus the emerging political awareness of American women.

When the all-male American Anti-Slavery Society was organized, Lucretia Mott and twenty other women formed a feminine counterpart, the Philadelphia Female Anti-Slavery Society. By 1837 the abolitionist societies had a combined membership of more than one hundred thousand, half of them women. Petitioning, which had helped end slavery in Britain in 1833, now became a major form of American antislavery activity, and women took to it with enthusiasm.

Monday was the regular petition day in the House of Representatives. On Monday, January 9, and on January 23, 1837, before the House once more voted to renew the gag rule for that session, John Quincy Adams rose to present a total of forty-five petitions from women. One can imagine the rheumatic Adams getting up slowly, painfully, from his mahogany seat, knowing that he faced the hostility of his colleagues, reading the names and demands of these brave women, shouting over the cries of "Silence him!" that filled the chamber: "Lydia Lewis and one hundred and fifty women of Dorchester praying for the abolition of slavery in the District of Columbia; Rachael Newcomb and one hundred and thirty women of Braintree . . ."

Cries of "Point of order! Point of order!"

"Abigail M. Emmons and three hundred and fifteen women of Franklin; Phoebe Weston and one hundred and fifty-six women of Westminster . . . impressed with the sinfulness of slavery . . ."

"A point of order!" Pinckney shouted. "Has the gentleman from Massachusetts a right, under the rule, to read the petition?"

Speaker Polk replied that Adams had "a right to make a statement of the contents" of the petition.

Adams pressed on. "Do most earnestly petition your honourable body to abolish slavery in the District of Columbia . . ."

"Mr. Speaker!" John Chambers of Kentucky shouted. "Mr. Speaker, I rise to a point of order."

The ex-President eased himself into his chair, still reading loudly. "And to declare every human being free who sets foot upon its soil."

House members immediately tabled the obnoxious documents, and Adams bounced up to tell them that the good ladies from Massachusetts had vowed to renew their petitions every year. The members reacted to the warning by renewing the gag rule for the remainder of that session.

Adams decided to probe the members' defense of the gag rule. He presented a petition from "nine ladies of Fredericksburg, Vir-

An Exceptional Marriage

ginia," who called for prohibition of the slave trade in the District of Columbia. But when John Mercer Patton of Virginia claimed that the women were free Negroes or mulattoes, and "infamous," the Speaker ordered the petition to be laid on the table.

With the House in uproar, Adams also prepared to present a petition sent by slaves. Before he could read it, however, he was attacked. "I object!" bellowed Joab Lawler of Alabama. Was Adams suggesting that slaves had a right to petition Congress? Waddy Thompson of South Carolina accused Adams of inciting the slaves to rebellion. Others shouted that he was a pawn of "incendiary fanatics." "Expel him! Expel him!" someone shouted. Adams told the Speaker that he had merely raised a parliamentary question about the slave petition: Was it in order? He then announced that the petition, from twenty-two slaves, was, in fact, against abolition!

The House exploded again with shouts. Its members quickly presented three resolutions; the first two called any petitions from slaves to the House disrespectful of the "feelings" of the House and the "rights" of southern states; they asserted that slaves had no right to make such petitions, only citizens had—even though that right was superseded by the gag rule. The third resolution made it appear that Adams had apologized to the House for his efforts on behalf of the petitioners. He demanded to speak in his own defense, and his speech was the most stinging he ever made. He accused the members of denying the right of petition for political reasons, an act "no despot, of any age, has ever denied to the poorest or the meanest of human creatures. When the principle is once begun of limiting the right of petition, where would it stop? The honourable gentleman, John Patton, makes it a crime because I presented a petition which he affirms to be from colored women, which women were of infamous character, as he says. I shall forever entertain the proposition that the sacred right of petition does not depend on character any more than it does on condition. It is a right that cannot be denied to the humblest, to the most wretched."

Petitions continued to tumble into Adams' office and home, and he continued to bring them to the House floor, testing the House

members with his parliamentary skill. He thrived on the adversity. Suddenly, at seventy, he felt uncommonly well; needling his opponents to exasperation was invigorating.

During these years, Louisa Adams read and listened, and explored her own feelings about slavery and about women. The inner turmoil this caused her cannot be overstated. Ill much of the time, still recovering from the shock of the death of John, her second son, Louisa entered a period of religious and personal self-examination. She started each day with a series of prayers, and then spent much time reading her Bible. She undertook a long religious poem, two lines of which contained this self-analysis: *She lived in error, faulty every day/Imploring God to guide her on her way.* In 1832 she began a detailed analysis of Old Testament history. Her feelings of not being well educated enough threatened to halt the project several times. But she overcame her sense of inferiority and wrote a sixty-page report.

The work made her study the Bible harder than she ever had, and look deeply into herself. She felt an uneasiness with her searching. Her doubts centered on the questions of equality and the Biblical treatment of women. Were women closer to God than men? Louisa said that in the Garden of Eden "woman and man were co-equal, and this is proved by their perfect equality after Eve had tasted the forbidden fruit." Further, she asked, "If woman is to be considered inferior to man, why was she made the Mother of Men after her Sin?"

From these religious origins Louisa's questioning broadened. Woman, she said, was at first the object of her husband's eye, but after bearing his children, she became a "secondary object," and soon she faded "into a mere automaton used as occasion required, and at other times she remained an unwelcome burthen." Louisa wrote that women must be alert, that the world places all weakness and frailty on their side. "The power, the property and the law are all on the other side, as well as publick opinion; which, created by man, is always in favour of himself."

At this time of questioning, Louisa had the chance to read Abigail Adams' letters, as Charles was compiling his grandmother's correspondence for a book. Abigail's letters to her husband, written in the 1770s, during his absences at the Continental Congresses, conveyed the certainty of her respected place in family and community. Hers was not a limited role, but a valued position as "farmeress," mother, teacher, employer, revolutionary.

Louisa found her mother-in-law's letters "full of energy, buoyant and elastic." She was also impressed with Abigail's message to her husband. While he was in Philadelphia in 1776, working on a draft of the Declaration of Independence, Abigail had made a declaration of her own. She wanted women to gain their independence along with men. "Do not put such unlimited power into the hands of the Husbands," she wrote. "Remember all Men would be tyrants if they could. If particular care and attention is not paid to the Ladies, we are determined to foment a Rebellion, and will not hold ourselves bound by any laws in which we have no voice, or Representation."

Abigail Adams' letters articulated many of Louisa's own feelings about equality, about the laws men wrote to govern women. The moment was gone when, as Abigail had wished, women might have achieved equality with men in a single document. Opposing them now were not only men, but also the majority of American women, who felt content with their subservient status. The door, which had stood so wide open, was now bolted shut. A few women, however, had begun searching for the key. Abigail Adams' letters, Louisa said, were "treasures," documents of a lost opportunity and guideposts to the awakening.

IN MAY 1837, two weeks after the Anti-Slavery Convention of American Women, two sisters, Angelina and Sarah Grimké, set out on a speaking tour of New England sponsored by the Female Anti-Slavery Society. The sisters were daughters of a South Carolina slaveowner, and could recite the horrors of slavery from firsthand observation. Their tour caused a furor: the Grimkés addressed integrated audiences composed of men and women and free blacks. Moreover, they demanded, along with the freedom of the slaves, the freedom and rights of women.

All of New England was in an uproar. Here was a direct con-

An Exceptional Marriage

frontation between the Quakerism of Philadelphia—to which the sisters had converted—and the Puritanism of Boston. The Congregationalists refused to read notices of abolitionist meetings from their pulpits, and one minister warned against dangers to the good church ladies from other women who "intinerate" as "public lecturers."

And what were these dangers? Angelina Grimké, small and delicate in her simple Quaker dress, spoke out. "We have given great offense on account of our womanhood, which seems to be as objectionable as our abolitionism. We are willing to bear the brunt of the storm, if we can only be the means of making a break in that wall of public opinion which lies in the way of woman's true dignity, honor and usefulness." Sarah Grimké demanded equal pay for equal work, and drew a parallel between women and slaves. She urged women to abandon frivolity and become conscious of their own worth.

At meeting after meeting throughout New England, the Grimkés spoke freely. Women must cast off their restraint, their embarrassment in the company of men. They must look to themselves for solutions to their own problems. They must read, pray, speak, act to overthrow slavery. The sisters urged white women to reach out to slave women. "They are our countrywomen—*they are our sisters;* and to us as women, they have a right to look for sympathy with their sorrows, and effort and prayer for their rescue."

On a warm June day in 1837 Angelina and Sarah Grimké, escorted by abolitionist leader William Lloyd Garrison, rode to Quincy to visit John Quincy Adams, at home during the congressional recess. They had been pleased with his defense of the right to petition and with his opposition to the gag rule, but they were equally displeased that he opposed as impractical the abolition of slavery in the District of Columbia.

The four discussed John Quincy's unwillingness to speak publicly in support of the abolition movement. His reasons, noted in his diary, were that his principles and personality made "it necessary for me to be more circumspect in my conduct than belongs to my nature." The Grimkés could not understand this equivocating. Either Adams was for abolition, or he was against it. The discussion was soon stalemated, and Sarah later wrote that they "came away sick at heart."

The climax of the Grimké crusade came on February 21, 1838, when Angelina spoke before the Massachusetts state legislature:

> I stand before you as a citizen, on behalf of the twenty thousand women of Massachusetts whose names are enrolled on petitions which have been submitted to the legislature. These petitions relate to the solemn subject of slavery. And because it is a political subject, it has often tauntingly been said, that women had nothing to do with it. Are we aliens because we are women? Are we bereft of citizenship because we are mothers, wives and daughters of a mighty people? I hold, Mr. Chairman, that American women have to do with this subject, not only because it is moral and religious, but because it is *political,* inasmuch as we are citizens of this republic and as such our honor, happiness, and well-being are bound up in its politics, government and laws.

For the first time in America's history a woman stood in a legislative hall and argued for the rights of women. As Sarah listened to her sister, she thought, We abolition women are turning the world upside down.

CHAPTER THREE

LOUISA Adams never met the Grimkés, but she closely followed their tour, read their speeches and pamphlets, and found in them connections with her own thinking. Louisa's attitudes about slavery were changing. She now felt "dislike of a system harassing, distressing and degrading to the finer feelings of the heart." Still, she argued for gradual emancipation. "We ought to reflect on their situation," she wrote in 1838, "ere an unfortunate, uneducated, unprepared race should be let loose upon the world without means to provide for themselves or their families and without the religion which prescribes our moral duties."

But as conservative as Louisa was in her social attitudes, she was radical in her politics. "The abolitionist excitement was tremendous," she wrote Charles after listening to a debate in the House. It "inspired a degree of ardor to my hotspur head, full equal in force and energy to their own."

Louisa was now involved every day with the issues of slavery and women's rights. On January 11, 1838, she wrote to Sarah Grimké, setting forth her ideas of women's rights based on her reading of the Bible: that God created man and woman equally.

Sarah soon replied, thanking Louisa for her "valuable & interesting" letter, and saying she thought Louisa's ideas on the creation of Adam and Eve "one of the strongest arguments in favor of the equality of the sexes which has yet been suggested."

Through her letters Sarah Grimké had a profound effect upon Louisa. She sent her books and articles about slavery and asked her opinion regarding a pamphlet of her own recent writings. Louisa protested that her education was inadequate to comprehend all that Sarah taught. She poured out her heart. Her female education, she wrote, made her feel inferior to her husband and other men. Her mind had been wasted with "amusement in the lighter branches of literature, rather than in those solid works which mend the heart and strengthen and improve the mind."

Step by step, Sarah elevated Louisa's vision, encouraging her examination of her fears and prejudices. She urged her to study slavery and emancipation in the Bible, where she would find "indignation & wrath against the oppressor & the imperative command to cease from wickedness." She also led Louisa to make the connection between slavery and women's rights, challenging her to ask herself whether she, as one of "the white slaves of the North," was any different from the black female slaves of the South. Now sixty-three years old, Louisa began to define herself as a woman. She was moving toward an answer to that basic, Adams-like question: What is my purpose in life?

WHILE Louisa and Sarah continued their correspondence, John Quincy relentlessly pursued the fundamental right of petition, and grew to understand, as Louisa did, the broader issue of equality. On August 2, 1838, for example, he told a gathering of women in Hingham, Massachusetts, that "I consider the ladies of this congressional district as much my constituents as their relatives by whose votes I was elected." It is said that women have no political rights, Adams went on, and their petitions are treated by Congress as if they had no rights at all. "But all history refutes this position," he said. He would continue to speak before Congress on "the great question of human rights—the right of petition—the right of women to be heard by the government."

There was something lovable and brave in this old man with the wheezing voice and acid tongue. American women of a wide political spectrum cheered his defiance, and Adams himself gloried in the agitation he was causing. Now in his early seventies, he rose at three every morning when Congress was in session, sorted petitions until eight, breakfasted on boiled milk and stewed peaches, and went to the House for twelve to sixteen hours. His vitality was intertwined with his work. Even when, in 1840, he tripped and dislocated his shoulder, he disobeyed doctor's orders and returned to his desk the next morning, feeble and shaking but determined. Louisa found it "utterly impossible to keep him quiet." Adams understood his need to stay in the struggle. "More than sixty years of incessant active intercourse with the world has made political movement to me as much a necessity of life as atmospheric air," he wrote in his diary. "The world will retire from me before I shall retire from the world."

Adams, who had been so badly beaten just thirteen years earlier, now thrived. In 1841 he even let the abolitionists convince him to join in their defense of thirty-nine kidnapped Africans who had revolted at sea on the schooner *Amistad*. For two days Adams argued their case before the Supreme Court. It was his position that since the men had been found in a state of freedom—after their revolt—they should be set free. If they were not, Adams said, could any human being of this nation be certain of the blessing of freedom? When the court ruled in Adams' favor, he was filled with joy, and wrote to his abolitionist friends: "The captives are free! 'Not unto us! Not unto us!' but thanks, thanks, in the name of humanity and justice to *you*."

Adams continued to have bitter fights on the House floor as he challenged the power of the slaveowners and sympathizers. In

An Exceptional Marriage

January 1842 his opponents decided to silence the cantankerous old man. Adams, as he always did, began the new session by presenting antislavery petitions, proceeding until the Speaker applied the gag rule. But on January 25 Adams read a petition from forty-six citizens of Haverhill, Massachusetts, asking Congress to immediately adopt "measures peaceably to dissolve the Union of these United States." The petition set off a tumultuous protest. Finally Thomas Walker Gilmer of Virginia submitted the following resolution:"Resolved, That in presenting to the consideration of this House a petition for the dissolution of the Union the member from Massachusetts has justly incurred the censure of this House." Here was the southerners' chance: censure would rid them of Adams once and for all.

One after another they rose to speak. The nastiest was Henry Wise. Tall and lean, a Virginia aristocrat and slaveowner, Wise denounced Adams as a "white-haired hypocrite" whose policy was "not yet, not yet, wait a little longer, keep up the excitement, agitate-agitate, keep the slaves in this District like mice to make experiments with." He went on for almost two hours, then closed viciously. "That one should so have outlived his fame! To think of the veneration, the honor, the reverence with which this person might have been loved and cherished." Adams, Wise said, ranked with Benedict Arnold and Aaron Burr. "The gentleman is politically dead; dead as Burr—dead as Arnold."

Adams was barely able to control his temper against Wise's "filthy invective." When he began his defense, he turned it into a defense of human freedom. In his speeches he drew upon the stored strength of years of self-discipline, of early rising and exercise, of his reading of the Bible and Cicero. This was the struggle he had spent his life preparing for. Adams carefully laid out his reply by first detailing the violations of the southerners—their attempts to destroy the rights of habeas corpus, trial by jury, freedom of the mails, of the press, of petition, of free speech itself. Through it all, he was interrupted by threats and questions of order, which only made him tougher.

Adams stood before the House for a week, and no one dared tell him to slow down. After the sixth day of speaking, still in full tongue, he informed the House leaders that he would need another week to complete his arguments. But he offered to sit down if anyone moved to table the question of censure, never to have it taken up again. John Minor Botts of Virginia so moved, and his motion rapidly passed, 106 to 93. Adams had won. But he was not finished with them yet. Before adjournment that same day, the old curmudgeon presented nearly two hundred petitions, and after they were tabled one by one under the gag rule, Adams went home in high spirits. He was scarcely able to crawl up to his chamber, but he did "with the sound of 'Io Triumphe' ringing in my ear."

IN HIS late seventies John Quincy Adams basked in the love and awe of his grandchildren and a public adulation unequaled at any other time in his life.

The family compound in Quincy swarmed with Adams grandchildren, who visited the grandfather they always called the President and the grandmother they addressed as Madame. Charles had built a home on the hill above the Old House, and he and Abby and their large family spent vacations there. Every summer Louisa traveled north with Mary and her daughters, Looly and Fanny, who joined the growing number of children produced by Charles and Abby. Louisa found herself the disciplinarian, while John Quincy, in contrast to himself as a father, often seemed a softhearted old grandpapa.

"Summer was drunken," recalled grandson Henry Adams. The children overran the farm, swam in the sea below the town, marched through the woods, and watched the Plymouth stagecoaches raise dust along the road connecting Quincy with Boston and the world beyond. Summer intoxicated them all.

The only dark cloud had come in 1839, when Fanny had suddenly taken ill with a painful abdominal inflammation—perhaps appendicitis—and, just eight years old, died. That year the Adams house in Washington again grew "painfully gloomy," and Looly stayed out of school for the entire winter.

John Quincy loved his grandchildren and knew that it was no small thing when they loved him. But he tolerated no laxity in his heirs. One day Henry, who stood at the head of his class, stubbornly told his mother he would not go to school. The old President emerged from his study and, without saying a word, gently but firmly took Henry's hand. Silently grandfather and grandson went out the front door, down to the gate, onto the road. John Quincy walked Henry the mile to school, took him through the front door to his desk, saw him in it, and turned and walked back home to his study. Not a word had passed between them, and none was needed.

Charles and Abby found their own children trying. Charles was a good and fair parent but a hypochondriac who thought he shared all the children's diseases. Abby was more sensible but less durable. She was vulnerable, weak, entirely dependent on Charles and her father. In 1843 she was suffering from "nervous depression," headaches, stomach disorders, deafness, and an incessant ringing in her ears. John Quincy saw clearly what was troubling his daughter-in-law. "I believe the chief if not the only cause of her complaint," he wrote Louisa, "is the care of five small children at once."

In July, Abby's physician recommended "a change of air and Scene," and she agreed to take a holiday with her father and oldest son. But to everyone's surprise, John Quincy decided he would go along, too.

Abby's trip disintegrated almost from the start: she felt "dreadfully homesick," and worse, delegations of admirers waylaid her father-in-law at their hotels and stopped their stagecoaches. Abby wrote that at Saratoga Springs, John Quincy basked in the adulation of hundreds of women, and when he departed, they filled the balconies of the hotels and "waved their handkerchiefs." Everywhere they stopped, admirers fired cannons celebrating his arrival; they mobbed him and begged him to change his itinerary and speak to them. Adams tried to resist, but this sentiment was soothing after the painful years of his presidency and the abuse from the House.

Entering Montreal, Canada, Adams found people waving American flags along his route, and in Niagara Falls, a large crowd welcomed him in the rain. A few days later, the good people of Buffalo sailed a Great Lakes steamer to fetch him, and he went aboard, dragging Abby and her father and son like excess baggage. In Buffalo, Abby wrote Charles, "he was received with five thousand cheers and all honors."

Abby and her father tried to quit the tour. John Quincy could not turn down any invitation, and he had worn them out. "I am so cross I can't speak to him," she said. Adams promised that he would not stop at a certain town; but precisely as he spoke the promise, a woman rushed up and urged him to attend a reception there, and he said yes. Later, when invitations from Auburn and Syracuse arrived, John Quincy said yes to both. Abby told Charles she was "cross as a bear." Finally she rebelled, and went on to Saratoga Springs with her father and son.

On his own, Adams slowed not a step. As his train churned across New York State, he wrote in his diary: "Crowds of people were assembled along the track, received me with cheers, and manifested a desire to hear and see me." Adams' popularity reached a level never before equaled by any member of his family.

In October 1843 he traveled to Cincinnati for the laying of a cornerstone at that city's observatory. He was seventy-six, but he rode the railcars and steamers through the approaching cold of winter with boyish vigor, and walked torchlight parades and made late-night speeches. In Cincinnati, he rode under a wide banner that crossed Sixth Street and said JOHN QUINCY ADAMS, THE DEFENDER OF THE RIGHTS OF MAN. Adams, however, did not overlook the women. After one speech, a "very pretty" lady kissed him on the cheek, and he promptly "returned the salute on the lip," he said, "and kissed every woman that followed, at which some made faces but none refused."

Adams spent a week in Cincinnati, and returned home exhausted. The doctor ordered him to bed, and Louisa felt compelled to use her "smart tone" to make JQA obey. Within a few weeks he had recovered health and vigor, and when Congress opened on December 4, Adams immediately presented petitions against slavery and started arguments opposing the annexation of Texas. He had drawn deeply from a summer and autumn of public acclaim.

An Exceptional Marriage

VICTORY SEEMED TO FILL John Quincy Adams' old age. On December 3, 1844, he introduced a resolution to rescind the gag rule, as he had at each opening session of Congress since 1836. To his surprise, the House voted 105 to 80 to adopt his resolution, and the gag rule quietly ended. Adams had worn his opponents down, and won.

John Quincy then turned his attention to the question of the annexation of Texas and the possibility of war with Mexico, which he rightly saw as tied closely to the spread of slavery. "On the subject of War," Louisa said, he "is almost *savage*," and "he thinks the Country on the road to ruin."

Adams went to the House every day to join the debates. Louisa, more and more a nurse to him, thought him "totally unfit to go to Congress." His memory troubled him, his voice was weaker, he was absentminded, "and often neither seems to hear or see." Yet he could not be kept home.

One hot morning two days before his seventy-ninth birthday, Adams impulsively turned during a walk and made his way toward his favorite swimming spot. As he approached, he started peeling off his clothes. Some young men were already churning the Potomac, and one whispered, "There's John Quincy Adams." The old gentleman waded slowly into the river and swam for half an hour, savoring the cool and refreshing feeling, before wading back to the rock where he had tossed his clothing, drying himself in the hot sunlight, dressing, and walking home. He returned the next two mornings, despite temperatures in the low seventies that caused him to shiver as he tried to dry in the sun. Louisa soon put a stop to these shenanigans. "In his present weak state," she wrote Abby, "he frightens me almost out of my life."

In November 1846 Adams accepted the unanimous nomination by the Whigs in his congressional district. He did not have to campaign. His fellow citizens returned him to Congress with a majority of sixteen hundred votes. It was his last election.

Victorious, John Quincy Adams left the Old House and spent the rest of the month with Charles and Abby in Boston, an annual custom, while Louisa went on to Washington. On November 20, after breakfast, Adams started out for a walk with a friend, Dr.

George Parkman, to visit the new Harvard Medical College. Suddenly he seemed to trip, his knees weakening. With the help of Dr. Parkman he staggered back to Charles's house. Adams had suffered a slight stroke. While in no pain, he realized that he had little strength or power of thought. Later he wrote, "From that hour I date my decrease, and consider myself for every useful purpose to myself or my fellow-creatures, dead."

Louisa hurried to Boston. "He is severely stricken," she wrote to Mary upon her arrival. His right arm to the shoulder and right leg from the foot to the knee were numb, and his speech so slurred that only Abby could understand him.

Adams now drew up his last will, and the precision of its thirty-three detailed articles showed that he was not as "dead" as he had proclaimed. He divided the bulk of his estate among Louisa; Mary Hellen Adams and her daughter, Mary Louisa; and his only surviving son, Charles. He left portions to other grandchildren, nephews, and nieces, and scattered his tokens and mementos. To Charles he offered the same opportunity his father had given him: to take full title to the Old House and its land by paying twenty thousand dollars into the estate.

By February 7 John Quincy was well enough to leave for Washington. Soon after his arrival he attended a congressional session. When he walked in, House members stood and applauded the old man they had tried to silence. Here was a statesman of the era, a living link between the nation's beginning and its coming of age. Adams was present at every House session, but he rose and spoke only once—against a proposal to give the owners of the *Amistad* a fifty-thousand-dollar indemnity.

Louisa and John Quincy quietly celebrated their fiftieth wedding anniversary during the summer of 1847 in Quincy, then returned to Washington and opened the F Street house "to the multitudes." They gave a New Year's party, which seemed as festive as those they had given when JQA was Secretary of State. That winter a new generation of Adams ladies sang for their guests, and two of their young gentlemen, said Louisa, "screamed" Swiss mountain songs, accompanied by a guitar "tuned to the highest pitch of discord."

An Exceptional Marriage

On February 21, 1848, John Quincy arrived early at his desk in the House and, before the day's session began, spoke with several members sitting near him. At about one o'clock the Speaker called for ayes and nays on a resolution calling for the awarding of medals and the thanks of Congress to various American generals who had fought in the 1847 campaigns against Mexico. When he called Adams' name, the old man, who thought the Mexican War "most unrighteous," stood and replied with a firm "No!" against the motion—which nonetheless carried the House overwhelmingly.

After his ringing "No!" Adams sat quietly at his desk while the House clerk read another resolution. A reporter at the press table fifteen feet away noticed a deep color tingeing Adams' temples. John Quincy tried to speak, and started to rise, clutching his desk for support, then slumped over an arm of his chair and fell to the floor. "Look to Mr. Adams!" someone shouted, and House members rushed to him. The chamber filled with the whisper "Mr. Adams is dying."

It was fitting that Adams, who so valued duty to his country, would fall while working at his desk in Congress. Members carried him out of the hall on a sofa to the Speaker's room. He revived enough to ask for Henry Clay, who arrived weeping and spent an hour holding his old friend's hand.

Louisa came at two fifteen and bent down to her husband's face, but John Quincy did not recognize her. Four physicians had gathered around Adams, and friends of the family insisted that Louisa return home, which she did. JQA could speak a little, and had no pain. That evening he murmured his last words, "This is the end of earth, but I am composed."

For more than two days the old statesman lay dying. The entire U.S. government adjourned business and waited and prayed. Louisa returned to her husband's side, then passed the second night in one of the committee rooms, reclining on a sofa.

After Adams' collapse, John G. Palfrey, a member of the House, and a close friend, had sent a messenger to the telegraph office. New lines between Washington, Baltimore, Philadelphia, New York, and Boston had only recently been opened, and often failed, but Palfrey kept a young man standing by during the next two days, getting messages through whenever he could. His first, sent to Charles Francis Adams, clicked later that afternoon into the Boston Magnetic Telegraph. It began: DEAR ADAMS: YOUR FATHER FAINTED HALF AN HOUR AGO . . . Charles rushed from Boston.

Several times John Quincy's pulse stopped, only to return even stronger. But on the evening of the twenty-third, when Palfrey briefly left his place in the Capitol, a messenger hurriedly called him back. By the time he reached the Speaker's room, he found it crowded but silent. John Quincy Adams had died.

Louisa learned the news almost as soon as Palfrey. She remained in the F Street house with Mary and the younger Adamses. Palfrey visited that evening and found her "comfortable and calm."

The nation Adams loved and served fell to mourning. The House members unanimously agreed that one member from every state and territory would escort Adams' body home to Quincy. President Polk directed that all executive offices in Washington be closed for two days; the national flag was flown at half-mast and army officers wore crape. At dawn on every military post, thirteen guns were fired, and in Washington, every half hour from sunrise to sunset a single cannon boomed in mourning for the old gentleman, followed at sunset by "a national salute of twenty-nine guns."

On February 26, from dawn until the funeral procession began at noon, the rumble of cannons filled every minute. Adams' silver-mounted coffin, decorated with the American eagle and covered with evergreen boughs and early spring flowers, had lain in state for two days in the House. At ten minutes before noon the Speaker called the House of Representatives to order, and as the bell on Capitol Hill tolled, walking to its slow rhythm, the President, Vice-President, the justices of the Supreme Court, diplomats, army and navy officers, senators, Charles Francis Adams, Mary Hellen, and, finally, Louisa Adams, entered and seated themselves. The service marked the first of dozens that would take place over the next month. Not since Washington's death had there been such a public mourning, and not until the death of

An Exceptional Marriage

Abraham Lincoln, then an obscure House member, would there be such an enormous funeral procession.

A week later, the congressional Committee of Escort took John Quincy home by funeral train for burial. Flags along the route flew at half-mast, and people lined the tracks, with their heads bowed. In Boston, a huge crowd met the train, and the coffin was placed on a carriage pulled by six black horses trimmed in crape, with heavy black plumes on their heads. The procession made its way to Faneuil Hall through streets thronged with mourners. The following day, the coffin was taken to Quincy, and as the body entered the town, small cannons were fired from the top of Penn's Hill, where John Quincy as a boy had watched with his mother the battles of the Revolutionary War. The procession paused at the Old House and at the church; neighbors carried the coffin into the family tomb and put John Quincy Adams to rest with his mother, father, sister, and his sons George and John. And as citizens and dignitaries filed past the vault, one of the members of the Committee of Escort stepped forward, and with trembling voice said in the soft tones of the South, "Good-by, Old Man."

ALTHOUGH ill almost continuously after John Quincy's death, Louisa Adams lived comfortably. She received rental income from a house in Washington which John Quincy had purchased from her sister Harriet Boyd. In addition Louisa's brother, Thomas, who had died some years earlier, had left her ten thousand dollars; and her funds, placed in Charles's care, were now earning five hundred dollars in interest every quarter. She was, Charles assured her, well off. She refurbished the parlor at F Street, bought new horses for her carriage, and entertained again.

In April 1849, with spring "bursting on us in all its natural beauty," Louisa suffered a stroke. She grew deaf and her eyesight dimmed. She spent the next three years in "quiet and contented infirmity."

Charles traveled to Washington every six months to see his mother; his father's death had changed him. He told Louisa that "the first feeling of standing alone, and having others looking to me for guidance is novel and startling." Earlier Charles had served in both branches of the Massachusetts legislature. In 1848 the Free-Soil Party had nominated Martin Van Buren for President and Charles Francis Adams for Vice-President, but they were defeated.

Louisa cherished the visits and attention of this son "whom I never deserted." She still felt guilty about having left George and John when they were children, "a penance which I trust God in His mercy will pardon and accept."

During her last years, Louisa lost sight of, but not her interest in, the women's movement. Although she was too old and too timid to join in the activities of the feminists, she had a combative desire to find some small way to give meaning to her life as a woman. Louisa thought about it, prayed for it, and when at last the idea came, it arrived with the suddenness and the power of a true and good act.

In 1846 she had hired a cook named Julia, planning to take her to Quincy that summer. But Julia was a slave, and Louisa had found that she could not take her north without posting a large bond against Julia's escaping. In 1847 Louisa had again wished to take Julia with her to Quincy. But Julia's owner refused. For one thing, Julia, by working as a cook, had already purchased half the cost of her freedom—that is, half her value on the Washington slave market. She needed two hundred dollars more, "and that must not be risked," said Louisa with irony. So Louisa herself bought the title to the enslaved black woman and set her free.

John Quincy Adams had negotiated great treaties, expanded the nation sea to sea, brought armies to peace, and, as an old man, stood alone against the slaveholders, but he had never reached out to one frightened, lonely human being. Louisa Adams did. In so doing, she freed part of herself.

During the winter of 1852, Louisa fell gravely ill. A victim of strokes and a weakened heart, she could not sleep or defeat the pain that raged within her; her hands and arms puffed up "like cushions." Finally, on her deathbed, heavily dosed with pain-killing opium, her mind drifted. She asked every day if Clay were dead. She dreamed that Charles had come from Quincy but was

An Exceptional Marriage

ill and walking with a cane. She asked about Mary, Abby, and Looly.

Louisa loved spring best of all the seasons. In the May preceding his death John Quincy had written to her from New England and reminded her of those springtime days of their youth, when they had read from the Song of Solomon the incomparable words of the coming of the season:

> *For, lo, the winter is past, the rain is over and gone;*
> *The flowers appear on the earth; the time of the singing of birds is come, and the voice of the turtle is heard in our land;*
> *The fig tree putteth forth her green figs, and the vines with the tender grape give a good smell. Arise, my love, my fair one, and come away.*

Louisa had remembered, and had written back that she welcomed the end of life's struggles, ambitions, toils, and the "blessed promise held forth to us, in the prospect of that eternal Spring which shall know no change, but which shall endure for ever and forever." Now she rallied and sank, rallied and sank, stubborn to the end. She seemed to be waiting, and only when April flowered to May did she let go. Surrounded by the blossoms John Quincy had planted around their F Street home, Louisa Catherine Adams, her life's promise fulfilled, died at noon, May 15, 1852.

Writer on the Run

For Jack Shepherd, one of the great pleasures of being a journalist is waking up every morning and wondering, What's the new thing for today? That kind of curiosity has long been a part of Shepherd's life: at age eleven he was producing a neighborhood newspaper in northern New Jersey that had a circulation of fifty-five and sold for a penny a copy.

Since then, as a reporter for *Look* magazine and later as a free-lancer, Shepherd has written on subjects ranging from civil rights sit-ins in the South to the drug culture in the northern cities, from drought in East Africa to war in Nigeria. His books have covered topics such as forest conservation and the politics of famine relief. He has written screenplays and television documentaries, and is the author of *The Adams Chronicles*, the book prepared in conjunction with the 1976 Bicentennial television series of the same name. It was his work on that project that spurred him to write the personal biography of JQA and Louisa, his ninth book.

Jack Shepherd

Jack Shepherd lives on an eighteen-acre homestead in Norwich, Vermont, with his wife, Kathy, their two teenage children, and various cats and stray dogs. The author of *The Runner's Handbook* (with Robert Glover), Shepherd is a dedicated jogger, and most days runs the five miles between his home and the Dartmouth College library, in Hanover, New Hampshire, where he researches new books and magazine articles. He writes continually, turning experience into prose. But he always allows himself a break at the end of April. "Then," he says, "there's trout fishing."

PHOTO BY EDWARD BONNER

TEXAS DAWN

A CONDENSATION OF THE NOVEL BY
Phillip Finch

At their feet lay the valley that they and
their children would battle to possess.

ILLUSTRATED BY DAVID BLOSSOM

At the close of the war, three Confederate Army soldiers struck out across the country to tame the wild range into what would become the biggest spread in Texas.

Now, a rigorous lifetime later, the daughter of one of those soldiers is being laid to rest. But her story, the legend of Rose Ellen Fowler, will not be forgotten—not if young Donnie Lee has anything to say about it. As he and his friend Sue Everitt piece together Rose Ellen's colorful life, they learn of the grit that built an empire—and of true love's power to defy the passing of the years.

The World of the Circle Three Bar

Trail Drives
- First trail drive – 1866
- Ray Newsome's first trail drive
- Newsome and Sample's trail drive
- Charlie Fowler's last trail drive
- Fictional

Donnie Lee: We got off school early to go to the funeral, even the Mexicans from down-valley that didn't know Miz Rose Ellen Sample—which was how I heard her called for most of sixteen years.

We stood out front, Tom Holloway and me, and waited for our mamas to pick us up and take us to the church. I peeked out the corner of one eye at Sue Everitt to catch her looking at me. Tom had joshed me pretty good about me wearing my Sunday suit, with the creases pressed so sharp in the pants. I did feel a mite strange until I saw Sue E. give me a sort of sideways up-and-down look and then a smile full-on. I stuck my shoulders back and smiled at her.

My mama and Tom's come along directly, together with our sisters, in the new Buick that was my daddy's to drive, him being straw boss of the southern division of the Circle Three Bar, biggest ranch in this part of Texas. Tom's daddy had come by in the morning with the pickup that he drove as straw of the Box CF, Rose Sample's place, and he and my daddy had left together.

That was something you might not have seen two years ago. Some say there was bad blood between the two outfits. You might be pals with a fella for as far back as you could remember, then one day all of a sudden he'd be calling you a Circle Three bum and you'd call him a Box C so-and-so and the fists would start to fly. It happened once with me and Tom.

Tom and I squeezed into the back of the Buick. His mother shoved a suit coat at him and said to get himself presentable.

Riding through town was right peculiar. It was shut down like Sunday midnight, and this was a Wednesday afternoon. Everybody was going to the old lady's funeral. You can imagine the tangle of cars and people when we got to the church.

Our daddies was waiting when we slid into the pew. Ahead of us was family of all sorts and the mayor and commissioners from six counties, plus the foremen of the two ranches and their families in the pew right in front of us. Behind us were hands and their kin and what townsfolk could squeeze in. The rest was outside and was to listen to the preaching, if you can believe it, over loudspeakers borrowed from the school stadium.

The organ was lowing, and soon the preacher begun to pray. While I did not listen to all the words, I felt sad all the same. She was a good old lady, from what little I knew of her. I had met her once in a while on the street and called her Miz Rose, the way she liked, and she always smiled at me. It did upset me some to think of her there in that wooden box.

Finally the words was finished. Then it was off to the cemetery, where there was an even bigger crowd. And the flowers! For every person around the grave, there must have been a dozen roses. I caught sight of Sue Everitt, and I must have been making eyes at her because my sisters giggled and my daddy squeezed my shoulder until I thought he would break it and he said, Damn your hide, Donnie Lee, show a little respect. This was a fine lady. That shut my sisters up right quick. I stared down at my boot tips sticking out from under my cuffs.

Then there was a line headed up to the grave. Everybody grabbed a flower out of the bunches setting there and tossed it onto the casket down in the hole. When I got closer, I saw two marble headstones standing side by side. The words on one of them said RAYMOND NEWSOME and then in smaller letters

CATTLEMAN and the dates, SEPTEMBER 2, 1866—APRIL 11, 1950. Green grass was just now sprouting out of the fresh earth over the grave, for this was the second time in just six weeks we had missed an afternoon of school for a burial.

I looked at the old lady's headstone to see whether they had put Sample or Newsome on it. But what it said was ROSE ELLEN FOWLER. It was the first time I ever heard her name that way. Under the big letters of the name was the same CATTLEMAN, which didn't strike me funny until later, and the dates, JANUARY 9, 1865—MAY 28, 1950.

I grabbed a rose and threw it in without looking.

On the way down the hill from the cemetery everybody drove a sight faster than they had driven up. Our family was together in the Buick. Side by side forever, said my mama in the front seat. I think that is so sweet, the two of them like that until the end of time. I seen her reach across and squeeze my daddy's arm. Myself, I could not see what the fuss was about.

Though I suppose you could not argue with what my daddy said—which was that she was a woman like they don't make anymore and had done a heap of living in her time.

CHAPTER ONE

THEY tramped down the Georgia road, three men weary from war, the trousers of their gray uniforms coated with dust.

"How far now, Charlie?" one of them asked.

"Four and a half miles."

Charlie Fowler was coming home, about to see his wife and his baby daughter, born since his last furlough. He thought of his wife, tried to imagine her face when she heard his plans.

These are our partners, he would tell her. Earl Newsome and Orrin Sample. They are going to Texas, and so are we. We're going into the cattle business, dear. We'll go from eighty acres to eighteen thousand. That would swing it. Olive always wanted to get ahead.

They had been married a year when the war came. He had

Texas Dawn

been nineteen and a farm boy. She had been barely sixteen, a girl from the town four miles away. She had been unsatisfied with the farm, he knew. He could not make her feel the pleasure he got from his eighty acres. He wanted her to be happy; now, after five years of war, he craved harmony more than ever.

"Charlie," Newsome said, "you change your mind, it is no hard feelings with Orrin and me. A thousand in gold is a lot for you to go putting into something you never seen. You got a family and a farm. Me and Orrin got nothing to lose."

"What are you saying? I want to do this," Fowler said. "We are going to buy that ranch."

The three men had met at a Confederate field hospital a few months earlier, all wounded in the same nameless skirmish, five days before the end of the war. Sample was nineteen, infantry, from Beaumont, Texas. Newsome was twenty-two, cavalry, from Front Royal, Virginia. Fowler was twenty-four, artillery, from Monroe County, Georgia. By the end of the fourth day they were closer than some brothers ever are, and they made plans.

Sample knew about that land in Texas. He had the dream. There were eighteen thousand acres belonging to his mother's cousin. She was a war widow who wanted to sell. Fowler had the down payment. Almost a thousand in gold, some inherited and the rest from selling off his stock and his single slave before the war. He had buried the gold before he went off to fight.

The two couldn't leave out Newsome. He was one of them. Besides, he could ride. And the three of them, together this way, made Fowler feel confident and sure, as if there were no limit to what they could accomplish.

They walked along the road, closer now to Fowler's farmhouse. At Fowler's right was Sample, squat and strong, with the face of a fat bashful boy on the body of a blacksmith. To the other side was Newsome, the tallest of them and the most handsome. His face was burnished and tough, with a crescent scar on one cheek and a nose that had been broken once. His way of moving was unhurried, athletic. All this suggested to Fowler a man who had done things and would do more.

Fowler thought of Olive, watching them approach, and he

walked faster. Through a break in the hedgerows that lined the road he saw the house, on the far side of his eighty. He burst through the bushes and into the tall grass that now grew in his fallow fields. Burrs and foxtails stuck to his pants as he ran.

He was halfway across the field when a hint of dread made him stop. Something about the house, something not right. Then he ran toward it faster.

The house was empty, the front door half open in a sad, wanton welcome. Weeds grew around the foundation. Fowler stood staring, then threw his head back to scream at the sky.

"Damn those bluebellies," he said. "Damn them to hell."

But then he saw that the Yankees had had nothing to do with this. Behind the house, where he had buried his gold, there were ragged holes dug in the red hardpan. A spade and a pick had been left beside one of them. When Fowler saw this, he knew that Olive had left and had tried first to find the gold.

She had never been able to remember his directions for finding the cache. One line from the north corner of the henhouse to the door of the shed. Another line from the house's back door to the big elm. Where the lines crossed, the gold was buried two feet down. He dug it up now, heavy gold pieces, in the tobacco sack he had filled five years earlier.

Fowler looked up at Newsome and Sample, who had been watching him. He felt the urge to apologize, explain. "She up and left me. She never was sweet on this place," he said. "And five years is a long time for a man to be gone."

A vague sense of duty made him set out to visit the neighbors to ask about Olive and where she had taken his daughter.

At the farm that bordered Fowler's on the west, a baby was squalling in a crib on the front porch. The three men stood and looked at it for a few moments.

"That is your daughter, Charlie," a woman said behind him.

Fowler picked up the bawling baby and cradled her against his chest. Her yelling grew louder at first but then subsided. She reached out with a chubby hand and grabbed his chin.

"I told you about my daughter, boys. Rose is her name, and ain't it fitting! Will you look at the color in her cheeks?"

Texas Dawn

The neighbor's name was Amelia Williams. She was in her forties, pudgy and graying. Her husband, Noah, was ten years older. They'd had two boys, lost one at Chickamauga, the other at Gettysburg.

"It's near five weeks that we've had Rose," Amelia said. "A lieutenant come through on his way home from the front, started talking Charleston to your Olive. She brought the baby here and said we could have your milk cow to keep the child fed. But you'll be needing the milk now that you have the child."

Fowler rocked the baby. "I have to be leaving her," he said. "Me and the boys here are off to Texas to be cattlemen. It will be some time before I can come back for her."

"Why, you can leave her, sure enough," Amelia said. "We love the little thing. She is a pure joy."

Noah killed a rooster that afternoon, and Amelia fried it. And there remained a splash or two at the bottom of Noah's squeezins jug. After dinner the men went to sit on the front porch; they watched the moon slide up over the trees.

"Noah," Fowler said, "I want to thank you for what you've done, caring for my daughter."

"It is the proper thing," Noah said, "and not such a trial. I want you to know if . . . if you can't make it back as soon as you plan, you can rest easy about little Rose."

"I know that," Fowler said. The couple would be happy, he thought, if he never returned.

Before he left the next morning, Fowler held the baby up at arm's length. He wanted to remember her in his hands—her laugh, the curl of the tuft on her head, her tiny clutching fingers.

He kissed her and laid her down in the crib. Then he walked to the road, with Sample and Newsome behind him.

SAMPLE's parents lived a few miles from the Gulf of Mexico, not far from the Louisiana line. They were renters, farming a cotton patch. His mother's cousin, Eliza, had been with them since her husband's death. She was ready to sell her ranch. But not to family. She didn't wish to pass on to kin the heartache and the trouble that went with that place.

"How much are you asking?" Fowler said.

"There are eighteen thousand acres. I would have to get ten cents an acre," Eliza said.

"Stock?"

"It's yours if you can find it. Cows and horses both."

"Buildings?"

"There was a house where I lived with my husband."

"What about barns, sheds, and the like?"

"You seem to have the idea that this is some sort of plantation. I and my husband hung on there for thirteen years and never did we feel that we owned the place. It belonged to the floods and the drought, the heat and the chill."

Newsome spoke up. "People say there is money in beef."

"There is. Out there a million cows is running free, waiting for somebody to catch 'em, and every one will fetch at least twenty in Saint Joseph."

"Twenty dollars a head," Sample said.

"If it was as easy as picking apples," she said, "everybody would be out there doing it. You would rather try to catch a buffalo than a Texas steer. That's why I don't want to sell to kin."

They needed two days of talking to convince her to sell. The fact that a stranger's money was to be down payment clinched it. Fowler paid her six hundred in gold. She took a note for twelve hundred more, payable in a year.

The place was easy to find, she told them. Follow the Brazos River fifty miles past the end of the white man's territory. South then until they found the biggest valley they ever saw. The ranch was there, in Mansos Valley.

"It's a Mex word," she said. "*Mansos* means tame. Somebody had a real wit."

She drew a map and wrote a list of supplies. These, and two mules to carry them, and horses for the partners, brought them close to the end of Fowler's gold.

The days were hot as they rode, and the men were grateful that Eliza had insisted on wide-brimmed hats. As they left behind the lush coastal plain, the land grew hilly and arid. The horses' flanks were wet and slick as they climbed.

Texas Dawn

One morning they reached the crest of a ridge, and the land they had been seeking lay before them.

They saw a vastness of grass, a high carpet pocked by thickets of oak and laced by deep gullies—arroyos, the native born called them—where manzanita brush and prickly-pear cactus grew among the rocks. The scope of it awed them. Unbroken hills stretched right and left beyond the eye's reach. To the west, across the valley, was another line of high hills. They were so distant that the men saw them only as wrinkles on the horizon.

Fowler blinked and looked at Sample and Newsome, who were staring out from astride their horses, out at the valley. He saw on their faces the look of men about to go into battle.

THE life that lay before them was fraught with every possibility of failure. But the three men were as fit for it as any could be.

The future would need men with deft hands, quick eyes, and the skills to use them well. Earl Newsome was such a man. He could ride, shoe, and doctor a horse; could carve a wheel spoke, frame a house, and sharpen an axe; could sole a boot, put a bullet where he aimed it. In seventy years it would be a Texan's conceit to imagine himself the man that Earl Newsome was: capable and laconic, a man of actions, quick decisions, impulse—built with just the right slimness of hip and breadth of shoulder. He was a tall man, and there was a masculine grace in his stride.

The new life would demand physical strength, too. Orrin Sample had that, and the will to use it. He was short, with heavy shoulders, wide chest, and stocky legs. He was not handsome, not even plain. He moved slowly, and his speech was deliberate, hesitant. He was a kind man, gentle in most situations, always unassuming. Yet he brought muscle to the partnership—and more than the other two would have guessed as they sat overlooking the valley that hot day in early September.

Finally, the new life would need thinkers. Skills and strength needed direction, vision beyond the next job. Charlie Fowler was a thinker. His acts were rarely automatic. He considered possibilities. He glimpsed the faint thread that ran from an act one day to its consequences later. He bothered to look at the future that sprawled ahead. His partners already were deferring to his judgment, waiting for his decisions. And his gold had bought them this chance.

That was the partnership. It was ideal for what the three men faced. There is no longer any job like the one that confronted them that first year in Mansos Valley. The land will never again be so gloriously, frustratingly open, the cattle never so wild.

Sample, Fowler, and Newsome made camp beside the Mansos River, near what was left of the homestead: a four-room board-and-batten house with a sagging roof, a lean-to shed on one side, and two corrals that were the only man-made enclosures for twenty miles in any direction.

Thousands of long-legged, lean-flanked cattle roamed the open grasslands and dense thickets that made up the property. Some of the cows bore the brand of the ranch that the partners had bought, and thus were theirs by law. Others showed the brands and ear cuts of two neighboring spreads, both abandoned during the war. Still others, never marked, were for the taking by the first person to mark their hides with a hot iron. The partners decided to brand as many cattle as they could that fall and winter, then start a roundup in the spring for the drive to a market. With the money they got, they would pay Eliza's note and buy supplies for the next year.

Newsome, who knew horses, said that the mounts they had bought in Beaumont would not be enough for the work they had to do. Each man would need a cutting horse for close work in a herd, another for rim-riding the canyons with their steep slopes, another for night-riding on the drive.

The partners chased wild horses for three days before finally trapping half a dozen in a narrow, closed arroyo. They got ropes on them and led them back to the corral, and Newsome spent the next three weeks breaking them to bit and saddle. In the last ten days he drew a chestful of pain with every breath; a truculent mare had planted a hoof in his ribs after throwing him. But when he was finished, the horses could be ridden.

The ranch's old branding irons were in the lean-to, and the men set to work. But they found the cattle quicker, more skittish,

Texas Dawn

and more long-winded than they had expected. The cows plunged through thickets and leaped gullies and matched the fastest horses' speed across the flatland. None of the men could throw an open noose. Their best hope was to run a cow into thick mesquite, then slip a noose over its wide horns as it struggled in the brush. Sample and Newsome roped the cows, while Fowler heated the iron and pressed the ranch's mark into the hide and then notched the ears.

After a few days their bodies ached from lumps and cuts and bruises and saddle sores. The idea of putting together a herd of these creatures and driving them several hundred miles seemed more improbable every day.

They were ready for help when Paco Alvarez and Camilo Ortiz came riding toward the campfire one evening. They were on their way home to Matamoros, Alvarez said. They needed a meal; Fowler motioned them down.

"We are vaqueros," Alvarez said. Ortiz spoke no English. "We been north, but we didn't find work. No better than when the war was on."

"What kind of work does a vaquero do?" Fowler asked.

When Alvarez realized that this was not a joke he said, "A vaquero, my friend, works with cows."

"How long have you been doing that work?" Fowler asked.

Alvarez shrugged. "I start when I am a boy in Mexico. Six years there. Then nine years up the Nueces. I learned to speak Americano there."

"Can you rope cows?" Fowler said.

Alvarez searched for the humor that Fowler so obviously intended. But he saw no hint of it in his eyes, steady on him across the campfire.

Fowler got up. "If you sat on your horse where it is now, and I was running away from you with my arms like this, could you throw the rope and catch me around my stomach?" He raised his arms above his head, spreading them wide in a semicircle.

Alvarez smiled then. "I understand now. Yes," he said.

He stood and walked to his horse, stepped up into the saddle, and picked up a coiled rope from where it lay slung across the saddle horn. "You are the cow, yes? And you want me to throw the reata over your horns and around your belly. But that is not how a vaquero would do it."

"Then do it your way," Fowler said. He ran, arms spread high.

Alvarez waited until Fowler was at the dim edge of the campfire's light, and then he threw. The rope floated out, kicking loose one coil after another. Fowler glanced over one shoulder, looked up for the rope that he thought must be descending on him. But at that moment the ground fell away from his feet, as the rope looped instead around one of his ankles. His chin was the first part of his body to touch earth again.

"Look at that," Fowler said dazedly as he sat up in the dirt. "Will you look at what he did? That is a marvel, for certain." He looked up at Newsome and Sample. "Partners," he said softly, "we need these boys."

The Mexicans hired on through the spring drive, working for food and ten percent of the take. By moving camp once a week, they could brand thirty head on a good day. At first Alvarez and Ortiz did all the roping. But the others took turns riding with them, and by January each of them could rope a cow and tie it.

The cold nights brought them together around the campfire. They tried to teach Ortiz to speak English. Alvarez, in turn, threw Spanish and cowboy slang at his riding partners. One night Ortiz broke silence with a song. Later they found that Sample could sing, too, more clearly and sweetly than any of them.

Sometimes they talked as they lay in their bedrolls. It was easier to speak of serious matters this way because they did not have to look at each other. They could say the words to the sky and the stars. Sometimes the talk was of women, of loves won, lost, and imagined.

Fowler alone did not talk of women. He had loved his wife, and there was a sadness, a hole in him that he was filling with work and with dreams.

BY THE end of January they were ready to herd. They needed men and food for the drive, so Alvarez rode south to Matamoros and returned with five more vaqueros. Newsome rode with

Texas Dawn

Fowler to buy supplies. They brought back a wagon and two mules, coffee, sugar, flour, beans, and a three-legged Dutch oven.

Meanwhile, Sample and Ortiz had not been idle. Before he left, Alvarez had found a long box canyon with sides too steep for even a longhorn to climb. There was a spring on the canyon floor, and some grass. They would need a place to keep the herd as it was gathered, he said. With old fencing, trees, and brush they cut and piled, Sample and Ortiz closed off the mouth of the canyon, leaving only a gate.

They began to herd at the end of February, and within a week they had put almost nine hundred cows inside the canyon. They could have tripled the number, but the grass was gone after a week and the cows were hungry and restless. It was time to move them, time to drive.

At dawn of the eighth day the vaqueros opened the gate. At first the cows poured through it. Then they broke through the fencing and the barrier of brush, and the canyon was empty in less than a minute. The herd was a dark mass of noisy life that shook the earth as it passed. But it was together, with mounted men strung out beside it to keep it contained.

Watching from the wagon, Sample chucked the reins and pointed the mules after the herd.

On this, their first drive, Newsome and Sample and Fowler were lucky men. None of the rivers were flooding when they forded. Though they passed through Indian Territory, they did not face Cherokee warriors. Men, horses, and cows stayed healthy. For the last two months of the drive the grass was good, and the cattle put on weight as they grazed up through the Kansas grasslands. And when the herd arrived in Saint Joseph, the price of beef was up.

The herd checked in at 811 head. Fowler got an offer of $31 a head from the first broker he visited and talked him up to $35. He left the office with a draft in his pocket for $28,385.

Newsome, Sample, and Alvarez were waiting outside. "We are rich men," Fowler told them, and held the piece of paper up for them to see. Then he walked across the street to a bank and cashed the draft.

They took hotel rooms. A double eagle slipped across the registration desk quieted the mutterings about cowboys. They bathed and got haircuts and bought clean clothes, and that night they ate French food, all ten of them at one table.

They whooped and shouted and sang, and they were all drunk when they left the restaurant, stumbling, leaning against one another for balance. Fowler hung back, and found Alvarez at his side. "Paco, can we do this every year?"

"You're a ranchero now," Alvarez said. "You own land as far as you can see. You own more cows than you can count. The cows are there. They keep making more cows."

"Paco, you'll stay with us, won't you?"

"This is much money, my share. I could buy a farm. I could find a wife, maybe. Get out of this wandering life."

The next morning the three partners were sober, and silent with awe at the reality of it. They paid the Mexicans, and what remained stunned them—Sample and Newsome because they had never had so much and were sure they never would again, and Fowler because he saw what the capital could do for the ranch.

They sold their horses, mules, and wagon, and with their earnings hidden in carpetbags, they took passage on a riverboat south.

As they traveled, Fowler prodded the others into making plans. They had to spend their money well. Another year's horses, mules, and wagons, and supplies, of course. Lumber and mortar to repair the old house, if they could find a way to ship the material. "And I think we ought to buy land," Fowler said.

"Land!" said Newsome. "If you ask me, we don't need it, long as there are cattle and range. It ain't only our cows that tallow up on our grass, and ours don't know where the property line is either, for that matter. I don't see it, Charlie."

"It can't hurt," Fowler said. His reason was more specific. One evening the past winter he had looked at the valley and pondered what it would mean if someone one day put a fence around his own property and chased out all but his own animals. Then you would need grass and water of your own. The more you had of those, the more cows you could run. Anyone could see that.

"Besides," he said, "if we can buy the spreads next to ours, our job will be that much easier. We won't spend time running down cows that turn out to have somebody else's brand on 'em. We'll know that every cow on our range will belong to us."

Then Sample spoke, watching the faces of the other two. "We ought to have our own brand," he said slowly, "that never belonged to nobody before. We can start to use it this winter, and in a few years there won't be a cow on the range that doesn't have our mark on it."

"Sure," Fowler said. "We will all think on it some and try to come up with a proper one."

"I been thinking already," Sample said. He brought from a pocket a piece of paper. The symbol drawn on it showed three horizontal parallel bars within a circle.

"These three lines," Sample said, pointing with a stubby finger, "is us. And the circle is because we are all three together in one, see? So it would be the Circle Three Bar."

At Vicksburg, Fowler left the steamer and bought a horse. He knew that now, if ever, he had to claim his daughter. If he waited another year, it would be a cruel thing to take her from the only home she had ever known.

NOAH Williams saw the horse coming up the road. When Fowler reached the house, Noah and Amelia were standing at the door. The little girl was between them, eyes wide and unblinking.

"Charlie Fowler," Amelia said. "I mean you no harm, but I hoped I'd never see you again."

"Amelia," Noah said.

"No, I understand," Fowler said. "But she's my daughter and I want her with me."

All day Fowler watched Rose, trying to comprehend the truth that this being, this miracle, was his daughter and part of him. Rose Ellen was nearly two years old now. She could walk and could speak some words clearly. She played with a calico kitten and a cloth doll stuffed with straw. When Amelia took up a broom to sweep the floor, Rose held one cut down to her own size and brushed behind her.

Charlie Fowler was shocked. He had imagined her still an infant in her crib.

"You'll be taking her tomorrow morning?" Amelia Williams asked during dinner.

"Waiting will only make it harder."

"I want to ask you about this place you're taking her to." Were there children nearby? she wanted to know. Women to care for her when the men were working? Schools? Doctors? And then, "Do you even have a house, I hope, for her to live in?"

"Not yet," Fowler said.

Amelia Williams stabbed with her fork at a scrap of food. "We won't let her go with you alone," she said calmly. "This so-called ranch is no place for a child who does not have a mother. You can take her if you want, but you take us as well. We will make the best of whatever we find there."

So in two days they sold their farm to the first taker; Fowler had decided to keep his eighty acres. They loaded their belongings into a wagon, and the four of them traveled by road, ferry, and trail to the ranch in Mansos Valley.

THE child found her new existence even richer than the one she had known in Georgia. The isolation of the place and the obstacles it threw up to the men did not concern her. She had Noah and Amelia, as well as her father and his partners.

She drew the soft side of the men to her and repaid love with love. Sample sang to her and bounced her on one big knee. Newsome built a crude house for her doll, even fashioned a bed from oak and dried rawhide when she outgrew her crib.

In her father she inspired wonder, for she was so unlike anything he had known. It was the beginning of an uncomplicated love that lasted as long as he lived.

She was happy, in part because the men were, too. She was sensitive, as children are, to undercurrents of emotion. During her childhood the partners were pleased with themselves and with their work, full of optimism and belief as the ranch grew. She sensed this and it brought her security.

She first sat on a horse when she was three years old. When

her father held her up to the saddle, she was startled but tried not to give away her fright. She wanted to please him. Not long after her fourth birthday he returned from a two-week trip to Austin with a tired little runt of an Indian pony, her first horse. She rode alone before she was five.

About that time Amelia began teaching her to cook. Her father was already spending evenings with her when he could, teaching her words and numbers.

It would not have mattered then if she had been homely. No one would have loved her less. But her face was delicate and symmetrical, except for a chin that soon asserted itself, strong but not overpowering. By the time she was four Fowler and the others realized that she was blessed with a natural beauty. She was, Amelia assured Fowler, taller than most boys at that age.

Except for Amelia, she knew only men. She acquired many of the skills that are supposed to be masculine: roping, shooting, hitting a nail on its head until it is buried. Less apparent, but just as real, were the confidence, pride, and self-reliance that she took from her father and the others.

She had lived more than four years on the ranch when the life that had been so full of love was interrupted. Neither it, nor she, ever was quite the same again.

Rose awoke before first light that day, a morning in early spring. Newsome was out on the range with most of the hands, getting ready for the spring drive. Sample and Fowler were going to ride out to join them, and Fowler would return in the evening. He was spending more time now with contracts and ledgers than with cows and horses.

Amelia was already up, cracking eggs into a skillet and boiling water for coffee. Rose Ellen followed the aroma of the coffee into the kitchen and clambered into her father's lap.

"How far are you riding today, Papa?"

"Up where the Mansos forks. Do you know where that is?"

She had not traveled more than three miles from the house since the day she arrived. But there was a hand-drawn map of the property tacked on a wall of her father's office. She studied the map often and asked questions.

"Yes, Papa. Where you catched the big roan last year."

"Where we *caught* it. It's about ten miles from here."

"Papa, I want to ride with you today. I can go that far."

"No." He bent to sip the coffee that Amelia poured for him. "And if you want to know why, it is because you don't ride well enough yet. You just aren't strong enough to ride that far."

She put her lips into a pout.

"And last of all, you don't belong out there," he said.

That brought a satisfied smile to Amelia's face. She did not approve of Rose Ellen's riding, or learning to shoot a gun, or wearing britches—which she did, at least half the time.

The sun had risen when they finished breakfast. Rose Ellen stood in the doorway after her father had lifted her up to kiss her. She clutched one leg, then released him, and stood watching as he and Sample mounted and rode off.

Amelia heated water for dishes. She did the washing; Rose Ellen dried. Then, since the day was the warmest in several weeks, Rose Ellen went outside to play in the sunshine, with the plains and the openness all around her.

After lunch she sat at the dining table to practice her letters. She would write her name ten times on a page; that would make her father happy when he returned.

Rose Ellen was fashioning the letters when she heard an unfamiliar noise from the back of the house, where Noah and Amelia were putting in a garden. It was a few steps to her father's office, where she could stand on a chair and look out the window to the back.

She saw three men she did not know beating Noah and Amelia. One of them was raising Amelia's shovel and swinging it down on her head. The two others were on Noah, grappling with him.

Rose Ellen heard a noise at the front door, then the scrape of boots on the floor. She hid in the first place she saw, a cabinet with solid doors in which her father kept guns and bullets and caps and powder. She closed the doors until only a thin slit of light showed.

Now she heard the footsteps crossing the front room. She became aware of the butt of her father's pistol against her shoulder in the hiding place. It was the approach of those scraping footfalls that made her reach for the gun, cock the trigger, and hold it with both hands out in front of her. The footsteps grew louder, and she told herself that she would have to disobey her father.

He had told her, the first time he took her shooting, "A gun is a tool to kill rattlesnakes, deer, coyotes. Shoot animals if you must, but not people. *Never* people." The urgency in his voice, and the way he phrased it, had told her that this was no ordinary command.

So she was going to have to go against her father. She thought, He might never love me again.

She heard the footsteps go to her father's desk, the drawers flung open and thrown to the floor, papers rustling. More footsteps, and talking, in the front room. Then the scraping soles were closer, and a shadow fell across the slit of light between the two cabinet doors.

The doors swung open. She looked at the face of a man she had never seen before. She pulled the trigger.

The cabinet, the room—the whole world, it seemed—filled instantly with blue-gray smoke. Her eyes burned, and the noise left a numb ringing in her ears. The pistol jumped in recoil and slammed against her face. She saw the man thrown backward, heard him hit the plank floor. Shoulders first, then boots.

The smoke cleared. The other two men came running into the room. They all looked at the body on the floor and then at her.

"It ain't but a child. A girl, I b'lieve."

"She's big enough to snuff out Jim's lamp. Look at that hole in his head."

"What's she got, a hogleg? That thing is 'bout bigger than she is."

"Go get it, Willie. Take it away from her."

The one closer to her stuck his pistol into its holster and began to walk toward her slowly. He spoke in soft tones. "Now, little girl, we won't hurt you. Give us the gun. It's all right."

She had disobeyed her father once. A second time would be easier. She lifted the pistol and aimed it high, her legs tucked in front of her. The loud click as the trigger notched into firing

position was louder than the man's voice, and carried across the room.

The men fled. They would tell each other later that there was nothing worth stealing anyway, no sense in staying.

Rose Ellen crouched in the cabinet until her legs ached. Finally she climbed out and walked outside to where Noah and Amelia lay. She sat beside them and sobbed.

Her father found her that evening beside the two bodies. She pressed her face into his chest and begged to be forgiven. She wanted him to hold her there forever.

Donnie Lee: We had dinner after Miz Rose Ellen's funeral, and when I was done I asked to be excused.

For what? my mama said. I never see you anymore, Donnie Lee; you're always running off.

Why she was being that way I did not know, but I opened my trap too wide. I said, There's nothing to do around here.

Well, go visit Gandy Meacham, she said. You ought to spend more time with him. We all should.

I stuck my hands in my pockets and fussed, and then I went to Gandy Meacham's bedroom. The shades was down, as usual, and the room was dark and quiet. Gandy Meacham was there in the bed asleep, or so I thought. He had been there in that room for a month, and sometimes did not move out of bed once a day.

He was my mama's grandfather. She gave him his name when she was small, the story goes, because that was as close as she could come to saying granddaddy. He lived most of his life in Wyoming, so I didn't know him. But when Gandy Meacham took sick, it fell to my mama to take him in. They stuck him in the back bedroom, and that was all we seen of him, except to set with him and bring him meals and help him to the bathroom if he was feeling spry.

I don't mean no disrespect. He was dying, and I knew it was a cancer, though the way we acted you would have thought it was some kind of sin to say the word. But Gandy Meacham was nothing to me. He never once did come to visit us in Texas, until he was ready to die. That was how I seen it.

There was a chair beside the bed. I set myself in it and looked at the old man.

He didn't sleep, exactly. Not once did I see him snooze and snore in the normal way. He lay there, not moving, his chest barely heaving the covers up and down. He breathed faint, like a sick little bird with a busted wing.

It was the pills, I think. My mama gave him pills from a prescription to keep him quiet so that he wouldn't hurt so much.

I set there thinking about Sue Everitt. How much time passed I do not know, but you could have knocked me down with a feather when the old man said, clear as you please, What day is it, boy?

I found my voice. Thursday, I said.

Morning or night? he wanted to know.

Night, sir, I said.

He drew a couple of breaths before he spoke again. I wanted to go, he said. I wanted to go to that funeral real bad.

You have to remember that the few times I had heard the old man talk in the past month he talked like he was out of his head. Now I asked myself why Gandy Meacham, who had lived probably fifty years without setting foot in Texas, far as I knew, would care about the old lady's funeral.

I'm sorry, Gandy Meacham, I said.

He said, Why do you call me that?

That is how my mama told me to call you, sir, I said.

My name is Quiller, he said. Quiller Meacham. I ain't your gandy anyways, am I?

No, sir.

You could call me Mr. Meacham, but I ain't been called Mister in twenty years. So Quiller it will have to be. Man to man. Does that suit you?

Yes, sir. Okay, Quiller, I said.

He said, You thought I was asleep. He reached under his pillow, pulled his hand out, and showed me two pills. If I took every one of these they give me, I would never be wide awake again. When your mama leaves the room, I sometimes spit them out. Even so, I get in a haze and I forget what day it is. I wanted to go to that funeral.

His voice was getting weaker. He wanted to know if there was a lot of people at the services. I told him there was, and how they closed down the whole town of Luray.

Humph, he said. She was a mighty fine woman. Everybody loved her, I 'magine.

No, sir, I said. She had her enemies.

Well, that don't s'prise me now that I think about it, he said.

I was ready to ask him how he knew her, him being in Wyoming whilst Miz Rose lived all her life here in the valley, when I remembered that in the olden times there was not so many people around and likely almost everybody knew everybody else.

We run out of conversation, I guess, because we just set there for a while in the dark like before.

He spoke next and said, I reckon you have things to do. You run along. Maybe go watch that new tellyvision.

The truth was that I was getting itchy to leave. We had the first TV on the ranch, and we could get a station in Austin. It was about time for Hopalong Cassidy, if I guessed right.

So I left the room and stretched out to watch Hoppy. It was a good show, as I recall, but I could not keep my mind on it. I kept thinking about Gandy Meacham and Rose Ellen Sample, and wondering what she had meant to him.

CHAPTER TWO

WITH Amelia gone, Rose Ellen was the only female on the Circle Three Bar. The closest woman was the wife of a neighboring cattleman, twenty-four miles away.

The men and the ranch had changed during the years Rose Ellen had lived there. Their eighteen thousand acres had become two hundred thousand. Having convinced his partners to buy land with the profits from their first drive, Fowler bought. An old land grant of thirty-four thousand acres that first year, another of twenty-seven thousand the next, smaller parcels in succeeding autumns. Then the big one, a grant of seventy-seven thousand acres owned by a family in Mexicali that had not been on the place since the war.

The partners had worked hard and had had some luck. Their first two years they had good drives. The third year they waited three weeks trying to cross the Red River in spate; as they waited, word came trickling down the trail of poor markets, beef prices so low that some ranchers were selling to the tallow factories instead.

So they held their cattle over. For the next year they slid by on credit and a smile. The following spring their herd was much larger than ever before, and prices were up again.

It seemed logical to Fowler that their ranch should eventually spread over every acre of Mansos Valley. The valley was thirty miles wide and stretched more than seventy miles from north to south. Along its western edge, hugging the base of the hills, was the Mansos River. As cranky and sporadic as its flow might be—swift and muddy during the rainy weeks; little more than ankle-deep during dry spells, which could last eight, nine months, sometimes longer—the Mansos was the only important and enduring source of water in that territory.

To Fowler the hills on the east and west seemed logical brackets for the ranch that he envisioned. He was not acquiring out of greed but to satisfy an instinct for order, wholeness. He was far past the point of being awed by the distances involved. He, who once had admired the breadth of his eighty acres, now could add five thousand to the Circle Three Bar as casually as most men might buy a rifle.

Six years after the partners first had ridden into this country, their property reached from one ridge of hills to the other, a thirty-mile stretch across the middle of the valley in a strip roughly ten miles long.

As the ranch grew, so did the ranch house near the banks of the Mansos. After six years its additions had engulfed the original four-room structure. The three partners and Rose Ellen all had rooms. Fowler had an office. There were a front room, a dining room, and a proper kitchen. The house was built of carpenter-finished wood, with glass windows and solid floors—not like the mud-and-stone huts on smaller spreads. The partners were proud of this tangible symbol of all that they had achieved.

Behind the house were some corrals, sheds, and a barn, a bunkhouse for the four cowboys who were kept on full time, and a cabin for the foreman. This was Alvarez, the vaquero who had returned one year after that first drive, broke and looking for work, having discovered that he was neither farmer nor husband.

The three partners themselves had changed so subtly and slowly that none of them was aware of it. They still worked hard, but they no longer were grubby adventurers. They walked now with the air of men who had accomplished something admirable. If they did nothing else, they would still have the Circle Three Bar to point to.

With Noah and Amelia gone, there was nobody to care for Rose Ellen during the drive that spring. So Fowler stayed with the child and watched his partners and their hands move the bellowing, milling herd north up the trail.

When they were gone, Fowler thought sadly that it was as if the place had been disemboweled. Take away the cows from a cattle ranch, and there is not much left. But he found as the days passed that he began to welcome this chance for rest and for solitude with his daughter.

She was unhappy. Barely three weeks had passed since the killings, and she was changed. He was not sure how a child was supposed to react to such a shock. But when he decided to finish spading the garden, Rose Ellen refused to go with him. She avoided his office. He caught her standing outside the room where Noah and Amelia had lived, looking inside. One night he awoke to hear her crying.

Before a week had passed, Alvarez returned, riding slowly up to the house. His left foot was bootless and swollen and hung free of the stirrup. Fowler helped him down from the saddle and into the house. The vaquero told his story.

The evening of the first day on the trail he had shaken the dirt out of his boots and walked barefoot to the edge of the Mansos. He had stepped on a rattlesnake. After two days of pain and delirium he had beaten the worst of it. The others, of course, had moved on with the herd. As soon as he was able to ride, he had pulled himself up on the saddle and returned.

They gave him the room that belonged to Sample. There he recuperated. Fowler cooked the meals and Rose Ellen brought them to Alvarez in bed. In a week he left the bed and in two he could walk. He would be able to care for himself and to look after the ranch, Fowler knew.

One night soon after Alvarez had taken his first steps, Fowler visited his daughter in her room. "I notice you ride real good these days, right straight in the saddle," he said as he tucked her in bed. "Do you get tired?"

"No, Papa."

"Suppose I asked you to ride with me as far as the sweet-water spring and back two times, maybe a little farther? Can you feature that?"

She squealed, sat up, put her hands on the collar of his shirt. "Oh, yes, Papa. I can do that!"

He wanted to take her away from the garden and the office. And he wanted to begin showing her the property that was as much her own as his. It was time she saw some of it.

"We may be gone a few days. Sleep hard so you won't be tired in the morning."

She did not sleep, except in brief stretches when her mind hummed with dreams. She was awake when her father lit the fire in the kitchen. She dressed quickly and ran downstairs. On the table were four canteens, food in sacks and cartons, and fresh bedding in a roll with the white canvas duck still spotless.

"I made up your bedroll," he said. "The blankets will keep you warm, and the canvas will keep you dry. We will take a mule so your pony does not have to carry so much."

When they had eaten breakfast, they packed the mule. Fowler showed Rose Ellen a packer's knot, told her to practice it, because he would have her loading the mule before the end of the trip. They said their good-bys to Alvarez, then mounted and rode off.

Texas Dawn

Rose Ellen did not look back at the house. The place was stained, her vision of it murky and gray, because of the killings. She was not sorry to leave it behind.

Soon they were in territory she had seen only from a distance before. The horses' legs swished in the grass, stirring up insects. Fowler took Rose Ellen past a field of bluebonnets, more flowers in one place than she could have imagined. She made her father stop so she could pick some. She grabbed clumps and stuck them in his pockets and her own and under the flaps of their saddlebags and in the mule's harness. When she had picked as many as she could, she stood back and thought that there were more bluebonnets standing now than there had been before. She lay down in the middle of them and looked up at the clouds.

They rode five miles that day. In the evening Fowler made camp where water trickled out of the side of a knoll. He built a fire and cooked a dinner of beans and molasses. The wind blew over their heads and bent the grass on the range. There were storm clouds to the west, purple stained with sunset orange and red.

Home was that way, her father told her, but they had come so far she could not see the house. It was no threat now. The impossible stretch of land gave her sanctuary.

They washed their dishes in a puddle that the spring made in the grass. Fowler crouched to swish his plate in the water and she did the same, imitating him exactly, balanced on the balls of her feet.

Her hair, grown long, was stuffed up into her hat, which she wore at the same angle as he wore his. The cuffs of her pants were shoved into her boots, just as his were. She stood up at the moment he did, and her version of his walk away from the puddle was as close as it could be without the bow of the legs, which put a rolling hitch in his stride.

He put more wood on the fire. She nestled against him, with her head on his shoulder, and he pulled blankets over them and told her stories about his first year on the range. To the west she could see lightning, so far away that she could not match the thunderclaps with the flashes.

"Don't be scared, Rose," her father said. "It is going past us. I don't believe we will even get wet."

"I don't mind if we do," she said.

She went to sleep happy. She knew something now that would never leave her: the land could make you feel good. It was big enough to let you escape from what bothered you. It could give you back what you had lost, fill you up where you had gone empty.

One day they stood on a promontory along the western range of hills. "This part is ours," he said, "and down in that arroyo is about where the spread stops. Royle Evans and his wife own past that. Maybe I can talk them out of it this winter."

"Do they have as much land as we do, Papa?"

"No. Not a third as much. Most people don't own as much land as we do, you and me and Earl and Orrin. There are some that don't even own a scrap of it. Do you understand?"

She shook her head no.

"I can't explain it any better. They don't own any land, is all. Some little girls don't have a pony. And some papas don't have any land."

He turned and looked down at her. "It's good to own a lot of land," he said. "Land is different from anything else. You wouldn't want to own more jewels than anybody else, or more clothes, or more food. That would just be greed and pride. But the more land we have, the better this ranch is. And we want to have the best ranch. Remember that, Rose."

She did not grasp the sense of his words. But she felt the emotion behind them, and that she did not lose.

When they returned home, it seemed to Rose Ellen that the killings had happened someplace else, someplace to which she would never return.

After six weeks Fowler was restless, for the ranch was dormant during a drive. He decided to take Rose Ellen with him to San Antonio. And on this trip, too, she learned more about herself.

They rode into the city in the middle of a rainstorm and boarded the horses at a livery. Then Fowler and Rose Ellen threw their saddlebags over their shoulders and marched across

Texas Dawn

the muddy street to the best hotel in town. The door of the hotel was polished hardwood, with etched glass and brass handles. Fowler swung it open for his daughter, and in their muddy boots they clumped up to the front desk with its ornate carved facing. Rose Ellen had never seen anything so fine.

Across the desk the clerk's eyes narrowed. "Sir?"

"I'd like a suite with two beds. Your best."

"And how long will you and your boy be with us?"

Rose Ellen sensed contempt and waited for her father to correct the mistake.

"About a week," Fowler said.

"Papa!"

"Yes," Fowler said quickly. "She's a girl. My daughter. Take off your hat and show the man, Rose."

She glared at the clerk and snatched off her Stetson; dirty, matted clumps of hair fell to her shoulders. A man and a woman watched from a red velvet banquette not far from the desk. The woman drew in a breath and put a hand to her mouth.

The clerk reached back for a key but withheld it. "We must ask for a deposit of twenty American in advance," he said.

Fowler slipped a saddlebag from his shoulder, reached inside to find a leather drawstring purse, and came up with a gold twenty. He slapped it down on the desk and held out his hand for the key.

As they went up the wide staircase Rose Ellen said, "Papa, I don't like this place."

"Hush, we'll have a grand time. Keep walking, Rose; don't look back. Here, this way."

The suite had three rooms. In one was a brass rail bed, in another a canopied four-poster. Fowler swept his daughter up and tossed her on the mattress of the four-poster.

"Ain't this fine? A feather bed, soft as can be. This beats bedrolls on hard ground by quite a ways, I'd say."

But she would not be distracted from the new and startling fact that some people did not live the way she and her father did, and that these people for some reason thought badly of her.

They stayed three days in the city, bought clothes and gifts, and ate every evening in the hotel's dining room. Fowler wore a suit of hound's-tooth check, and he made her wear a flounced dress of pink silk. She noticed that people treated them with more respect then, and nobody mistook her for a boy. But the city was loud, busy, running a dozen different ways at once. The evening of the third day she asked her father when they could go home.

"Anytime we choose," he said.

The next morning they rode out of town.

Two days beyond San Antonio they stumbled across a sight that thrilled her more than any of the city's novelties. At dawn, above a watering hole, they surprised a herd of wild horses. There were hundreds, and they moved, startled, in a fluid formless unit. They flowed up the side of a ridge, then along the crest, silhouetted against the bright new sun. They raised dust, and their manes and tails flew, and the special light of dawn burst through the dust and waving hair in starburst patterns. Then they were gone, and there was only copper sunlight glinting off the water.

She never had a summer like that one again. It remained in her memory like a series of vignette photographs, bathed in that same warm copper tone that had streaked through the manes and the tails of the wild horses, and they were images of nothing but happiness and love.

Fowler, Rose Ellen, and Alvarez stayed alone in the ranch house until the end of September, when Sample and the four full-time cowboys rode in.

"We had a good drive, Charlie," Sample said. He was flushed, excited. "Two thousand one hundred and seventeen head to market, and we got thirty-eight and a quarter."

"Where is Earl?" Fowler said.

"Natchez, last I seen of him," Sample said. He jumped down from his horse. "Earl has hisself a lady."

EVERY year it was the same, the libidinal stirring that began as a faint flutter in the spring. With it you could mark the progress of the Circle Three Bar's herd up the trail.

Texas Dawn

Fording the Colorado River, the first landmark barrier in their path, awakened the desire that the men worked so hard to keep buried during the winter. Once they reached the Kansas line, they were hounds on a scent. And when they finally collected their pay, the aching and yearning would send them bursting into the dance halls and saloons and bawdy houses of Abilene, which was now the market for their cattle.

Sample and Newsome were as bound to the rite as any of the others. This time, however, a few days out of Abilene, Sample told Newsome that maybe he would try to keep his money in his purse this year, no reason to go spreading it around the way he had in the past. "So I believe I will lay low," Sample said as they rode at the head of the herd. "The boys can go out and chase the painted pretties if they want. You?"

Newsome cleared his throat, adjusted his hat, frowned, and answered without looking at Sample. "Orrin, a man's a man," he said. "I'm going to step out some."

"Not me," Sample said. "Not this time."

When they reached Abilene, they went first to the brokers' offices, then to a bank. They booked rooms at a hotel and doled out the hands' pay. Sample and Newsome, in their room on the third floor, could hear the noise downstairs as the cowboys exploded out onto the street, shouting and hooting.

"Damn fools," Sample said. "Me, I will settle for a warm bath and a cold beer. How 'bout it, Earl?"

They each paid a dollar for a wooden tub half full of steaming water, six bits more for a shave and a haircut. They bought new clothes. It was early evening now, and they ate dinner and drank six schooners of beer between them.

In their room again, Sample let himself fall back on one of the two beds. "I might just sleep until next Tuesday," he said.

Newsome was standing by the open door, rocking on the heels of his boots. "I feel restless yet," he said. "Maybe I will wander about some."

"Do what you want."

Newsome returned two hours later to the dark room and eased himself down onto his bed. From the street he heard slurred shouts; he looked from the window to see a cowboy below fire five rounds from a pistol pointed at the moon.

"Gunfight?" said Sample.

"No. Some boy hellin' round, is all."

"And how is the town?" Sample said.

"Oh, 'bout the same. Maybe shrunk some. I just went up to Big Nose Annie's for a spell."

"There is a woman ugly enough to curdle a rattlesnake's blood."

"Annie weren't there. She sold out to a bunch of French chippies."

Sample took this in. "French . . ." he said. Then: "Hell." He turned on his side. "Earl, you done for the night?"

"Anybody that's been throwed as much as me is always ready for another ride."

"Maybe you'd ankle it up with me to that place. Just to look around."

Before the cowhand on the street could reload his Colt, they were dressed and out the door.

They were men who knew women mostly from memories and dreams. Women were a mystery to them, and a vexation. Not just women, but women's allure and the need they evoked. They complicated an otherwise simple and satisfying life. Yet troubling as women might be, they still drew men like Sample and Newsome to a respectful, timid proximity.

Each year, as they returned from the drive, the men rode by train to Saint Joseph and from there to New Orleans by boat. This time through Saint Joseph, Newsome, feeling flush and fancying himself a dandy, visited a tailor. He had money and he would show it. He bought silk shirts and striped pants. Then a pair of kid leather gloves, the color of a fawn's underbelly. He paid and was leaving the shop when he saw the sash: satin, red, six inches wide. He tied it around his waist.

So Newsome was in full splendor two days later when he first saw the woman standing on the loading platform in Saint Louis. He and Sample had ridden a packet down the Missouri and were waiting for the southbound *Robert E. Lee*.

The woman stood ahead of them in the line at the ramp. She

was tall for the day, and slender. She wore a bonnet that would have suggested dowdiness but for the clean lines of her face and the sheen of her blond hair. She held a fringed parasol, balancing it on one shoulder with three fingers touching the knob in delicate fashion.

She was alone, Newsome noticed. He nudged Sample. "Orrin, lookee there."

"Some woman. Where's her man, I wonder."

"She don't appear to have one," Newsome said.

They spoke too softly for the woman to hear, but she sensed their boyish excitement. She turned her head as though to peer at her admirers, but her eyes remained downcast. Then she flicked them up briefly. Her glance lingered on the striped pants, the silk shirt, that sash. Most of all, that sash. She smiled.

Newsome writhed within, a splendid agony. Nothing was ever easy with women.

They met that afternoon. Newsome was walking the upper deck when he saw her at the rail, looking down into the water. He moved to within a few feet of her, the limit of his daring.

She turned and smiled at him again, casual and open, as though they were old friends. "Lovely day," she said softly.

"Surely," he said. He gripped the rail and stood, rigid and miserable, managing only to breathe, and that with some effort. He told himself, Say something before she leaves. You'll hate yourself if you don't.

"Whar-bouts you from?" he said.

"Natchez."

"I been past it on the river."

"Yes?"

"Every year me and my partners and our boys ride the *Robert E. Lee* from Saint Looie to N'Orleans."

"Cowboys?"

"They is cowboys, the hired hands. Me and my partners are cattlemen."

"Texas?" she said.

"That's right."

"Do you have a large ranch?" In asking, she made the first

symbolic step across the chasm between them. This was going better for Newsome than he had dared to hope.

He, too, stepped closer. "Fair size," he said. "Bigger'n three hundred sections. A section is a mile square."

"And cattle to go with all that land?"

"Oh, yes, ma'am. More'n we could bother to count."

"That sounds positively fascinating," she said. "You must tell me more about it sometime. I should return to my cabin now. The sunlight goes to my head, it is so strong."

She was gone before he could reply. No matter. His head was awash with possibilities; he must go to the saloon, have a whiskey, and contemplate the amazing situation.

By that evening Sample and the hands had heard of the encounter. In the dining salon, the group fell silent as the woman entered and followed a steward to a table.

"There she is," Sample said. "She is a sight."

"Lookit that woman," said a hand. "Quality."

"Now shut your traps, you bunch of yahoos," Newsome said fiercely. "Y'all act like you never seen a lady in your life."

"Boss, she looked over. She looked right over here."

"Will you shut your mouth or do I do it for you?"

"She did it again, Earl," Sample said.

Newsome swallowed. He tried to affect nonchalance in turning to look at her. But he caught her with eyes down, studying a menu. He turned back. The second time he turned, a few moments later, she was sipping from a glass, apparently absorbed in thought.

The third time, their eyes met. Again that smile, as though she were just now noting his presence. She raised her hand in a tiny wave, then returned to her menu.

"She's about invited you to go over there," said Sample.

Newsome spoke through clenched teeth. "Please don't raise a commotion."

They finished their dinner without another word. Newsome did not look at the woman. He stayed locked in his seat, staring down at his plate. When the table had been cleared, he ordered two whiskeys and drained each with a swallow.

Finally he asked Sample, "She still over there?"

"Yep. Best make your move if you're gonter."

Newsome rose and walked toward where the woman sat. He felt the eyes of the men follow him. The woman noticed him when he was a few steps away and beginning to falter.

"How nice to see you," she said. "Won't you sit down, please?"

He felt giddy as he slipped into a chair.

"We should have an introduction," she said, "to make this proper by the book."

"Earl Newsome," he said. His hand went up to the brim of his Stetson, hesitated, then pulled the hat off. "And you, miss?"

"Mrs. Irene Weaver," she said. She saw his shoulders slump. "Please. I don't believe the late Mr. Weaver will object."

She suggested champagne. He ordered a bottle of the most expensive. She asked him about Texas, about the ranch, about the drive he had just finished. Maybe, she said, he would walk with her about the upper deck. The sun was down now, and the night was mild.

"Perhaps," she said, "you think I am presumptuous. Most women would be more reticent. That is not my way, sir. I simply don't hold with some of the popular conventions. Not that I overstep the bounds of propriety. But this trip is too brief, as life itself is, for some of the silly rules that others thrust upon us. Don't you agree?"

He did. Indeed he did, if he understood half of what she was saying.

Sample had gone to his cabin. He was dozing when Newsome burst into the room and shook him. "Orrin, wake up, pard. I need some money."

"Money? How much? Five? Ten?"

"Couple hundred, maybe."

"What in blazes for? We have to go to the captain and have him open the strongbox."

"I know. That's why I'm here. He said the two of us together had to be there when he opened it. Come on."

Sample dressed and followed him up to the office, where the first mate was on duty. The officer pulled out of the safe a small locked satchel that they had left there that morning. The two partners took the bag into a corner.

"Earl, what is this all about?"

"Tell you when I got the time, pard. I'll put back what I don't use. I ain't took a cent outta this ranch in years, and I ain't going to bust us tonight, neither." Newsome counted off fifteen twenties, then snapped the bag closed, and left.

After seeing the bag replaced in the safe, Sample hurried after Newsome and caught him in the social hall. Newsome walked from one table to another, scrutinizing the poker players. At one table he spotted a gold pin on the lapel of a thin man in gambler's blacks. Set in the pin was a sparkling diamond.

"That thing real?" Newsome said.

"Yes."

"How much?"

"I don't wish to sell."

"I'll give you three hundred in greenbacks," Newsome said. He flung the bundle down on the table.

"Sold, it appears," the gambler said, and gave him the pin.

Sample followed Newsome to the upper deck. The woman was waiting there. When Newsome gave her the pin, Sample heard her say as she handed it back, "You do it. You're giving it to me; you find a place for it."

Newsome hesitated, then sank the sliver of gold into a fold of fabric high on her bodice. The woman raised herself on her toes to kiss his cheek.

Sample watched. The act, so simple and unaffected, brought a rush of emotion to him, which he tried to understand as he left and returned to his cabin. There was embarrassment; he had been an intruder. Some jealousy, maybe. And, when he considered it, there was a touch of fear. But that was loco, he told himself. He had nothing to fear from a kiss on Newsome's cheek.

Newsome joined him soon in the cabin. There was awe in his voice when he spoke. "Pard, that is some woman. I can't believe all that has happened to me. I wanted her to come with us, Orrin, to see the ranch. She said that wouldn't be right." He coughed softly, groped for his next words. "But she said I was welcome to get off the boat at Natchez, get myself a room, and keep seeing her there. That is what I will do."

"Why, you old fox," Sample said. "Go to her, Earl, if that's how it is."

Sample tried to sound hearty and full of cheer. But even as he spoke, envy and fear surged inside him again.

IN HER cabin, Irene Weaver unfastened the buttons at the back of her dress. While her fingers worked, her mind turned over the day. She had to be cautious, had to be sure. She would only have so many chances in the time she had left.

Poverty taught you to make the most of chances. And she had been poor. Her father was a blacksmith in Shreveport, Louisiana. A smithy's earnings made thin slices when divided among nine children. Even after two of her brothers died of scarlet fever and a sister of pneumonia, there never was enough.

Irene was born beautiful, and the beauty had survived bad food, home remedies, drafty walls, and coarse lye soap. It managed to make itself obvious even through patched dresses and the severe bun of hair—both her mother's doing.

When she was sixteen, she married the pharmacist who had a shop down the street from where her family lived. Everhall Weaver was thirty-three and dour beyond his years. He owned a carriage with a matched set of grays, and a gingerbread cottage across town. That clinched Irene. She settled into the cottage and avoided the old neighborhood. She visited her parents as often as she needed to forestall their visiting her.

Once she recovered from the heady excitement of a well-stocked pantry and store-bought clothes, Irene examined more critically the life to which she had committed herself. It had its drawbacks. She sensed that there was a limit to how high any pharmacist could climb.

With a suddenness that startled Ev, they were living in Natchez, he was owner of a drayage company, and they were the parents of a baby boy. Irene had found the drayage company for him; it belonged to a distant relative of one of her friends. Ev felt as if it had all happened slightly faster than he could follow,

Texas Dawn

but Irene pointed out that their house in Natchez was better than the one they had left. The drayage company would be a money-maker, properly run. Best of all, he was a businessman, no longer a shopkeeper. They were moving up.

Within a year she had bought the dresses and attended the dances and parties that were her admission to Natchez society. She needed fine clothes, new furnishings for the house, a nursemaid for the baby. Ev was appalled. The scope of their expenditures was awesome.

But the debts always were paid, for he was putting all of his effort and most of his hours into spurring on the business. He wished he had more time for his son, he told Irene. She consoled him. He couldn't do everything, she said. Little Ray loved him all the same and one day would appreciate all that his father had done.

Three days short of his fortieth birthday Ev Weaver died at his desk in the drayage warehouse. Irene failed to realize the implications at first. When he died, the money faltered but the debts did not. She knew nothing of the company, had left those details to Ev. So she sold the business and paid the debts. It was a lesson learned. Never again would she fail to understand, and most of all to control, her financial security.

But as she looked out at Natchez through a black lace veil, she despaired of her future. It would take a special kind of man, a generous and substantial man, to fill her material needs now.

In a letter of condolence a friend in Saint Louis had invited her to visit. Irene found a family to keep her son. She put away her widow's weeds and traveled upriver to Saint Louis. She stayed a month, long enough to convince herself that to find the right man she must leave Natchez and establish herself where there were more men, money, prospects.

She was racing time—racing the inevitable depletion of her funds and racing age as well. She saw the beginnings of lines at her eyes, at the corners of her mouth. Her face was showing the first signs of an unhappy pinch.

She had been returning to Natchez when she met the cowboy. She had to trust her instincts, she knew, and her instincts told her that this man owned all that he claimed and was what he seemed to be. That had been the most difficult part, believing that a man could be so boyish, so vulnerable to feminine ways. But it could not be an act, she decided. It was too perfect, too complete.

Texas was far from genteel society and all that she knew and valued. But if need be, she would change Texas to suit her tastes. For this she believed above all else: there was nothing that could not be altered if one made enough effort.

OCTOBER passed, and November. One evening Fowler told Sample that they might have to make plans to buy Newsome's share if he did not return.

But in mid-December, Newsome came up the trail to the Circle Three Bar driving a covered buckboard, with a woman beside him. A young boy rode in the back seat with trunks, cartons, hatboxes. While Sample, Fowler, Alvarez, and Rose Ellen stood outside the house, Newsome climbed down from the seat, walked to the other side of the carriage, and put out an arm for the woman to touch as she stepped to the ground.

Newsome made the introductions. He wanted everybody to meet his wife, Irene, and their son, Raymond.

Donnie Lee: It was history class, and what the teacher called a Living History project, that finally got me together with Sue Everitt.

History was the best part of the day for me, since my seat was beside Sue E.'s. I felt good being next to her that way, but I had trouble keeping my mind on what was said. This was double bad because Sue E. was the straight A type and I wanted to look sharp for her. Most times it didn't work that way.

The day after the funeral we walked together to the cafeteria and she said would I eat lunch with her because she wanted to talk to me about this Living History project.

We was supposed to team up with somebody else in the class

and do a composition on something that had to do with the history of the valley. It had to be something that wasn't in books, something we got from talking to people who actually knew it the way it was back then.

Sue E. said, What do you think is a good topic, Donnie Lee?

I didn't have a clue. Did I feel dumb.

Well, she said, I've been thinking I would do Rose Ellen Sample.

I piped right up. I said, I thought this was supposed to be a Living History project. I recollect we buried that old bag yesterday. Soon as I said it I was sorry. I was trying to be smart, is all. But Sue E. looked at me like I was a big *cucaracha* that just climbed out of the crack in the wall.

You shouldn't make fun of the dead, she said. Especially not a woman like her. Did you ever stop and think how hard it must have been for women back in those days?

I reckon not, I said.

I have, she said. That is why I want to do a project on her. She must have been a great lady.

Everybody says so, I said. I reckon you're right.

Then maybe you'd care to work with me on the project, Sue E. said. You know the people in the valley, you know who we can talk to.

Nothing ever made me feel more proud than hearing that. Like I was special. Like she thought I had the goods to help her with her A. Right then I knew I was in love.

That evening I made myself concentrate on who to talk to. Tom Holloway's daddy, who was Rose Ellen Sample's straw. Stallworth the banker did business with everybody in the valley. But he was not nearly as old as she'd been. I kept trying to come up with somebody who'd have known her from a long time ago.

Then it hit me.

Gandy Meacham, right under this same roof, in a room right under mine. Gandy Meacham went back that far, and somehow he knew her then.

I went downstairs and into Gandy Meacham's room. Quiller, I said, you awake?

He just barely budged, opened his eyes like they was sewed shut. What is it? he said.

I said, I thought maybe we could talk. Like last time. Maybe we could talk about Miz Rose Sample.

What you want to know about her? he said.

All about her, I said. What she was like, the way she acted—all such stuff.

Not now, he said. Too tired. My head's woozy. Come back tomorrow, you hear? He reached out and took me by the arm. He give me a squeeze, about as hard as he could.

CHAPTER THREE

The grown-ups set aside the argument long enough to eat supper. They were silent when the cook brought the steaming porcelain tureen of soup. They ate with their eyes down at their food, silver spoons clicking against the glazed plates.

That suited Ray and Rose Ellen. It meant they could slip unquestioned from the table while the adults stewed over the latest sharp words. After they glanced at each other, Rose Ellen left first, crossed the parlor, and went outside. She walked to the stable, threw a saddle across the back of her new mare, and was tightening the cinch when Ray appeared. When he led his pony out, she was mounted and waiting for him.

"Where to?" she said.

"We got a couple more hours' light."

"Indian Oak," she said. It was their name for a lone tree on a hill nearby.

They rode at a gentle canter until they were out of sight of the house. Then each put spurs to horse, and the animals exploded forward into the open country.

At a gallop they picked paths through the brush, the rocks, and the gullies, each rider intent on a race. Rose Ellen found in her mare a reserve of speed that let her pass the boy in the flat. At the base of the hill he drew even. Then it was straight up, Ray pounding his hat against his pony's side. Rose was bent over the pommel, the reins loose in her left hand while the right found a grip in the mane.

It was the mare by a head as they charged over the top. Then Rose Ellen was tightening the reins as she vaulted out of the stirrups. She hit the ground with legs moving and dived across the brown grass to slap the tree's trunk.

He was half a step behind her, and he sprawled across her legs as he reached for the tree.

"Mine," she said, breathless.

"Damn."

"Don't you curse around me, Raymond Newsome."

"I reckon I will if I want."

She pulled herself up from the ground, sat against the trunk so that she could look out over the valley. He sat beside her.

They were children no longer. They had grown into skinny parodies of the adults they would become. At thirteen Rose Ellen had her full growth, but the sharp edges of her elbows, knees, and cheeks were more obvious than they would be soon. At twelve Ray was already showing the long legs, wide shoulders, and strong arms of a man.

Below them the river was luminous, the low sun at an angle that let its light reflect off the water.

"Don't get sore," she said, "just because I won again."

"That mare has got speed to waste. Give me that mare and I could beat you to the top and whistle 'Dixie' while doing it."

"It ain't speed. It's heart. That mare has got more sand in her than the whole Mansos River. And there ain't nothing wrong with your pony that a fair rider wouldn't straighten out." She looked at him. His jaw was set. She knew that she had gone too far. That's just the way he does when he is stung, she thought. Puts on like he is so tough and can't nothing hurt him.

So she said, "You about flew over that arroyo back there."

He said nothing, but his jaw relaxed.

"That's a deep one," she said. "I was just behind you, and I says to myself, There ain't no way he's going to jump it. But there you went, like it wasn't but a crack. I wouldn't have tried it if I hadn't seen you do it first."

"It's a good pony." He grinned. "Jumps a long ways when it has to."

Then it was better, back to the way they were most of the time, which was more as one person than two. They were rarely apart, and it had been that way almost from the beginning. That first day Rose Ellen had shown Ray the horses and the barns and led him down to the river. She had coaxed off his brogans and teased him into the water with his pants rolled up around his knees. He had been a frail little boy then, frightened and unsure. It was a new life and a new country, all so different from Natchez and what he had known.

She had decided to cure him of his fright. After all the years of living with adults, she was ready for the company of a child. He would be her pard, she decided. She taught him to ride—on the sly, using her little pony—so that when Earl thought his new son ought to learn something about horses, Ray shocked him by climbing into the saddle and trotting around the corral.

Their being together was natural. When Rose took her lessons from her father, Ray was there, too, learning the same things. If Rose weeded in the garden, the job went twice as fast with two. And if one was going to ride in the hills, the other would follow.

Soon they had their own existence that only incidentally touched that of the adults. At first Irene had tried to keep Ray indoors. This was all new to him, she argued, and he ought to step into it gradually. But he had confounded her by leaping into the new ways. He grew nine inches in two years, showed muscles in his arms, turned acorn brown in the sun.

Ray and Rose Ellen were growing up together in a universe of their own design. Yet even with this melding they were different in ways beyond gender. Rose Ellen was the talker if there was talking to be done. Ray kept his feelings close. They could both be hurt. And the closer you were, she was learning, the easier it was to hurt and be hurt. But Ray would take hurt like he could take it forever, and never cringe. She cried out against it.

Rose Ellen realized the differences because she had considered the matter and judged it. Ray took it in without question, and there was the biggest difference. She was her father's daughter this way above all. He was his stepfather's son, taking on Earl's manners by inclination and by imitation.

Alone on the hilltop, they climbed the oak, she boosting him to the lowest branch, then taking his hand and scrambling up the trunk. Together they went hand over hand to the top, until each could stand on a thin upper branch and feel daring.

In the house in the valley, the four adults were sitting in the room they now called the parlor, the original front room of the old house. The place had seen many changes in the years since Irene arrived.

First a new room for the two of them, Earl and Irene. Then a room for Ray and closets for Irene's clothes. Earl deserved an office of his own like Fowler's; and Luz, the Mexican woman Irene found to cook and clean, needed quarters. They kept a carpenter on salary for eight months making the changes.

After a few months Irene had sent for her furnishings. The cattlemen now ate with silver, from china plates, and walked on plush rugs, and sat on chairs covered with velvet. This was Irene's world, within the walls of the house. She cared about the workings of the ranch—too much for Fowler's taste—but she got what she needed to know from the men and from the ledgers. No need for her to walk out into the sun and the dirt. That was for the others.

"Now," Sample said, "let's just talk this thing out. If we hack away at it, we can come up with something we all like."

This bickering had plagued them for the last several years. It had forced Sample into the role of mediator.

"We can talk around it all you want," Fowler said. "I still can't see buying cattle now. I think we can get the Taylor spread, and if that means buying no stock this year, then so be it. The Taylors have some stock anyways, which would go in the deal."

Irene said nothing, but looked at her husband and put a hand on his shoulder so solidly that it was almost a nudge.

Newsome cleared his throat. "Now, Charlie, what we was thinking—Irene and me, that is, and maybe Orrin won't give us a fight on it either—is that it's . . . it's cattle that brings money from the brokers, not land."

He glanced at his wife, saw her head tip forward slightly. Doing fine. He rolled on, the words coming easier.

"Now, land, the way it works in these parts, don't mean much. There is folks in this valley running five hundred head that don't have much more land than what their house sits on. Their cows roam, and the land is open. Like Tom Adams, that sold us his six sections a while back. He took his money and bought himself a herd down Matamoros way, and here he is back this winter running them Mexican cows right on the same land. Ain't nothing changed except our money is in his pockets now."

Irene put a hand on her husband's arm. "Why buy the Taylor place when our cattle graze on that land already?" she said.

Fowler stared at them. This dream of his, this vision of a single ranch up and down the valley, he had never shared. He believed that it would mean nothing to them. He also believed that they would be grateful for this land one day. "What if it changed?" he said. "What if we had to keep our cows only on land that we owned?"

"How, Charlie?" said Newsome. "How we going to make our cows stay where they belong? How can you fence all the land we own and keep the fences standing? You're talking crazy. You don't need fences when you got brands."

Fowler was motionless in his chair, silent. But within himself he cursed small minds, small visions.

On the hill, high in the oak tree, Ray and Rose Ellen looked across the valley in the evening sun.

Ray started moving out on the branch. "I can go way out here," he said.

"Don't you fall."

"I ain't scared. And I can go farther. See, way out here."

"Don't, Ray." The sight of him halfway out on the limb made her chest tighten. "You're real brave. But don't."

He moved for the trunk when he heard the first crack. But the branch splintered in front of him and he fell. He hit two limbs on the way down and broke them both. His body thumped heavily on the ground, and he lay there fighting for the air that the blow had knocked out of his lungs.

Texas Dawn

She jumped down when she reached the last branch, ran to him, and turned him face up. She was crying.

"Don't cry, Rose, don't do that."

"You hurt bad?" she said.

He gave a tentative flex to neck, legs, arms, fingers. "Shoot, no," he said.

His shirt was ripped, front and back. His pants were torn down one leg. His face was unmarked, but both arms, his chest, and the exposed leg showed deep scratches where blood was welling. "My maw is going to tan me," he said.

"You can't go in looking like that," she said. "We have to clean out the scratches, too."

They rode slowly down the hill to the edge of the Mansos. He obeyed when she told him to take off his shirt and sit on the bank. She dipped her bandanna into the river and wiped the cool cotton down his arms, then his chest, his back, his legs.

They made their way home. From inside the house there was shouting. No one noticed as they rode into the stable.

"Hold it, Rose," he said. "We can't let my mother see me like this. She'll keep me beside her for a month."

"Then we won't let her see you. Stay here," she said.

She went in the back door of the house and reached Ray's room without crossing the parlor. It was easy to gather up the clean jeans and shirt that he needed, get out undetected through the back door, and return quietly to the stable.

The sky was smudged black over red when they walked together into the house, front door this time. He must be hurting, she knew, but he walked as if he did not carry a mark. And there were none that the change of clothes did not cover.

The adults were rising out of their chairs in the parlor.

"Raymond, I never see you around here," Irene said. "Where do you spend your time?"

And Fowler spoke, more sharply than usual. "Rose Ellen, you've got lessons to do. I regret the day I stuck you on a horse the first time."

The two young people caught each other's eyes. Then Rose Ellen went to her room.

She closed the door behind her. She pulled off her boots and stretched her skinny body on the bed. With her arms folded beneath her dark hair she watched the last minutes of sunset stream through her window. She was not so much thinking about Ray as feeling him. And though she had no word yet for the feeling, the truth was that every bit of her young girl's being was suffused with love for Raymond Newsome.

Orrin Sample left the house and walked to the tack room beside the stable. He stuck two fingers into a jar of saddle soap, soft and fragrant with a rich smell that he liked. He smeared a dollop on the saddle that lay before him on a bench. Today's argument had drained him, as they all did. Irene and Earl tugged at him one way, and his loyalty to Fowler drew him another, though Charlie never tried to sway him as the Newsomes did.

He could not fault Charlie Fowler for the way he had run the ranch. Sample could look around and see what Charlie had done in thirteen years. Land almost without end. Plenty of money. And something better. Power might be the word for it. When he walked the streets of Abilene, Austin, San Antonio, Sample stepped aside for nobody.

He yearned sometimes for the simpler life they'd had, three together, before the ranch had grown so large.

Sample rubbed the saddle soap into the leather and thought, I am the same, at least. I haven't changed. And a moment later: The hell you haven't. You are older and you want more, just the way Earl and Irene do—just the way Fowler does, too.

Everything changes, he knew. Even Texas was changing, with towns where once there had been grass. There were schools and churches, county commissioners, roads. Sample told himself, You can't cry over what is lost, because everything changes.

The sun was dropping behind the hills when Charlie Fowler left the house and walked down to the Mansos. Maybe he was wrong, he thought. Maybe it was foolishness, this idea of more land that he carried with him all these years. Maybe it is pride alone that keeps me battling, he thought. And pride is a poor reason.

For a while he had almost believed that they could do anything, the three of them. But now the dream seemed more distant than ever.

He listened to the stream running over the rocks. He looked around, saw that the far hills to the east still reached into daylight. He realized that he had never seen the valley, one end to the other, at one time. Fowler did not know how high a man would have to climb to see every square mile of it all at once. Higher, he thought, than he could reach.

Earl Newsome watched Fowler walk slowly up from the stream, head down. Looking beaten, Newsome thought. He did not want to hurt Charlie. But he wanted more to please Irene, and she had ideas, things that he would never have realized without her. No reason for Charlie to be so mulish, he thought. No reason for him to behave that way. There was plenty for all on this ranch.

Earl paced the kitchen while his wife knitted in the parlor. He was full of desire tonight, and he knew that she would not disappoint him. Not tonight. Not after he had spoken up to Fowler as she had urged him.

The clock struck seven thirty. Newsome took a rifle from the rack in his office and brought it to the kitchen with a can of oil. He checked the action and oiled the moving parts and wiped the barrel clean. He did this with five guns and was working on his sixth when Irene rose, put her knitting into a basket, and left the parlor.

When Newsome saw her in the hall, he replaced the rifle in the rack and followed her to their room. She was bending over a dressing table, with a lamp burning before her, examining her image in a mirror.

"Hello, darling," she said when she saw him, and she showed him a smile that Newsome wished he saw more often. It warmed him, as always, and it gave him courage now.

He walked to her side and kissed her on the nape of her neck. This time she did not seem to object. He had learned to be careful; often his attentions annoyed her. He had not married a cow-town chippy. Irene was a lady.

Tonight she turned from the mirror, put her arms around his

neck, and kissed him on the cheek. "I'm so proud of the way you stand up for me, Earl," she said.

"I will do anything for you," he said, and he meant it.

She pressed her lips against his, and he felt like a man again.

THAT spring Sample alone took the herd and the hands to Abilene. Fowler stayed behind again. He could not run the ranch from horseback on the trail. And this time Newsome, too, stayed back. That was Irene's idea. If Fowler could skip six months' riding, so could her husband. More than one man bossed the Circle Three now.

Sample found a good market. When he returned, he noticed a change. Earl and Irene were gone from the big house. They were building four miles upvalley, living in a cabin now with their new home half finished.

Better for all concerned, Fowler told him.

Sample discovered another change a few minutes later. He answered a knock on his bedroom door to find Rose Ellen, come to welcome him home. She greeted him as she always had, with arms around him, holding him tight.

"Orrin," she said. "I missed you. I always do."

She squeezed him again. The body that he felt against him had changed during those months. She was no longer a girl. She had some growing to do yet, but she was going to be a beautiful woman. He could see that.

She sat with him and talked. There had been terrible fights while he was gone, she told him. You had to be careful what you said, because everybody had a short fuse.

That night, when he should have been sleeping, he thought of Rose. The difference in her touched off longings that he had been careful to keep in check. He told himself that this was wrong, thinking this way. She was no woman yet. And she was still Charlie Fowler's daughter.

After a few days he told Charlie that he would be spending some time with Earl and Irene, maybe camping there nights. They needed help, and work was slack around the ranch now.

He did it to get away from Rose Ellen. But during his second day there, she rode up the trail with her hair flying behind her. She pulled up and called for Ray. The boy came out from the frame of the new house. "Ray, can you go riding?" she said.

"No more'n an hour," Earl answered for him.

The boy went for his pony, tied to a picket stake nearby. Rose Ellen looked up and saw Sample on the roof, straddling a rafter. She waved and called his name. At that moment Ray swung into the saddle, and the two of them rode off together.

And Orrin found himself envying the boy. Mostly he envied the way Rose's eyes followed Ray every moment that the two of them were together. Orrin knew then that he would have to leave the house where she lived. He had to be away from her.

In two weeks the Newsomes' house was framed and roofed and walled, so Sample returned to the old ranch house. Newsome removed the furnishings that Irene had brought from Natchez. Irene hired away the housekeeper, too. So the first evening without her Fowler cooked steak and potatoes for three. They ate together, Fowler and Sample and Rose Ellen, using tin plates from the chuck wagon. Irene had taken all the rest.

They ate without speaking. Finally Rose Ellen excused herself to finish a book.

Sample poked with a fork at the remains of the meal before him. "Charlie," he said, "you up for some talk?"

"Talk? If you want."

"This is hard. I don't know which foot to lead off with."

"Orrin, don't go coyoting round it. It can't be all that bad."

Sample sucked in a breath and spoke. "Charlie, I think I'll be going off on my own to live."

Fowler sat back in his chair. "Damn," he said.

"Don't take it personal," Sample said. "It's got nothing to do with you."

"No. Course not. All my friends are up and leaving. But it's got nothing to do with me."

Sample could not tell him the real reason he was leaving. "Charlie, things is changed. With Earl gone, it ain't like three partners sharing everything. This house is yours now, yours and Rose Ellen's. I'm just a maverick here."

"We'll split the place down the middle if that makes you feel better. You take one side, leave the rest to me and Rose."

"No. Only one way to make it right in my mind."

Fowler put his hands to his face, ran his fingers over his chin. "What do you say to a swallow or two?"

They took two cups and a bottle, and they walked outside, beside the stable, where they had a view of the valley. In the bunkhouse they heard Alvarez and one of the hands crooning to chords strummed on a guitar. Fowler filled a cup, handed it to Sample, filled the other, and corked the bottle.

He drank from his cup. "Somewhere we lost it," he said in a moment. "Not all of a sudden, but gradual, so nobody noticed it for a long time. But it is gone now, plain enough."

"Maybe it ain't really lost."

"Oh, it's lost, pard. It is lost all right. Things won't ever be the same as when we started out. But maybe it ain't so much to lose."

Another gulp. Sample waited.

"I mean," Fowler said, "there was the three of us young bucks, we thought we could lick the rest of the world if we fought with all the grit we had in us. But maybe we weren't so special, more lucky than special. Could be we got too big. Things got easy, and it all went to hell."

He drank once more, and this time Sample spoke. "We couldn't help getting big, Charlie. We wanted it. Not one of us would have raised a hand to stop it even if we knew how it would turn out. We wanted it too much, all of it."

The next morning Sample packed his belongings. He discovered that for the first time in his life he owned more than he could carry on a single horse. He was loading a second horse when Rose Ellen came out of the house. "Papa told me," she said. She sensed that his leaving had to do with her. She was not happy about it, but she understood.

Orrin kissed her on the forehead, pulled tight the last hitch on his pack, and rode up the trail toward the house where Earl and his family were living now. Irene had offered the old cabin beside their house until he built a place of his own. She seemed always there to help whenever he needed it.

Texas Dawn

EARL NEWSOME, IF HE HAD known the depths and the power of what churned within his wife, would have said that she was a right quick study. Sharp as mesquite. Clever as a coyote. Could lay lower'n a lizard at high noon.

But after eight years of marriage he suspected no such thing. He would have been astonished to learn that within her first week at the ranch she had decided that she had married the wrong partner in this enterprise.

She had realized that the place swung around Charlie Fowler. None of the three partners was stupid, she had thought, but Charlie knew how to use his mind, and he trusted it. That put him one big step up on the others. She asked herself why Charlie had not gotten rid of the other two already, and she could not escape the conclusion that he was a decent man who cared as much for his partners as he did for himself.

As she learned more of the ranch, she marveled at what Fowler had accomplished in so few years. Left alone, he might do great things in the valley. But so would she. And Irene would not be happy with her own destiny in the hands of another, no matter how capable.

Sample had been in the cabin five days when she asked him to dinner. By now, she thought, he'll have had enough of his own cooking.

She found Luz in the kitchen. "I want you to make that tamale pie tonight," she said. "The one you do with the corn bread. And I believe we will have wine, a good bottle from that case that was shipped from New Orleans."

She had Luz heat some water, and she washed her hair. Then she sat doing needlework beside a window, until the sun had dried her hair and she could brush it down her shoulders. She perfumed her neck and put on a dress that she had not worn since she came to Texas. It had a high, tight bodice, and it was nipped in at the waist. Earl would like that dress, she thought. And so would Orrin. Tonight she wanted Orrin to like her.

Sample came to dinner wearing fresh clothes and clean boots. No need to have dressed special, she told him. She wanted him to feel at home. She hoped he wouldn't need an invitation next time.

He drank the wine, and Irene kept the glass full. The tamale pie was as good as he had ever tasted. It was his first meal in nearly a week that hadn't been burned.

After dinner she offered him a soft chair in the parlor and they talked. Somehow the talk drifted to Fowler and the ranch. Sample defended Charlie, his friend.

"That's very loyal," Irene said. "I admire that in a man."

"You don't know how far we come since the end of the war."

"But you all had a part in that, didn't you? I know Earl did his part, and I'm sure you did, as well."

He nodded. "I did, some."

"Charlie Fowler is your friend. I know," she said. "And I'm not one to say anything if you happen to be content with the way you've been treated."

There was more talk, but Sample went home turning that phrase over in his mind. "If you happen to be content . . ." Sure, he was content. No reason not to be, that he knew.

Dinner with Earl and Irene became a habit. The cabin was lonely after fourteen years in the big house with the others. The Newsomes' house was there at the top of the hill from his cabin, and he could not ignore the light that glowed from the windows when darkness came.

Sometimes they did not discuss Fowler. But just as often Irene would, and always in words that disturbed Sample later. One night she asked Orrin how often he went over the ledgers. He answered, "Oh, now and again." He was ashamed to admit that he had never thought of questioning Charlie's figures.

Fowler and Newsome were still speaking, rigidly civil but at least talking. When the drive was a month away, they spent a day with the hands, roping and branding. For Fowler this had overtones of days past. At midafternoon Newsome reined in at a spring near the branding fire, to drink and splash his face. Fowler joined him at the pool, squatting beside him.

"The cows get sprier every year," Fowler said. "Or maybe it is just me slowing down."

Newsome nodded. "Maybe some of both." He moved as if to stand up and leave. So Fowler spoke.

Texas Dawn

"Earl," he said, "we have been through a lot together."

"We have." Newsome's answer was cautious, neutral.

"I want to talk to you," Fowler said. "About things not being the way they used to be with us, the three of us."

"There's four of us now, Charlie."

"That's so. And that gets straight to what I want to palaver about. The way we lock horns now over every damn thing. That ain't right."

"That seems to be the way things come out."

"But why? When it was just us three, did we ever gouge each other the way we been doing the last few years?"

The two men stood, and Newsome said, "What are you telling me, Charlie?"

"I'm saying maybe we should look and see where all this bad will comes from. I know you love Irene, but look at what has happened since she settled here."

"Maybe you said enough, Charlie."

"And maybe you ought to be your own man again instead of letting a woman speak for you."

Newsome's right hand drove into Fowler's stomach, bent him over. Then Newsome tossed him to the ground and went toward him again. Before Sample and one of the hands could pull Newsome away, Charlie Fowler was dazed, bloody, and beaten.

That night Irene told Newsome that she was pregnant. "I think it is time we set out on our own," she said. "Don't you?"

She needed six days to sway Sample. On the seventh the three of them called on Fowler. He looked at them through eyes puffed nearly shut, spoke with lips stiff from half-healed cuts.

"We want to split the place up," Newsome said.

Fowler stared. "You, too, Orrin?" he said.

Sample looked at Newsome and Irene, and he nodded.

There were pens in a jar on Fowler's desk. He took a broad-nibbed one and an inkwell and walked to the surveyor's map of the valley on the wall. He dipped the pen in the ink, placed the point down carefully, and drew two heavy black lines across the paper.

"Sliced in three," he said, "like carving a roast. Lines run east

Texas Dawn

to west across the valley, so we each get a piece of the river and some good grassland. You can have your choice. I'll be happy with whatever you leave me." He put down the inkwell and pen.

Newsome and Irene walked to the map. "Orrin, we would like the northerly piece that the new house is on," she said. "Does that suit you?"

"Sure," he said. "If they's all the same, you keep the piece with your place on it. You, too, Charlie."

"Then yours is the third one in the stack," Fowler said. "I am in the middle, with fine neighbors to the north and south of me. We will have to do this legal." He was angry, but was trying to

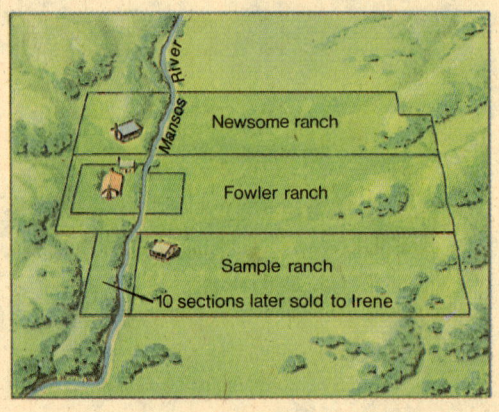

keep his voice under control, not wanting to lose his dignity.

"Is that all?" he said. "You got what you come for? You sure you're getting your due?" He waited; they were silent.

"Then get the hell out of my house, all of you," Fowler said. He pointed a trembling finger at them.

They left. Fowler saw Rose Ellen standing outside the office. Her troubled face drew him to her. He put an arm around her.

"You heard?" he asked.

"Yes."

"You understand? There's no Circle Three Bar anymore. It will be three ranches, and you and I will own one. I like that idea, Rose. We won't have to share a spread any longer."

"Can I still be friends with Ray?"

Fowler was angry. His voice rose. "His ma and pa are no good, and the apple doesn't fall far from the tree. No, I expect you can find better than a Newsome for a running mate."

Her eyes filled with tears. She turned from him and ran to her room. He heard a sob burst out as she shut the door. He had to swallow the urge to go to her, tell her that she could be friends with the boy if she wished. But he wanted to spare her the rough handling that she would get from any child of Earl and Irene's.

Later that day Ray heard the same. Earl surprised Irene by telling the boy, without prompting, to have nothing more to do with Rose Ellen. With a ranch of their own now, Earl told him, he would have to learn the business. It was time he worked instead of riding the day away with Rose Ellen.

The next day, and every day for a week, Ray and Earl rode together, chased cows, and practiced roping. Earl gave him a horse from his own string, a nimble cow horse with good speed and quick feet, able to match a heifer's dodge and feint. Young Ray rode as if born to the saddle. Newsome decided that with more hard work he would be a hand worth having. So Earl pushed him from first light to sundown.

Each night the boy would bolt down his supper and then collapse in his bed. But there were moments before he slept, and moments in the saddle during the day, when he thought of Rose Ellen. He imagined her watching him roping, and in his imagining all his throws were perfect: every loop caught a cow.

After a week Earl took a day off. He had legal business with Fowler, and he told Ray to go out alone and work. But Ray did not push himself as hard as Earl had pushed him. That night he had more time to think about Rose Ellen.

He wondered whether he would see her again. Maybe it would be years. Maybe never. When he was sure that Earl and Irene slept, he dressed, picked up his boots, and crept from the house.

Outside, he pulled on his boots. The horses were tied to a picket line. He could do without a saddle; he untied his new horse's reins, swung up onto its back, and rode away at a trot.

The night was murky black, with a new moon rising over the

far hills. The boy reined in at a tree about a quarter of a mile from the Fowlers' house. He walked the rest of the way.

There were no lights. From the back door, he thought, he could get to Rose without coming near Fowler's room. With feet bare again, he was silent in the house until he pushed the door of Rose's room. The hinges squeaked and the noise woke her.

"Ray!" she said, surprised to see him.

"Keep your voice down, girl."

He walked to her bed. She sat up and grabbed his forearm. She was wearing a nightshirt with ruffles around the high collar and around the cuffs. Something—the darkness, the nightshirt, her touch, the danger—thrilled him. He pulled his arm away, though that was not what he wanted at all.

"I thought you would never come to see me again," she said.

"My pa told me no."

"Mine, too."

"Get your clothes on," he said. "I didn't come all this way just for a howdy-do. I got something to show you."

"You wait outside," she said.

He sat on the back doorstep. When she met him, they walked together toward the tree where he'd tied his horse. She took his hand, and he held tight, feeling a warmth and pleasure he had never known before. It had everything to do with Rose, with her being glad that he had dared to come to her.

When she saw the horse, she let go of his hand and ran. "Ray! Yours?"

"Yep. I call him Rojo. His hair is brown, but it does look red when the sun hits it right."

He helped her onto the horse's back and pulled himself up. She put her arms around his chest, and though her touch was light the breath left his lungs.

They had touched before, often. But it was a mystery to him that until now he had felt nothing when they touched. He could not imagine how he had ignored it.

They rode across the hills, and when open space stretched before them, he gave the horse more rein. They rode until she told him that she ought to go back. Her father might awake early.

He brought her to the tree where he had tied the horse, and she slipped down to the ground.

"You'll come to see me again?" she said.

"If I can."

"This is Thursday. We'll meet Sunday, after everybody is asleep. If one of us can't get out then, we'll try for Tuesday; and if not Tuesday, it'll be Thursday a week. That suit you, Ray?"

"Uh-huh."

She reached up and touched his elbow. He knew that he was supposed to bend down toward her. He moved as if a hand were pushing him down. He stopped with his face an inch from hers. She raised up on her toes to meet him and placed her lips against his, both hands on the back of his neck.

Then she was leaving.

"Rose," he said. "Where we supposed to meet?"

"Indian Oak," she said. She ran toward her house.

His own home was dark when he got there. He should be sleepy, but he had never felt more charged. For now he knew that he would not be kept from Rose Ellen Fowler.

CHAPTER FOUR

WHEN they should have been driving cattle to Kansas, they were splitting up the ranch. The money was easy, but they needed a surveyor and a lawyer for the land. Then they picked over guns, horses, tack.

Some things, though, defied division. Fowler, Sample, and Newsome gathered the hands and told them they could have a job with any of them. Alvarez looked at them and allowed that he would keep his bedroll where it lay, in Charlie Fowler's bunkhouse. The others decided they would all stay with Fowler and Alvarez.

Then Fowler got out the branding irons. The long rods were black, but the shaped metal of the brand was burned white by years of fire.

He thrust the irons at Sample and Newsome. "Maybe one of you knows how we can slice this brand up like the rest," he said.

Sample dug the toe of one boot in the dirt and said, "Charlie, you keep it."

Fowler spat. "I don't want the irons around here," he said. "They belong to a ranch that doesn't exist anymore. I've got new ones being made up."

Newsome held out a hand. "I'll take them," he said. "It's a good brand. You can read it in the moonlight."

That left the thousands of cattle. Sample was ready with a way of dividing them. Starting at one end of the range and working their way to the other, they would rebrand every animal they found that bore the Circle Three Bar mark. There would be three different irons in the fire, and the brander would use each one in turn. One for Fowler, the next for Sample, the third for Newsome. After they had finished, any cow that bore only the old mark was fair taking for any of them.

Fowler stayed away. He sent Alvarez and two hands. Newsome took Ray; it was the boy's first trip to work on the range. They made him the branding boy. For twelve hours every day he kept the fire hot, and across it, laid in order, the irons were glowing red. For Fowler the brand was a Diamond Five—he had cut a deck of cards; and for Sample, an O–Bar–S. Newsome chose an inverted V to be placed above the old brand, forming rafters over the old Circle Three Bar mark.

Hundreds of times a day Ray would snatch up the next iron in line and knock it against his boot to clean it of clinging ashes and coals. He would run to where a cowboy had lassoed the cow and would press the brand in until he could smell burned hair. His body was occupied by the work, but his mind was with Rose. The first Sunday night, the next Tuesday, and the Thursday after that, he thought of her going to the oak tree, waiting for him in the dark.

She'll think bad of me, doubt me, he told himself.

His first night back was a Sunday. He was exhausted, but he fought sleep, waiting for Earl and Irene to go to their room.

The night was bright this time when he rode. At Indian Oak, he sat beneath the tree and dozed for a while, but soon he awoke, sure that she was on her way. In the valley was a horse, traveling fast and trailing a plume of dust. Soon he could hear the hoofs beating the ground, coming over the brow of the hill.

She reined in, climbed down, her eyes on him. "H'lo, Ray. Your pa put you to work, it seems." She was trying to be calm, but the quaver in her voice gave her away.

"You knew," he said.

"I puzzled it out. Paco came home today, so I knew if you were ever going to come, it would be tonight."

She moved to him, put a hand on his face. It trembled against his cheek. He wanted to kiss her, say all the words that swam in his mind. But he hesitated, and she pulled her hand away.

They sat under the tree and talked, safe trivialities. He barely heard the words. She took his hand, and the pressure of her arm against his spun his head. He turned and kissed her.

She returned the kiss. Her arms were around him.

She tilted her head back and spoke. "Ray, don't push so hard against my lips."

"I reckon I kiss passable well."

"You don't if you hurt my lips," she said.

"Then maybe I just ought'n to kiss you."

"Maybe not. I am sorry that I troubled both of us to come up here tonight," she said as she stood up.

He regretted his temper's flaring. It was gone already and he was contrite. "I'm sorry I got riled when you said you don't like my kissing. We can try again."

"No. But maybe if you can get away Tuesday."

She rode away and left him on the hill.

When he returned home, lamps were burning in the house. He walked in by the back door and heard voices in his parents' room. Maybe, he thought, he could bluff his way through this one. He went to his room, pulled off his shirt, and walked back into the hall in jeans and an undershirt. Earl was walking toward him, his face pale.

"What's wrong?" the boy asked.

"Your mother," Newsome said. "Didn't you hear us? Your mother is ill, boy."

Ray went into his parents' room. Irene lay on blood-blotched sheets, her face a drained and pallid gray. He sat beside her bed, and first he felt guilty for having been gone when his mother took sick. But he knew that his being gone had nothing to do with causing it.

At first light Ray rode for a doctor, thirty miles distant in a cow town called McPherson, below the valley's south end. It was late evening when he returned with the doctor.

The doctor sent Ray and Earl out of the bedroom, and he closed the door. The pendulum of the big standing clock in the parlor struck the quarter hour. Much later the doctor came out. She had lost the baby, he said. Now she needed rest, six weeks at least.

Newsome kept watch over Irene. His restless vigil stopped Ray's trips to the oak tree; there was no predicting when his father might be awake.

That spring Fowler was the only one of the three former partners to lead a drive. Sample was building a cabin, for he alone had not had a house when the ranch was parceled out. Newsome stayed home with Irene to nurse her until she was well again. As the doctor's six weeks became twelve, she spent mornings out of bed, and the pallor left her cheeks. Newsome began spending his days away from the house and sleeping beside his wife in their bed.

One day he looked at her, and she seemed as healthy and as lovely as she had ever been. When she blew out the lamp by the bed that night, he reached to touch her.

"No," she said. "Please, Earl, not that."

He turned away, tried to swallow his hurt.

The next day, when he came home, he saw Luz with an armful of his clothes, going into a third bedroom that was beside Ray's. "Luz is moving my things," he said to Irene.

"It would be better this way, darling. Please understand."

"We are husband and wife," he said. He had to keep himself from shouting. "I don't believe I care for this."

"Do you want to lose me?" she said. Her voice was loud, too loud for him. He didn't want Luz, anybody, to hear what she was telling him. "I can't be pregnant again, Earl. I don't want ever again to go through what I've just survived. Surely your rights aren't so important that you would place me in jeopardy."

"No." He wrung his hands together. "But you don't have to put me out of our room. I swear it, I wouldn't let anything happen." He could stop touching her. But he did not want to be put out of their room for Luz and Ray and the world to know.

"We can't take the chance," she said. She was quiet now, placating. "I want you to know I still feel about you as I always have. We are still partners in every other way, darling."

He went out and did not come to dinner. He watched the sunset and he thought of Charlie Fowler, lucky to be out on the trail.

When he came into the house, he went to the room where Luz had carried his clothes. He lay across the bed. The mattress was stiff and unfamiliar. He wished he were on the trail now, lost to the world somewhere north of the hills.

When Fowler came home from the drive, he was as astonished at the six months change in Rose Ellen as Sample had been a year earlier. He had known, before he left, that she was no longer a little girl. When he saw her again, she was a woman.

He looked at her and imagined how she would strike a man. Strike him silly, he guessed. Long legs, a fresh and pretty face—when she kept her hair out of it—and a shapely form. And her eyes, dark and alive. He noticed the delicate movements of hands and lips when she ate. How did she ever learn that? he wondered. Still, she was not ordinary, even for a pretty girl. There was her jaw, which was strong and sharp.

He suddenly felt that this place was wrong for her. She was too good for the gritty dirt and the hills strewn with rocks, for the coarse shirt and jeans that she wore. He thought of her in a brocade gown and evening slippers, perfumed and with her hair done in fashion, not stuffed beneath the crown of a wide-brimmed hat. She would be beautiful.

She had become what she was because he had brought her here for his own happiness. She diminished the loneliness of the place, cut it down to a size he could manage. But, he thought now, what did she know of being a woman?

Texas Dawn

Fowler resolved to think of Rose's interests, put her above himself for once.

The next morning they rode to McPherson to buy supplies. Fowler excused himself in the middle of lunch and told her that he had business at the bank. He knew that the banker had a daughter a few years older than Rose. She had gone to a finishing school and had come back a lady.

The banker gave him the name and address of the school. In Denver it was, the Hardy Academy for Young Women. Fowler used the bank's stationery to write a letter of application. Then he posted the letter. He said nothing to Rose Ellen.

Two months later the notice of acceptance from the headmistress was waiting for him at the post office. Fowler scribbled a second letter and enclosed a fifty-dollar deposit.

For a few days he searched for a way to tell Rose Ellen what he planned. He found it the night he saw her leave the house and ride for the hills.

He awoke without knowing why. He heard a scuffling outside and from a window he could see Rose Ellen riding away from the stable. He dressed quickly, saddled his horse, and galloped off in the same direction. Soon he saw her again, riding up the side of a high hill.

He reined up and waited. It wasn't right to follow her, he thought. He ought to have faith in her. Then he saw a second rider coming from the north. The man—Fowler could see that much—seemed not to notice him, and rode up the hill that Rose Ellen had just climbed.

Fowler dismounted and climbed on foot. When he got to the top, he saw his daughter. Her back was toward him, a pair of arms wrapped around her. She was kissing a man whose face Fowler could not see.

Fowler kicked at the earth. Rose Ellen turned, startled. She moved her mouth but could not speak. The man released her and pulled away.

It was the Newsome boy. But not such a boy anymore.

Fowler heard angry words coming from his own mouth. He took two steps forward, caught Rose Ellen by the wrist. Ray reached for her to pull her free. Fowler flung a forearm at the boy's face and sent him sprawling.

Rose did not resist when he pulled her down the hill, her wrist in one hand and her horse's reins in the other. He told her to be ready to ride early the next morning and not to bother to pack too many pants or pairs of boots.

She cried when he told her what he planned. She turned alternately petulant, contrite, and sullen as they rode to Galveston, ferried to New Orleans, rode by steamer up the Mississippi to Saint Louis, and west from there by train. She told him that they were both going to feel terrible if he went through with this. He said then that she was right, most likely.

But until he had left her and walked down the stone steps at the school in Denver, he did not know how right she had been.

---- ⌶ ----

Donnie Lee: All morning I run over in my mind how I would let on to Sue Everitt about Gandy Meacham. She wanted an A, and I had the fella that would help us get it. The question was, Should I come right out and say so? Or should I string it out and bring Gandy Meacham out of the north forty while she wasn't looking? I wanted to make her happy and make her proud of me.

Come the end of history class, I told her I wanted to talk to her about our project.

She said, I'm sorry, Donnie Lee. Prom committee meets this lunch hour. You should have talked to me before class.

But then she said, Why don't we get together after school? T.J.'s, if that suits you.

It was a hamburger shack. We sat in a booth ordering pop and fries. When the waitress left, I said, Sue, I got our A living right in my own house. Gandy Meacham, my great-granddaddy, he knew Miz Rose when they was young.

She said, How far back?

I said it was some fifty years since he left the valley.

She wanted to know how well they was acquainted. And I told

her it sounded like they had been real good friends back then.

Our order came. She chewed on the end of a fry and got a look like her mind was someplace else. Then she looked at me and said, Bet they weren't.

Weren't what? I said.

She said, Weren't just friends. I bet they were—you know—boy friend. And girl friend. Like that.

In my mind I thought, Ain't that just like a girl to get such a notion? But I was learning to keep my head a good long step ahead of my mouth when I was around Sue E.

Could be, I said. You never can tell.

She said, Maybe we could see him tonight.

I told her that might not be such a good idea. I wanted to talk to him some alone and prime the pump. I didn't know how Gandy Meacham would take to Sue E., who was, much as I liked her, the flighty sort. I had a notion she might get under his hide.

I said, Let me talk to him tonight. He takes medicine and sleeps an awful lot, and he don't always make sense.

Then you call me right up tomorrow, she said, and tell me what he had to say.

I had a better idea. I said, I was thinking maybe you and me could get together tomorrow night, and I could give you the lowdown on what Gandy Meacham had to say and we could see a picture and drive around a bit.

She said, Why, that sounds like fun.

Well, great, I said. My hands must have jumped when I said it because I hit my glass and spilled pop all over the table.

When I got home, I threw my books and my jacket on the bed and went down to Gandy Meacham's room. But his eyes was closed shut, and I couldn't get a rise out of him.

That night at dinner my mama said, The poor old fellow was restless this afternoon, so I gave him a double dose of pills to help him get some relief.

A double dose.

I expect that will knock him out for a spell, I said.

CHAPTER FIVE

SAMPLE and Newsome and Fowler had changed the valley, not so much the look of it as the way it was used and what it would become. But that year there occurred two events, independent of each other and hundreds of miles apart, that would alter the valley as much as the three men ever had.

The first came a few days before Christmas, 1880. A man named Hart drove his one-horse carriage up the road that ran the western length of the valley. Hart was a salesman from Illinois. He had a definite aversion to cattle folk, with their closed minds and set ways. They shunned him and snickered at the special product he was selling.

All morning he followed the road north. He passed the smaller ranches, for he was after the three big spreads that were, he had heard, stacked one atop the other in the middle of the valley.

He did not stop at the first. That place looked like a squatter's cabin. The second one, up the road a few miles, seemed more likely. Charlie Fowler met Hart on the front porch.

"I'm a wire-fencing salesman, sir," Hart said.

"I never heard of a wire fence that would stand up to cattle," Fowler said.

"This one will," Hart said, "because it is different." He opened the leather case that he carried and held it out for his prospect to inspect the samples.

"What are these things?" Fowler asked, reaching inside.

"They are prickers," Hart answered. "Barbs, if you will. Mr. Glidden, who holds the patent, calls this a barb fence. Feel one." He added, "But not too roughly." He was too late with the warning. Fowler put his thumb to his lips and tasted blood.

"Sharp," he said. "But cowhide is a sight tougher than mine."

"No matter. A cow wouldn't want to tangle in this either. You can five-strand it, but four will do. Draw it tight with a team, tack it good to a stout post, and no cow will try it twice."

Fowler looked closer at the wire, saw how the thin barbed pieces were wrapped around the heavy-gauge wire. He imagined a cow running into it. "This is a wonder," he said.

Texas Dawn

Not once since Hart had been in Texas, selling his wire fencing, had he gotten this far with a cattleman without encountering laughs. "Maybe you would care for a demonstration," he said. "In my wagon I have a spool of the wire. We can build a small pen and see how a few of your animals take to it."

"No," Fowler said. "I believe you."

"Then you'll be wanting to place an order."

"I don't think so." Fowler replaced the strand of wire in the leather case.

"You are ahead of your day," he said. "You won't sell to cattlemen until we have a reason to keep our cows from chewing our neighbors' grass, and right now our neighbors don't object. So far there is enough grass to go around."

"But that will change," Hart said. "This wire will have its day in this country."

Fowler watched the salesman climb back into his carriage, and he thought, So now it begins. It had to happen sometime.

Irene Newsome was upstairs when she saw Hart pulling up at the house. She was downstairs in time to hear Earl sending the stranger away. "What is the matter, dear?" she said.

"No matter. This fella is trying to sell me some wire fence, is all. And I told him that any cow that tries will walk through any puny wire a man can put up."

"Not this wire," Hart said. He held out a piece for Irene.

Something in the salesman's face made her look closer. "You seem to believe in this," she said.

"I've seen it work," Hart assured her.

"I would like to keep this piece of wire," Irene said.

A week later she made a rare excursion out of the house. Her face shaded by a wide-brimmed bonnet, she was driven to Sample's cabin. There she told him that she had business with him.

THAT same day, in an apartment in Washington, D.C., a man and a woman sat at opposite ends of a sofa and spoke. The woman was nearly forty years old, but with a straight back and skin still smooth. The man was fifteen years older, balding and big-bellied. He wore a swallowtail coat and spats and gray trousers. There was a stiff celluloid collar across the neck of his starched shirt. A gold watch chain spanned his girth, circling the roundness of his stomach.

"There must be something you can do," the woman said.

The man's voice was a raspy bass. "How many times in the last month have we been over this? I am finished here. I must return home, and I cannot possibly take you there with me."

"After twelve years," she said. "Finished, like that."

"You knew this could happen," he said. "The voters grow weary. They clamor for change. Even a U.S. Senator is not immune to the effects of the fever."

She stood up, her back to the man. "Don't you care? Doesn't it matter to you, what happens to me when you're gone?"

He stood, walked to her, put a hand on her shoulder. "Of course it does. I do care." He kissed her on the side of her face.

She pulled free, her face hard. "No more," she said.

The man backed away. "My wife will be expecting me," he said. He walked to the door and let his hand pause on the knob. "The lease is up at the end of the month," he said. "But it is paid until then."

She stayed for a while in Washington. With the new term, there were new faces at the dinners and the parties. She held on to the hope that she would be discovered again, as she had been twelve years before. She could serve a man well now, with all that she knew of the city and its workings. But the invitations were few. That fall the parties went on without her, and she knew that she was finished in Washington.

In the middle of October the woman was on a train bound south. From Atlanta she took a branch line to the county seat. There she found the tax collector's office.

"I need some information," she said. "I am trying to contact a man, an old friend with whom I've lost touch. He lived in this county until after the war. He owned eighty acres. Fowler was his name."

The collector knew of him. He still owned the land; taxes paid in full. A queer business. Not a seed planted there for twenty years, but every spring the tax bill went to someplace in Texas called McPherson, and every summer the money came back.

She was at the rail depot the next morning, first in line when the ticket agent opened his booth.

"I need to get to Texas," she said.

IN THE daytime Rose Ellen could see the mountains from her dormitory window. The far peaks were sharp-edged, with blue-gray rock poking through the snow. Sometimes she could see the wind swirl the snow into graceful mare's tails. But she preferred the rolling foothills that lay between Denver and the high peaks. They were brown and bare and reminded her of Texas.

As she watched another twilight, Rose Ellen leaned her head on the windowpane. Her breath condensed against the cold glass. She wanted to be home. Without turning she spoke to a girl behind her, reading by gaslight. "The cold makes my fingers hurt. Second week of April and the pond is still frozen."

The other girl laughed into her book. "Don't blame the weather for your fingers hurting," she said. "Miss Charlotte's hickory stick has more to do with it. If you don't mind your ways, you won't leave here with any fingers worth mentioning."

Charlotte Ames was a small and fragile woman who, in words so soft they were barely audible, taught girls to be ladies. What her words lacked in emphasis, her hickory stick provided. A first offense against her rules of decorum brought the thick stick down on a table or the arm of a chair. When the stick moved a second time, it came to rest on the knuckles of the transgressor. Within a week after she had come to the school, Rose Ellen's hands were swollen and bruised.

She had taken every blow. They were less frequent now than they had been. And she knew that she could endure anything once she had survived Miss Charlotte's teaching her to walk.

Her first day at the school Rose Ellen had been walking down a hall when Miss Charlotte wanted to know what exactly was that act that she was performing with her legs and feet.

"Walking, ma'am," Rose Ellen said.

"You may call it walking, but I do not."

Miss Charlotte told Rose Ellen to remove her shoes. Then the headmistress knelt on the floor and held the hickory stick in her right hand. They would work on cutting down her stride, she said. She told Rose Ellen to take shorter steps.

Rose Ellen walked.

"Shorter." The woman banged the hickory stick on the floor.

Rose Ellen turned and walked again.

"Shorter," Miss Charlotte said again, fiercely, and this time she brought the stick down against the girl's bare toes. Rose Ellen bit her bottom lip to keep from crying.

"Walk! Shorter!" Again the stick bit Rose Ellen's toes.

Another day of this and the hip-rolling swagger was gone. Rose Ellen was putting the heel of one foot directly before the toes of the other, as if she had been doing it for years.

There were eighteen teenage girls in the school, every one the daughter of a suddenly rich prospector or rancher or merchant or thief. The girls were reclamation projects, the first generation of their families to have manners equal to the new, quick money.

Those who had been at the school longest showed the fewest traces of their origins. The newest student was a girl from Dallas, and Rose Ellen strained sometimes to catch snatches of her speech. The words had a comforting sound. Like the foothills around Denver, they summoned up memories.

She had nothing from Texas except those memories, a few clothes, and a slim packet of letters that she kept tied in a red ribbon. Three letters were from her father, sturdy and full of forced good cheer. The fourth was in an impatient scrawl that was different from her father's careful hand:

Dear Rose Ellen,
 I hope this gets to you. I heard the banker in town tell pa that you was at a school in Danver with this name, i hope it is right.
 Things are right fine in the new house. It is a cold winter, we had a norther blow down and freeze us a couple days, my rojo he stuck a leg in a hole and busted it but pa says that's all right, come spring I will ride the trail with him and his boys and I can have my pick of the string like the others, and maybe I can ride flank I ride so good.

Texas Dawn

> Last week Thursday I think it was I rode up to indian oak and it made me feel sad. I miss you terrible and hope that maybee you and me will see us again.
>
> Who knows maybee I will have to ride up to Danver some day.
>
> Yours very truly,
> Raymond J Newsome

She thought of him often. Most nights she took her feather pillow in her arms, closed her eyes, and imagined that it was Ray Newsome. That way she slept easily and happily.

"This book is about Boston," said the girl behind Rose Ellen. Her name was Amanda, and she was from Wichita. "I would like to go there, I believe."

Rose Ellen looked at her. "Boston? I don't know why."

"Boston is a great city. Women there wear beautiful dresses, and all the men are gentlemen. I want to learn to be like the best people, to walk with them and live like one of them."

Rose Ellen turned again to stare out into the darkness beyond the window. "I don't understand how you can call them the best without even knowing them. I don't expect I ever will meet those folks unless they come to Mansos Valley someday."

"You mean you'd go back to Texas?"

"Sometimes I'm of a mind to start walking south and not stop until I get there."

"Whatever for?" the girl asked.

There was an oil lamp beside the window. Flecks of snow were falling now, streaking white in the glow of the flame.

"Because it is my home forever," Rose Ellen said.

THAT night her father was sleeping under the sky, the herd bedded down on the trail just south of the Red River. With Rose Ellen in Denver, the ranch had been empty for him that winter. So he had spent days on the range, riding and roping with the hands harder than he had done in ten years. It would be a good year for his ranch. After the drive he would visit Rose at school.

Twenty-seven days uptrail from Charlie Fowler were Earl Newsome and his herd. He and his men had never before left so early on a drive. They needed the days because they were trailing up to Wyoming to sell beef to the army. That winter a major had come riding through the valley, offering contracts of thirty dollars a head, on the hoof, at Fort Laramie. Irene thought they should take the contract. It was good business, she said, to sell to a buyer who spends someone else's money.

ON THIS same night Orrin Sample was alone in his cabin. For the second year in a row he would be passing up the drive. That left time for looking back at his life, to see what he had done, what kind of man he had become.

Before he had known Fowler and Newsome, he'd not been a man to ask such questions of himself. Ten years into the partnership he would have answered them proudly: he had opinions worthy of consideration; he was part of a great enterprise.

Now the doubts were strong. He had been making mistakes since they'd split the ranch. For the second year in a row he had been late hiring help for a drive, and help was hard to find. He had hired two saddle tramps to rope and brand mavericks. But then he had slipped patching his roof, and he was hobbling when he should have been riding. The saddle tramps worked alone, and when they left him after two weeks, it was to start a herd of one hundred and fifty cows—bearing a new brand of their own—up the trail to Kansas.

Then Irene had come to call. Flustered, Sample offered her a seat inside the house and a glass of spring water.

"Orrin," she said, "I know you have found the going somewhat tough since we made the break. I feel badly, since Earl and I had a part in that. We would like to help if we could."

He said no, he did not need charity. Not yet.

"I don't mean charity, but a trade that would help us both. You can get rid of what you don't really need."

"Besides cattle, I've only got land."

"That's what I mean," she said. "Land."

He refused at first. They both knew that land was worthless. He had heard her say so fifty times to Charlie Fowler.

In the end she talked him into it. He gave in when she agreed to take her choice of the land, whatever she wanted. Even so he felt like a cheat when he took the money: sixty-four hundred dollars at a dollar an acre, to cover the ten sections of his land through which the Mansos River flowed, with its cool water and its grassy banks. He was grateful for her generosity.

He was not a happy man as he examined himself in the solitude of his cabin. Chances once spurned now seemed suddenly imposing. A wife, maybe, if he had not come to this remote place. Children. A life in which he did not need the charity of neighbors to survive. A life, above all, in which he would not be haunted, as he was now, by the mocking specter of what might have been.

THAT summer of 1881 Ray Newsome joined the company of men. He kept something of a boy's spirit, but his body was a man's and he did a man's job on the trail. He rode beside men and ate with men. At night he listened to their bawdy stories and told lies of his own in a man's voice.

The change went beyond that, to depths that Earl Newsome did not recognize at first. Even Irene saw only the outlines of it. But what she knew of it she liked. As they rounded up the cattle for the drive, she understood that he was no longer a bystander. She glimpsed in him the first quickening of pride in the ranch.

Never had anything satisfied Ray as much as this drive, moving the herd—his herd—up the trail. He liked to push his body all day, then placate it with a full stomach and dreamless sleep at night. He was ready for the notion when it came to him. He realized, This ranch will be mine. And it will be the best.

Ray no longer rode flank but took his place beside Earl at the head of the herd. When it was payoff time at the fort, Earl and Ray walked together to the quartermaster's office. Together they gave the man $100 for counting a herd of 932 as 1045.

Fort Laramie was no cow town, and the men were ready to play. Earl called them together and told them they could have Cheyenne for a couple of days or they could have Denver—all the same to him.

Ray did not draw a breath during the talk that followed.

Cheyenne was closer, somebody said. But Denver is a for-real city, said another. Then a hand named Adams recollected a show he had seen in Denver—1877 it was, or 1878—with girls dancing about in their scanties and going out into the crowd.

That carried the night for Denver. Ray expelled the breath he seemed to have been holding for five minutes.

Denver was a big city, the biggest he had ever seen. Bigger than Austin, which he had visited once. They reached town in the afternoon, left their horses at a stable, and found a hotel. The cowboys made plans in the lobby. One of them called to Earl, "Hey, boss, you going to let that youngster bust loose tonight?"

Newsome looked at Ray standing beside him. "He can speak his own mind."

Ray shifted his weight from one boot to the other, hands jammed into his hip pockets. "I might like to look around some."

"I thought you might," Earl said. "Go on, then. But don't do anything to make me ashamed of you, understand?"

The cowboys took Ray to the first saloon they found, just a few doors from the hotel. One of them ordered a round of whiskey for the bunch, and another said to Ray, "You ever drink whiskey? Beer, even?"

"No."

"Make it a beer."

Ray drank it down. The taste was strong and foul in his mouth. Probably alcohol straight would not be so bad, he thought. So next time around he ordered whiskey and got no argument. That burned the throat at first, but it slid down easily enough. He ordered a second whiskey and drank it.

The cowboys began to leave, first a pair, then a third, then two more, until he was alone at the bar with Adams.

"We got to go with the boys," Ray said. He had to say it slowly. His mouth was thick.

"You don't want to go where they are headed," Adams said. His hair was long and gray, curling up the back of his neck. "Next year, maybe, but not this trip. You stay. Get good and lathered, which ain't going to take you till the sun goes down, and then go on back to your pappy."

He nodded at the bartender. "Another whiskey for the young buck here."

Ray gulped this one. He put the glass on the bar, tugged at the waistline of his pants, and told Adams he had something to do. He went to the livery stable and got his horse.

"Lookin' for a school," he said to the stableboy. The words came out hard. Ray considered the possibility that he was drunk. "School for girls."

"If I knew of one," the boy said, "I wouldn't tell anybody else about it. But I don't, pard."

Ray rode his horse into the street, into the evening shadows. He swayed and held tight to the pommel. For a while he rode from one edge of town to the other, hoping to find the school that way. Twice he asked for directions, but he could not remember the street names and the turns he was supposed to make. Then the sun went down, and he could no longer read the street signs.

The motion of the horse made him feel sick. He was away from the center of the city, on a street lined with houses, when he got off the horse and sat on a corner. He hoped that sitting would soothe his stomach.

When he looked up again, he saw a man standing before him. The man wore a dark blue suit with brass buttons, and there was a badge on the front of his jacket. He tapped a smooth club into his palm and looked down at Ray. "And," he said, "what manner of distress have we here?"

THAT evening Rose Ellen went upstairs, as usual, when she finished her supper. The other girls in her room had gone home for the summer. She could be alone, open the window, listen to the crickets.

Charlotte Ames gave herself credit for changing the rowdy Texas bumpkin into a credible version of a lady. Rose Ellen was sedate now, had achieved that languid and almost soporific state that was the Ames ideal. But what Charlotte Ames took for composure was no more than boredom.

Rose Ellen sat by the open window, lit the oil lamp at her

elbow, and read. She was tired, for no reason. So she put the book aside and closed her eyes.

A man's voice woke her, a voice that she did not know, calling her name in the street. She looked outside and saw a figure on horseback. "Rose Ellen Fowler," the voice said.

Miss Charlotte leaned from a window and screamed, "Miss Fowler cannot see you. You are drunk and filthy and disgusting. Go away, please."

"Rose Ellen!" the man called again.

And then she knew. Something in the voice gave it away, changed though it was since the last time she had heard it.

"Ray?" she said from the window.

"Yep. Come to take you riding, girl."

Miss Charlotte screeched up at her, "Stay where you are, young lady. Don't let that man near you. He will do you harm."

"Let's go, Rose."

"He won't hurt anything, Miss Charlotte. He is a friend of mine from Texas. Maybe we can let him in the parlor for a few minutes. That will quiet him down."

"Jump, Rose. It ain't far. You can do it."

"Young man, I'm warning you. Go away this instant. Clara, lock that front door. Ramona, see to the back."

"That's it. That ties it," he said.

He rode the horse up the three stone steps to the landing, leaned down in his saddle, and tried the door. When it did not budge, he dismounted.

Rose Ellen stepped back from the window. She could not watch. She heard a succession of sounds: a splintering of wood, shrieks and screams of female voices, and a shattering of the front door's etched glass. She heard Ray's heavy boots clopping down the hall, then up the stairs.

She thought, My Lord, he is coming for me.

"Rose!" he shouted. His voice reverberated up the stairwell, breaking nine months of quiet. "Rose Ellen, where are you?"

She opened the door. He looked at her and grinned, the expression so ludicrous and the sight of him so welcome that she smiled back at him.

Texas Dawn

"Let's go," he said.

He was different. The boy she had known would never have done this.

They started downstairs. The girls and Miss Charlotte stood wide-eyed, then stepped back when they approached. Rose Ellen realized that they were afraid of Ray.

"I am going out," she said, "with my friend here. Please don't worry. He won't let anything happen to me."

Outside, he pulled her into the saddle behind him. They galloped out of town. She clasped her arms around his chest and thought of stories her father had read to her from a book. They were stories of women trapped in castles and knights riding to rescue them. The stories had never meant much to her. But she had never before needed rescuing.

"You ain't angry?" he said.

"No. I am happier than I have been since the last time we were together."

"I had to find you. First I thought I couldn't, but I got some help from this fella said he was po-lice. I told him I was looking for my sister."

They found a grove of aspens beside a brook. Ray pulled up there, jumped down, and helped her off the horse. He picked out a flat, clear spot among the trees, and they walked there hand in hand. Ray breathed in the night air. His head was clearing.

He looked at her, his hands on her shoulders, to make himself realize that they were together again. He pulled her to him and kissed her. "Rose, I love you."

"I love you, too," she said.

They sank down to the grass. His hands searched, moving across her face, her arms.

"I want something," he said, "and I don't know how to ask, and I ain't even sure I am supposed to have it."

"We've done everything else together," she said. She reached for the buttons in back of her dress and pulled them free.

Later he cradled her against him, her head tucked under his chin. "I never knew," he said "Never had no idea."

"That is the way it is supposed to be," she said. "I could see

where it might go wrong. But the way we just did it is the way it is supposed to be."

He said, "We'll get married, I 'spect."

"It seems the reasonable thing."

"Not right off. I want to, but it will take some doing, from your end and mine."

"Then we will work on it, won't we?" she said. "If it is something we both want, we will work on it until it comes out right. I'll face what I have to here and then square things with Papa."

Ray brought her back to the school, kissed her once more, and watched her walk up the steps and through the broken door.

Finding his hotel took some work. When he got there, he did not sleep. That next day and most of the ride south to Texas he saw with the clarity of a traveler in a strange land. He looked at the world through new eyes, a man's eyes.

Charlotte Ames kept Rose Ellen confined to her room for three days, as though she carried a contagious fever. A girl brought meals to her door, knocked, then scurried down the stairs. Rose Ellen was grateful for the solitude. The night had changed her, too. Suddenly she could not fathom the unhappiness and the torment that she had felt in this place. It was a triviality now, a nuisance. She could not take it seriously.

The quarantine ended with Miss Charlotte rapping on her door, telling her that her father had been informed in a most detailed letter. And her supper was on the table downstairs. That was the end of it. Her crime had exceeded Miss Charlotte's capacity for punishment. There was one final penance: the wondering stares of the other girls.

After six days her father arrived for a visit, trail-weary from the drive to Kansas. They held each other and she cried. Miss Charlotte, standing in the door of her office, requested him to do her the kindness of speaking privately with her.

Rose Ellen waited in her room. When her father walked in, he sat on the edge of her bed and she sat across from him in a chair. "That Miss Ames says you had some fling. Who was this young whelp you been carrying on with?"

"It was Ray Newsome," she said. "And he is no whelp."

"Son of a gun," he said softly. "What is it with you two?"

"We don't like for people to try to keep us apart."

"Do you mean to marry this boy?"

"I do."

"Well, damn, I don't know what to do."

"If you would listen, Papa, I would tell you that he is good and kind. Different from you in some ways. Too quick to move sometimes. I wish he sat on things for a spell the way you do. Some ways, though, he reminds me of you. Real proud. Full of respect for himself is what I mean. That is a good thing for a man to have. Or a woman."

"I don't know what to say, Rose. I did not feel kindly toward him before I came here, and your words can't change that."

"I'm sorry, Papa."

He cleared his throat. "This school was a mistake. You don't belong in a place like this. It was wrong to stick you among people who would try to change you. I don't blame you for being happy to see a face that you knew."

"They changed me for the good, Papa. I have learned all sorts of things that I didn't know before. And I got some book learning, too. That doesn't hurt."

She walked to where he sat, put her hands on his cheeks, and kissed him. "I'm grateful to you, Papa. You did the best thing for me, always have. But to be honest, I think I've gotten most of the benefit from this school that there is to be had."

"Well, you do seem to be a finished woman," he said. "If you went home now, you would be the jewel of the valley."

"Let's go home, then," she said.

"You want to take the train and the steamboat?"

"I want to wear some pants and ride," she said.

They rode together as they had ridden that summer ten years earlier, mindless of care and time, covering the miles. She told him stories of Miss Charlotte and the hickory stick in a way that made him laugh. They were out of Kansas and four days into Indian Territory before Ray Newsome's name came up. Within a week they were discussing whether Ray might be able to court her without his parents' permission.

Texas Dawn

Charlie Fowler had taken his daughter's side, a move both emotional and pragmatic. He knew, having heard her speak about Ray Newsome, that she would not be shaken loose from her heart's hold. To stand against a stampeding herd of longhorns would be as fruitful. "If he is the man you think he is," he told her, "he will find a way through this."

They'd been home for a day when she saw Ray in the distance, on horseback. She stepped out on the porch and waved. He galloped over to her.

She squinted at him. His head blocked the high sun.

"Come down off that horse and greet me proper," she said.

He did.

"You look right fine," he said. "Wearing a dress, I see."

"Around the house I do, unless I want to ride."

Fowler appeared at a corner of the house and saw them standing there. Ray stepped away from Rose Ellen, then toward Fowler, slow, calm.

"I know that you don't like me. But before you throw me off your land, I am telling you that I mean to marry your daughter."

"My likes don't seem to carry much weight," Fowler said. "You don't have to stand there ready to scrap. It has been some time since I threw that punch at you, and I wouldn't presume to start in again."

Fowler saw the young man's arms relax at his sides.

"Maybe," Fowler said, "you would excuse yourself from my daughter and come have a few words with me."

They sat in the front room, and Fowler studied him. Afraid, Fowler thought, but sitting on his fear so it doesn't show. Ready to stand up for himself. Good for him. Then he spoke. "You won't have to come around here like a fox to a henhouse any longer. My daughter says she wants to marry you. As long as that is so, and you behave, if you follow my meaning, then you will be welcome."

"Thank you."

"Earl and Irene won't be happy to hear of your plans."

"When I think of a way, I'll tell them. And it won't take me long, so's we can get on with this marriage."

Fowler put up a hand. "The marrying will wait, if it is meant to be. Six months from now, or a year, if you two belong together, you will still be ready for marriage. I want to know if you can court my daughter the proper way, and can make your arrangements so that you can keep her as happy as she deserves to be."

"I will," Ray said, the voice almost defiant. "I wouldn't do it any other way."

It was Ray who asked Orrin Sample's help, a favor. He wanted Sample to ask Earl to let him work three days a week with him that winter. "This isn't for you, Orrin. It's for me," Ray explained. "I want to get out of that house so I don't have to account for every hour."

"What can you do here that you can't do at home?"

"Court Rose Ellen Fowler."

The answer shocked Sample and touched off a welter of emotions that threatened to break out on the surface. Anger. Jealousy. A woeful sadness. He let the feelings wash over him as the boy looked at him, puppy-dog earnest, waiting for an answer.

Sample found his voice. "Planning to marry her, are you?"

The boy grinned, and Sample found himself hating him, wanting to pound the smugness out of him.

"Uh-huh," Ray said. "If I worked for you down here, I could see her two, three times a week. You wouldn't have to tell tales if I passed my evenings at the Fowler place. And you'd get a good day's work out of me in the bargain."

Sample scrambled in his mind to find a way to refuse without betraying why. "It seems underhanded to me," he said finally. "I am your father's friend. Am I to help you deceive him?"

Ray said, "Don't you care about Rose Ellen?"

"I have known her since she was two years old." Longer, he thought, than you have. "Natur'ly I care about her."

Ray said, "And don't you think she is a fine girl?"

This time Sample did not have to keep the truth out of his voice. "She is as good a girl as the Lord put on this earth."

"Don't you see that puts you apart from my ma and pa? She is Charlie Fowler's girl, and that is all they need to know."

Sample had no answer to that. He sent the boy away with a promise to think about what he asked.

Sample knew that he still had not broken free of Rose Ellen. She did not dominate his thoughts as she had before. But in the past year he had thought of her often, and the thoughts sometimes were fantasies of her living in his cabin, sleeping beside him, having his children. He told himself that the thoughts helped him bear more easily the days when he heard no voice but his own, talking to him.

He decided to speak to Charlie about this—Charlie, whom he had not seen in more than a year.

Fowler's greeting was friendly in a vague way. In the front room, he nodded Sample to a chair. The two men sat straight-backed and stiff in their seats.

"I don't mind telling you, Charlie, I felt a mite odd coming up the road," Sample began. "You and me, not having said a word in some time."

"We have both been busy," Fowler said.

"Yes," said Sample. "I thought you might have some ill will toward me, not that I would blame you if you did."

Fowler could not hold him at a distance. Not Orrin, his friend. He smiled and saw Sample do the same.

For a while they traded gossip, spoke of the weather. Rose Ellen came into the room and sat on the arm of her father's chair. Sample watched her while he talked.

"I came," he said, "to talk about Ray Newsome. He said to me yesterday he was going to come courting Rose."

Sample told them what Ray Newsome had asked. Their reactions hit him hard. Rose Ellen seemed happy to hear it. A slight smile showed on Fowler's face, and he said, "How about that? The young fella acts like he is serious about getting what he wants."

Sample dreaded the answer he would get, but he asked the question anyway. "And how does it strike you, Rose?"

She looked hard at him. He thought he saw a wisdom there, an understanding. He could believe that she knew everything that was going on inside him.

"Orrin," she said. "You do what you think is right. Lying is wrong, and there are some who would call this a lie. But if you can see your way through this, you'll make me very happy."

Her words made the difference. He wanted to see her happy.

Earl was quick to grant the favor. Work was slow on his spread and would be for some time, he said. Better to have Ray help a friend than to be idle. They settled on Tuesday, Wednesday, Thursday of each week. Ray could save traveling time by staying with Sample those nights.

Ray arrived early the next Tuesday morning and worked with Sample building a corral until midafternoon. Then he cleaned up for the evening, while Sample made a stew. The boy changed into clean clothes and came into the kitchen whistling.

"I made dinner," said Sample. "Look, fresh meat."

"Thanks," Ray said. "But if I hurry, I can eat with Rose Ellen."

Sample watched him run for his horse and gallop off.

Later that week, after Ray had returned home, Sample visited Fowler again. The two men had a good evening together, and the visits became regular, whenever Ray was not there. These hours were some of the best Sample had known in a long time. Earl was not the man he had been. But with Charlie the illusion survived, however tenuously, that time's effects were not so great.

After one of these visits Fowler and Rose Ellen watched Sample walk, slightly drunk, to his horse. She turned to her father and said, "I feel sorry for Orrin."

"I feel sorry for him, too." Fowler put an arm around her. "Because he has nobody like you in his life."

One night in late October, Sample came for dinner. Rose Ellen was bringing a roast to the table when they all heard a wagon outside. Rose Ellen put the platter down and went to the door.

A woman climbed down from the wagon and looked at the figure in the doorway. "You wouldn't be Rose Ellen?" she said.

"I would."

The woman stepped onto the porch, closer to Rose Ellen. She wore a black silk dress covered with a film of yellow trail dust. There was something disquieting to Rose Ellen about the familiar, nonchalant way the woman studied her face.

Texas Dawn

"You turned out beautiful," the woman said.

Rose Ellen heard her father behind her. She looked at him, and his startled, frozen face gave her a shiver of fear.

"Who are you?" Rose Ellen said.

The woman said, "Just your mother, Rose."

CHAPTER SIX

THE man in the buckboard looked impatient, standing with one foot on a trunk. He asked if they wanted it on the porch.

Sample said a quick good-by.

"Charlie," Olive Fowler said, "the question is whether the bags stay in the wagon and I go back to town or you invite me in and the wagon goes back empty."

"Well . . ." Fowler said. "Well, you can't go back tonight."

The man brought the trunk and a portmanteau to the porch, then shook the reins and drove off. Rose Ellen stepped back from the doorway; Olive walked into the house.

In the front room, Fowler lit the oil lamps, and Olive took a seat. Fowler hesitated. Rose Ellen guided him to the sofa, where they sat together, looking across at Olive.

Fowler tried to sort out the emotions that fought to be recognized. He was judging the effect of the years on his wife, wondering which question should come first. Rose Ellen studied Olive to find echoes of her own looks. She was angry at the intrusion and unable to stifle a fear that she did not yet understand.

Olive Fowler was relieved. She had actually gotten into her husband's home, was seated in his chair. She knew that surprise had served her well so far, but would soon lose its effect. So she tried to sense and ride the currents lapping around her.

Sure that silence worked against her, Olive spoke. "At the courthouse, there in Georgia, they said they sent your tax bill to McPherson, and I thought you were living there. You can feature how surprised I was to find I still had more than twenty miles to go from the town. I could have stayed there overnight, but I couldn't get this far and then wait longer."

Fowler nodded. He was trying to slow down the whirring of

his mind, but she took his silence for animosity and prattled on.

"I think Rose has your mother's eyes, don't you, Charlie? And my mother's figure. My mother had such a fine form."

"Olive," Fowler finally said, "why have you come here?"

She looked at him and Rose Ellen. Their faces were immobile.

She said, "I got myself in a spot, Charlie, and had no place to go. I was at the end of the road. Nobody to turn to, nobody who cared what happened to me. I had my mistakes for company.

"I thought of you and Rose. And I told myself, Charlie Fowler is the last man who ever treated you right; maybe he won't be too hardhearted if you go see him."

Tears ran over her dusty cheeks, making clear pink channels. She dabbed at them with a handkerchief.

"I was ready to come live with you on that eighty acres, if you'd have me," she said. "That place I left as if it were nothing, it began to look like paradise to me."

The tears gushed now. Fowler started from his seat to go to her. He felt Rose Ellen's hand, holding him back. But Olive sobbed into her handkerchief, and Fowler moved to stand beside his wife's chair.

He felt awkward in putting out a hand to lay on her shoulder. "Olive," he said, "there's no call for that."

"I've been a horrible woman, Charlie," she said. "I don't deserve any kindness. But I need help. Any finger you lift would help me. Just letting me into your house like this—you've given me another night to go on living."

He said, "Sure, you'll stay here tonight. We've got plenty of beds. And you must be hungry."

She shook her head. "My stomach is too tied up. But I won't fight you if you offer me a hot bath and a place to sleep."

He was glad that she had stopped her bawling. "Rose will heat some water for the bath. Please, Rose?"

Rose Ellen left without a word.

"Charlie, she isn't a bit happy about my being here."

"You've got to understand—"

"I do. I can't blame her. Suddenly the mother she never had appears at her doorstep. I understand."

Texas Dawn

She touched the hand on her shoulder. "Charlie," she said, "you never went to court against me?"

"Divorce, you mean? No, I didn't. Never had a reason good enough. It is a long way to a courtroom from here, and it never seemed worth the time nor the trouble."

Later, while Olive was asleep upstairs, Fowler and Rose Ellen ate a cold dinner. They did not speak until he laid down his fork and said, "You think I did wrong, letting her stay tonight."

"Yes," she said. "I don't want her here. She has no place in this house. We built all this without her. We can enjoy it without her. I don't care for her."

"I do," he said.

The words surprised her.

"You have nothing about her to remember," he said, "but that isn't so for me. She married me and bore me a child, and the memory of that isn't so easy to bury."

Rose Ellen said, "I would hate her if she had done to me what she did to you."

"I did. For a long time I did hate her. But hating can't live on itself. I loved her once, and there is still something left, Rose. If she'd given me a choice, while she was at a distance, I'd have said no, she shouldn't come here. But she came, and I could not turn her away."

"Give her money. But don't let her stay, Papa. She makes me feel that something is wrong in this home of ours."

"Nothing's wrong," he said. "We're too strong together for that."

Rose Ellen crouched at the edge of the Mansos. She dipped a soapy shirt into the stream and shook it until the flowing water had rinsed it clean. Washing clothes was not a tedious job when she put the tub beside the river. She liked the sound of the water, and the high banks here made it a private place.

So she was doubly irked when she heard Olive Fowler's voice in back of her.

"You're making a terrible lot of work for yourself," she said to Rose Ellen, "when you have a spring to draw water from right behind the house."

Rose Ellen twisted the shirt until it stopped shedding water. She flapped it and laid it with a pile of wet clothes on a flat rock.

"Besides," Olive said, "the clothes need heated water to come clean."

Rose Ellen looked at her. "They rinse out better when I can dunk them in the running water," she said. "And if I make more work for myself, I don't see it is anybody's affair but my own."

Olive looked at the clothes on the rock, shifted her gaze to Rose Ellen, and said, "Tonight I am doing dinner. You don't have to worry about it. I believe I will do beef in a pastry shell. I'm sure Charlie has never tasted the like of it."

Rose Ellen slapped a pair of pants into the stream.

"I got the recipe from a French chef in Foggy Bottom," Olive said. "He cooked for Andrew Johnson's Secretary of State."

She walked up the slope to the house. Rose Ellen wrung the last drips from the pants and threw them on the pile.

Olive had been in the house ten days and already seemed to have rooted herself. Charlie Fowler showed no inclination to make her move. She was becoming part of the scenery, blending in like a tawny mule deer against an October hillside.

At first she had come and gone silently, almost cringing. Lately she spoke at the dinner table, asked questions, advanced opinions. More and more, Rose Ellen thought, she was acting as if she belonged here.

Rose Ellen hung the clothes on a line in the sun and went back up to the house.

Olive was in the kitchen, slapping and kneading dough. Two days earlier she had offered to cook her first meal, had ventured that she felt uncomfortable being waited on. Charlie should let her earn her keep while she was resting. That was the word she had used. "Resting."

The dinner had been delicious. Charlie had complimented her twice. Twice too often for Rose Ellen. Now Olive was taking a second dinner upon herself, just assuming that she had every right to be in the kitchen.

Rose Ellen walked up the stairs to her room and began to think about Ray. This was Tuesday, and Ray would be coming.

Texas Dawn

CHARLIE FOWLER, ALONE AND ON foot, heard the sound of his boots crunching in the gravel of a dry streambed. Five rabbit carcasses dangled from his belt. He thought that a sixth would give them a meal, with enough left over for stew.

He had not hunted in ten years, so six rabbits in a day would be a feat. And Olive had mentioned rabbit the night before. "Lapin," she called it. She said it was a delicacy in Washington City, served in all the best homes. The thought of surprising her had given him the nudge he needed to reach for his double-barreled shotgun.

Her third night in the house, Olive had mentioned Washington casually, implying that she had lived there a long time. The next night she had said so, specifically. Twelve years, she said, almost thirteen. Fowler did not press her for details. She would share those with him when she was ready.

As he reached the edge of the streambed, a rabbit scurried through a patch of brush, across Fowler's line of sight. He raised the gun to his shoulder and squeezed the trigger. The rabbit spun around awkwardly and fell to the ground. It was a fat buck.

When Fowler got home, he smelled beef cooking and heard loud voices. Olive and Rose Ellen were arguing about how clean clothes should be folded. As he walked into the kitchen, Rose Ellen brushed angrily past him.

"Charlie! You brought rabbits!" said Olive. She was wiping her hands on an apron. Rose Ellen's apron, he saw. "I don't imagine you got all those nice big rabbits on your own," she said.

He could not resist smiling, a silly, proud smile. "Every one," he said. "But you have something else cooking."

"It is no loss. The hands will eat it. We can't let this rabbit go wasting. You have wine? I once learned a tasty wine sauce for rabbit."

The rabbit was fresh and good. Rose Ellen ate a few bites before she got up from the table and said she would ride down the road to meet Ray.

"She has been cross the last week," Fowler said. "Not her nature, normally."

"Two women sharing a household is hard sometimes," Olive

said, letting the thought slip out as if it were a matter of fact that two women now shared this house.

She noticed that Fowler did not challenge her.

WHEN Rose Ellen met Ray, they rode to Indian Oak. They sat under the tree, and she rested her head on his shoulder. They had not made love since the night in Denver. She liked to feel his arms around her, but she told him that she could do without babies now, and her will prevailed.

"Ray, you have to get me out of that place," she said.

"Things that bad with your ma?" he said.

"Papa has a soft spot as wide as this valley. And she found it."

"She treats him real good, going on what I seen last time."

Rose Ellen kicked at a clump of dirt. "Men! Is that all that matters, somebody treating you good? A man will bed down in a den of shake-tail snakes if they don't bite him first off."

"She can't be all that bad," he said.

"She is. If she doesn't leave, there won't be room for me. And I don't see Papa making her go. You are going to have to take me away from there, get our own house started so we don't have to let in anybody we don't want."

"I was thinking, maybe the drive would be a good time to tell Pa about us. If I get him alone, seeing my side, then Ma will have to foller along."

Rose Ellen kicked again at the clod of dirt. "I don't know that I want to wait that long," she said. "I don't want to push you. But if you love me, and you think it is right, I want to marry as soon as we can. Your ma and pa will have to hear it sometime."

"I'll tell them," he said. "Friday, when I get back home."

"I have this terrible feeling something is closing in on us, and we are running out of time to get away from it. Like when you run a cow into a box canyon," she said. "The cow always thinks there is a way out the other end. I feel like something is running us toward a box canyon. We can't see ahead of us, but we think there is always daylight at the other end. And we are running out of time to turn away." She began to cry.

"Something is changing, Ray. I want to have a happy life with you forever. We think we have all the time to do that, but maybe we don't. I want to marry you, grab the chance while we have it."

She held her face against his shirt. He put his arms around her.

IN HIS dining room, Charlie Fowler swallowed the last scrap of rabbit and said, "You are a fine cook, Olive."

"Thank you, Charlie, very much." She took the compliment with eyes averted. Then she said, "Would it be forward of me to suggest a brandy to top off the dinner? I noticed a decanter in the cupboard."

They sat on the sofa in the sitting room, clinked glasses in a toast to health. They drank.

"You have been here almost two weeks," he said. "What do you think of this spread?"

"It is big. So much land with nothing on it but cattle. And quiet. At first you must have missed having people around."

"We were busy," he said. "Work is a blessing that way. And we couldn't have everything. What I would have done without Rose Ellen, I can't say."

"But a daughter can't be everything to you." Olive moved closer to him. "Charlie, I want you to know . . . if I can do anything to please you . . . well, I wouldn't mind, not in the least. We are still husband and wife, you know. That is not changed."

When she had gone to bed, he sat alone and thought of his daughter. He wanted her to know what simple joy a man gets from a woman's smile, a woman's compliments. A daughter would not understand the power women had over men to raise them up and dash them down, turn them about-face with only a wink, a nod, a word.

Mostly he wanted Rose Ellen to see his vision of the life that lay ahead for him after she married. She had sustained him so long. But soon she would be tending to another man in her own home. Little enough would be left for him then.

He walked to Olive's room. He saw that her door was open a crack, with a line of light at its edge. He pushed it open.

A single low flame of an oil lamp lit the room. Olive was sitting up in bed, her back against a pillow, her hands clasped in front of her on the blankets. She was wearing a lace peignoir. She smiled at him.

"Your invite was more than I could turn down," he said. He reached out and touched her skin above the peignoir's neckline.

"Charlie," she said, "can things be the way they were before? You wouldn't send me away now, not after this?"

"I wouldn't," he said. "Believe me, I wouldn't do that."

Donnie Lee: All along I thought that my mama would not want me bothering Gandy Meacham about Miz Rose Sample and past times. But in nine or ten hours I would be at Sue Everitt's house, and I still did not have a lick of news about the project. When I saw my mama head for Gandy Meacham's room with those pills and a glass of water, I knew I had to do something.

I said, Ma, I wish you wouldn't give Gandy Meacham his pills right off.

She wanted to know why.

I want him to talk to me, I said, and the words don't come out right when he takes the pills.

Why, I had no idea you were such pals, she said. What is so important that you two have to talk about?

About the old days, I said. And I want to take what he says and use it in a paper for history class. Actually, me and a girl is doing this paper together.

I waited for the top to blow. But instead she said, Donnie Lee, I think that is fine. That old man has a treasure locked inside his head, and it makes me feel good that somebody is taking the trouble to get at it. You go on and talk to Gandy Meacham about his cowboying days. Just take these pills with you and make sure to give him two or three when he starts to hurt too bad.

Then she asked me who was this young lady. A nice girl?

Real nice, I said. Fact is, I'm taking her out tonight to talk about the project, and I want to know can I use the Ford.

Your daddy will be home for lunch, so ask him then.

I took a pencil and a notebook with me into Gandy Meacham's room. He was awake, staring up at the ceiling. I said, Howdy, Quiller. I asked if he wanted to take the pills. I didn't want him hurting on my account.

Just one, he said. That will take away some of the bite without knocking me out. After he took it, he said, I recall you saying you wanted to talk to me. What was it exactly?

About the olden days, I said. Especially about Miz Rose Sample. For school. We're supposed to learn about historical people.

He laughed, though it come out more a wheeze.

Tell you one thing, he said. Back then, didn't none of us think that school kids would be talking about us.

Soon as the pain let up, he said, I had a brother a year older than me. That was Lynn. Him and me cowboyed up in the Panhandle country until one day in 1890, I think it was, or 1891, we decided to hoof it out of there. We rode the grub line until we come to this here Mansos Valley. We stopped at the first spread we come to, which was the Circle Three Bar, and that was how me and Lynn come to work for Raymond Newsome.

He stared up at the ceiling for a while, like there was something the matter with it. But there wasn't—he was just looking and not really seeing it at all, I'd guess.

I said, Quiller?

Life, he said. Life. You think you got a handle on it sometimes, but you don't. Nobody does. You do things, simple things that you figure don't make a bit of difference one way or the other, but later it turns out they change everything. Lynn and me, we didn't have to stop at this valley. We could have passed on through. And everything would have been different.

He said, The first time I seen her she was in mud up to her knees. She was wearing a man's shirt and pants. When she slogged out of the mudhole, she had on a pair of men's brogans, shoes you would call them, at least four sizes too big for her. Not even cowboy's boots. See, the Box CF—that wasn't the name then, but it's the same spread—was not much of a money-maker. She didn't have the money to ruin a pair of boots, so she put on this pair of brogans when she had to walk in the mud. It was a drought year, and the cows was getting stuck in the wallows all the time.

She was trying to get the heifer out all alone. I couldn't let her go it by herself. So I climbed through the bob-wire fence, he said. Ray Newsome's bob-wire fence.

He stopped talking, and I seen him clench his jaw. He was hurting again.

Then he said, I thought she was a beauty, right as she was. Most men today, if they seen her that way, would not say so. The years was tougher on females then, I believe. You get a woman working out in the sun, doing a man's job the way she done, it is tough on the looks. She had a good form, but not soft the way women usually are. Wiry and tough is more like it. But I said to myself, Now, there is a *woman*. She didn't have an ounce of quit in her, and she wasn't afraid to get dirty to do what she had to do.

Gandy Meacham stopped talking all of a sudden. He turned around on his side and propped himself up on his elbow. Then he said, See, Donnie Lee, s'pose that was a man instead of a cow in the mud, a man that she cared about. You think she wouldn't do the same for him, if she would get kicked and dirty just for a ten-dollar cow? The woman who will do that will go halfway to hades and back for a man she cares about.

Leaning on his elbow was too much for him. He lay back against the pillow. And he said, Donnie Lee, better get me them pills. I don't believe I've got any more talking in me for today.

That's okay, Quiller, I said, giving him the pills.

He took them and said, You talk for a change. You are a fair-looking fella. You must have a gal to tell me about.

I said, I got my eye on one. Her name is Sue. And I am talking to you for her and me both, since we are doing this history project together.

Well, then, you bring her around, he said. Next time. I mean it.

I said I would. Then I remembered one thing.

Quiller, I said. I know this is silly as all get-out, but I have to ask you anyways. For Sue.

Go ahead, he said.

I have to ask you if you and Miz Rose was in love.

He smiled and said, Hell, boy, ain't you figured that out yet? 'Course we was.

How do girls know these things?

Pretty soon he was asleep and I left him.

When my daddy came home for lunch, I stood in front of him, and he said, Is there something you want, Donnie Lee?

I wonder if I could use the Ford tonight.

Not to go out looking for trouble with a bunch of other boys, I hope, he said.

No, sir. I have to see this girl. It's about the history paper we are working on together. I thought it would be a sight easier for me to drive than for you to be hauling me back and forth.

He said, Who is the girl?

I told him, and he looked at my mama and said, Cloyd Everitt's girl. The new doc in town. Nice folks, I hear. He looked back at me. I guess it would be okay. I'll knock off early today, so I'll see you before you go.

What a fuss they made before I left. Ma making sure my pants looked just right and my hair was combed, my sisters giggling and making faces. Even Daddy got into it. He walked out with me and said, What do you plan to do with this young lady tonight? When you are not working on your school project, I mean.

I thought we would get a bite and maybe see a picture.

He said, You got money?

Two fifty that I saved, I said.

He dug into his pockets for the keys to the Ford, a 1940 model that we owned and not a ranch car.

He also come up with two dollar bills. Better take this, he said. I would not want you running out of gas.

My ma come out on the front porch. Crying, if you can believe it. You would of thought I was going off to war, not just my first real date with a girl.

I was careful backing out of the driveway, and I drove slow down the road, thinking about the strange ways of kinfolk.

CHAPTER SEVEN

IF HE was a man, he told himself, he should act like a man. So as soon as he returned from Sample's ranch, Ray Newsome told Earl and Irene that he was going to marry Rose Ellen Fowler.

Earl Newsome, as was his nature, exploded. And Irene, as was her own, said nothing, but watched carefully.

She saw that Earl reacted as a matter of course. His wishes had been subverted, therefore he was angry.

She also saw that Ray stood up to the anger. So he knows what he wants, she thought. No budging him.

"We can send you away from here," Earl said. "You think she would care for you then, a drifter with no place to go? Would you go live with her and her father?"

"If that's what I have to do, I will," Ray said.

"We don't want that," Irene said. "Does her father know?"

Ray nodded. "He is with us. Not at first, but he is now."

She threw questions at him, poked and probed, but found no seams in his resolution. "Raymond," she said, "you must know that you've startled your father and me. We're not antagonistic, not at all. But we would like to discuss it between ourselves. Will you give us that? By tomorrow evening we can talk it over again without anger."

He saw it as a retreat, and was happy to cease fire. He walked away and left them alone in the room.

"If that don't blow me over," Earl said. "Him. Just a boy. Telling us he is getting married, no two ways about it."

Time, she thought. Must have time. Ray is too strong now. Fight him now and you lose. But maybe time will change that.

"Darling," she said, "you know that young people have a way of changing their minds. For this reason or that, or no reason at all. If we give them time, one of those young lovers could have a change of heart. So much the better. If not, the girl has her qualities. Maybe their marriage is not such a bad thing, anyway."

Irene knew that she could never let it happen. Rose was strongheaded, and she had ideas. Ray's mother did not need another such woman in the family.

Earl shook his head. "Woman, I can't keep up with you," he said. "I would have figured you dead against it. Instead you are halfway to talking it up. Suits me. We will just get them to wait as long as we can before they go off and do it."

The next evening Ray rode to see Rose Ellen. He found her beside the Mansos, looking into the water.

"How did you get away?" she said. Then she laughed and grabbed him by an arm. "You came with news. You did, didn't you, Ray Newsome? You told them."

He saw that her eyes were red, the lids puffed. "Who made you cry?" he said.

"I got into a terrible fight with that woman. Papa stuck up for her and I didn't want her to see me cry, so I came down here. So how 'bout it, cowboy? You going to take me away from here?"

"Sure. Just as soon as we have a chance to get ready, so as to do it right."

She stepped back. "What does that mean?"

"There is a whole heap of things we didn't think of. Like, where are we going to live? You don't want to live with my folks."

"No."

"Well, my pa, he said he would build us a house, half a mile or so up from our place. Not big or fancy, but enough for the two of us. But he can't do it until after this next drive."

"Eight months? Nine, ten? I don't want to wait that long!"

"I told him that. But I can't miss the drive. Pa needs me. So it's five or six months we won't be together anyways."

He reached to hold her. She pushed him away. "Oh, Ray, I don't like it, not a bit."

"Please, Rose. I done the best I could. It was hard enough as it was. I don't want them to hate me. I didn't want to yell and fight with them. I thought I done pretty good for us."

She put her hands on his upper arms, felt the hard, thick muscles beneath his shirt. "You did," she said. "That woman has made me impatient, that's all. But I can wait if you can. What is a few months when something you want so much is waiting at the other end?"

He held her in his arms under a purple Texas sunset. A bank

of clouds splayed out dark and sullen across the sky. His clasp
was strong and insistent. He stroked her hair while he whispered
in her ear, soft words like the gentle and mindless night songs of
trail drivers, who hope to pacify the herd with a lullaby.

ONE night Rose Ellen awoke in her bed, crisply conscious of
an escape from her quandary. She had to wait until after the
Newsomes' drive before she could be married. She did not want
to stay alone with Olive for half a year. And she wanted to be
with her father once more before her life changed.

She would go with him on his own drive. She'd talk him
into it. The logic of it thrilled her.

When her father balked at the idea, she spent a day riding with
him, showing him again that she could rope steers and ride steep
ridges as well as any man. He still refused and told her that he
feared for her safety.

"Who will be your pardner?" he asked. It was custom for
cowboys to work together and sleep shifts as a pair.

"You will," she said.

"The trail scout works long hours, rides twice as many miles
as anybody else," he said.

"I can keep up."

"The boys, they like to strip down and get themselves wet
when they get near water. It keeps 'em from getting too gamy.
You won't be able to do that."

"I'll find a way."

"Cowboys can cuss the spots off a pinto, and they won't alter
their ways because a lady is around."

"They have been cussing around me since I can remember.
Maybe I will hear a word I don't know, but I doubt it."

"Rose," he said, "cowboys on the trail think of women all the
time. There is no telling what one of them might try with you."

"Papa, do you hire crazy men? I mean, out-and-out howling-
at-the-moon crazy men?"

"I try not to."

"Then I don't believe I have a worry. Any cowboy who tries
anything with me will have to think about what I'll do to him

when he sneaks into my bedroll. Not to mention you. And Ray Newsome, when he finds out. A cowboy would have to be pure loco to buck the three of us. And you don't hire crazy men."

"If I say yes, will you wear your blouse and your pants loose? Will you keep your hair tucked under your hat the way you did when you were a little girl?"

"That is what I plan."

He laughed. "Wait until they hear about this in Wichita."

On the morning the herd started up the trail she rode more erect than usual, shoulders square. She knew that the start of a big job brought pride, if it did not intimidate. There was also a touch of awe, because the herd was so large, so mighty. The cattle bellowed. The long raked horns jabbed up at the morning light like so many hundred dancing knives. But these few riders, with their horses and their wits, would move the roiling black mass up the trail, hundreds of miles to their goal.

Alvarez was foreman of the ranch, and usually the job of trail scout fell to him. He'd ride well ahead of the herd, finding spots for camps, seeking out water and grass, searching the banks of high rivers for a likely ford. But this time, with Fowler on the drive, Alvarez stayed close to the cattle, and Fowler was scout. He enjoyed seeing the country that the herd would cross in a few hours, liked being alone with his horse in the open spaces. This time Rose Ellen rode with him, and he liked that even more.

Six days out of the valley a rainstorm hit. The rain came down in thick drops that popped loudly against the brim of Rose's hat, against her slicker, against the earth. The dry ground soon turned muddy. So heavy was the rain that it formed an opaque gray veil that periodically dropped and lifted before them.

They pushed north for an hour into flat and open land. The cattle trail in this region was a band several miles wide. In summer it was easy to follow, from the millions of hoofs that had pounded the ground, from the grass eaten close to its roots. But they were early on the trail this year and the downpour was washing out signs of passage.

They rode for another half hour until Fowler stopped and peered ahead through the rain that cascaded in front of them.

As the rain hammered, Rose shouted, "Which way is north?"

He looked up to find a glare of brightness in the clouds that would show him the sun. But the only light was diffused, seemingly without source. "The way we are headed, I think. Might as well go back to the herd now," he said.

They turned the horses around. A few minutes later they reached the edge of a ravine. There had been no ravine in their path when they left the herd. Then they knew that they were off the trail. They rode for a few hundred yards along the ravine's edge, hoping to find where it grew shallower and ended. But it went down as far as they could see in the rain.

Fowler shouted, "I reckon if we get to the bottom and follow it to the end, it will empty us out on the trail again and we will find the herd."

She nodded, and they started down. At first the ground was soft, and the horses sank in to their fetlocks. But soon they reached boulders, smooth and rain-slick. There was no way around the large ones, and the horses had to walk from one rounded rock to another. Fowler had not ridden his horse on such terrain before. It was a good mount for hard rides, long-winded and strong. But on the rocks now the horse was skittish. Rose Ellen's horse was more nimble, and she took the lead.

Even through the drumming of the rain she heard the hoofs skidding behind her, heard the horse's deep sound of fright, heard Fowler's yell, angry and surprised. She turned and saw the horse tumble sideways and send Fowler twisting out of the saddle. He landed hard behind a big rock, out of her sight.

She reined in, then jumped down and ran to her father. His Stetson was cocked to one side, and blood was coming from his scalp. She pushed aside hair matted in the wound and saw the white of his skull where the rain carried away the blood.

She felt sick and frightened. Behind her the fallen horse lay on its side, kicking and squealing. She put her father's hat over his face to keep the rain off, then went to the horse and saw the broken bone that poked through the skin of one foreleg. She pulled her father's rifle from its saddle scabbard, levered a round into the chamber, and pulled the trigger.

She ran back and knelt by her father. In a few minutes the rainfall became thinner, and her father moved and mumbled.

She lifted the hat. "Papa, thank God you're alive," she said. "How do you feel?"

"Like a steer danced a fandango on my head." He stretched and moved limbs, muscles, joints, until he was standing. "The horse?" he said.

"I had to shoot him. Busted leg."

He rode her horse and she walked beside him, on down the ravine. When they were close to its mouth, cattle calls reached them. It was their herd.

Fowler cleaned his wound and bound it, but it still hurt. That afternoon the jogging of the horse sent surges of pain through his skull. He could not sleep that night. His tossing woke Rose Ellen and she stayed awake with him. In the morning light he looked haggard and drawn.

"You need a doc," she said. "You should see the size of the lump on your head."

"I have to be with the herd in Kansas," he said. "Work my bargain with the buyers. Paco can get the cows there, but it ain't his job to haggle. Those are my cows, not his."

She said, "They are mine, too. I can bargain."

He smiled through the hurt. "Maybe you can," he said. "But you can't travel alone to Kansas with a bunch of trail hands."

"I can," she said. "And I will. I am sending you back with the rustler. I will do his job." The rustler in an outfit was a boy on the edge of manhood, learning the cowboy's trade from the busy end: assistant to the cook, errand runner, the lowest-ranking member of the trail society.

This year the Diamond Five rustler was a fifteen-year-old named Sam. Now Rose Ellen took him aside and told him what to do. "Get my father back to the ranch. Don't hurry him too much, but don't waste time either. His head will hurt some no matter how slow you go. What I'm trying to say is get him home fast as you can without killing him."

"Yes, ma'am."

She held her father tight, then stood back as he slowly forced himself to climb into the saddle and swayed there atop the horse.

"I'm fine," he said. "Just fine."

Fowler and Sam rode south. Fowler's head felt huge, distended. The pressure of the hatband was too much, more like a tight iron strap than thin leather. He cut a slit at both ends of the crown and tried to ignore the pain. He gripped the saddle horn as he rode. There was dimness at the edges of his vision. He felt weak, somehow light-headed with all the hurt.

"Got to stop," he said. His motion off the horse was almost involuntary, as much a controlled fall as a deliberate step. He sat heavily on the ground. His forehead was suddenly wet.

"I hear water running on the other side of that bush," Sam said. "I'll bring you some to drink."

The boy filled the canteens and carried them back to Fowler and the horses. Fowler was on his side with his eyes closed.

Sleeping, Sam thought. He sat in the shade of a cedar tree and let him rest. The boy did not mind the wait. The grass was green, the bluebonnets were in bloom, and the air carried the fresh taste of spring. But soon his conscience nagged at him. They should be on their way again. He walked to Fowler and shook his shoulder gently. "Mr. Fowler," the boy said.

Then Sam drew back his hand and looked hard at him. Having never before seen death in a human, he was slow to recognize it in Fowler's face, his skin, and his limbs.

Somehow he got Fowler's body across the horse and tied him down. He rode without stopping for a day and a half, returning Charlie Fowler for the last time to Mansos Valley.

OLIVE sent the boy to tell Sample. After the boy ate and went to sleep, Sample sat alone to prepare himself for the night and the day ahead. He had lost a friend, and he faced the palpable fact of his own mortality. He saddled a horse and rode off.

First he stopped at Fowler's home and spoke to Olive. She seemed more frightened than bereaved. He took Fowler's body off the horse and carried it into a bedroom. Then he headed up the trail to the Newsomes.

"Poor Charlie," said Newsome. "This is bad, Orrin."

"He'll have to be buried soon," Sample said.

"How about up on the hill where we used to chase the deer?" Newsome said. "Where the laurel grows so thick. There is a clearing that looks over his place. I'll get tools from the shed."

Newsome carried a spade, Sample a pick. The rainstorm of three days earlier had passed through the valley, too, so the ground was damp and yielded to the steel.

"It pains me," Newsome said, "to think that Charlie went hating me."

"He didn't." Sample brought the pick up over his right shoulder and swung it down in a swift, vicious arc. "It wasn't in Charlie to hate for long," he said. "To keep hating is work. You have to have nothing else on your mind. That wasn't Charlie. He had plenty else to think about."

Sample twisted the point of the pick free from the earth. "Anyways, it wasn't you that riled him. Don't take it wrong, but you know what I mean."

"I didn't think he was cheating us," Newsome said. "He didn't go about things the right way, but that was just his manner. We done wrong, didn't we?"

"Prob'ly."

"We can put everything back the way it was. I'll make Irene see. Rose Ellen will go along with it, don't you think?"

"Ain't likely," Sample said. "Charlie wouldn't have done it, even if you'd asked, and I don't see Rose Ellen doing it. You can't put back together something that was broken like that."

"Charlie had ideas. He had big plans."

Sample turned to face Newsome. "Earl, this is just the wrong time to talk about Charlie's plans. It's too late now. So don't go on about it."

Sample felt the grief come over him. He swung the pick into the ground, again, again. For Charlie, he thought. Dig it deep for Charlie.

THE two women, dressed in black, met for the first time the next morning. They rode in a buckboard with Ray, while Earl and Orrin brought the body in a wagon. It was wrapped in a canvas shroud that Orrin had sewn, and it rested in a coffin that Earl had finished just an hour earlier. There was a wooden headpiece with Fowler's name carved into it: Newsome's work also.

Ray and the two men lowered the coffin into the hole. They stood looking into the grave until Sample swore softly, reached for a shovel, and began flinging dirt on the coffin.

Olive and Irene watched from the buckboard, in a patch of shade beside the mountain laurel.

"This must be a shock to you, especially after being so long apart," Irene said.

"You can imagine," Olive said. "I don't know what I will do. Rose Ellen won't have me stay. We didn't get along."

"But she won't know for some time," Irene said. "Even if we could get a message to her in Kansas, it would be months before she returns." She took Olive's hand and patted it. "You must stay with us a few days. You don't want to return alone to the house." She smiled.

"Besides," she said, concern in her voice, "it is possible that the future is not as dismal as it seems."

Irene waited until Newsome and Sample had combined their herds and had begun a drive up the trail a few days later. Then she sent to McPherson for the lawyer.

His name was Belford Tefler. He was sedentary in a community of active people, so his paunch was unusual. But he carried his head and moved his eyes in the manner of a hungry hawk. Irene liked that.

He sat down with Olive and Irene, asked questions, talked about probate courts and rights of survivorship. Irene listened to the words and thought, There are so many ways of getting what you want in this world.

Rose Ellen made her way north with the herd. For a few days she thought constantly of her father. Gradually, with the passing of weeks, the thought that he might have been seriously hurt seemed more improbable and too great a burden to carry. She worked hard, taking her sleep in short naps, when she could get it, for even at night she helped with the herd.

Texas Dawn

Within a week after her father had left the drive, she got her first indecent proposal. She discovered that a good laugh was the best rejection. It stopped a man without bruising him, gave him a chance to pretend it was all in fun. Before they reached the end of Indian Territory, she had laughed with nearly every hand in the outfit.

Just inside the Kansas line, local farmers met them on the trail with rifles and shotguns. They wanted the herd to turn back. They were afraid of Texas tick fever.

Alvarez wanted her advice. He was trail boss, but the cows were hers. She decided: turn the herd back for a few miles, then turn around again and stampede. See if the farmers will stand up to six hundred sets of long, crooked horns. They did not. She considered the seventeen head that they failed to retrieve afterward a small enough toll to pay for passage.

In Wichita, she sold the herd for a good price. At the hotel where the hands always stayed, she was walking away from the registration desk when the clerk looked down at the signature and called, "Miss Fowler? Something for you. It has been waiting a few weeks."

He ruffled through papers and came up with an envelope addressed in Ray Newsome's hand. In her room, she tore it open and read:

My darling Rose,
  I need to tell you this. Your pa is ded, he died on the way home after he hurt his hed, we buryed him on a hill behind the house. You no how bad I feel for you. Rose I'm sorry really I am.
                                        Your darling
                                        Raymond J Newsome

CHAPTER EIGHT

THAT year the homesteaders in Kansas tried hard to stop the surge of beef up through their territory. Some drovers sold to brokers who had set up offices near the border. The prices were lower there, but the cattlemen saved time and aggravation. Sample and Newsome were among them. So they cut four weeks off their drive and returned to the valley before Rose Ellen and the Diamond Five hands.

Newsome was not ready for what he found there. After eleven years of marriage he realized that he did not understand his wife, that she could still astonish him.

She told him that they now owned the Diamond Five.

"Twenty-five thousand is a bargain when you consider what we got," she said. "Olive was anxious to sell. She doesn't much care for Texas."

Irene asked him whether he had heard of such a thing as a probate court. She hadn't, herself, until the lawyer told her about it. A probate court decided what happened to a man's property after he died. There wasn't one in this county; they'd had to go to Austin. But it was worth the trip, when the judge decided that Charlie Fowler's ranch belonged to his widow.

Earl said, "Not a cent for Rose Ellen?"

"Olive had a good lawyer. The one from McPherson, named Belford Tefler."

"Not so long ago you were saying that land was the last thing we need. What the hell is going on?"

His voice was loud. She knew he was angry, and she knew his anger was always best met with calm.

"Think for a minute," she said. "In the beginning it was you and Charlie and Orrin, equal partners in the ranch. Now it is just you and Orrin, and he doesn't even have his full share anymore. You have the rest, and you do things your way. Are you complaining, Earl? We own about all of the old Circle Three Bar that is worth owning. Aren't you proud of that?"

He shook his head. "I can't be proud of something I had no part in."

His son, Ray, wanted Rose Ellen to get this news from him first. He told himself that he could make her realize that this was not the disaster it seemed. On the day she returned, he found her sitting on the porch with tears in her eyes.

She held him tight. "Oh, Ray," she said. "I thought I was done with crying. Then I saw this, the stable empty, cobwebs in his office. He loved this place so. He wanted so much for it. Now it is up to us, Ray. We have to make it all that he wanted."

She sniffled and rubbed her face against his shoulder. "At least Olive is gone," she said. "That is something, anyway."

He felt helpless in the face of what he had to tell her.

"Rose, I want you to listen and stay together," he said. " 'Cause there is something you have to know right now." Nothing to do but throw it out plain. When he finished, he tried to avoid her eyes, swollen and red and looking at him through a wet film.

"I don't understand," she said.

"The ranch belongs to my ma and my pa now. But it's all in the family, as they say, and since you'll be marrying me directly, I don't see that it makes much difference."

Her eyes turned cold and furious. He spoke faster.

"See, in a way they was doing us a favor, my ma and pa. If Olive had held on to the place, it would be out of your hands forever. But now, likely they will give it to us to run, just like our own."

She stepped back from him. "I have to think this thing through," she said. "We will talk after a while. For now, will you get into the bunkhouse and tell Paco and the others what you just told me. I don't have it in me to repeat it."

Her horse was still saddled. She rode away from the house, her mind fixed in sorrow, in anger, in hurt, unconscious of a destination. But when she reached it, she knew it was where she wanted to be. She got off the horse, drifted a few steps, and sat cross-legged in the grass.

She was looking over the valley from a hilltop. She could see the river bright in the high sun, could see the house where she had grown up, could see across to the eastern hills. These things comforted her.

She sat and wept, her chest heaving. She let the tears run down her face. The horse grew restless and wandered away, but she did not notice. There was the evening sun, and then the moon. Still she sat and wept. During the night a wind came up and rustled the grass and dried the tears.

Before the sun rose, she had grasped all that her father's being dead meant. She understood that she had no place anymore in the home she had known. She also knew that she could not leave the valley.

By midafternoon, when Ray rode toward her, she had decided what she would do. Getting up, she brushed the dirt and grass from her pants.

"I knew you'd be here at Indian Oak," he said. He got off the horse and stood in front of her. "About this buying the ranch," he said. "My mother, I think she wants to stop us from getting married, Rose. She figures if she gets you mad enough, you won't want any part of the Newsome family."

Rose Ellen said nothing.

"See?" he said. "That means we ought to get married. Right now. Without waiting. I mean, when you are done with your mourning. She won't like it, but she won't do anything about it. I'm her only son. She can't get rid of me."

"I can't marry you," she said.

"Rose, you don't know what you're saying."

"I thought on it all night. That was the first thing that came clear to me. I can't marry you."

"You're down on me for what my ma did. You can't take it out on me. Rose, we will last the two of them out, and then it will be all ours and our laugh on them."

"Don't you see?" she said. "What is mine, she took from me. And now you come to me and say I can get back what is mine just by marrying you and waiting for your folks to die. Well, it is not so easy. I never would have believed how fast you can hate something you loved; I feel like that place is tainted. It doesn't make me feel good the way it did. It just makes me remember what was done to me."

"Then we won't go near it," he said.

"Will that change her being your mother? She's powerful smart, Ray. She is better than anybody I ever saw at getting what she wants, figuring out this and that to work her way around every little problem. I can't live with you knowing that she is there, trying to get you free of me. That is no way to live. It's like sleeping with one eye open."

He held his hands up before her face, a gesture of supplication. He clenched them into fists. His knuckles were white. "Do you love me?" he said.

"Yes."

He felt tears coming to his eyes. "But you won't make everything right and marry me."

"No."

"I don't understand," he said.

"Last night I decided, the way a question is put to you can be more important than what you're asked," she said. "Like if somebody stopped you out on the range and pulled a pistol on you and told you to take a drink of water from his canteen. It wouldn't matter how thirsty you might be—if it's put to you that way, you wouldn't let a drop past your lips."

He stopped crying. He stared at her. "It's just pride that's behind all this," he said. "You'd make us both miserable for pride."

"It runs both ways," she answered. Her voice was soft and even. "You love me. You say you want to marry me. But I would bet my life you won't do the one thing that would keep us together."

"Just say it," he said, "and watch me do it."

"Leave the valley with me," she said. "Go so far away that your ma can't get to us. You give up what is coming to you, so that it won't be like I am marrying you to get back what is mine. I can leave the valley if I have to, if we'll be together, start fresh, with nothing but our own selves."

"Now, Rose . . ." he said.

"I'm ready. Go down there and say your farewells and come back and get me and I am yours."

"I can't do that."

"You could, but you won't," she said. "I don't blame you, Ray. I wouldn't if I were you. It's a bad deal. You are in line to own the best part of this valley."

"It isn't fair. You can't expect me to give that up."

"I have to go now," she said. "I have something to do." She began to walk down the hill.

"If that fella," he shouted at her, "the one with the water, if he stuck that canteen in your hand and shoved it up to your mouth, I do believe you would cut off your own arm to keep from drinking."

She stopped and looked at him. "I would," she said. "And so would you, Ray Newsome. Besides me, you're the only one I know who would do that." And she walked away and left Ray Newsome on the hill.

This time she knew where she was going. She found her horse at the bottom of the hill and rode south on the trail beside the Mansos. She watched the valley as she rode, trying to see and smell and feel all that it held out to her. The day was bright and warm. Cattle drank at the river, which flowed low now, around islands of sand and rock.

Soon the trail brought her to Orrin Sample's cabin. It was a rectangle of unpainted shiplap siding, with a shake roof and stone chimney, nestled in a stand of trees.

Sample was splitting wood behind the cabin. When he saw Rose Ellen, he felt the racing of his heart. "Rose, come rest yourself," he said.

She sat down on the porch, a wide front stoop, and Sample sat beside her. His face was red and wet.

"About your pa," he said. "You have my feelings, my sympathy. I felt real bad, Rose. I miss him terrible."

"I know."

Her smile helped him put his awkwardness aside. "I don't believe you seen the place since the cabin's built," he said.

"This is a real lovely little grove," she said. "Those are gum trees, I believe, and a couple of cottonwoods, too. You don't see many of them this far out in the valley."

"And a few loblolly pine," he said. "They like the water, you know. Right in this spot, I don't know why, the water is real close to the surface. And the trees keep the house cool."

He stood. With a nervous gesture he slapped his palms against his thighs. "What can I do for you, Rose?" he said.

"I need help, Orrin. You know what Irene did to me."

"Yes. Earl and me, we didn't know she was up to that. Earl would've stopped her if he'd known."

"Maybe, but it is done now. I am alone and I have no place

of my own." She felt weary, old. "Orrin, would you marry me?"

He was stunned. "Rose, you don't know what you're saying."

"I want you to take me for your wife. I don't know what I will do if you say no."

He paused, then said, "What about Ray?"

"I can't marry Ray. He is Irene's son, and I am too proud to do it that way."

"I don't want you marrying me to get even."

"That is one thing I would not do. You are a good man, Orrin, and have been my friend as far back as I know. You want to know why I ask you this? Because I want to stay in this valley. I can make you a home here. I can be good to you and kind. I'd try to give more back than I ask. And I wouldn't ask you to do this if I didn't know you wanted me.

"I won't say I'll stop loving Ray. I don't know about that. But I promise to put him behind me and not look back, and that's different from the other."

The next morning they rode to McPherson, and when they returned in the evening they were husband and wife.

Every day for a week Ray Newsome rode to the old house beside the Mansos and to Indian Oak. He did not find Rose Ellen. The Diamond Five hands said they had not seen her.

He came home one night and found guests. John Sears and his wife owned ninety-five sections north of the Circle Three. Irene thought they might be ready to sell, and so they had been invited to dinner.

In the middle of the meal John Sears said, "The talk is that an old bachelor bit the dust the other day. Another good man gone to ruin. Your old partner it was, Orrin Sample."

"Can't be," Earl said. "Who would have the old bear?"

"That's the best part," Sears's wife said. "Just a girl it was. Charlie Fowler's daughter. Rosetta, was it?"

"Rose Ellen," Ray Newsome said softly. He put down his knife and fork, mumbled excuses, and left the table.

Later Irene went to see him in his room. "I don't know how she could have done this to you," she said.

"I hate her," he said. "I hate you, too. You did this to me."

"Be glad you are rid of her, Ray," she said. "She was so flighty and impulsive, too strongheaded. You don't want that in a wife. You'll find someone, soon enough, who is more suited to you. Someone more . . . manageable."

Donnie Lee: There is nothing comes easy, my daddy says, that is worth having. And when I picked up Sue Everitt on Saturday night, I had to believe him.

I don't think I was ever more ready for anything than to be alone with that girl. But first I had to wait for her in the Everitts' front room and get the treatment from her parents. Her mama was not so bad, only snuck looks at me as she was clearing plates from the table in the dining room. But her daddy started asking me questions. Like, how long did I have my driver's license? And I'd have her back before eleven, wouldn't I?

Though when I seen Sue E. walk down the stairs I could see why he wouldn't want to take any chances. She was wearing a dress. I believe it was blue, with a white belt, but I could not say for certain. Girls spend so much time picking clothes, when all the time it is not the clothes that men look at, but at the lady underneath it all. And Sue E. was just fine.

We drove to the Rialto and sat through most of *Sands of Iwo Jima* before I finally said, Sue, you look real pretty. I whispered it in her ear, which was the closest I'd got to her all night.

Why, thank you, Donnie Lee, she said. These old things, I just threw them on.

Oh, how I wanted to touch her. I got my arm up on the armrest and put it against hers. She didn't seem to mind. It took me a while longer, but eventually I just put my hand on top of hers. And she held on to it, sort of laced our fingers together.

This happened right in the middle of the last big shoot-out in the picture, so it wasn't long before the lights come up and we had to leave and I had to take my hand away.

At T.J.'s, she made me repeat, word for word, all that Gandy Meacham had told me. She listened to the story about the heifer and the mudhole and said, Uh-huh, yes, uh-huh. Then she said, What a sweet thing, that part about a woman doing all she can to help a man. I want to see your great-grandfather for myself.

It was only nine twenty. I said sure, why not. I have to admit I wasn't exactly ashamed for my mama and daddy to see Sue E., beautiful as she was. So we got in the car and drove home.

My mama stared bayonets at me for bringing home somebody without her having the time to clean and primp. But my daddy didn't mind and seemed to take a shine to Sue E. He bowed real low to her, but not like he was making fun, and he told me git in the kitchen and bring some lemonade, where was my manners?

Presently Sue E. come straight out and said, I wonder if it would be possible to meet Donnie Lee's great-grandfather. I've heard so much about him.

My mother said, He isn't well, you know. But he ought to be able to talk for a spell.

Sue E. and me walked into his room together, and I made the introductions. Gandy Meacham's eyes looked bright and he acted right glad to see me. Then he crooked his neck and run his eyes up and down Sue E. He said, Danged if you ain't a looker.

I knew then that if it wasn't for the pills he still had every card in the deck.

I don't believe Sue E. even blushed. She just said, Thank you kindly, sir.

Gandy Meacham give a smile, like to crack his face, and said, An old geezer like me can get away with such talk.

Why, Sue E. said, a gal doesn't mind what age fellow such talk comes from as long as he is a gentleman.

He said, So you want to know about times long gone.

About Rose Sample, she said, and about you, too.

He said, I would a sight rather talk about her. But we will get around to me if we talk about her long enough.

She was an unusual woman, Sue E. said. Must have had a lot of determination in her.

He said, The way I heard it said was, she had a load of hell in her neck. You ever heard that one? It means if she had her head set one way, nobody and nothing would turn it. Rose Ellen had more hell in her neck than any woman or man I ever knew.

I seen him grit his teeth the way he did when the pain made him stop talking. Sue E. reached for his hand and held it while his face twisted up. It was a strange sight, her smooth young hand on his, which was old and spotted, wrinkled and hard.

Sue E. saw his face relax, and then, like nothing happened, she said, In what way do you mean? She waited for him to talk.

Well, like the town, he said finally. The one you go to school in. That town was built by Ray Newsome. Rose Ellen was sure he done it out of spite for her. Understand, for a long time Ray Newsome had a mad on for Rose Ellen. You best be ready to suffer the consequences if you said her name to his ears. He would not let the railroad through to her land. He would not let her cattle cross his land to the depot either. And she said fine, she did not want to touch her foot down on his land. The railroad people got on him about that, and he backed down. But she said to hell with him anyways, and she found another way of doing it.

Sue E. said, That is what I mean by determination.

He said, Maybe. Some would call it pure cussedness.

Sue E. looked at me and then at Gandy Meacham and said, Sometimes you need cussedness to get what's coming to you.

Gandy Meacham cracked that smile again, and I saw him squeeze Sue E.'s hand. He said, Donnie Lee, where did you find this young lady?

You could have lit a football field with the look on Sue E.'s face when he said that. And I wondered, Do you have to be eighty-some years old before you learn how to make a girl that happy?

We did our good-bys, and I drove Sue E. to her house. She looked at her wristwatch and said, Donnie Lee, it's only seven minutes till. No need to rush these things.

No, I reckon not, I said.

Somewhere I found the nerve to lean over and kiss her. I must have done something right, because next thing she was moving over to me and planting a kiss that like to curl my hair.

Ξ

CHAPTER NINE

They named the boy Charles, but "Charlie" it would always be. He was born pink and healthy, one afternoon in October of 1885, in the cabin his father had built in a moist grove of gum trees and cottonwood and loblolly pine.

There was a newly hewed cradle waiting with fresh bedding. After the child had fed for the first time from his mother's breast, Rose Ellen Sample walked slowly but steadily to the cradle and laid him down there to sleep.

Rose Ellen was happy. Orrin needed her presence, her caring, and her femininity in a life that had been barren without it. She cooked for him and kept the house, as she had for her father. The marriage did not change her life so much from what it had been, though it was far from what she had imagined it might be with Ray Newsome.

Ray ran the Circle Three Bar now. Eight months after he had helped to bury Charlie Fowler, Earl Newsome died of heart failure. More than two years later, Ray saw Rose Ellen for the first time since she had married Sample. The sight of her on Sample's arm, her belly swollen, stirred what had been festering for so long, a bitter love turning incompletely to loathing, assuming giant proportions in his mind.

Irene noticed the change in him. She guessed its cause and she could see its effect. He sank himself deep into the ranch to make it prosper and dominate the valley. The Circle Three and Rose Ellen became tangled in his mind, their being the outlet for and the source of his frustration. After a while he could put it into words: Make her sorry. Show her what she missed.

He bought land, and the ranch grew. Soon the Newsomes' holdings surrounded Sample's land on every side.

One evening Ray and Irene sat at the dinner table long after Luz had cleared away the dishes. "We need more space," Ray was saying. "We need more grass, more feed. There must be twice as many cattle as there were ten years ago. If they would fan out some, it would be better, but they don't leave the water.

There are places they eat down to the roots, bad as sheep."

"But if you clear out some of our cows, you will only be making room for others' cattle to eat our grass," Irene said. She meant Sample's. Except for the O–Bar–S, they owned every acre in that part of the valley. She left the table and returned with the short length of barbed wire that she had gotten a few years earlier from the salesman. She gave it to Ray. "It is time we talked about this."

He glanced at the wire and put it on the table. "Barbwire fence," he said. "I've seen it all over Kansas. I am sick of seeing it. Homesteaders use it to stop us on the trail. Last year we carried cutters to get through it."

"Maybe," she said, "we need it for the same reason the homesteaders do." Then he saw. In his mind he saw a fence across the land, dividing the valley.

"You could do so much," he said. "Keep your own cattle where you want them, give the land a rest one place or another. But cattle folk won't like it."

"We will show cattle folk," she said.

In the last ten years there had been a consolidation. Smaller ranchers had sold to the bigger ones, until by 1885 there were only seven spreads in the valley, the smallest seventy-four thousand acres. Ray's house, whitewashed and roofed with tin, was the finest in the valley; Sample's cabin, weathered gray by sun and rain, was the most primitive. The Circle Three kept a dozen cowboys on permanent payroll; Sample kept Alvarez, who had come over after Fowler's death. But these were degrees of the same prosperity. Even balanced against seasons of drought and down markets, these were good times for cattlemen. Sample and Rose Ellen still lived better than most people in Texas or out of it.

The difference was of vision. Ray Newsome's wealth and his holdings could not increase fast enough to suit him, while Sample already had more land than he had ever hoped to own. With Rose Ellen and his son, he had all that he had ever wanted.

Charlie seemed to change by the week. He was strong, perpetually hungry, full of an uncommon energy. He learned to crawl and soon rubbed his knees and hands red on the cabin's wooden floor. They started teaching him to walk, Sample coaxing him forward while Rose Ellen kept him upright.

One morning Orrin and Rose were playing with Charlie when Alvarez rode up to the cabin. He came to tell them that hands from the Circle Three were building a fence to keep them from the stream.

Rose Ellen rode with Sample to the river. They found the Circle Three's hands digging holes, planting posts. Rose Ellen saw spools of wire beside the canvas tents they had pitched on the land. They were west of the cabin and at least half a mile from the river.

Rose Ellen shouted, "Get off this land with your infernal fence. We will tear down every post that is stuck on our property."

"Rose," Sample said, "just a minute."

"They can't put fence on our land," she said. "Tell them, Orrin. Our cattle can't get to the water."

The hands from the Circle Three looked up and waited.

"Tell them," she said. "This is our land, Orrin."

Sample said, "I don't believe so, Rose."

"Orrin, our land goes clear across this valley, from one range of hills to the other. My papa drew it that way on his map."

"I sold it," Sample said. "To Irene. She wanted to help me out, a couple of years back."

"You sold your water?" Rose Ellen said. "You sold the only thing that keeps your cattle going?"

Sample began to ride slowly back to the cabin, head bowed. She saw the sag of his shoulders, and the sight made her want to be beside him. She spurred her horse and caught him.

"I'm sorry," he said. "I never seen it coming. I ain't sharp enough, not like your pa was."

"We will make do," Rose said.

The fencing took weeks. That gave Sample a chance to gather most of his cattle, but it was a bad time to sell. The market was down, and cattlemen were holding their beef out for the next season, hoping for higher prices. Within three months Rose Ellen's ledgers showed they had sold four thousand eight hundred and seventy head to other ranchers. They kept out only three hundred head and five horses. Sample thought that the springs and seeps on his land would support no more.

Early one morning, while the last section of fence closed around them, Rose Ellen and Sample rode up the valley to the Sears ranch, bringing Charlie with them.

Sample said to the man and his wife, "Rose and me would like to buy your place."

Rose cut in. She said, "The fact is, we need a place with water."

John Sears had been trying to speak. Finally he said, "I would like to sell to you folks, but I can't. Ray Newsome come to us months ago with that lawyer of his, and they trotted out some deal. The lawyer calls it an option. The way he explained it when he paid us the money—"

"Two thousand it was," his wife said.

"Yes," said Sears. "What he bought was the right, he told us, of having first crack at buying our spread before we sold to somebody else. So I can't make a deal without talking to him first and giving him a chance to top you."

Sample swallowed. His throat was hard and dry. "You have a fine place," he said. "I can see why Ray would want to get hold of it."

"Oh, it ain't just us," the woman said. "The Pratts, too, and the Hesselbarths that I know of for certain. I hear the Martins also signed. It looks as if Ray Newsome means to own this valley from bottom to top."

They were riding home when they met a Circle Three cowboy on horseback. The fence was almost done, he said, and the boys had found a few head of Sample's stock on the Circle Three side. He told Orrin to claim them now.

"Show us where these cows are," Rose Ellen said.

There were five, penned in a corral beside the Circle Three stables. Rose Ellen handed Charlie across to Sample and climbed down from her horse. Before Sample could stop her, she pulled the Winchester rifle from his saddle scabbard.

Ray ran to the window when he heard the first shot. He saw Rose Ellen with one arm braced against a corral post, sighting down the barrel of a repeater. Her face was impassive, her lips thin. One dead cow was on its side in the pen. She fired again, and another cow fell dead in the dust. Rose Ellen fired again and again and once more. Then she said something to one of the Circle Three hands.

After she and Sample and the baby were gone, Ray sent for the hand and told him to repeat her words.

"She said, 'Tell Mr. Ray Newsome that he can keep our cows.' That's all," the cowboy reported.

The fence would be Irene's legacy. In two years she was dead of a stroke. But she died knowing that her son and her ranch were all that she had wanted them to be.

THE sun was hot, high in the sky. In the grasslands, Rose Ellen and Alvarez were digging a wide, shallow hole in the ground. Sample and his son, Charlie, were digging a trench from the hole, up a hill toward a cropping of green brush and thick grass, where water seeped.

The boy was seven years old and strong enough to work a small spade. Like the others, he wore a wide-brimmed hat, a bandanna around his neck, and a cotton shirt. They were soaked with sweat, but the drying moisture made their skin cool, and the shirts were loose enough to let in the breeze.

"This big?" the boy said to Sample.

"No. Half that. There ain't much water. You understand what we are doing? We are opening up the seep to let the water down this ditch, into the tank your ma and Paco are working on."

They worked in the sun, their movements deliberate, endless, identical, until their shadows stretched across the grass. Sample came down the hill and stood at the edge of the hole where Alvarez and Rose Ellen were working.

"About done," he said. "I have to hack away at the seep and dig a few more feet of ditch."

They walked up the hill and found Charlie trying to dig through the roots of the brush. "Here," Sample said. "Leave that part to me, boy. He is a real steady hand, Mama, as good a worker as his pa ever was."

He shoved the spade into the ground, bringing the narrow

trench up to the base of the seep. There he dug a shallow basin to catch the water and channel it into the trench. Soon there was a trickle in the black soil. Sample dug some more, and then the trickle made a growing puddle in the basin. When the basin was full, the water lapped into the trench.

The four of them watched the slow progress of the water down the trench. The porous ground absorbed most of the trickle.

"It might make the tank by midnight," Sample said. "Might get a couple of inches deep."

"Enough to let five or six cows drink," Alvarez said.

They rode toward home, their bodies drained by the heat and the work.

They were used to a simple existence now. The big herds were gone from their land. Without the Mansos for water, their land supported few cattle. Each year Sample had sold off enough to keep the herd at about three hundred and twenty head. During dry years he had to sell even more.

In a good season they made enough to buy clothes and food and to pay Alvarez, who was sixty now. Rose Ellen kept a garden and preserved food, and was teaching her son to read and write by lamplight in the evenings, as she had been taught. Because three hundred and twenty head are not much work for good cowmen, Sample had time for other things. He had added two back rooms to their cabin and was building a system to bring running water inside the house.

They were not poor, but they lived without opulence. And in a way they were scratching their own survival out of the land. They were holding out against Ray Newsome, who in the last five years had cast the Circle Three's boundaries out past the northern end of the valley. He had bought the Searses' spread, and the Pratts's and the Martins' and the Hesselbarths'. A family named Gilmer still held out against him. But they and the Samples were the last.

Irene was three years dead. Her passing had brought sadness to Ray, but he was glad to stand alone on the ranch. He could not forget Rose Ellen and had stopped trying. The truth was that he indulged in his unhappiness. He would not allow the

Texas Dawn

wound of his only failure to heal. She was his by right, he argued to himself. Until she was restored to him he would use her to prove himself.

He built the town to show her his power.

The Central Texas Railroad came to the valley in 1887. The railroad had a charter from the state legislature, but Ray Newsome had title to the land. And he had his lawyers, and he had his nerve. Ray was glad to see the railroad come because that brought the cattle markets closer. But he wanted to show his muscle. So when rail crews punched into his property, Ray Newsome told his men to set dynamite charges in the path of the tracks. His cowboys could blow holes faster than the rail crews could fill them. Then, where the track was supposed to run between a hill and a rock cliff, Ray Newsome himself set the charges that blew tons of rock into the pass.

The next day two directors of the Central Texas arrived in a private railroad car and asked to see Ray. He came with Belford Tefler. The directors did not seem unfriendly, so Ray shook their hands and drank their whiskey. They sat at a long conference table in the middle of the car.

"Mr. Newsome, you are a young man, and somewhat impetuous," said one of the directors in a loud voice. "A man of direct action, evidently. But you can't stop the railroad."

"I already have," Ray said.

"What you are doing is illegal."

"I asked my lawyer here and he told me what I already knew," Ray said. "There ain't no law against a man blowing up his own property if he wants."

"We have a right-of-way," the other director said indignantly. "A state grant."

"The state can't grant a right-of-way across private property," Belford Tefler said.

"There is precedent."

"You boys could get your lawyers to argue with my lawyers if you want," Ray said. "They prob'ly could argue up a ball of fire, but you don't have time to waste. So if I can just hold you off a few months, you lose."

The first director dropped his voice and said, "Mr. Newsome, the railroad is progress. It is important to the economic well-being of this region. At this moment the town of McPherson is languishing, waiting for the arrival of the rails."

"That is what I wanted to talk to you about," Ray said. "McPherson is half a day's ride from here. A far piece to go for a box of cigars or a sack of flour."

"But if you don't let the rails through, there soon won't be any town at all. You don't want that."

The chairs around the conference table were high-backed and sturdy. Ray's did not creak when he tilted it and balanced on the chair's two back legs. He folded his arms across his chest.

"I might build a town of my own," he said.

This was the first that Belford Tefler or anybody else had heard of his plan. Ray wanted to build a town. He wanted stores, a doctor, a hotel, a sheriff's office, all that McPherson had.

"And a railroad depot," he said. "Pens for stock waiting to be shipped. Offices for cattle brokers and buyers. The thing is, gents, I want to make this a good big town that lasts for a while. But if your railroad goes any farther than it does right now, my town won't be different from any other whistle-stop on the line."

By the next day Ray had what he wanted. His new town would be a railhead for that spur of the road. The rail rights down the rest of the valley were his. He let the tracks come within five miles of the Circle Three ranch house. He found a level spot and laid out the town with a surveying crew. Main Street was parallel to the tracks, two hundred feet west. He marked ten streets running parallel to Main Street and ten more that ran east to west. He divided each block into building lots.

After the workmen arrived, their hammers pounded for five months. They built pens and loading ramps, warehouses, stores, a jailhouse, and a bank building with a vault. The Central Texas printed brochures to promote the town as a freight center. One day, when the town was almost ready, a special train brought in businessmen, speculators, and cattle brokers.

Ray had a land office on Main with a salesman and a map showing streets and lots. Three lots sold to saloonkeepers the first morning. Other merchants leased space in the buildings along Main. Belford Tefler moved his practice from McPherson and brought with him a barber and a doctor.

They christened the town on the Fourth of July. It was only a formality; cattle already bawled in the pens, the jail cells had held a dozen fractious cowboys, the saloons had twice already swept the dirty sawdust from the floor and replaced it.

Red, white, and blue bunting hung from the eaves of the depot on the occasion. County officials, executives of the railroad, even a delegate from the statehouse sat on a platform. There were speeches; all went on too long. Then Ray hung a slab of wood from two hooks on the depot's eaves. The name of the town, painted on the slab, was INDIAN OAK.

The town quickly reached that stage where growth invites more growth. Businesses sprouted and brought in employees, and more businesses sprouted to serve the employees. Tradesmen and merchants came down the rail and settled in. By 1890 Indian Oak was the county seat.

A FEW years later Rose Ellen bore a second child. They called her Dora. The baby was light-haired but ruddy, and to Rose Ellen she had something of Charlie Fowler's face when he had brooded, thoughtful and clouded. She liked to see that there was something of her father in the children she brought to life.

One evening Sample was shoeing a mule while Rose Ellen nursed the baby. She watched Charlie practice writing in a notebook. He bit his lip, frowned, and labored over the letters, until Rose Ellen said, "You've done enough. Go find your papa."

The boy returned in a few seconds, panic in his eyes. "Mama, Mama," he said. "It's Pa. He's hurt bad."

She laid the baby in the crib and ran to the shed, where Sample kept his forge. She found him curled on his side, a few feet from the hind legs of a mule that was tied to a post.

"The damn jenny." He gasped for air. "I dropped a nail and bent down to get it. I know better than that. She cut loose. Got me right in the gut."

There was a crescent welt low on his abdomen. Rose Ellen got him to bed and gave him some laudanum. By the next morning, when Alvarez returned with the doctor from Indian Oak, Sample was sweating with fever.

The doctor lifted Orrin's nightshirt and looked at the billowing black-and-purple bruise. Then he took Rose Ellen outside. A kidney, he said. And infected now, to judge from the swelling and fever. She could try to keep the fever down, and pray.

For three days Orrin groaned and tossed and moaned, helpless and in misery. He died the morning of the fourth day.

She and Alvarez dug his grave not far from the cabin. When they got near the bottom, they found water. It would have been as good a tank, she told herself, as any that she and Orrin ever had dug together.

CHAPTER TEN

"RAY?" said the voice. "Did you hear me?"

Ray Newsome found himself looking out the window. It was the only open window in the room, and it had brought in a breeze that turned his eyes toward the sunshine.

"Yes," Ray said. "Ah . . . no. I didn't, at that."

"The Baldwin engine we wanted is four months to build from the day we order it, and shipping on top of that. But there is a short line in Nevada that is selling off some of its rolling stock. They have a two-four-two in good shape and some cars, too."

"If the engine looks good, buy it," said Ray. "No need to buy a new one if we can get around it."

Once a week Ray met with his business managers in his office. He had split the ranch into two sections, each with a foreman and a manager. There was a manager for the packing plant he had built a year earlier on the east side of the tracks.

Now he was building a railroad, a narrow-gauge short line from Indian Oak to the south end of the valley. The Central Texas was helping him with financing, because Ray's line would bring in even more cattle to be shipped north and east.

"I talked to the engineers," the railroad manager was saying. His name was Harmon. "They say we need to trestle twice over the stream, once about five miles south of here and then about fifteen miles south again of that."

Harmon stopped. Ray was looking out the window again.

"Go on," Ray said. "I'm listening."

Harmon talked on. It was a drone to Ray. After a while he gave up trying to follow it. This wasn't normal. He usually hunched over the table and stared at his managers the way a hungry dog waits for a scrap of food. But today they got noncommittal nods, grunts, silence.

He spoke again when Bartell, the manager of his wholesale warehouses, began to talk about increases in shipping prices.

"We have any candy?" Ray said.

"What was that?" said Bartell.

"Candy. Do we carry that wholesale? The kind that comes in a box, fancy candy."

"Well, um, that's a specialty item, sir. Mrs. Roth sells it in her bakery."

"Hmm. How about perfume? The good French stuff."

"Jenkins, the druggist, keeps some. Would you like me to get some for you, Mr. Newsome?"

"I surely would," Ray said. "Much obliged. And get a big box of chocolates while you're at it." He gave Bartell twenty dollars and sent them all away. When they were gone, he paced the room. He thought about how it was going to be tonight.

He was going to see Rose Ellen.

He had told himself that before, and each time he had lost his nerve. This time was going to be different. In his mind he said the right things. He had all the apologies and explanations, then the sweet talk that she would be ready for when she had been with him for a while. He was sure they needed only a chance to rekindle the old love.

After Bartell brought the candy and the perfume, Ray rode to the house he had built in his town. He wondered where Rose Ellen would want to live. Maybe, he thought, she will want her old place. The foreman of the southern section lived there now. If she wished it, so it would be.

He dressed three times. First, in a business suit. But when he looked in a mirror, he wondered, How will she remember me? Not riding in a buggy dressed like a chairman of the board. Like a cowboy, on a tall, strong stallion.

He still had those clothes. He hadn't stopped riding the land, and it kept him strong and slim. He put on faded pants, a plain shirt, and tied a bandanna around his neck. But he knew that he looked wrong. He was no longer a sixteen-year-old boy.

He settled on blue cotton trousers, a collarless white silk shirt, clean boots, and a Buckeye-model Stetson, broad and tall and elegant. This time he looked like a prosperous young man going to call on his ladylove.

When he went outside, the stableboy saddled the big gray for him. Ray put the candy and the perfume into a saddlebag. He mounted and rode down the valley.

He had to fight the impulse to turn back. He had waited too long, he told himself. When he first heard of Sample's death, he had considered writing a note, telling her that he was sorry. But he crumpled half a box of stationery trying to find the right words. When the chance for the note passed, he thought he ought to wait a few weeks before he visited her in person. But after three months he talked himself into four, then six. Sample had died in August, and now Ray faced the first week in March.

He rehearsed the words that he thought she would want to hear. The fence. It was Irene that talked me into the fence. It was wrong, but I was upset and I wanted to hurt you, Rose dear.

The children are beautiful, Rose. I could love them like they was my own. We'll hire us a teacher to come live with us and make sure they get nothing but the best.

The past? You can't let it get to you, Rose. Here we are, the way we ought to be. We been through a lot, but we're still young. Got our best years ahead of us. You are more beautiful than you ever was before, and you was a real beauty. You're a *woman* now, Rose—that's the difference.

He reached the fence that marked his property line. When he passed through the gate, he got the idea of leaving his horse some distance from the cabin and walking the rest of the way. She would not hear him. He would knock on her door, and she would be facing him before she knew what was happening. It was years since he had ridden the road into Sample's property.

When he was closer to the cabin, he tied the horse to a tree. He took the candy and the perfume from the saddlebag and walked until the cabin came into view, partly hidden by trees. Lamps burned in the house. He heard a boy's happy shouts, a baby crying. Then quiet. She must have put the children to bed.

He waited in the trees. He was just getting up the courage to walk to the house when the door opened. She stepped out on the porch. And a man stepped out with her.

He was tall and broad-shouldered, this man. He had a deep voice that carried out to where Ray stood. Her voice followed, light, with a laugh in it. This was not the lonely widow he had expected. They were now sitting on a bench.

Ray could not move; they might see him. It seemed like hours. Their talking became too soft for him to hear. He saw Rose Ellen turn her face up to the man. They kissed, and then stood and went into the cabin, and the lamps went out.

Ray stood among the trees for what seemed like hours. When he walked back to where his horse was tied, he tore the cover from the box of chocolates and flung them into a field. He pulled the cap from the perfume and threw the open bottle away.

He let the horse plod up the road. He had almost reached his gate when he heard a horse behind him, trotting. He slipped into an arroyo beside the road and watched as the horse drew near.

The rider was the man he had seen with Rose Ellen. He recognized the square, wide shoulders. He glimpsed the man's face; he could make out no features that were familiar to him. But he did see the brand burned into the horse's left flank.

The brand was a circle enclosing three bars. A brand, Earl Newsome had once said, you could read in the moonlight.

SHE had met him when Orrin was still alive. She was pushing a heifer out of a wallow that day, up to her knees in mud, heaving against the rear end of the bleating cow, when he spoke.

"You ain't going to do it that way," he said.

She caught her breath as she looked up at him. He was grinning down from a horse, on Ray Newsome's side of the four-strand fence.

"You can keep your opinions to yourself," she said. "They aren't worth much over here."

She pushed some more and only drove the heifer deeper into the mud. She wanted the cowboy to go away. She was sure that she could not save this cow, and she did not want anyone to see her fail, especially not this cocky youngster.

Then she thought, Failing would be easier if he failed, too. "I'm so happy for Ray Newsome," she said, "that he can afford to pay his hands to sit in the saddle all day and admire the sights. If you are so smart, you try."

He climbed between two strands of the wire and walked to the wallow. He stood beside Rose Ellen. He told her to push behind the cow's forelegs while he pushed from the rear. In a few seconds the heifer was out of the mud, running away with eyes wide.

"Obliged," she said.

He was hardly more than a boy, if you looked past the tanned and leathery face. Twenty-two, twenty-three, maybe. "Always glad to help a neighbor," he said. "Who is Ray Newsome?"

"You must be new to the Circle Three."

"My brother and me just come from up Panhandle way."

"If you stay around, you will find out that Ray Newsome owns the ranch you work for. You will also discover that he would not look kindly on your helping out anybody on my spread."

"Bad blood?"

"Bad as it gets."

He made a motion of turning to look one way, then another. He said, "I don't believe the gentleman is anywheres about."

He stuck out his hand. "Quiller Meacham," he said.

Three weeks later he brought over one of their strays at the end of a rope. Dinner was on the table, and Sample invited him to stay. After that he came every few weeks to visit. He brought toys for Charlie, a knife, a spinning top.

A few days after Sample died, he came by again.

With his hat in his hand he said, "Mrs. Sample . . . Rose . . . I want to tell you how bad I feel. Orrin, he was a good man."

He was back on his horse when he said, "Oh. And if you need some help, Ray Newsome don't own me all day every day."

She knew she would need help. Alvarez could not do the work he had done even five years earlier. So Quiller came at least once a week after that. He chopped wood, fixed a leak in the roof, helped her brand calves.

In December she asked him if he and his brother would leave the Circle Three to hire on with her.

"I don't believe so," he said. "But thank you."

She tried to smile. "You think I would be tough to work for?"

"I don't care about that," he said. "But I don't want to be your hired hand. I don't want it that way between us."

Several days later she was not surprised when he kissed her on the cheek before he left. It began that way, slowly, and they stayed friends throughout it.

One night she told him, "I have been a lucky woman. I have known at least two good men. One in a lifetime is more than some women get. I had my papa. I had Orrin. Then there is you. Don't let me down, Quiller."

By now she was watching him closely. He was smart, and she found him patient, gentle, confident. He was good to Charlie and Dora. He had a feeling for the land and the ranch. One night she thought, If you are strong enough to take it all, I won't stop you. I'm yours and so is all I have, if you know how to go about getting it.

They were in love. He had most of his evenings free, so he ate with her and slept beside her until early mornings, when he had to return to his bunkhouse. The size of Newsome's ranch was a blessing in that way. He was just a face among dozens of cowboys, and no one cared how he spent his nights.

One night he brought another hand to dinner. Josiah Benton was a toothless old man with a stubble of beard and sunken cheeks. The skin of his hands was cracked, and there was black grease under his fingernails.

"Josiah and me been setting 'crost from each other during breakfasts these days. Won't nobody else talk to Joe, since he ain't a cowboy," Quiller said.

"And what is it," Rose asked, "that you do on the ranch, Mr. Benton?"

"I'm a machinist," Josiah said, and went back to his dinner.

"He's the handiest son of a gun I ever seen," Quiller said. "If it moves, Joe here can fix it. He come from Nebraska. He worked for a comp'ny up there. Tell her what kind of machine they made, Joe."

Josiah swallowed. "Hydraulic rotating machines," he said.

A smile creased Quiller's face from one cheek to the other. "And tell her," he said, "what those machines do."

"Oh, they can do many things. But me, I would use them to drill deep-water wells."

To a woman who had learned to be thankful for a tepid inch of brown water in a hole, the idea seemed impossible. But out of courtesy and with a hope that she would not admit even to herself, she asked him questions. "Seems to me everybody would want a machine like this if it worked. Why haven't I heard of it? Why isn't it famous?"

"The fellas that own the patent give up on it," Josiah said. "They didn't know how to run it."

"Who did?"

"Me. It was my machine. It was their idea, but I made it work. But when it come to their big chance, they told me to ankle it out of the way. They didn't want to cut me in."

"But it is still there," Quiller said. "Still in Nebraska."

"If this machine is such a wonderment, why haven't you told anybody else about it? The Circle Three would like more water."

"Nah," Josiah said. "They pay me wages and get my time. I got no reason to help them. But Quiller here, he is a friend to me. If he lets you in on it, it's all the same to me."

She said, "I cannot get away from the feeling that this is going to cost me money if I say yes."

"They owed money," Josiah said. "The sheriff come and put a lock on the door. But if you was to pay their debts, they would send their number one model down to you, first thing."

"And how much," she said, "would that be?"

"Eighteen, nineteen hundred."

She had the money. And Quiller persuaded her. Then she knew how much she trusted him.

Eventually the machine parts arrived at the depot in six long wooden packing crates. Quiller brought them out to the ranch in her wagon when he had a free day.

But the spending was not finished. She had to hire Josiah and two helpers. She had to buy pipes and lumber and fittings.

They built a derrick fifty feet high. It was in the middle of a field, about a mile from the house, where there were no springs or seeps that she knew of. That made it like nine tenths of all the land on the O–Bar–S.

She could see the operation from her kitchen window. The first day she made three trips from the house, with Dora in her arms and Charlie trailing behind. The machine threw up loam, sometimes dark sand, sometimes rock and gravel. But dry, all of it. Not enough water, she told Quiller that night, to wet a tick.

The second day she made just one trip, and after that she only watched from her kitchen window. They worked for a week. Josiah told her they would be needing more pipe soon.

"I bought six hundred feet," she said.

"And I put all but sixty down the hole," he said.

"No more," she said. She felt angry, ashamed to have let herself be taken in like that.

The next day Quiller was off, and he came over. He told her quietly that he would help them drill the last sixty feet. She was in the front room that afternoon, darning socks for Charlie, when she heard the back door, then Quiller.

"Rose," he called in a strained voice.

She put down her sewing and went to the kitchen.

He was holding his Stetson, brim up. He let go of the hat. Water poured out of it and splashed on the kitchen floor. His clothes were wet.

They ran hand in hand to the drilling rig. It now stood above a swelling of water that poured from the hole. Josiah Benton leaned against the derrick and smiled a toothless smile.

"In fifty years this well will run just as strong," he said. "You have to figure out what to do with all the water."

She knelt, cupped her hands, and drank. Cold and pure and sweet. She put her head down in the pool and felt the water rush from the wellhole and buffet her face.

The next week she bought more than a thousand calves. She hired four hands, and a woman named Inez to help with the children. She built a bunkhouse and kept Josiah and his crew working, drilling until there was not a spot on the ranch more than a mile and a half from fresh, flowing water. The water gushed from some wells. Others needed pumps, so Josiah built windmills to bring the water to the surface.

That year she changed the name of the ranch. She did something that the place had not deserved before. She gave it her father's initials and enclosed them in a box, and the spread became the Box CF.

One afternoon when Quiller was free, she put lunch in a basket and rode with him into the pastures. They spread a blanket not far from a new windmill, where the excess water made the grass grow tall and green. It was a soft cushion under them.

"You have been a part of this," she said. "Lately it feels wrong when you leave and go back to the Circle Three."

He did not answer. He picked a long blade of grass and put it between his lips.

"I shouldn't have said that, maybe. It isn't a woman's place to talk that way," she said. "But I don't know that I ever learned my place, Quiller."

He looked at her. "You want more out of me than you are getting. I been tempted, I have to say that."

"What holds you back, Quiller? This ranch is going somewhere. It could take both of us along with it. What stops you?"

"I am a cowboy," he said. "I like to be loose on my feet. I like to do what I want, and when. A loose rein, you might say."

"Quiller, that is nonsense. Two years you've been at the Circle Three, and I don't see you trying to jump the fence. To go where? Do what? Be a cowboy someplace else?"

"Say . . . say I married you, if we're talking about that. And say I decided this place and this valley didn't suit me no more. I couldn't up and leave, could I?"

"No," she said.

"There. You see why I'm shy of settling down? Rose, don't push me. I got to take things at my own speed."

"You can leave at your own speed, too, you know!"

"Maybe I will, right now," he said. He left her alone to gather up the food, fold the blanket, return to the cabin.

He was back a few evenings later, and they fought again. This time it was about fences; she wanted to put some up. "You can't tell me," she said, "that it doesn't help the grass if you keep cattle off and give it a chance to grow."

"It helps some," he said. "But I think you could spend your money better. What this place needs now is more cows."

"It is my money," she said. "If you know so much, you should have your own place by now to do what you want with it."

She regretted the words as soon as she heard them. "I'm sorry, Quiller," she said. "That was terrible."

"Maybe you have something there. It's plain, ain't it, that the only way I will have anything in life is by marrying you?"

Her words and all that lay behind them were with him later at the bunkhouse, when his brother told him to pack his saddle-bags and roll up his blankets. The big boss himself, Mr. Ray Newsome, wanted to see him in Indian Oak.

Quiller was ready to leave, and the leaving felt good.

For a while Ray Newsome had forgotten about her. The night he saw another man kissing Rose Ellen, he was sure he would not care about her any longer.

He had tried to keep busy with work. His railroad was pushing down the valley, and several times a week he rode to the end of the line to see how far it had extended. Then he heard about Rose Ellen's water.

He thought about how happy she must be. She would prosper, after all that he had done against her. That was how she entered his mind again.

Now the stranger who had left her home that night nagged at him. He knew from the brand on the horse that the man was one of his own hands. A few days at the grub table and a few casual questions gave him a name. The next day Ray asked his foreman to point out the cowboy named Quiller Meacham.

Soon he had convinced himself that Rose Ellen might yet come into his life if that cowhand were out of the way.

---- ⌶ ----

Donnie Lee: Sue E. was with me every time after that when I went to talk to Gandy Meacham about Rose Ellen. There was something between Sue E. and the old man that I could see but could not explain. The questions I asked him was never quite right. Sue E. would get impatient and so would Gandy Meacham, like they knew all the lines and I was slow catching on. After a while I gave up and let her handle it.

She was the one who got the story out of him about how he had come to leave Texas. I'd figured that he just up and left on his own. But there was more to it, and he told it all one night.

He said, When Ray Newsome wanted to talk to me, I was still sour about Rose Ellen not giving me enough slack. Newsome called me in and offered me one thousand dollars and a train ticket to get out of town and stay gone. I knew he was doing it to buy me off Rose Ellen. She had told me about the bad feelings between them. But there in Newsome's office I knew it was not just the bad feelings but the good that was once between them.

Quiller said, At first I refused. I didn't want any part of it. He told me I was out of a job no matter what I decided. There was only one other place in the valley, and that was the Box CF with Rose Ellen. And I was to the end of my string there. It was marry her or nothing. I was thinking I couldn't just jump into something as serious as marrying. I told myself, Hell, if you are leaving anyways, you might as well take the money and the ticket. And that is what I did. That afternoon I was on the train, and I never did come back until now.

The tears busted out on Sue E.'s face right about then.

Quiller said, When you are young, you think your chances come along thick as flies. You think you got all the time to pick the one that suits you when you are ready. But it ain't that way.

When the chance comes, you got to take it. I didn't get but one Rose Ellen come my way and I sold that chance. Six months later the money was spent and I was married to a gal that I didn't care about, and all I got out of it was a daughter. And eventually you, Donnie Lee.

He said, I sure wish I'd left that money on Ray Newsome's desk. And I wish I'd gone straight to Rose Ellen even more.

CHAPTER ELEVEN

THE fastest and the most beautiful horse on the Circle Three was a big chestnut gelding. Two weeks after Quiller Meacham had left the valley, Ray pinned a note to the gelding's hackamore and told a ranch hand to take it to Rose Ellen.

The note read, "For you. Respectfully, Ray."

He waited all day, too nervous to work. Late in the afternoon the ranch hand came back, the chestnut on a lead. The note was gone. Ray asked what had happened.

"She read the note," said the hand. "Then she told me to take the horse back, she couldn't keep it."

"How did she say it? Like she was riled?"

"No, sir, I wouldn't say so. She had a smile on her."

The next day Ray sent the hand back to Rose Ellen with the chestnut and a black mare and the mare's colt. This time the hand returned without the horses.

"First off she looked a mite cross," the hand said to Ray. "Then it was like she couldn't stay cross and she smiled. She said to tell you she didn't have room in her stable for no more of your calling cards. She said next time you got something to say, you better say it in person."

He called on her the next day with a big bunch of wild flowers that he had picked along the way. When she came to the door, she looked at him for the first time in more than eight years.

His presence at her door startled her. She had expected him sometime, but she could not have prepared herself for it. She could feel her heart beating fast, insistent.

He didn't look so different, she thought. Paler than she had remembered. The thrust of his jaw made her throat tighten; she had seen him do that so often before, a gesture of bravado when he was shrinking inside.

"Those lovely flowers will wilt in the heat," she said. She opened the screen door and took them from him. "Come in and sit down." She hoped to sound matter-of-fact. "Little Charlie has made a mess, as usual, but I think you can find a chair that isn't full of toys."

Ray took off his hat and sat down. She carried the flowers to the kitchen, filled a jar with water and put them in it, then returned to the front room. He watched her and saw lines at the corners of her eyes where there had been none before. Her hands smoothed her skirt and went to her hair, where a few strands had fallen from the bun at the back of her head.

"I'm taken aback. I didn't expect you here," she said.

Her voice sounded flatter now. But she was still Rose Ellen, he thought, and he would put the music back in her voice.

"You like the horses?" he said. "Ain't that chestnut a beaut?"

"For a fact, it is. I didn't know what I ought to do. I thought I should send them back, but then Charlie Fowler didn't raise me up to be a fool."

She sat a few feet from him. Time to find out if this is the Ray I knew, she thought. "It would have been easier to make up my mind," she said, "if I'd known why you were doing it."

"Maybe I wanted to show off some." The words jumped out before he could try the sound of them in his head. "And I wanted you to think good of me."

"You expect those horses to do a lot."

He thought, Please don't fight me, Rose. He gripped the hat in his hands and said, "Rose, I want us to be friends again."

"It doesn't happen as easy as saying. Words don't make it be."

"Can we walk somewhere?" he said. "Just to get out in the air? Doesn't have to be far. Up the road a ways."

She left the room to tell Inez she would be gone a few minutes. Then Ray followed her out the front door. They tramped through the field behind her cabin.

"If you stay around," she said, "you'll find I'm different from the girl you knew."

"Somewhere inside you," he said, "part of you is the same."

That made her angry. "You can see that?" she said. "You are with me five minutes and you can see right inside me, know what I am clear through?"

"I don't have to see. I know. I'm not so different either. Same old Ray, when you get down to cases."

"Some parts of that fellow I liked," she said. "Some parts I didn't."

"Rose, about that fence a few years back—"

"No," she said. "Don't talk about what is gone. It won't work if you do. We can't fall back on the good parts of what we had before, and we can't get tripped up by the bad. You and me today is the only way we have a chance."

"You want to try it?" he asked. "Friends, I mean."

"We have to go it slow," she said. "Don't go expecting too much from me."

From that moment he pursued her. He was cautious at first, almost formal in the way he behaved with her. She was defiant, daring him to make a mistake. But he did not.

She was ready for his attentions. Quiller's leaving—without explanation, without even good-by—had rocked her. And she remembered why she had loved Ray before. He was manly, with a gentleness that came from strength. He was handsome and he could laugh and he made her feel beautiful. He loved the land, as she did. She felt her defenses giving way.

One night he gave her an emerald ring. The stone was as big as her thumbnail. "I can't take this," she said.

"You don't like it? I'll give you a bigger one."

"No. It is beautiful." She kept the ring. But she thought, We live so differently. He has so much.

Another evening she went with him to a dinner party in Austin. Ray had bought her a gown, yellow silk with a high, tight waist and a cascade of flounces down the skirt. Not in years had she worn such a dress. She powdered her face and put long curls in her hair.

Texas Dawn

They went to Austin in a special Central Texas excursion car. At the party she met politicians and railroad men and businessmen. Their eyes followed her, staring at her.

Ray spoke into her ear. "You are beautiful," he said. "You belong in this life."

For a while the gown felt wrong on her after muddy pants and a shirt. But the music played and she danced and drank champagne, and soon she was enjoying the party, and it was the ranch and hard work that seemed distant.

At daybreak the train returned. They rode into Indian Oak, Ray with an arm around Rose Ellen. At the depot they stood on the platform. Ray took her in his arms, buried his face in her hair, her neck.

"This is a good life, Rose. All it needs is you to add that last part. The part that means most to me. Marry me."

"You live high," she said. "Not the way I'm used to."

"Telling me you don't like it?"

"It has its advantages," she said.

She was close to saying yes. The two of them like king and queen in this valley that would be all their own. But she would not be rushed into it. "I need some time," she said.

When Ray left after bringing her home, she kissed her children, said hello to Inez, and finally fell asleep around noon.

The baby's shriek woke her. Inez burst through the door.

"Fire!" she screamed. "Miss Rose! Bad fire in the kitchen!"

"Get the children out," Rose Ellen said.

She yanked on clothes. The fire snapped and popped in the kitchen, and smoke streamed in tiny insistent curls from spaces between the boards in the wall of her room. She grabbed extra clothes for herself and a pile of papers that Sample had kept tied with string in the bottom of the closet. The deed was among them. She ran into the children's room and took more clothing for them. Then she went outside and stood watching her home burn.

It went fast. The flames raced through the kitchen, and then the wind spread them across the roof. Rose Ellen put one arm around Charlie. Inez cradled the baby in her arms and cried.

Alvarez saw the smoke and came running. He stood with the

others and watched. In less than an hour the cabin was gone. Only a few tongues of flame flickered from the ashes.

"Where are we going to live, Mama?" Charlie said.

"Right now we have the bunkhouse," she told him. "There are beds there, and room for all of us."

"Are we going to get a new house?" he asked.

"You know it," she said. "We live here. This is where we belong. We'll build a house up again, is what we'll do."

Then she considered her words and knew that they were true. This was her life. The years and the work she had spent here had claimed it for her. She could never leave it. Nothing Ray Newsome could give her would ever mean as much to her as what she had already.

When he heard of the fire, Ray went to see her. He found her among the ashes, her arms and her face black. She was shoveling out charred wood, cleaning the foundation for a new house.

They sat together under a cottonwood tree. "I can't marry you," she said.

"I have heard that before," he said.

"This isn't the same. We were kids then, and there wasn't much difference between us. That isn't so anymore. You want me to come into your life. But I have things here I can't leave behind. I worked too hard for them."

"You mean this spread," he said. "You can keep your ranch, if that is what bothers you."

She took his hand and held it tight. She wanted him to understand. "This ranch is part of it," she said. "But there is more. Like the way I live and the way I look at what happens around me." She touched his cheek. "We aren't like most," she said. "We got a lot inside us, and it is strong. For years we've been changing in separate ways, and we've been too long apart. Every day you find something that is important to you, and you put it with all the rest that is important to you, and pretty soon you've got too much to give up for somebody else."

He stood up. He slapped his hat against the tree. "Tell you one thing," he said. "The second time is easier than the first. I been as low as I can get with you and I know what it's like."

Texas Dawn

"It hurts me, too," she said. "There's a part of me that wants to go along with you."

"Then you won't be happy," he said. "Not all the way. A part of you won't let you forget."

"You have it right," she said. "But a long time ago I stopped trying to be happy all the time. You can't have it."

He put the hat on his head, and he looked at her. "I hope you don't think it will be different with anybody else," he said. "Any other man, it'll be the same."

"I know that," she answered softly. "I will be going it alone from here on."

Not long afterward she heard that Ray had married the daughter of one of the Central Texas directors. Her name was Lucille Wheelock. The news created in Rose Ellen a certain melancholy. But the feeling passed.

Ray changed the name of his town. He took the first two letters of his wife's name and put them with his own name and called the town Luray.

The year 1895 brought two events that stood out in the procession of days. In April, Lucille Newsome gave birth to a boy. She and her husband named him Robert E. Lee Newsome. And in June, Charlie Sample died of a rattlesnake bite before his mother could get him to a doctor.

CHAPTER TWELVE

Ray Newsome left his office in Luray and walked around the corner to the livery stable. The cowboy who was sitting in the corner reading the Luray *Clarion* saw him, threw aside the newspaper, and jumped to his feet so fast his spurs rang.

"You ready, Mr. Newsome? Didn't nobody tell me. I'd have her ready for you if I'd knowed."

"Just get it," Ray Newsome said.

The cowboy went to the back of the stable. Ray heard the wheeze and the cough and the wall-shaking bang in the same sequence as always. Even the horses were accustomed to it now. White smoke that burned the nostrils drifted to the front of the stable. Then a surge of rattles, and an automobile rolled to the stable door. The cowboy moved across to the passenger seat. Ray Newsome sat behind the wheel and pulled a pair of goggles over his eyes. The car lurched forward, through town, south to the ranch house.

His car was the first in the valley, a new 1910 Thomas Flyer with wooden spoke wheels and brass fittings. He lived in every way now the life of the rich and privileged. In 1901 he had torn down the home that Earl and Irene had built and replaced it with a Victorian mansion designed by an architect in Kansas City. He had house servants—maids and butlers. He and his wife and their son had visited Europe three times, bringing back paintings and furniture and rugs for their home.

In his room, he washed the road grime off his face and put on a fresh starched shirt and tie. His custom-tailored clothes were cut more fully every year. He wasn't yet fat, he told himself. But he was heavier. He blamed his job; he got out of the office so seldom.

When he went downstairs, his wife was seated at the dining table. Lucille turned her face so that he could kiss her cheek. He went to the other end of the long table, where his place was set.

"Where's Bobby?" he asked.

"In his room. Sent home again," she said. "Fistfighting."

"He likes to mix it up," Ray said.

"Such surroundings he is in here," she said. "The sons and daughters of cowboys, tavernkeepers, even Mexicans. He should be with his own kind."

"He is with his own kind. This is where he lives. It's my town, practically my school. I gave them the land to put it on. How would it look for me to send him away?"

A butler came in and served them cold cucumber soup.

"I'll talk to him," Ray said.

"Please do. And while you are about it I wish you would correct the way he speaks to me. So smart and full of sass."

They finished the meal, and then Ray went to his son's room. He found the boy lying on the floor, his feet propped against a wall. He had a pocketknife and was shaving thin slices off a piece of wood. Shavings were scattered on his chest and on the floor.

Ray looked down at him. "Your mother tells me you had a problem today at school."

"Nothing much," the boy said without taking his eyes off his hands. "I got in a beef with Ezra Paine's son."

"Him? Tiny as he is?" Anger blossomed in Ray. "Stand up when you talk to me," he said. "And put away that knife. Look at the mess you're making."

The boy expelled a big sigh. He slowly took his feet off the wall, folded the knife, brushed the shavings from his chest, and got up. He was as tall as his father already. He was not yet so full in the shoulders and the chest, but the outlines were there in the big bones, and he was still growing. He stood now with hands on hips and calculated boredom on his face.

"Why can't you stay out of trouble?" Ray said. "And your mother says you have been smart to her again. You show her respect or you'll have me to deal with."

"What are you going to do?"

"Put you over my knee and whup you if I have to," Ray said.

The boy looked into his face. "Maybe. But not for long."

"Clean this mess up," Ray said. He went downstairs to his study and closed the door, as if by doing so he could shut out his problems. At the office he was master of his world. Home was different. Here the problems evaded his touch.

Bobby was turning out bad. But Ray knew no way of getting what he wanted from the boy. He didn't know how to provide the ingredients that go into a good son. He had taken for granted that the boy would be eager, as he himself had been, to take part in the ranch. But Bobby had never shown an interest in what his father did or how the money came.

The boy did fight too much. When he felt generous, Ray convinced himself that his son had spirit and feist. At other times Ray told himself the truth, which was that Bobby was spoiled, slothful, and a disgrace.

His failure with his son might have been easier to take if Ray had not felt that he was fighting the battle alone. Lucille was no happier with Bobby than he. But she seemed as detached from this problem as she was from everything else.

Here the failure was even more vague. Ray could not say how he would make his marriage different. He would want Lucille to care more, maybe. To show more feeling. Perhaps, he thought, he was asking too much of her and too much of marriage. He did know that he could be happier, that he had reservoirs of joy and fulfillment that had not been tapped for many years.

But he also carried with him the lesson, long and hard in the learning, that nobody ever gets everything he wants.

Rose Ellen was washing dishes, and her daughter was talking about college. Dora was finishing her last year of high school and she wanted more education.

"I don't think English literature will help you much on the ranch," Rose Ellen said.

"Mama, they don't teach agriculture at Barnard."

"Why do you want to go so far away? They have a good university right up in Austin."

"I want to go east," Dora said. "I want to see something besides cows and grass for a while."

Rose Ellen scrubbed a plate and dipped it into a pan of hot water. She had known for several years now that Dora would leave when she got a chance. The girl loved her mother, but she felt nothing for the ranch and the valley. She could hardly ride and rarely did. She spent her time reading books and magazines from Boston, New York, Philadelphia. She had never been east of Saint Louis, but she knew Manhattan better than she knew the back sections of the Box CF.

Rose Ellen wiped her hands on a dish towel. She put her hands on Dora's shoulders and gripped hard. "I am forty-five years old," she said. "People die that young. So tell me the truth. If I died tonight, what would you do about the ranch?"

Dora's lower lip trembled. "I'd sell it, Mama, if I could. I wouldn't stay here. I'd be too lonely, and there are other places I want to live."

"I don't know where you got your ideas," Rose Ellen said, "but I can't blame you for them. It is just hard for anybody to swallow that someone they love doesn't care about the same things they do. What is important to me means nothing to you. And I have to say that what you care about doesn't mean so much to me. So there we are."

"I don't want to hurt you, Mama," Dora said.

"I will send you to school in the East if you want it so much. You knew I would. Some things just take getting used to."

She held tight to her daughter. She faced years alone now, alone on the ranch and alone with her love for the valley, and that was not easy to take.

THE smoke and the noise bothered her. So Rose Ellen Sample stepped out on her front porch and looked over her land. The laughter and the music seeped through the walls.

A blast of wind caught her in the face. It was cool and damp; what had been a warm, bright June afternoon was suddenly dark now. To the north the sky boiled purple. The grass on the lawn bent flat in the wind; specks of grit stung her cheeks. In the near pasture the cows huddled together. Nothing blew like a norther.

It was Dora's wedding day. She had married Gerald, a Philadelphia boy, and was going to live in the East. What Rose Ellen had feared during Dora's college years was fact now.

The front door opened behind Rose Ellen, and Inez stood beside her. "She's ready to leave," she said.

When they came in, Dora was standing at the bottom of the stairs that led up from the front room. She had changed from her wedding dress and was wearing a long black skirt with a jacket and a white blouse. The visitors from the East—college friends, the groom's family—were behind her, talking among themselves in the accents that Rose Ellen found so flat and clipped.

The groom's father carried a valise in each hand. They were all leaving for Philadelphia that evening, and Dora with them.

Dora put her arms around Rose Ellen. "Thank you, Mama," she said. "This is such a happy day. I'm sorry I have to spoil it for you by going away now. I promise I'll make Gerald bring me back to visit real soon."

Rose Ellen said nothing. She knew that the valley of the Mansos was a long way from Philadelphia.

Outside, the bags were loaded into a wagon. The visitors filled three carriages.

"Why, it looks like rain," Gerald's mother said. "And an hour ago there wasn't a cloud."

"We call them northers," Rose Ellen said. She was standing on the porch with Inez beside her. "They throw a chill in the air, but they blow by quick most of the time."

"I should hope so," the woman said.

The carriages lurched forward, away from the house. Rose Ellen squinted as she watched them go. She brushed away moisture that formed at her eyes.

The wind was strong, she thought. Even for a norther.

Rose Ellen began to mark time's passing as much by events as by dates. Dora's marriage was the same summer the Circle Three Bar began to bathe its cattle in a tick dip. The Box CF did it a few months later, and that was the end of Texas fever.

The next spring Paco Alvarez died, and so did Lucille Newsome. The drought summer followed that. They had water from wells now but no irrigation system, so when there was no rain there was no grass. Ranchers had to dump their stock on the market for lack of feed.

Rose Ellen bought her first automobile the year the geologists came to the valley, wanting to look for oil. That was 1916.

At first Rose Ellen refused. She had heard that drillers defaced the land. She ran a cattle ranch, she told them. Her interest was in grass and water.

Ray Newsome let them drill. In 1918 they hit their first gusher, on land that had once been part of Charlie Fowler's Diamond Five spread. They pressed Rose Ellen for permission to drill on the Box CF. Finally she relented when they promised to keep the drill sites clean. They found oil on her property, too.

There was never enough to make her rich. But for the first time she had an income to keep her going if the price of beef ever dropped drastically. As it would, a decade later.

Not long after the oil wells, electricity came into the valley. Soon after that it got telephones. And in 1924—Rose Ellen marked

Texas Dawn

it as the year she planted Rhodes grass in some of her pastures—Robert E. Lee Newsome, his father's sole heir and abiding disappointment, drove his Packard into one of the power poles that now lined the main roads of the valley. He killed himself and a young woman named Rita who was riding with him.

"A TRAGEDY," Inez said. "A true tragedy." She put a cup of coffee in front of Rose Ellen and sat in a chair on the other side of the desk at which Rose Ellen was examining a ledger.

"A tragedy," she said again. "I don't know how the Lord can allow such things to happen."

Rose Ellen looked up from her ledger. Her hair was mostly gray now, and there were lines and pouches on her face. But she still had her sharp jaw and an even glare that could intimidate a stranger. She used it now on Inez, who was, she knew, immune to it. "Are you still talking about that baby?" she said.

"Yes. Miguel is his name. The poor child. Now he's an orphan."

"As well as a bastard."

Inez frowned and looked away. "Rita was a good girl, Lord keep her. I don't blame her. You want to blame somebody, blame that Newsome boy. He gives her a child and then won't marry her. But you can't hold the father's sins against the child."

Rose Ellen looked down at the ledger. "I don't hold anything against the baby. How could I? I've never even seen him."

"You will," Inez said. "I'm bringing him here for two weeks. I have to care for him for a while."

Rose Ellen's face turned up from the figures once more. "You're not!" she said. "Let Ray Newsome take the baby in; it's his responsibility if what you say is true."

"Miguel is of my family. Rita was the daughter of my only sister. I must take a turn with him. His grandmother isn't well and she can't do it alone."

"Fine." Rose Ellen waved a hand in the air. "But don't ask me to help. I'm a busy woman."

A few days later Inez brought the child into Rose Ellen's home. She carried him in a cradle into her own bedroom. Rose Ellen looked into the cradle for a few seconds. Then she went into her office to read. But soon Miguel began to cry, and the sound made its way to her ears. So Rose Ellen left the house and went riding. She was sixty years old, but she could still ride for hours when she wanted to.

The ranch was orderly, tamed, placid. Usually these qualities made her proud. Today they irked her. Her spread was too polished for her liking, too well run, if that was possible. It was self-perpetuating now, strong enough to survive drought and bad times. It needed her no more, she thought, than did the windmills that ceaselessly pumped water from the earth.

The thought startled her. I have taken this place as far as it can go. Nothing more to do here.

That evening the baby cried again. They were eating dinner, and Inez got up from the table to go upstairs.

"Bring him down," Rose Ellen said. "Probably he wants to be around people."

Inez carried him down, squalling. Rose Ellen took the baby and cradled him, rocked him as she had rocked her own children so long ago. She thought of Charlie, and of Dora, who had a daughter of her own now. Rose Ellen had seen Dora just once since her marriage, on a visit to Philadelphia.

"Miguel, Miguel," Rose Ellen crooned. The baby stopped crying and closed his eyes.

Rose Ellen always woke early, so she began to feed him in the mornings. She began to look at his face for traces of Ray Newsome. And when the two weeks were up, she drove to visit Ray at his ranch house.

She still saw him a few times a year. Usually it was to mediate fights between their hands. There would be a fence-cutting, or some punches thrown in a bar, or stray shots fired into the night. There was a rivalry, a residue of the old bitterness. So she saw Ray sometimes, and it was not difficult for her to drive her pickup north on the valley road one afternoon, to pass through the wrought-iron gate that bore the Circle Three Bar brand, to walk up the steps of the big house and call on him.

She said, "Ray Newsome, there is talk you have a grandson in Luray. Is this true? We both know the child I mean."

"Rose Ellen," he said, "I never knew you to care so about somebody else's strays."

"There was a time," she said, "when your strays were meat on my table. You didn't answer my question."

"What is it to you?"

"Say I am an old lady with more time on my hands than is good for me. Just tell me what you plan to do for the child."

"I don't plan to do anything," he said. She studied him to find in this hard man traces of the boy she had known long ago.

Miguel's grandmother and the county agency were happily surprised to have Rose Ellen Sample adopt the orphan. In spite of her age she was healthy. She would give the child a good home.

She and Inez brought him to the ranch. But he was Rose Ellen's child. She dressed him in the mornings and took him with her when she drove in her pickup. When he was old enough, she gave him a pony and taught him to ride, as she had taught Ray Newsome once.

He was an obedient and attractive child, and he cared very much about the ranch. He grew up working beside the hands in the pastures and looking over Rose Ellen's shoulder in the office. On his sixteenth birthday she changed her will. Miguel Sample became the sole heir to the Box CF.

---— Ξ ———

Donnie Lee: We got our A on the history project. It was Sue E.'s idea to use Gandy Meacham's own words, like he was telling about Rose Ellen Sample himself. That made the story sound more real, she said, and she was right, for the teacher even asked if Gandy Meacham could come talk to the class.

I told him about the teacher's invite. He laughed as loud as he could manage and said that was right funny, for he was twelve years old last time he'd been in school and that time they invited him to leave.

Summer finally come, but Sue E. and me still saw each other almost every day. Somewhere during that history paper she become my girl.

We didn't stop visiting Gandy Meacham either. I seen about the beginning of July that his good days was getting fewer and fewer, and his bad spells was lasting longer. That made me want to be with him as much as I could when he was right.

He and Sue E. and me talked about all manner of things. One thing Sue E. and me both steered around was any mention of Ray Newsome and Rose Ellen Sample. But one day Gandy Meacham himself said, Donnie Lee, what do you think of that boy Rose Ellen called her son?

I said there wasn't nobody I knew ever said a word against him for anything he done. Though there was those who was down on him for things he couldn't help.

Like being half Mex, Gandy Meacham said.

I said, That is part of it.

Sue E. said, If you listen to the talk around town, there are some that are jealous that he ended up with so much because of Miss Rose and wasn't blood kin to her.

People set stock in blood kin, Gandy Meacham said. As if there ain't any other sort. He lay back on his pillow. His eyes was solemn and sad. He looked up at the ceiling and didn't say nothing for a spell.

Then he said, I need something from you. I want you to come see me tomorrow when your folks has gone to bed, Donnie Lee. And you, too, Susan, if you can make it.

I knew there would be no keeping her away.

He said, This is important to me. Don't you let me down.

CHAPTER THIRTEEN

RAY Newsome sat in the hot sun. With a handkerchief he dabbed at his forehead, his upper lip. A few feet away the Mansos Valley High School marching band was tooting and thumping through "Anchors Aweigh," so loud it made his ears hurt.

He was sitting on a bench beside the track that circled the high school football field. The stands behind him were full of the people of Luray and the valley. Soon he would have to look for a second into the eyes of his grandson, and then the ordeal would be over.

When Miguel was going to school in town, Ray had sometimes glimpsed him in the schoolyard or on the streets. He'd had the same gawky build and narrow face that Ray had seen in Bobby. He wondered how many of his son's ways were in this youngster.

Few, it seemed. The boy's name had appeared often on the school honor rolls published in the *Clarion*. Ray had the habit of scanning the list, looking for it. Still, he had never wanted to be seen with him.

It had happened once, when the boy was in the eighth grade. The principal had asked Ray to award the prizes in the school's oratory contest. He had accepted. He took his seat at the front of the auditorium stage. He was stunned to see Miguel Sample walk in as one of the three finalists. When the boy spoke, Ray did not hear what he was saying at first. Then the words filtered through. Miguel was talking about the valley.

It was a good place, Miguel was saying. Some places in the world were easier to live in, but the valley was good to people if they worked hard and respected it. It gave a living to hundreds of people. And when you looked around you, you saw what people could accomplish with the land if they worked enough.

It had been the best speech, and Ray found himself pinning the blue ribbon on the boy's shirt, sure that the audience silently reproached him for having rejected his grandson. He had vowed never to let himself in for such embarrassment again. But now he faced it one more time.

The valley's young men had returned from World War II, and the townspeople wanted to honor them. A band and speeches—a proper welcome home. Mansos Valley's first citizen could not refuse the request to shake hands with them, one by one, as they marched past the stands of the football field.

They were grouped by service. Now the army came; then fourteen young men in naval uniforms were at attention in front of him. Ray Newsome moved down the row, addressing each by name, shaking hands and sometimes clapping him on the shoulder.

"Johnny," he said. "Good to see you back home. . . . Luke. You look good, boy. It was a cruiser, wasn't it? North Atlantic? You was a long way from home."

But he could not keep his attention away from the far end of the stadium. Seven marines waited there. And one of them was Miguel Sample.

The bandleader waved his arms, and the brass section hit the first notes of "From the Halls of Montezuma." The marines marched up the track to within a few feet of Ray Newsome. They stood at attention, their shoulders back and their chins thrust out. Miguel was third from the left.

When the song was finished, Ray started down the row. "Andy Merrill," he said. He pumped the first marine's hand. "We're proud of you, young fellow. I mean it."

"Thank you, sir."

Then the second. "Jimbo. You was busting windows with a slingshot not too far back. Next I hear you're a sharpshooter on Saipan, winning medals. I guess the practice come in handy."

The marine grinned.

Then Ray Newsome took one step to his right and looked into his grandson's face.

Miguel's eyes did not move. Ray forced the words up his throat. "Well," he said. "Look at the medals you got there. You must be a real hero."

Miguel did not know what to say.

Got to make him say something, Ray thought. This looks all wrong. "What you plan to do now that you're back?" he said.

Miguel had an answer for that. "Going to ag school this fall. A and M."

"Good," Ray said. He was relieved. "Good for you." And he moved to the next marine.

After the last of the speeches all the people in the stands cheered and rushed down onto the field. Men and women sought out their sons and embraced them. Rose Ellen shouted Miguel's name, and he ran to her, took her in his arms.

Ray Newsome watched until he could bear it no more. Then he turned away and walked to his car.

Texas Dawn

THE BIG PICTURE WINDOW in Ray Newsome's third-floor office presented a view of downtown Luray, with the railroad depot, the warehouses, stockyards, and packing plant on the east side of town. In the ten years since construction of the red brick office building, the changes in the view from that window had never been drastic enough for Ray Newsome to notice. But the day that he went to visit Rose Ellen, he found himself nervous, distracted, and he focused his attention on what he saw from the window.

Two days earlier Rose Ellen had fallen down the stairs and broken her hip. Though he disliked hospitals, he felt he ought to visit her. There remained between them some unacknowledged feeling, a bond that was wispy and unspecific but still real.

He was edgy as he waited to leave. She could still do that to him. Visiting hours were from one to three in the afternoon. He had half an hour to wait, so he was passing time by examining the view that he usually neglected.

His eyes rested on the stock-auction barn across the tracks. He removed the gold-rimmed bifocals he had resisted until the summer of 1947. He polished the lenses with his tie, then replaced them and squinted at the barn.

The last time he had noticed, it had been painted a gleaming white enamel, and the red letters of RAY NEWSOME STOCK SALES, INC. had been bright and distinct. Now it looked terrible.

There was an office intercom on his desk. He shouted into the speaker, "I want Harris!"

Among his employees were four young men Ray called his bird dogs, his errand boys. Harris was one of them. He hurried into the office. Ray pointed a damning finger toward the window. "Would you look at that stock barn?"

"Uh-huh," Harris said. He wasn't sure what was supposed to be wrong. The paint? he thought. But the building looked no shabbier now to him than it had for the last three years.

"Look at that paint job," Ray said. "Even with an old man's eyes I can see it is in rotten shape."

"Yes, sir," Harris said. "Looks bad."

Ray jumped out of his chair. When he was angry or excited, he was still capable of startling agility.

"Who let that happen?" he said.

"Well, Mr. Newsome, I don't know exactly."

"Let's find out," Ray said. They left the office building and walked east on Chisholm Street. "Makes me sick. What would a visitor think, coming to town and seeing that? He'd think that Ray Newsome must be seeing hard times."

Harris walked beside him. Ray Newsome paid his bird dogs well, but they earned their salaries with excesses of patience. The old man had a way of suddenly fixing on some obscure detail of his businesses. He now seemed convinced that his reputation hung on a paint job.

When they reached the barn, Harris fetched the auction manager and a maintenance man, really just a boy.

To the boy Ray said, "Why hasn't this barn been painted?"

"Nobody told me to, sir."

Ray glowered at the auction manager. "I'm telling you," he said. "I want it painted. Now. Right away."

Suddenly Ray felt tired. He sent Harris to get his car and driver. Then he went inside the auction barn and sat on a wooden seat. The paint was a triviality, he knew. But details were important. He wanted everything to be right.

The car arrived, and as they headed out of town, south to the hospital, Ray realized that he had brought nothing for Rose Ellen. He made the driver stop beside a field where bluebonnets grew in patches, and he picked a handful of flowers.

When he entered Rose Ellen's room, he wished he had not come. Miguel was in a chair beside her bed.

Ray smiled at Rose Ellen. "I see you got comp'ny already," he said. "Maybe I'll come back in a while."

"No," Rose Ellen said. "If I let you go now, I'll never get you back here. Pull up a chair."

Ray sat opposite Miguel. "Brought you some flowers," he said to Rose. "They ain't store-bought, though."

"Picked fresh is better," she said. "They're beautiful, Ray. Put them in that glass of water."

When he had done it, she said, "Ray, you know my boy, Miguel."

"Right," Ray said. "A pleasure." He looked quickly at the young man, then back at Rose Ellen. "Well, how you comin' along?"

"I will live," she said. "The doc tells me this kind of thing happens to people our age."

There was a silence of a few seconds that Miguel broke. He had to go to town, he said. He would return in half an hour. He kissed Rose Ellen's cheek and said a polite good-by to Ray.

"Does it hurt you bad?" Ray asked.

"It hurts more to know I won't get on a horse again."

He rubbed his hands on the knobs of his knees. "You always was one for riding," he said. "If I shut my eyes, I can see you like yesterday on that long-legged mare, the one you—"

"Don't," she said, almost sharply.

So he made his voice upbeat again. "I talked to Faulk up at the statehouse yesterday. He says we are getting pavement down the east side of the valley if he has to tar it himself, next year at the latest."

"Is that a fact?" she said, and once more they were casual friends, with the safe wall between them. They talked about politics, grain prices, electrical rates.

Then they fell silent again. Finally Ray said, "This morning I was shaving, and I was thinking the way I do when I shave, thinking about Jay McClellan that passed on last week. He wasn't but fifty-five, fifty-six. Then I realized that everybody in this valley is younger than we are, Rose. You and me, we remember things that nobody else walking around here has seen."

"I noticed that a while ago," she said.

"It is good to talk to you now and again," he said.

"Same for me."

"Don't it bother you?" he said suddenly. "When everybody you knew before is gone, you got to know your time is near, too. Don't it bother you?"

"Some," she said. "But I'm lucky. I have my son. I don't want to rub your nose in it, Ray, because done is done, but having him around changes things."

"He keeps you from getting lonely," Ray said.

"That is part of it," she said, "but just a small part. The mos important is the peace I get knowing that the one possession I love in life is going to end up with somebody who cares about it as much as I do."

When Ray went back to town, he saw the auction barn. There were half a dozen workmen on ladders, painting one wall. It was green paint, not white, that slopped from their brushes.

He made the driver stop at the barn. Then he got out and yelled, "You idiots! What the hell you doing?"

The auction manager heard him shouting and came out.

"The color," Ray said. "That's green. This is supposed to be a white barn with red letters."

"We couldn't find enough white," the manager said. "You said you wanted it done right away, so we took what we could get."

"Aw, no," Ray said. "Don't anybody care about my place but me?" He heard the question he had just asked. And he already knew the answer.

EVEN in his own DC-3, Ray Newsome grew weary of the flight home from Laramie.

It was a long trip for a man seven weeks short of his eighty-third birthday. But he still ran the Circle Three, and when there was land to be bought in Wyoming, he did the buying. Now the Circle Three Bar would have a place to fatten its cattle in the summer before they were shipped to market. The deal was closed, but the work had tired him.

When the plane touched down, his limousine brought him to the ranch house. Ray walked up to his room on the second floor. He had a maid turn off the air conditioner and open a window to let in the evening air. He asked for the five back numbers of the *Clarion* that he had missed while he was in Wyoming.

It was a small-town paper, and he liked that. He liked to read about people he knew, who walked the streets of his town and lived on checks from his companies' payrolls—about their bowling scores, their bake sales, the visits of their relatives. He also liked to know what they were reading about him in his own newspaper.

He was feeling sleepy in the middle of the third paper when he saw the headline. Two photographs showed a pretty blond girl named Loretta Foster and the young man, Miguel Sample. Both, said the article under the photographs, were June graduates of Texas A & M. Miss Foster was the daughter of Mrs. Eunice Foster and the late Mr. Charles Foster of Amarillo. The wedding would be held this coming Saturday, at three p.m., in the home of Mrs. Rose Ellen Sample of the Box CF Ranch.

The next day was Saturday. When Ray awoke, the nightstand clock said nine twenty. The room felt hot. He had slept eleven hours and was still not rested. That didn't surprise him. Even sleeping was an effort now, and he was always tired. He ate breakfast, then told the maid to send for his car. He walked outside and got into the front seat. "Drive," Ray Newsome told the driver. "Drive anywhere that is mine."

The ranch rolled up to meet him in the limousine's windshield, then peeled away and disappeared in the mirror. Railroad tracks. Asphalt roads. Cows that grazed in the green grass, and horses that ran with flying manes as the car sped past. The mantis heads of oil pumps dipping and raising, dipping and raising. A cowboy he did not know rode a horse he did not recognize, through an irrigation ditch that he had long ago forgotten. And fence, fence forever.

They drove east, to the base of the hills that had seemed so distant and foreboding to Ray Newsome when he was a child. There he told the driver to turn south. Then they were going down the valley, their course meandering through oil fields and pastures. He wanted to see it all, to comprehend that it was all his and that the time was short when he would be able to hold it.

Near the south end of the valley Ray had directions for the driver. Up this road, down the next for a few miles. A right here, a left there. Then a turn that took the limousine up the gravel road that led to the Box CF and Rose Ellen's ranch house.

Forty-two people were sitting in the parlor of the house, on metal folding chairs that had been rented in Luray. Rose Ellen sat in the front row, and while she waited for the minister to appear, she hoped for a breeze to cool the room.

She heard the guests' chatter fall away, voice by voice, behind her. But that was wrong, she thought. The minister was still in the kitchen, five minutes to go yet. She looked around and saw the people whispering, staring.

Ray Newsome was standing at the back of the room. His body was bent and his eyes searched the faces. She thought he looked frightened. It was an effort, but she pushed herself up and walked to him. He saw her coming. Not stern, but smiling. She was welcoming him.

She put out a hand and said, "Come, Ray, here."

"I come for my grandson's wedding," he said.

"Yes," she said.

"Not because I have an ounce of good in me," he said. "I come because I need something."

She raised a hand and put it on his cheek. "We all need something," she said. "It's okay. We all do."

THE next Saturday was theirs. Ray married Rose Ellen in the same parlor. She held his hand as they spoke the vows, her grip strong and reassuring. Then he put a ring on her finger, and they kissed, tenderly. And for the first time, Ray Newsome knew peace within himself.

They had already spoken to the lawyers. Both ranches would eventually be Miguel's.

Ray added one clause to his will a few days before he died. It concerned a hill on the west side of the valley that had been within the original holdings of Charlie Fowler, Earl Newsome, and Orrin Sample. Because Rose Ellen's passing followed so closely his own, she did not ever see or know what he planned for the hilltop.

But there, in February of 1951, a crew of workmen erected a pedestal of native stone beneath the branches of a solitary old oak tree. They fastened to it a bronze plaque with raised letters that said ROSE ELLEN.

A life-size statue of a young woman was placed on the pedestal. It was a curious work. The head of the young woman was slightly bowed. The eyes were somber as they gazed down on the valley. And the arms were spread wide in the all-embracing posture that the old Mexicans used to call *brazada*.

Donnie Lee: We went back to see Gandy Meacham that night, the way he asked. It took some doing. Sue had to wait outside by the window while my folks batted the breeze in their room. Finally I saw their light go dark. I waited for a few minutes and snuck down to Quiller's room. I opened the window for Sue to crawl through.

When he seen her, the old man's face got a dozen crinkles, all pointing up. I tole you I wanted something of you, he said. And this is it. I want you to take me where she is buried.

First thing, I thought of all the reasons why not. Like getting the old man dressed and getting him to the car, and what I would catch if my folks found out, and what I would do if he died on me.

We'll do it, Sue E. said. Won't we, Donnie Lee?

You bet, I said.

Gandy Meacham pulled down the covers. He was dressed underneath them. He was wearing a flannel shirt that was way too big for him, and brand-new jeans that wasn't broke in, bunched up around his waist where he tightened his belt. It was some belt. It had a silver buckle in the shape of a longhorn's head, with two red stones for the eyes.

He said, I dressed myself. Took a while, but I done it. These is my burying clothes. I made your mother buy them, Donnie Lee. I told her I wouldn't have none of any fancy black suits.

Then he raised up a bony crooked finger and pointed at the closet. My hat and boots, he said.

With these on, damn if he didn't look like an old cowboy instead of a sack of bones.

We got him out the window and into the car. The motor caught quiet as you please, and we headed toward the cemetery. There was a big full moon out and it shined a pearly white down on the valley, with a scrap of cloud sliding past now and then.

At first I couldn't get the point of going out to a grave. Then I decided he wanted to do something for her, anything he could. It didn't matter that she would never know of it. And what was left but to go out and stand there? Me, I was doing it on account of Sue. I could tell this was a big deal to her. Not to say that I begrudged the old man his hour, for I had come to care for him, and he had been good to me.

I parked the car. We got out and walked through the cemetery. I was carrying Gandy Meacham in my arms. Any other time it would have been spooky, the big moon shining and a wind rustling the tall grass, that being the only sound save our own footsteps. But there was something bigger that rode over all the rest and left no room for spooks. Maybe it was the three of us, together that way, knowing so much about each other when you think about it.

Then Gandy Meacham said, Tell me when we's close.

I stopped maybe half a dozen graves away. I said, Them there. The two new ones. Hers is the far one.

Let me down, he said.

I did. He started off, tottering like a baby, but we knew we had to let him alone. He walked right over Ray Newsome's grave, and just when it looked like he was going to pitch over, he reached out and caught himself on Rose Ellen's hunk of marble.

He stood there, just touching the stone. His head was bent down. Sue E. begun to cry, without making a sound. She hugged me, and all the time we watched the old man in the moonlight.

I wondered what was going through his mind about that gray-headed old lady that I used to see on the streets of Luray.

Then it hit me. He never did see her that way. To him she was still young and beautiful, always was and always would be.

He was standing, not hunched over at all anymore, but right straight and with his shoulders square. He was no old man now. Not in his head, anyways. He was young again, same as her, and they was in love just the way they'd been before.

Maybe it was his winning that put the starch in his backbone. I mean, he did win, if you look at it one way. Ray Newsome had his ranch and married Rose Ellen for a short spell. But what good did it do him tonight, all that work and all that scrapping, the hating and the loving and the pride that was in him? Tonight Quiller Meacham could think of Rose Ellen while he breathed in the night air, hold her in his heart just as sure as I held Sue E. in my arms. For the night, Rose Ellen and living was his.

Texas Dawn

I seen all that in the poor old man who stood there in the Texas moonlight. I seen that, and more. And it come over me like a big cloud over the moon, and made me hold tight to Sue E.

I was scared, not from ghosts and graves, but from what I seen. All this time I had been thinking that me and Gandy Meacham was so different, him being old and me young, him sick and me healthy.

But I seen now we wasn't so different. Like I had Sue, he had Rose Ellen. The hand that touched her gravestone was the same that must have touched her a hundred times. The eyes that looked on grass and marble and moonlight had looked on her young face and seen love.

We was the same, him and me and all the rest of us, him past things that I had in front of me yet, but both of us walking the same road, with others before us and others behind. So what made us different? A few years, is what. A few years.

Which, I seen in that moonlight, ain't so very much at all.

Young Man Gone West

"I'd like to think," says Phillip Finch, "that most readers will recognize something of themselves in Rose Ellen Fowler." One reader who is certain to is Finch's wife, Robin Chapman, upon whom the character of Rose Ellen is based.

"I met Robin in California," he says. "I was working as a newspaper reporter; she was a television newscaster. I could tell immediately that she had the qualities I admire most: independence, inner strength, knowing what she wants from life. These are qualities that I later infused into the character of Rose Ellen—my ideal woman."

Finch, a Washington, D.C., native, went west after graduating from the University of Maryland, and covered sports for the San Francisco *Examiner*. He has been in love with the West ever since.

"History is much more recent in this part of the country than it is back east," he says. "Out here you can still find people who have an immediate touch with things that happened a hundred years ago." Like Donnie Lee, Finch listened to an old man talk for hours about life on the range in the early days; an old Nevada cowboy was one of his primary sources for the lore and history that went into *Texas Dawn*. "There's something to be said for recent history," says Finch. "If that old fellow were transplanted back to Texas a century ago, he could pick right up on his job, because it hasn't changed that much."

Phillip Finch

Today, Phillip and Robin Finch tend their own piece of history—a 1920s town house in Portland, Oregon. Robin anchors a local television news program; Phillip has given up reporting and now writes novels full time. Although he has since turned to other subjects, *Texas Dawn* remains a large part of his life. "When I finished the book, I felt as though I really wanted to meet Rose Ellen Fowler sometime—except I think I already have."

A new love and a vital mission
brought her to a

CROSSING IN BERLIN

A CONDENSATION OF THE NOVEL BY
Fletcher Knebel

ILLUSTRATED BY JIM SHARPE

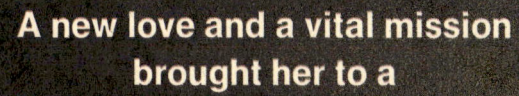

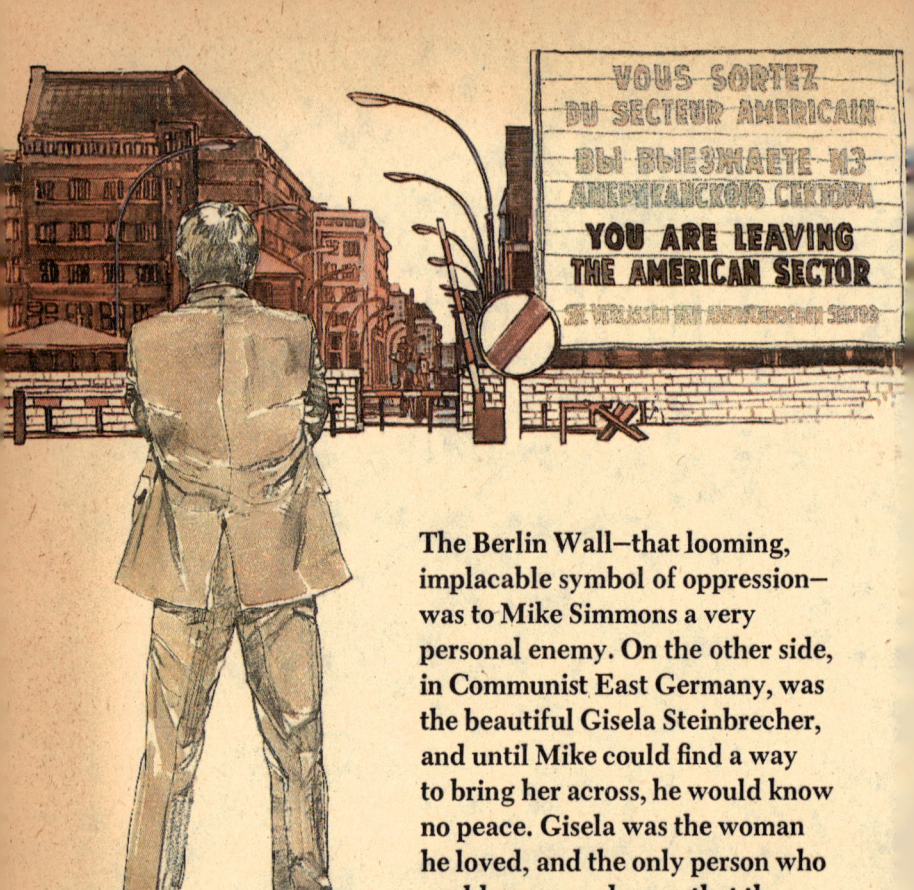

The Berlin Wall—that looming, implacable symbol of oppression—was to Mike Simmons a very personal enemy. On the other side, in Communist East Germany, was the beautiful Gisela Steinbrecher, and until Mike could find a way to bring her across, he would know no peace. Gisela was the woman he loved, and the only person who could expose a danger that the East Germans were determined to keep secret.

Somehow, Mike had to beat the Wall. And beat his own private terrors as well....

An engrossing new thriller from the author of *Seven Days in May*.

CHAPTER ONE

HE HUDDLED in his sheepskin coat, shelter from the night wind that whipped across the Platz der Republik. Leipzig's gritty, late November air held the threat of snow flurries. People bent to the wind as they plodded past, homeward bound after a day's work in the publishing houses, metalworking sheds, and fur marts of East Germany's second largest city. They gathered at the streetcar stop near the sooty old Park-Hotel, and their frosty breath rose like steam in the glow of the electric sign that unrolled the news of the world a letter at a time.

Despite the piercing cold, Mike stood with his German-English dictionary in hand and watched the recapitulation of the day's developments according to East Germany's Marxist theoreticians. ADDIS ABABA: ETHIOPIA THUNDERS WELCOME TO DDR HEAD OF STATE . . . BERLIN: IRMA REICHENBACH, DDR BACKSTROKE CHAMPION, TRAINS FOR ASSAULT ON 100-METER MARK . . . WASHINGTON: USA PRESIDENT MCCULLOUGH CEMENTS MILITARY-INDUSTRIAL PACT.

In the doorway of the Astoria, Mike pushed aside the woolen drapery that shielded the hotel's foyer from the chill of the streets, and at once the lobby's warmth embraced him. He unbuttoned his coat and shoved his fur hat into a side pocket. A clatter of voices filled the lobby and the adjoining dining room and cocktail lounge. The evening hour drew men and women to East Germany's second most popular pastime, eating and drinking. The number one avocation was tramping through the stores with string bags, searching for the battery, the winter coat, the shoes, the olives, or the toothpaste that just might have appeared on the shelves since the last hunt.

At the reception desk, Mike was handed his room key by Frau Gotsche, the least amenable of the three women clerks. Stout, matronly, and in unfaltering command, she seldom smiled, rebuffing any pleasantries by the guests.

The Astoria itself, on the other hand, buzzed with conviviality. It was the first night of a convention of East-bloc printers and publishers, whose self-assurance stamped them as among the Communist elite. Mike saw but one person he recognized in the crowded lobby, an East German woman with whom he'd traded banalities about the weather at breakfast. Tall and blond, she stood out in this serviceably dressed throng because of her fashionable sweater, a bright orange creation with a loose, cowl-like neck. Mike caught her eye and she smiled and nodded. He waved, resolving to look her up later.

In his room, Michael Ralph Simmons washed, then changed from his work clothes to a white shirt, tie, and jacket. Not a bad day, he thought as he knotted his tie. The Swedes who had awarded a subcontract to his company, Todd Elevator, Inc., were highly competent and pleasant to work with. In another three days he would see completed the installation of a bank of passenger lifts and two service elevators in the eight-story hotel the Swedes were building.

As for East Germany, Mike felt ready to leave. A month was enough in this muted country—officially the Deutsche Demokratische Republik (DDR)—that held its inhabitants captive behind the Wall and the mined frontier. He longed for the turbulence and discords of the West, for shops without interminable queues, for the strident colors and absurdities of what, on the other side, they called freedom. He thought of his daughter, Sally, a student at Cornell University. Would she show up at his New York apartment, or would she spend the whole Christmas season with her mother? His son, Dave, was an army helicopter pilot, stationed at Fulda in West Germany, little more than a hundred miles from here.

Only three more nights to go. Mike Simmons always kept track of time through nights rather than days. Like his hidden self, the night seemed fragile, vulnerable, in need of company. By day Mike sold elevators and had them installed, earning merit badges for his composure and reliability. His nights, on the other hand, cloaked mythic dreams and the stony tread of terror. He had once awakened with a start to hear his own scream of fright dying in his throat.

But this night was still young, far from the mutters of midnight, and as he walked the long corridor toward the elevators, his thoughts ran to the familiar. Food, for one thing. The veal schnitzel again, or perhaps venison for a change?

The dining room was packed. Mike stood uncertainly, scanning the hall for the East German woman he had noticed earlier and waiting to be seated by one of the waitresses.

"Mike!"

It was Sven Alsten, chief of the Swedish team building the hotel. "Come join us," Alsten called. Mike caught a flash of orange next to him. A lucky night? He walked to the table, the target of appraising glances from Alsten's dinner companions and a smile from the tall blond woman in the fashionable sweater.

The Swede, a partying bachelor, had surrounded himself with comrades from the printers' convention. Mike was introduced to a Russian named Yuri something, to an agreeable, slim female who held a high position in the East Berlin Ministry of Culture, and to Frau Gisela Steinbrecher, the uncommonly attractive woman in orange. She edited publications at the Technical University in Dresden. Mike squeezed in at the end of the table between the Swede and Frau Steinbrecher.

"*Prost!*" Yuri, the Russian, poured half his beer into Mike's glass and brandished his stein. Mike clinked and drank.

"A thirsty capitalist," said Yuri approvingly. "And smart enough to sit beside beauty." He gestured toward Gisela.

They had been speaking German, but now in deference to Mike

they switched to English. "What news from the West, Mr. Simmons?" asked the slender East Berlin bureaucrat.

"Don't ask me. I've been over here almost a month now."

Alsten described Mike's job of supervising the elevator installation in his building.

"So the American is here to raise all good Socialists to the stars." The Russian managed to mangle the English language almost beyond recognition.

"And help bring the American dollar back to the upper floors," said Alsten. They all laughed.

"As bad off as the dollar may be"—Mike couldn't resist the temptation—"it still brings ten East marks in Leipzig."

"You are also a currency trader?" The subminister of culture smiled, but her voice had an edge of challenge.

Mike backpedaled. "Of course not. I'm just talking about what's common knowledge in the street." Common knowledge also noted that a foreigner arrested for black-market currency dealing might be slapped into jail.

"Have you been to the opera here?" asked Gisela Steinbrecher, in a bid for safer ground. Her blond hair curved to her shoulders, and she had an engaging way of holding his glance with hers just a fraction longer than necessary. He sensed a budding of mutual interest.

"Yes, last night. They did *Salome*, not one of my favorites, but beautifully sung and staged. As a production, tops."

"As good as your Metropolitan in New York?" Gisela blushed slightly as she labored through the English.

"As good, certainly. A fine performance, even though I never cared for all that agonizing by Salome when she holds John the Baptist's head on a platter."

They ordered dinner from the crisply efficient waitress, ate while Alsten and Yuri debated the merits and shortcomings of Leipzig, and then drank more beer. Later they were joined by a friend of Yuri's, a tipsy Russian with a gleaming gold tooth, and two drinking companions from the convention—a Bulgarian woman who published textbooks and a hearty Rumanian printer.

The Rumanian complimented the woman from the Ministry

of Culture on her perfume. Pleased, the lady functionary said she had bought it in a hotel Inter shop. There the East German authorities permitted Western goods to be sold to any customer who offered Western currencies in payment. DDR marks were no good in the state's own luxury shops.

With the easy-humored cynicism that was as prevalent among Communists of high status as among politicians and businessmen of the West, they all began to tell stories of how they beat the system. Yuri said that he and his comrade had a steady supply of Western goods because their boss had good connections in the Soviet Union. Gisela told of her aunt in Stuttgart who sent her packages of clothes.

"Including this?" asked the subminister of culture, fingering the orange sweater.

"Yes." Gisela saw Mike admiring her. She blushed again, and he became acutely aware of the warmth of her body beside him.

The Bulgarian publisher said that she abided by her country's rules, but that every person had the right to an occasional transgression just to avoid the monotony of perfection. They ordered more beer, laughed, and gossiped. They were successful Communists, secure in their professions, and they enjoyed the company of their peers.

"You all tell jokes about us Russians behind our backs," said the comrade with the gold tooth, "but you are afraid to tell them here. So, I will tell a joke against the Soviet Union. You know why so many comrades get in line to see Lenin in his glass coffin at the Kremlin?"

"No. Why?" Alsten, the Swede, obliged.

"Because it's one line where the goods won't be exhausted before they reach the counter." The Russian had stumbled through the wilderness of English and was applauded.

Emboldened by the Russian's success, Mike decided to tell a story of his own. Risky, perhaps, but he had only three nights to go. "Two DDR soldiers were patrolling along the Berlin Wall," he ventured, "when one soldier asked, 'What would you do if the Wall suddenly collapsed?'"

At mention of the Wall, the face of the East German bureaucrat tightened and the Rumanian dropped his eyelids like blinds. Mike ignored the warning signals. "The second soldier said, 'Why, if the Wall collapsed, I'd climb a tree.' 'Climb a tree?' asked the first border guard. 'Why would you do that?' Replied his partner, 'To avoid being crushed in the stampede.'"

No one laughed. Alsten made an awkward business of clearing his throat. In the ensuing silence, Mike felt Gisela rap his ankle, then slowly rub the spot with her foot, as if to assure him that the rebuke was friendly. He glanced at her, but she colored faintly and stared without expression at the Rumanian across the table.

"That story is offensive to our brothers and sisters of the DDR," said the Bulgarian woman. "Besides, it's an old joke."

Yuri, the senior Russian, spoke with a more judicious air. "Our friend may be excused for not knowing that the Wall was built to prevent willful imperialists from sabotaging our fraternity of socialism. Not you, of course." He shook his finger at Mike. "But your government and its lackeys."

"Well, the Wall has been a fact of life for two decades now," Alsten said.

"The Wall—" Mike felt a sharp warning rap at the ankle. "I've only seen the Wall twice," he concluded lamely.

But south of the Berlin Wall he had seen forty miles of the mined, fenced, electrified, patrolled, and dog-guarded frontier from a U.S. Army helicopter piloted by his son, First Lieutenant Dave Simmons. He had seen the rich fields and pastures scarred by a gash a hundred meters wide, the watchtowers spaced at close intervals, the runs where snarling police dogs raced back and forth along the ten-foot-high fence, and the sinister mines, which just a month earlier had shredded a teenage boy bent on flight to the West. And all this was not to keep some enemy out but to keep the citizens of East Germany in.

The scalped terrain of the death strip might have bordered a Nazi extermination center or a prison camp in Siberia. Mike understood why his son, who flew a sector of the frontier almost daily, despised the Wall and its eight-hundred-and-fifty-mile chain link counterpart that separated the two Germanys.

Soon the talk turned to less flammable topics, but without the easy humor now. The Wall had thrown its shadow.

Conversation fell into several groupings, and Mike found himself stumbling about in fractured German and English with Gisela. At last Frau Steinbrecher asked haltingly whether he spoke another language.

"I get by in street Spanish," he said.

"*Español!*" She let out a little cry of joy. "*Lo hablo, yo. Estudié el español cinco años en la escuela.*"

So, she had studied it five years in school. Her voice had a fetching throaty timbre.

"Tell me something about your work and how you live," Mike said in Spanish. "I've been here a month, but I've only been in a few offices and just one home."

"I have a doctorate in chemistry and I'm in charge of editing university publications," she said in her German-accented Spanish. "I have a nice office, and the ten people who work for me treat me with great respect, just as if I deserved it."

Her laugh had a light, self-deprecating touch. Her husband, she went on, was an assistant professor of physics at the Technical University.

Mike felt an unexpected twinge of jealousy at the mention of a husband, even though he had noted her wedding ring and had speculated that such an attractive woman, apparently in her thirties, certainly must have a husband.

She liked swimming and music, she told him. She would love to visit the West whenever the state cleared her to attend a publishing convention. Her husband, Karl, could never understand this desire. He, it appeared, was a passive conformer, an uncritical servant of the Socialist state.

She asked about his life in America, and as he talked about himself, Mike became aware that they were communicating on a number of levels. He could feel their legs touching, the rhythm of their breathing, a meshing of unspoken thoughts.

So it came as a disappointment later, when he suggested that she come to his room for a nightcap, that Gisela gave him a flat "*No, señor.*" She added in swift Spanish, "*No vengo a su cuarto.*"

Crossing in Berlin

"Oh? You won't come to my room?"

"Instead you come to mine. Number two four nine. It is off the main corridor, near the stairs. *Dos cuatro nueve*."

"Enough Spanish, you two." Yuri raised his beer stein. "Join the crowd."

"We all switched to English out of politeness to you, Mike," said Alsten in mock reproof, "and then you desert us for a private chat in Spanish."

"Excuse us," said Gisela, again with faint roses in her cheeks. "I will speak English if it kills me."

"And it will," roared Yuri. "A terrible language, English. Not fit for the lips of such a beauty."

They all talked on, inhibitions dissolved by alcohol.

Gisela at last pleaded fatigue and made her adieus despite a chorus of protests. But it was another half hour before the two other women said good night and Mike felt free to leave.

"See you at the shack tomorrow noon," said Alsten.

Riding the elevator to his floor, the third, Mike recalled the parting words of Mark Jacoby, vice-president for Todd's overseas division. "One last thing, Mike," Jacoby had said. "Take it from an old hand who's spent a lot of lonely nights in the Communist countries. If you think you've got something going with an East German woman, forget it. Five to one she'll be a security agent or informer, and you'll wind up in deep trouble. You don't need that, Mike. And Todd sure doesn't need it."

Gisela an agent? Did East Germany train its secret operatives in the delicate art of blushing? He stood in the third-floor corridor, pondering. Ah, the hell with Jacoby's advice. Mike Simmons could take care of himself. He headed for the second floor.

The door of number 249 stood slightly ajar, cracked perhaps half an inch. He rapped softly, entered, and stood quietly, adjusting his eyes to the darkness. "Gisela?"

"*Buenas noches, señor*."

He took a few tentative steps toward the low voice. Mark would call him a fool. Yet he felt a familiar tremor, the night nearing those hours of silent alarms when nameless fears and sometimes terror loitered in the recesses of his mind.

Lights from the street filtered through the drawn mesh curtains, casting pale, shifting geometries on the wall. Gisela came toward him, wearing a blue cotton bathrobe and holding a finger to her lips to signal silence. She bent her head slightly, her chin tucked in, suggesting both entreaty and vulnerability. Mike was beguiled.

When he kissed her she responded willingly but briefly, then brought her lips close to his ear. "We must speak softly like this," she whispered in Spanish. "While there's only the smallest chance that this room is monitored, I cannot take that chance. Neither can you."

"Whatever you say." He embraced her. Gisela kissed him, this time with fervor, and again put her lips to his ear. He anticipated a whisper of affection.

"I must get out of this country," she said slowly and distinctly. She gripped his hand. "You will help me, Miguel."

GISELA's words were Spanish, but the insistence and the imperative tone were quite German, rupturing at once the web of intimacy that she had woven. His spirits sank. He felt used. It was not he whom she wanted, but an escape channel to the West. Mark Jacoby's warning echoed.

Mike withdrew from Gisela's arms. "I don't know if it's possible," he began in a normal voice. Gisela clapped a hand over his mouth.

"No. You must speak into my ear like this," she whispered.

"Okay, we'll keep it low." He'd play it her way, but he too would maintain caution.

"Your mood has changed." Between her whispering and her German-accented Spanish, Mike had to strain to catch her words. "I don't blame you. But I can't help myself. I have learned something that leaders of the West must be told."

Mike boosted his defenses a notch higher. Of course. It was the timeworn scenario: beautiful female agent enmeshes foreigner in escape plot for which, when she turns him in with a poignant smile, he is tried and sentenced to prison. Well, artful Gisela, you will not hook Michael Simmons.

Crossing in Berlin

A loud knock split the room's silence like a cleaver.

Mike froze and Gisela clutched him. Act two? Now police would burst through the door. . . . He caught his breath, awaiting the crash. He could feel Gisela's heart racing and he heard her whimper. With fright? Lady agent acting? If so, she was superb, for her fear enveloped him like a cold fog.

Another knock on the door, peremptory this time.

"*Wer ist da?*" she called, near panic in her voice.

The muffled reply carried a name that sounded familiar.

"Oh, it's one of those Russians." Relief flooded her speech.

She wrapped her bathrobe tighter and went to the door. When she opened it, Mike saw the bulky form of Yuri and heard him say something in muddled German.

"*Nein, nein.* You go to your room," Gisela commanded. "You're drunk. Sleep it off now, and I'll see you tomorrow."

The Russian staggered off down the hall. Gisela moved to the bed and drew Mike down beside her. She huddled close to him.

"What did you think when you heard the knock?" Mike asked.

"I was terrified. I had no idea who it could be. And you?"

"I was sure it was the police. I assumed you'd trapped me."

"Ssh. Not so loud. You thought I worked with the police?"

"And why not?"

"How awful! You thought I asked you here as part of my job!" She framed his face in her hands and gazed deep into his eyes. "I am very honest with you. I want to get out to the West. I must. But also I was attracted to you. Do you understand?"

"Tell me more." The thought that she still might entrap him, while diminished, had not entirely faded.

"Perhaps you are impossible, after all." She sighed. "First, you're an American, naïve about world politics and about what it means to be a prisoner in one's own country. Second, you're a man without appreciation for the ambivalent feelings of a woman." She laughed softly. "Consider, Miguel. Why would the state bother with an installer of elevators when it has much more important people to watch? Have you such a large ego? Or so many military secrets? Anyway, I would make a ridiculous agent; Karl says I can't hide my emotions."

Karl? Oh yes, her husband, the professor of physics.

"It would be wonderful to share and trust with Karl. But if he knew that I planned escape, he would be shocked. In the end, he might betray me."

"But you are taking a chance with me. I'm a stranger you've never seen before."

"I see very few people from the West and none in the informal atmosphere at the table tonight. I felt I could trust you. And I wanted to be with you too. . . . Oh, I don't know." She clung to him. "How can I sort out such strong feelings? Many things are true. . . . I must get out, I tell you. For my own sake, yes, but also because I have urgent news. Every day that passes increases the danger."

"What is this big news?"

Outside, the wind moaned thinly at the window ledge. The time, Mike guessed, must be nearly two a.m.

"You must listen carefully," Gisela said. "Did you ever hear about what scientists in the West call—I say this in English—the greenhouse effect?"

"Greenhouse. Hmm. Yeah, I think so. Isn't that a theory that increased burning of fuels puts more carbon dioxide in the atmosphere? That it can change the climate in some way?"

"Yes, yes." She squeezed his hand. "At the Technical University in Dresden, I have a brilliant friend, a chemist, Otto Kleist, who for some years has been doing computer calculations on the rising level of carbon dioxide in the atmosphere. This year he came up with numbers that frightened him—and me too."

Whispering, Gisela poured the story into his ear. Scientists in the West had calculated that with ever increased burning of fossil fuels—oil, coal, gas—the world would face a crisis of climate early in the next century. As the amount of carbon dioxide in the atmosphere crept upward, global temperatures would rise, melting polar ice caps, raising the level of oceans, endangering coastal cities, and shifting great deserts northward.

But Gisela's friend, Professor Kleist, had concluded that the world faced catastrophic climatic changes many years earlier than had been thought. If the industrial nations did not curtail the burning of fossil fuels at once, the world's most abundant breadbasket—the corn, wheat, and soybean states of the American Midwest—would become an arid waste. Famine and disease would stalk the continents. By 1990, Kleist predicted, salt water two to ten meters deep would flood many of the great seaports, inundating such low-lying areas as Florida and the Netherlands.

"Last summer," she said, "Professor Kleist wrote a paper, fully documented, that warned of world disaster within ten years. He urged that it be disseminated to scientists, most of them in the West, who are working on the carbon dioxide problem. Instead, authorities ordered him to cease all research on the matter and destroy all copies of his report.

"He refused, stating that he would take his case to the head of state. So the secret police ransacked his office and stole his tapes and notes. Not a trace is left of the intricate calculations he had amassed over the years. Otto was beside himself with rage. He appealed for help to a high university official, a friend, he thought.

"That brought prompt results." Gisela's voice was bitter. "The state ordered him out of the university and confined him to his flat in Weisser Hirsch, the old residential suburb overlooking the Elbe. Otto is not allowed out of his yard, permitted no visitors, no telephone. People who write him get no reply. Men in gray raincoats pace up and down his block."

Far away a siren screamed. Down the corridor a door banged, and a male voice cursed thickly. The small hours tiptoed amid random terrors. "But why?" asked Mike. "I don't understand. Why would the state silence a man who thinks the world's in trouble for consuming too much fuel?"

Gisela sighed. "You would have to live here to understand fully. Although it's small, the DDR ranks eighth in industrial output among nations of the world, and the Socialist Unity Party—the SED and its politburo—wants ever more production. Nothing must stand in the way of bigger and better output.

"And our major fuel—a leading export too—is brown coal, lignite, which releases heavy amounts of carbon dioxide. If we had to cut way back on brown coal, it would ruin the DDR."

"And how do you fit into this?" He felt unhinged, disconnected. He wondered if Gisela had concocted the account in order to persuade him to help her escape.

"I carry all of Otto's conclusions in my head," she answered, "as well as his methodology and some supporting calculations. In short, I know enough so that any expert in the West would understand the data within a matter of hours. I could write it all out for you to deliver. But I must get out too. For myself. Out of this prison that the DDR has become."

"If you know so much, I'm surprised the security people didn't implicate you along with the professor."

She moved away from him. "You're still suspicious of me?"

"Reverse the roles. Put yourself in a strange hotel room in, say, Rumania, and how would you feel? Look, Gisela, if I'm to help you, I've got to trust you completely. I have to question you to clear away doubts."

"So you will help me?" she asked eagerly.

"I haven't decided. Please, can't you understand?"

She brushed his cheek with a kiss. "Yes, yes. Oh, Miguel, I need your help so badly. . . . What else do you want to know?"

"How come Professor Kleist disclosed all his research to you?"

"I'd been calling on Otto for some years in my job as editor of technical papers. We grew to like and trust each other, so I helped him write and polish his final report."

"Didn't the secret police question you about editing his stuff?"

"The Staatssicherheitsdienst?" The name for the secret security police, the SSD, slid off her tongue like sand down a chute. "The *Stasi* quizzed all of Otto's friends, but I pretended the material was too complicated for me. Besides, I was a leader of Freie Deutsche Jugend—the Communist youth organization—my husband is diligent in Party affairs, and my sister is related by marriage to the head of the Party."

"When did you decide to escape?" He kissed her shoulder.

"The day the *Stasi* put Otto under house arrest. From that moment on, life here became unbearable. Not that I don't approve of socialism, because I do. Without the ugly repressions we have here, it is the most humane of systems. And for the material things, the most satisfying. Did you know our per capita income now surpasses that of Great Britain? We have food, shelter, and security until we die."

"Now you sound like a Party official addressing a factory brigade meeting."

"You must understand me. This country is my home," she said with feeling. "I was born here and I have lived here thirty-eight years, nowhere else." She took his hand. "May I tell you about my family, Miguel?"

"Of course. I want to hear."

Her family, she said, never recovered from the deep wounds of World War II. Hitler's maniacal drive into Russia took the life of one grandfather, a Wehrmacht captain. Her maternal grandparents perished in a British bomber raid on Hamburg. Her father was wounded in France, never regained his health, and died before she entered the university. The massive Anglo-American bombing of Dresden left her, a two-year-old, unharmed. Her mother, however, came out of it grotesquely scarred and demoralized. She had died a year ago. Now only Gisela and her sister, Frauke, survived. Frauke lived in Kaltennordheim, in the border zone, and could be visited only with a pass.

"I tell you all this so you can appreciate why I feel as I do about this land that has suffered so much. Frauke said something recently that helps explain us. 'We are,' she said of the DDR, 'a clean, decent, orderly, hardworking, prospering, sports-proud, cultured people—and we're in jail.' For me, that says it all."

"Tell me about your husband."

"Karl is a good, steady husband, reliable and generous. But he is not so concerned with me anymore. The old love has wilted. We have been strangers for years. He has his science and his stamp collection." After a long pause she said, "I could wait for an opportunity to go to the West on editorial business, but my travel chances are not great."

"How would I be able to help you?" Mike pictured the border zone as he had seen it from the air, imagined the watchtowers and searchlights, the savage dogs, the land mines. What could he do against such barriers?

She said, "It would be foolish to talk about it unless you agree to help me. Will you, Miguel?"

"I must consider a number of things—myself, my family, the company I work for. I'll have to think it over."

"The printers' convention ends day after tomorrow. I have one more night in the hotel."

"Then I'll give you my answer tomorrow night."

"You must say yes, Miguel. You must." She kissed him fiercely.

"I admire your courage. You're an extraordinary woman."

"We must not be seen together except in a crowd," she whispered breathlessly. "So give me a signal of some kind tomorrow night at dinner."

"Okay. Let's see. If I wear a brown turtleneck sweater, that means yes, I'll help. If I wear a shirt and tie, then the answer, sadly, is no."

"Tomorrow I shall pray for a brown sweater," she said.

Upstairs in his own room, Mike stood for many minutes gazing out the window. The wind picked at crevices of the massive railroad station across the Platz der Republik. A long red-and-white banner, BUILD THE FUTURE THROUGH SOCIALISM, tugged aimlessly at its cords. The streets were deserted. Mike felt stabs of the old and nameless fears. These were the black hours, the alleys of the night.

CHAPTER TWO

MIKE hung his yellow hard hat on a peg, took off his rain jacket, and stepped over to the kettlelike iron stove. A brown-coal fire warmed the board hut that served as construction headquarters for Sven Alsten and his Swedish crew.

"Another lousy day," said Mike.

A driving rain pelted the drafty shack. Through one misted window he could see the raw hulk of the unfinished Interhotel. Through another loomed the scalloped tower of Karl Marx University, tallest structure in the city and formerly known as Leipzig University. Now the skyscraper was the world's only institution of higher learning that boasted a posh nightclub on its twenty-seventh floor. Leipzig, ancient home of medieval fairs and Johann Sebastian Bach, had undergone fateful changes.

"How are you coming with those door locks?" Alsten was a fine engineer from Stockholm with a prodigious appetite for work and play.

"Sven, you ought to dock the pay of anybody who fools around with those elevators." Mike slapped the rough planked table. "I mean it. That's the third time some guy has pried open those doors." He blew on his hands, rubbed them for warmth. He felt edgy enough today without the added frustration of broken contact arms. "How about some coffee, pal?"

"Coming up." Alsten filled two mugs with Costa Rican coffee, which an assistant had brought through customs in his luggage.

"Let me show you what we're up against." Mike set his mug on the table, then sketched outlines of the elevator shaft on the back of an invoice. "Look, every floor has a door-lock assembly for each shaft. If this contact arm breaks, the elevator stops dead. That's our safety guarantee. But prying open the doors has got to bust the contacts. It's not the cost of the set that bothers me; it's the lost time."

"How much time?" Alsten blew on his hot coffee.

"Well, I had two spare assemblies, but I used them on those other breaks. I figure maybe two, three weeks to get some in."

"Three weeks!"

"I might do better if I bring them myself. Look, don't blame us for the delay. If you don't take some disciplinary action, this is likely to keep on happening."

Alsten heaved a sigh. "You know that means dealing with Lanz?" Werner Lanz was the Party brigade leader on the job, charged by the SED with looking after the welfare of some one hundred union members building the hotel.

"Just so I can do it in here where it's warm." Mike held out his hands to the big-bellied stove. "Will you do the interpreting?"

"I suppose I'll have to." Alsten shrugged. "Let's get this over with." He leaned out the door, summoned a nearby workman, and asked him to fetch Brigade Leader Lanz.

Werner Lanz made his headquarters on the opposite side of

the hotel skeleton in another shack, dubbed SED Haus by the workers. He arrived shortly, little dampened by the rain.

"Herr Alsten. Herr Simmons." Lanz bowed slightly after taking off his raincoat. He was short and wiry, with swift, birdlike mannerisms. "You wished to speak with me?"

"Yes. We have a problem, Herr Brigade Leader." With Alsten translating, Mike first complimented the intelligence and know-how of DDR workers, then eased into the matter of the broken contact mechanisms. He said Lanz should know that he was urging Alsten to impose penalties on any person tampering with the elevators.

Lanz listened raptly, then delivered a long, singsong reply, in which he extolled the devotion of his men to socialism, to solidarity, and to the advancement of the DDR through superior buildings. Given such lofty commitment, it was unthinkable that members of his union should interfere, either intentionally or accidentally, with the elevators.

Nevertheless, Mike replied, somebody had forced open the doors on the third floor of number four shaft, cracking the contact arm and rendering the elevator immobile. This was the third such incident, and it must not be repeated or completion of the building would be greatly delayed.

Ah, but the brigade leader had personally investigated the two previous incidents and had found that no one had forced the doors. On the contrary, the malfunction had occurred because of defective material in the door-lock assemblies.

"Defective material!" Mike's temper spurted. How could the brigade leader have tested the broken parts? Mike himself had taken them out in the process of replacement.

Lanz replied that he had not tested the parts. But since his comrades had not forced open the doors, how else to explain the malfunction save through defective material?

"What kind of specious reasoning is that?" Mike was boiling.

"Calm down, Mike," said Alsten quietly.

Mike got himself under control with an effort. Choosing his words, he told Lanz that Todd Elevator's defective parts had never exceeded a fraction of a percent.

Ah, but Lanz had read stories in the press of massive recalls of American automobiles because of parts failures. The combatants lofted their arguments back and forth, while Alsten sought to moderate and to modulate. In the end, Mike paid homage to the honor and integrity of the East German construction workers, and Lanz withdrew his allegation of possibly shoddy workmanship at Todd plants. He promised to post a notice that would ensure the future inviolability of Herr Simmons' well-crafted elevators. Then, amid a flourish of adieus, Werner Lanz walked out into the rain.

"Sorry I blew my stack," Mike said to Alsten. "I don't know what got into me."

A workman arrived with the daily hot lunch, and Alsten sniffed at the containers. "Hmm. Bockwurst, potatoes, and carrots." Alsten pulled battered chairs up to the table. "What did you think of that crowd last night, Mike?"

"Man, talk about expense accounts. Those Communists know how to run up the tab."

"People are people the world over." Alsten cut off a chunk of bockwurst. "I got some good laughs, though."

"I did too, but my story didn't. I guess it's because they're ashamed of the Wall."

"It's more than shame," Alsten reflected. "They're prosperous here in East Germany now, but they're still prisoners. Resentment over the confinement runs deep. Things look placid on the surface, but the fellow who strays too far from the Party line runs the risk of being put away."

"It's tough to escape, right?" Mike welcomed the opening.

"Less than a couple hundred a year make it now. The state has fifty thousand *Grenztruppen* patrolling the East German border to make sure nobody gets out. That's a lot of guards for a country no bigger than your state of Virginia."

Mike agreed with a nod, then asked casually, "Anybody ever approach you to help with an escape?"

"Yes. A young fellow who works on this job began dropping hints about getting out, but I had to turn him off." Alsten lifted his hard hat and plastic raincoat from the wall pegs. "I can't afford to take a chance. We figure to bid on a lot more work here—worth millions."

Mike worked through the afternoon with his mixed crew of Swedes and East Germans. Final phases of the installation—checking, adjusting, testing—went slowly. He tried to shut Gisela and her troublesome plea out of his mind, but conflicting images kept flickering—gray watchtowers with gun slits commanding stretches of raked red turf, feverish whispers, a bright orange sweater, the frenzied barking and lunging of German shepherds on a dog run.

Darkness had fallen by the time Mike made his way across the Platz der Republik with the homegoing crowds. In front of the cavernous rail terminal he passed a squad of Soviet soldiers, engulfed in brown greatcoats, marching toward a train. Mike had seen uniformed Russians infrequently. Few of the troops the U.S.S.R. maintained in East Germany were permitted to mingle with the native population.

Delegates of the printers' convention milled about the Astoria lobby. Mike looked for a flash of orange, but failed to see the woman who had so suddenly entered his life. In his room, he took his time showering, shaving, and inspecting himself in the mirror. A bit fleshy, that one hundred and eighty pounds on a five-eleven frame. A few more strands of gray in the black hair. Not a bad profile. Some women still thought him attractive. Gisela too?

Padding about the bathroom, toweling with vigor, Mike realized he was postponing the moment of decision. He put on his shorts, undershirt, trousers, and shoes, then pulled open a dresser drawer and looked down at its contents. To the left rested two turtlenecks, one gray, one brown. To the right lay half a dozen shirts. He hesitated only momentarily. Reaching down, he picked up the brown sweater.

So, he had made up his mind. Energy coursed through him. He felt new, fresh, recharged, ready for any challenge.

On the way to the lobby Mike pondered his decision. A stranger might conclude that he had acted out of fancy for a woman and antipathy for a regime that imprisoned its people. Only half right, he knew. The fancy for a woman, yes. But he hated the Wall, not only as a symbol of mass oppression but as a forbidding presence that evoked dark terrors of his Nebraska childhood.

Mike's father, an itinerant plumber, had disappeared when his son was but two years old, and a year later Mike's mother died of pneumonia. The little boy went to live with Dolly Peck, a cousin of his mother's, and her husband, Mac, a Bible-quoting, dogmatic fundamentalist. Childless themselves, Mac and Dolly believed that the essence of education lay in putting the fear of God into the younger generation. They harried little Michael with admonitions to love, worship, and fear the Holy God, with emphasis on the fearing.

For his boyhood lapses of behavior, Mike was exiled to the basement of the old frame house in Omaha. Mac or Dolly would place him on a stool in the middle of the bare-walled room and shut the door. Usually his sentence lasted half an hour, but in cases of "wicked sacrilege" or serious infractions of the conduct code, the couple forced Mike to remain on the stool for an hour. Mike dreaded "the dungeon," as he knew it, and came to hate every crack and splotch on the basement walls. Fear frequently reduced him to shivering and sobbing, and occasionally he screamed with terror when he imagined phantoms and monsters poised for attack. He knew that the Pecks could hear his screams, but not once did they shorten the period of punishment.

Fortunately for Mike, this ordeal lasted only a few years. While he was in second grade, a sister of his long-vanished father moved back to Omaha and prevailed upon the Pecks to let Mike live with her and her husband. Laura and Roger Murray were decent, kindly people who reacquainted the boy with the solace of love, home, and friendship. But the curse of those basement walls had remained. The looming walls and hooded phantoms of the night hovered in the shadows through his marriage, through the growing up of his children, Dave and Sally, on Long Island, through his divorce, and into the bachelor years that followed.

The nightmares almost always involved walls: high walls, dark walls, walls that moved in to crush him. And now he faced an actual wall, which might be battled and conquered through the person of an immensely intriguing woman. Could the subconscious be cleansed through struggle in the outer world? Perhaps by helping Gisela Steinbrecher to escape, he might somehow exorcise the private terrors that pillaged his sleep.

As Mike strode through the lobby toward the dining room, bright orange flared in his path.

Gisela stood riffling the pages of a magazine. She looked up, and her glance told her what she wanted to know. She flashed a radiant smile. "What a heavenly color you're wearing." She said it in Spanish, her voice low and seductive.

"Will you join me and the others for dinner, *Frau Doktor?*"

"No. We must stay apart." She spoke rapidly. "I have arranged for an apartment where we may talk normally. Go there at nine thirty prompt. Number Ten Hainstrasse, a block behind the *Information Zentrum*. You go up three flights to apartment thirty-one. Now I go to dine with the others from last night. You must eat somewhere else."

Mike saw Frau Gotsche studying him from the reception desk as he left the hotel. She quickly averted her eyes.

He dined at Auerbach's Keller, a restaurant that traced its lineage to Goethe. Afterward he sauntered past the old town hall with its enormous blue-and-gold clock and through the twelfth-century marketplace to Hainstrasse.

The approach to number Ten was through a courtyard between a confectionery and a luggage store. He made his way to the building's entrance and mounted the wide, curving stairway. Gisela answered his soft knock at the apartment door.

They moved eagerly into each other's arms.

"When I saw the color of your sweater, Miguel . . ."

"I loved the look on your face, my love." The Spanish *mi amor* slipped out unsummoned.

Gisela kissed him slowly, and he savored the distinctive scent that he now associated with her. No matter what happened between him and this woman, he knew he would never forget that unique aroma of breath and body warmth.

"This is the apartment of my friend Ulli." Gisela swept her arm about the room, which served as both parlor and bedroom. "It is ours for two hours. Ulli comes back from her mother's

about midnight." Gisela placed a pair of chairs near the coffee table and tuned the small radio to the government-run Berliner Rundfunk. A symphony filled the small apartment.

"That's too loud, isn't it, if we're going to talk?"

"We set the radio over here like this." She placed it on the floor near the door. "Who knows? The walls may be thinner than we think."

Gisela took his hands in hers as they seated themselves. "So, Miguel, what do I do to get out of the DDR?"

He was astounded. He had agreed to help, not to lead or initiate. "I haven't the vaguest idea. I don't know the first thing about arranging an escape. That's your end."

"But I know nothing. You're the widely traveled man from the West. You know many people over there."

"Sure, I know people, but none in the escape racket. I have no idea how to start."

"Then we must find out together, no?" She made it sound as easy as a phone call.

"Well, yes. I suppose so." He felt carried along by this singularly determined woman, yet lost too.

"I will tell you what I've heard." Gisela proceeded in businesslike fashion to cover the options. "First, there's the Baltic route."

But that, she said, was impossible in winter, and it required great endurance and stamina, which she did not possess. And the defector who attempted a shorter swim, across the Elbe where it formed a natural border with the Federal Republic, faced almost certain death by machine-gun fire from swift river patrols.

Then there was the flee-for-fee network, the shadowy organizations that spirited East Germans across the border beneath automobile seats, in freighted crates, and even in Allied military vehicles, which passed through Checkpoint Charlie without inspection, under the old Berlin agreements. They provided false passports and forged papers.

"But the latest price quoted is fifty thousand marks," said Gisela, "and I have less than three thousand."

Tunneling, a favorite method of escape in the early years of the Wall, had been all but abandoned, she said. Constant patrols, informers, and sophisticated detection devices made it a lethal escape venture.

Gisela talked of other escape routes—a visa for Yugoslavia and then across the lightly guarded frontier into Greece; a boat crossing of the northern Elbe during a heavy nighttime snowfall; walking out with a forged West German passport.

"They say the best route now is at places where they're renewing the fences." Gisela's voice rose above the dreamlike passages of the radio symphony. "In places where they're 'modernizing' the frontier, the fences are taken down temporarily and the mines are cleared away so the work crews won't get killed. This leaves unfortified gaps several hundred meters long."

Mike thought back to that day in October when he had flown with Dave along the border near Fulda. His son had pointed out a spot where guards had been exploding and removing mines preparatory to installing a new escape-proof fence.

"Yes," Mike said. "I've heard that too."

Gisela brightened. "Maybe we should concentrate on that way."

"Look, I'm leaving in a couple of days, but it just happens that an accident on the job makes it necessary for me to come back here again. Before I do, I'll try to find out where the fence is down." Mike frowned. "But how would you get near such a place? You need a pass to be anywhere near the frontier, don't you?"

"As I told you last night, my sister, Frauke, lives in Kaltennordheim near the border. I have a permit to visit her. It helps to be a good Party activist."

"And how am I to get word to you?"

"Why," she said brightly, "we will meet right here two weeks from tonight. My friend Ulli adores affairs of the heart, and she'll let us have the apartment anytime."

"Is this an affair of the heart, Gisela?"

She gazed into his eyes. "I think so," she said seriously. "But I wonder, Miguel. Do I feel these stirrings because of love or because you agreed to help me? I'm not sure. But I do have great warmth for you."

"And I for you."

She leaned forward for a kiss.

Then they began to talk of ways and means. If he needed to get in touch with her, he should contact Ulli Beitz at the cultural events ticket counter in the *Information Zentrum*—the visitors information center. Gisela showed him a framed photo of Ulli, a pleasant woman of thirty-odd years with a great mass of dark hair. Gisela also gave him her home address and her phone number at the university, but these were to be used only when other channels failed.

Mike gave her Sven Alsten's phone number and that of Walter Delaney, who ran Todd's European operation through his West Berlin office.

They devised a simple code, based on elevator parts, to cover elementary situations. They tried to translate such terms as hatch, sling, platform, door lock, counterweight rails, hoist machine, and safety switches into Spanish, but in a few cases fell back on the English word. They wrote down the code, but Gisela vowed to destroy the paper after she had committed the meanings to memory. She also made up a brief coded exchange in German for Mike's use at the ticket counter with Ulli Beitz.

The symphony had given way to a string quartet playing light chamber music. Mike glanced at his watch. It was eleven forty.

"You must go now, Miguel." She brushed him with a parting kiss. "I'll wait for Ulli. Remember, two weeks from tonight here, eight o'clock. . . ."

"I don't like your walking back to the hotel alone at this hour."

"The streets here are safe. This is a well-run prison."

CHAPTER THREE

MIKE paced about the dreary waiting room where he and a dozen other transients awaited the return of their passports. Checkpoint Charlie, a cluster of prefabricated shacks, offered a narrow aperture in the high, thick concrete wall that split Berlin for nearly thirty miles. Not far from the control station lay the bald expanse of Potsdamer Platz, its East Berlin turf packed with vehicle traps and spiked with searchlight towers.

"Ahman . . . Sharlief . . . Finster . . . Giovanni . . . Herr and

Frau Dubois." The gray-uniformed control officer had begun handing out passports. One by one the travelers grasped the booklets and clattered out of the metal shack. Mike stood alone, his name uncalled.

"Simmons?" he asked.

"*Noch nicht fertig,*" the official said. Not ready yet.

Mike continued pacing. He had now passed half an hour in this bare, chill room that smelled of disinfectant, musty clothes, and stale tobacco smoke. Finally his name was called by the control officer, who stood behind his counter holding out the blue booklet embossed with the haughty gold eagle. Why did it take so long? Mike wanted to ask, but of course the inquiry would merely compound futility. He took his passport and moved along a planked walkway to customs. The officer approved Mike's single piece of luggage without looking inside.

Farther on, at the currency window, a voice asked for his passport and currency declaration. Upon entering East Germany a month earlier, Mike had signed a paper stating the amount of money he was bringing in. Minutes passed. Mike pulled on his fur-lined gloves and stamped his feet as he waited. The voice asked that he step inside, please.

Now what?

The small room held a wooden table, a desk lamp, and two chairs. On the wall hung a photograph of the chief of state, Chairman Heinrich Volpe, wearing glasses and looking benignly professorial.

"*Sprechen Sie Deutsch,* Herr Simmons?" The officer in his gray uniform held Mike's passport and currency statement.

"*Nein.*"

The officer passed into an adjoining room, shutting the door behind him. Through a small window Mike could see about fifty yards away the white line that here separated the two Germanys. It crossed Friedrichstrasse, binding the pavement like a bandage. On this side, red-and-white barriers and posts cut a zigzag pattern, making it impossible for vehicles to speed across the border, as many had in the early days. On the other side stood the prefab huts where Allied military men monitored entering cars.

"Good afternoon, Mr. Simmons." This time it was a pleasant-looking woman with an ingratiating voice. "A few questions if you don't mind, sir." She spoke English with a British accent.

"Let's see. You brought in five hundred and twenty-three West marks, twenty-seven dollars, and three thousand dollars in American Express checks. Isn't that a great deal of money for twenty-nine days, Mr. Simmons?"

"Not for a businessman."

"Ah, yes." She drew a slip of paper from his passport and consulted it. Mike became alarmed; just what was all this? "Todd Elevator, Inc. Is that correct?"

"That's right."

"How much did you spend in the DDR, sir?"

"Oh, about twelve hundred American dollars, mostly for food."

She needed to know exactly how much money he had left, so Mike counted his remaining funds.

"Seventeen marks missing. How regrettable." Another pleasant smile. "But I think we may consider you in order." She handed him his passport. "By the way, did you entertain anyone?"

"A few for dinner. Perhaps four or five people all told."

She folded the slip she'd taken from his passport into precise quarters. "Including a Frau Steinbrecher of Dresden?"

The jab of a needle could not have startled him more. He tried to steel himself, hoping his face did not betray him. "Why, yes, I did." Suddenly the cramped room felt cold.

The customs woman smiled. "You needn't get—what's your American word—uptight? I knew Gisela Steinbrecher, Gisela Helmich then, during our school days. A hard worker and active Party member. We wish more people from the West could talk with such an excellent example of the modern Socialist woman."

No words, however disarming, could mask the chilling implication of Gisela's name being mentioned here.

"And what is your name, please?" he asked.

"Frau Müller."

He held out his hand. "A pleasure, Frau Müller."

After accepting his handshake, she said, "So, a safe journey home, Mr. Simmons. Will you be returning soon?"

"Yes, I must bring some spare parts for the elevators."

"Perhaps we shall meet again, then. Good day."

He walked swiftly from the hut and along the planked walkway, carrying his single bag. At the exit, he showed his passport to a soldier, who then pressed a button to open the last gate in the East German security complex. The iron gate clanged behind him, and Mike crossed into West Berlin.

Who was the informer? That assistant subminister of culture, or whatever her title was? The desk clerk, Frau Gotsche? She had seen him talking to Gisela. What did this mean for the escape plans? The questions swarmed like threatening wasps.

Mike hailed a cab and taxied to a hotel on Augsburgerstrasse, just a few blocks off Kurfürstendamm, or Ku'damm, as West Berlin's chief boulevard was sometimes called. Here flocks of tourists surged past theaters, shops, sidewalk cafés, movies, restaurants, and nightclubs.

West Berlin throbbed with life this late November afternoon. Fashionable women, leather-coated young men, jeans-clad adolescents thronged the streets. What struck Mike Simmons, only a few minutes away from the queues of the East, was not so much the contrast in abundance—shopwindows laden with luxuries, bustling crowds, a splurge of cars, clothes, and cafés—but the difference in color and rhythm.

East Germany was a nation of monotones, its houses, buildings, and cities ranging from somber brown to the hue of ashes. The overall impression was drab and depressing. By contrast, West Berlin glowed with color. It offered shimmering advertisements, entertainment posters and displays, splashy clothes of every style and cut, and the rainbow dance of cars and motorcycles.

West Berlin pulsed with exhilaration, clamored with life. Horns blew. Barkers cried. Traffic hummed. There was a certain vivacity, a certain heedless chatter that was missing in East German cities. Ordinarily Mike would have immersed himself in West Berlin's delights, promenaded, seen an afternoon movie, or stopped somewhere for a drink. But today Gisela held his thoughts in leash. No matter where he turned, he felt the tug of his promise.

After settling into his hotel room, Mike called Walter Delaney at his office and arranged to meet him in late afternoon. Next he placed a call to First Lieutenant David Michael Simmons in the helicopter pilots' ready room of the 11th Armored Cavalry Regiment in Fulda, down near Frankfurt am Main. Luckily Dave was the duty officer, and Mike reached him at once. They had not talked since the night before Mike crossed into the DDR.

"Remember the day we went over your regular route and you showed me where repairs were being made?" Mike thought it prudent to avoid specifics on the phone.

"My regular route? . . . Oh, sure. What's up, Pop?"

"I can't go into it now, Dave, but I have a friend over there who wants to take a look."

"At the repairs?"

"Yes, wherever they might be right now. Do you follow me?"

"Yeah, I think so." Dave's voice took on a note of eagerness. "Take a look in passing, we might say?"

"Right. Dave, I'd like to come to Fulda and have a talk with you. How soon are you free for dinner?"

"How about Friday, Pop?"

"Okay. I'll see you Friday evening."

Mike napped briefly, then met Walter Delaney at the Roma, a smoky Italian bar and pasta house on Marburgerstrasse two blocks off Ku'damm. Delaney ordered small beers, which in Berlin meant glasses only slightly smaller than ski boots.

"*Prost!* Glad you made it back from the land of stupid slogans and kiddies' bedtime hours. If you're not off the streets by nine p.m. over there, you're liable to get rolled up in the sidewalks."

Delaney was a rough, burly sort with full jowls and a ragged, smoker's voice. He was a phenomenal salesman whom rivals in business regarded with awe. He was also the only man known to have called his chairman of the board a dumb jerk without losing his job.

"Walt, I need some door-lock assemblies for the Leipzig job. How soon can I get them?"

"We can have them here from the Frankfurt warehouse in twenty-four hours. How many do you want?"

"I guess I ought to have half a dozen. Some idiot's forever forcing our doors."

They talked about spare parts and progress on the Leipzig job; then Mike broached the subject that so engrossed him. "Walt, over there I met a woman who wants to get out. I want to help her, but I haven't a clue how to start."

"Didn't Jacoby give you his company lecture about steering clear of those Communist sweeties?"

"He did." Mike grinned. "And I didn't."

"Tell me about her. I don't mean her name or where she works." Delaney waved his beer glass. "Just the good stuff."

Mike ran through the whole script, including the incident at Checkpoint Charlie. Why he trusted Delaney implicitly he did not quite know. Perhaps for the same reason that Todd Elevator customers did. Delaney had a disarming natural warmth.

"Your woman doesn't sound like an SSD agent," he said when Mike finished. "You say she didn't mention that chemist, Otto Kleist, the second time you saw her?"

"Not a word. Although I didn't realize it until this morning, coming up to East Berlin on the train."

"An agent would have harped on that theme again, to keep her story straight." Delaney took a long swallow of beer. "I hope that story's a fake. That's all we need right now—a lot of carbon dioxide to choke to death on. Still, your deal with her is dicey, Mike. You must know that. These two Germanys are crawling with spies, informers, agents. At the same time they have millions of open contacts, visits, and trade negotiations. . . . There are even two lawyers, one in West Berlin and the other in East Berlin, who get together every few weeks and set a price for the Federal Republic's purchase of East German political prisoners. Can you believe it? So, all the security stuff is a waste of the people's money, if you ask me."

"How do you read that little business with Frau Müller at the checkpoint? That scared the hell out of me."

"I see that in one of two possible ways," Delaney said. "One, your friend is suspect and they'll nail her for something. Two, she is indeed a sterling Party type and the praise from Frau Müller—

if that's her real name—can be taken at face value. Either way, you're on notice that they've got you in their sights."

"You don't think I ought to keep that date with Gisela?"

"Whoa, Mike. I don't tell anybody what to do."

"But if you were me," Mike insisted, "would you keep it?"

"No way. I intend to sell a lot more elevators behind the Wall, and I wouldn't jeopardize that business for any woman."

"Even if you were in love?"

"Love!" Delaney gulped on his beer. He wiped his mouth and eyed Mike critically. "Let me ask you a question. Suppose this gorgeous creature said to you, 'Mike, let's face it, we're desperately in love, a love unique in this sorrowed land. However, I like it here and do not intend to leave. Therefore I want you to live with me in the DDR.' Would you stay?"

"No." Mike laughed. "Of course not."

"So much for love." Delaney sat moving his glass in small circles. "I don't mean to be rough on you, Mike, but it helps to cut to the guts of the deal, right? If a man's feeling for a woman can't survive a difference in customs and systems, it ain't love. So, if you're going to help the lady escape, you'd better have another reason."

Another reason? There was the feeling that was beginning to dominate his thoughts. Last night he had dreamed of the Berlin Wall ripped apart by lightning. The strip that split the two Germanys had become allied with his own tortured images of walls and with the grisly phantoms that plagued his nights.

"Walt, I hate that Wall." His vehemence surprised them both.

Delaney eyed Mike with new interest. "That's why you're going to help this broad bust out? Because you hate the Wall?"

"In part, yes. I think the Wall is an abomination in a fairly civilized continent."

"Civilized!" Delaney hooted. "Man, you're in the country that only yesterday, as time goes, cremated six million Jews. Not that the Germans are much worse than the rest of our great and noble human race. There're about a hundred countries on this globe where they'll pull out your nails just for making fun of the top guy."

"The Wall's a symbol of those atrocities, for one thing. I can't do anything about all those other places, but maybe I can get one person across the Wall. One person." Mike could not tell Walt about the other reason, the night terrors and his need to banish them somehow.

"Now what you want from me is leads on where to find help."

"Right."

"Okay, there are some refugee organizations that'll have some tips and, of course, the flesh traders who'll deal for money. Oh yeah, there's a member of the British Frontier Service called Spider Butler. You can reach him at their headquarters in Helmstedt, which is on the border. Like you, he hates the Wall, and he'll do his best for anybody trying to breach it."

"Do you know any of the professional escape people?"

"No, but I can line up some names with a few phone calls." Delaney raised a finger. "But it costs, Mike. The rate's up around thirty thousand dollars a head. You want to spend that kind of money?"

"No, but I'd like to hear the propositions."

"Okay, I'll leave what I find out for you at the hotel tomorrow." Delaney summoned the waiter for the check.

Mike accompanied Delaney to the nearby subway station, then walked briskly back to his hotel. At the front desk, a clerk handed him a folded slip of paper. "This arrived by telephone just a few minutes ago, Herr Simmons."

Mike read it in the elevator on the way up to his room. "Pop. New switch on your project. It's urgent you get here tomorrow. Call me soonest. Dave."

CHAPTER FOUR

Disco music thundered in the concrete guardhouse of the regimental headquarters of the U.S. 11th Armored Cavalry, where Mike Simmons awaited authorized contact with his son. The elite Blackhorse Regiment patrolled a section of the armed frontier on the outskirts of Fulda. An hour by train from Frankfurt, Fulda was a hilly, bustling city of sixty thousand Germans, baroque architecture, and a massive twin-towered cathedral. To the east stretched the lethal strip of earth and fence that severed the two Germanys.

Lieutenant Simmons arrived in the guardhouse like a booted invader, his husky frame swelled by a padded winter combat jacket. At six feet three he towered above his father. Though the family resemblance was unmistakable, Dave had green eyes in place of Mike's brown, and a broad, firm jaw that gave him a look of resolution and tenacity.

Father and son embraced fondly, but with that certain awkwardness of men who had not shed the memory of parent and child roles.

The two men left the guardhouse and walked through the thin, fading light of a wintry afternoon.

"I came as soon as I could, Dave." Mike had to stretch to keep up with his son's stride. "What's up?"

"A new gap in the border. But it'll only last a few days. You and I are going to check it out."

Lieutenant Simmons obviously throve in the role of command. He walked with a long, confident stride, a slight swagger in his gait. He returned salutes with flair, greeting enlisted men he knew with the proper mix of friendly interest and the restraint of rank. Mike had forgotten his son's appetite for army life.

In the solid old stone building that housed Dave's air troop, Mike followed his son down a corridor to a small room containing a battered desk, two chairs, and several metal lockers. Maps covered the walls, and a radiator hissed quietly.

"Let's wait here until the captain of air troop can see us. Just tell him you're visiting. No details, okay?" Dave, his father noted, had picked up a staccato style of speech. "Tonight we'll take a ride in the Opel and I'll show you where the fence is down."

"You sure it's all right, Dave?"

"No problem. We give plenty of VIPs a night briefing at the border." He settled himself on the desk top and swung his shiny black boots. "I'm glad you came right away. This particular gap in the border will only last a week to ten days, no more. Who's coming across?"

Crossing in Berlin

Mike quickly ran through Gisela Steinbrecher's story. "She says she already has a pass for the border zone."

"Is this woman, ah, important to you, Pop?"

"I . . . I'm not sure, Dave. I think so."

"I have a reason for asking." Dave rushed ahead, eager to flee the delicate subject of his father and women other than his mother. "It's dangerous to cross even when the mines are blown and the fence is down. People can get killed."

"We know that. She's ready to run the risk. Of course, I'd like some handle on the odds."

"Sure, that's why we're here. I want you to get the whole picture. Come over here."

They stepped to a wall map, which depicted the border area patrolled by the 11th Cavalry via helicopters and armored trucks. "Okay, we're here." Dave pointed with a pencil. "This jagged green line is the border in a section we call the Parrot's Beak. Now the open place in the fence is right here, not far from the town of Melpers. See it?"

Mike peered at the map. "Yep. About how wide is the gap?"

"Call it three hundred yards. They blew the mines the day before yesterday. Today they are trucking up fencing material and digging new postholes." Dave carried on with his briefing. Eleventh Cavalry intelligence estimated that the *Grenztruppen*—the *Grepos*—would take from a week to ten days to erect the new wire-mesh fence with improved S-70 mines affixed to alternate fence posts. These mines fired TNT and shrapnel laterally along the fence whenever someone touched a wire strand. Right now, however, the three-hundred-yard stretch stood open. Fortunately the nearest dog run was a mile north. Also, this area stood midway between watchtowers. Last night and the night before, searchlights had raked the area every half hour from seven p.m. to five a.m. An East German foot patrol of two border guards had passed through the open area once every ninety minutes, an armored truck every four hours.

"You add it all up, Pop," concluded Dave, "and I figure a defector from the DDR has about a fifty-fifty chance of making it."

An enlisted man knocked; he brought word that the captain

was ready to meet Dave's father. The door to Captain Orville McCutcheon's office bore the self-mocking legend SANCTUM SANCTORUM. The captain wore spectacles and, except for his closely trimmed hair, might have been a young college professor. He liked to emphasize informality of command, "free" staff brainstorming, and combat readiness. He stressed all three as he chatted with the Simmonses about the duties of the air troop.

"We're here to keep a sharp eye on the Germans across the border and to absorb the first shock when and if the Russians attack. Of course, we're alert at any moment to handle problems arising from IBCs. My men—"

"What's an IBC?"

"Pardon me, Mr. Simmons. Army terminology. Illegal border crosser, anyone coming to our side at other than control stations."

"Illegal by the DDR's definition or by ours?"

"Illegal, even deadly, on the other side," said the captain. "Over here, once an IBC is across the border on West German soil, we give them all the help we can. That includes returning the fire if DDR troops shoot across the line. That's happened—not often, but we have to be ready."

After chatting with the captain for a few more minutes, the Simmonses said their good-bys and walked across the highway to the Europa, the small, neat hotel where Mike had taken a room. There he and his son continued their talk over a dinner of *Kohlroulade*—ground meat in cabbage leaves—a salad, and a rich, creamy cake with the coffee.

"I gather you don't like the Wall any better than I do, or you wouldn't be here." Dave toyed with his demitasse.

"I'm beginning to hate that Wall, Dave. It's becoming an obsession with me."

"Welcome to the club. It's not an obsession with me, but I sure hate it, and until somebody threatens me with a court-martial, I'm going to do what I can to crack it. . . . Only, just to be on the safe side, let's keep this try between us, huh?"

"Sold." Mike eased back in the armchair. "You'd think our policy would be to help as many people as possible get out of East Germany."

Crossing in Berlin

"Not really. The West likes to make propaganda out of the Wall, but I know a Brit named Spider Butler who—"

"Oh. A friend gave me his name as a man who might possibly help. British Frontier Service in Helmstedt?"

"That's the guy. He's famous on both sides. Worked the border for almost thirty years. He's convinced everybody's secretly happy with the Wall. For one thing, it's good insurance against a reunited Germany." Dave pushed away from the table. "Well, let's look at the spot where our IBC will come through . . . we hope."

Dave drove his dark blue secondhand Opel cautiously in the moonless night. Patches of thin ice clung to the highway, which looped past bare fields and clusters of white cement-block houses with red tile roofs. Many of the houses were already dark, though it was only eight thirty.

After a drive of perhaps twenty miles, Dave pulled off on a dirt road, halted the car, and switched off the headlights. Ahead of them stretched a narrow valley between low, sloping hills. Dave said, "We've got about a quarter-mile walk to the border."

The cold air nipped at their faces and hands. Mike drew the sheepskin collar of his jacket about his ears as they walked along the road in silence, Dave carrying a bulky instrument of some kind. Several lights shimmered in the distance.

"That's Melpers, over in East Germany," said Dave in a low voice. "Village of a dozen houses. Only screened Party people allowed to live there."

Several hundred yards from the car they came to the debris of an abandoned farmhouse. Dave led his father behind the ruins.

"This will be our station the night your IBC comes across."

"Please, Dave. IBC sounds as inhuman as the Wall. Her name's Gisela."

"Sorry, Pop. I use army lingo without thinking." He took the instrument he carried out of its case. "This is an ambient light scope. On a dark night, you can make out a human figure at five hundred meters. Here, try it."

Mike stood at a corner of the farmhouse and peered to the east through the scope. In ghostly perspective he saw the blurred outline of the fence to the right and to the left, with a long gap between. Some distance to the east he could make out a secondary fence, also with a large opening. As he searched with the scope that turned darkness into a kind of witches' twilight, he saw movement. Two figures. He handed the scope to Dave.

"That's the American patrol from Alpha—our observation post. They walk three miles south, then back again. Look, the middle of that creek over there is the frontier. That is your crossing. Now, let's get back to the car. We shouldn't hang around here."

In the warmth of the Opel, Dave talked steadily as they drove back to Fulda. The overcast parted to expose a few stars and occasionally a sliver of moon.

"I looked up the moon tables." Dave had taken full command of the operation. "No moon next Tuesday night. Can you get word to Gisela in time for her to cross then?"

"I'll try. It's awkward to reach her."

"Well, Wednesday and Thursday are alternates, but no later. By Friday they'll start wiring those new S-70s that can blow you as full of holes as Swiss cheese."

Dave outlined his escape plan with military precision as he steered the Opel over the winding highway to Fulda. He scheduled the crossing for seven fifteen p.m., midway between searchlight sweeps. Gisela should hide in the woods that covered a ravine on the East German side. Dave would signal twice with a flashlight at exactly seven fifteen, whereupon Gisela should emerge from the ravine and crawl on her stomach toward the stream that marked the border. As soon as she began her crawl on the flat ground, Dave would hurry forward to cover her with an automatic rifle. Gisela should not get to her feet until she was well past the boundary brook. Safely into West German territory, she would run with Dave for the protection of the tumbledown farmhouse.

Under no conditions should Gisela leave the wooded part of the ravine until she saw the flashlight signal. If a mishap occurred during her crossing, she should use her judgment in choosing whether to crawl back, or stand up and make a run for it.

Dave would supply a detailed topographical map of the area. "The big question," he said, "is how she's going to get to that ravine. We've heard that often anybody moving within five kilometers of the border, even with a pass, gets questioned."

Dave came up to his father's hotel room to continue the planning. He wanted everything precisely clear, nothing left vague or subject to chance. Mike would fly to Berlin tomorrow, cross to East Germany with his boxful of elevator parts, and try to contact Gisela at once. As soon as she committed herself to a night, preferably Tuesday, Mike should return to Fulda. Dave would try to contact Spider Butler for help on the operation.

Mike grinned. "Sounds fine to me. You're the commander."

Dave shook his father's hand. "Until Tuesday, Pop. And listen. I'm awful glad we're in this together. Really." Dave's shy smile, so at odds with that firm military jawline, seemed to hover in the room after he left. Mike undressed and eased into bed.

Three hours later he awoke with a start, his heart pounding, his forehead damp with sweat. Somewhere behind brooding walls he heard the methodical tread of terror, those hollow steps that stalked his nights. Not until the window took on the first pallor of dawn did the childhood trauma disappear and permit him to fall into a fitful sleep.

Two DAYS later Michael Simmons joined the quiet, orderly line at the cultural events counter in Leipzig's *Information Zentrum*, where Ulli Beitz sold tickets for the theater, concerts, and special attractions.

As he drew nearer the marble counter, Mike saw that Gisela's friend was a somewhat harried woman of perhaps thirty, with a drifting smile and a lush tumble of black hair. As she looked up, she brushed away a strand with the back of her hand.

"Have you tickets for Herr Simmons?" He stressed his name.

"Interhotel Astoria?" She appraised him with new awareness.

"Yes. Room three eight four."

"Ein Moment, bitte."

She left her counter, disappeared to the rear. Several minutes passed before she returned and handed him a slip of paper, fixing her eyes on his with a look of deep intensity.

Mike did not open the envelope until he was inside the hotel construction shack. Ulli's message read: "I will try to reach her. Be in your room at the Astoria at 1400 today."

That gave him four hours to handle replacement of the doorlock assembly. He rounded up two men and settled down to work on number four shaft. After he had completed the job, he visited briefly with Sven Alsten and told him that he would return in a week or so for final trials of the equipment. He reached his hotel room with time to spare.

The phone rang a few seconds after two o'clock.

"Herr Simmons?" Ulli's voice.

"Speaking."

"Your theater party will meet tonight at the same place," she said in slow, measured German. "Eight o'clock." She hung up.

The afternoon dragged despite the sunny weather and a temperature that reached almost springtime levels. Mike changed into his exercise suit and running shoes and ran under the Platz der Republik, past the park on Goethestrasse, and around the opera house. He returned for a shower and a light supper, then spent an hour going over the topographical map Dave had provided.

The minutes crept forward, and at last, shortly before eight, he set out for Ulli's flat. As he prepared to turn from Brühl into Hainstrasse, Mike noticed a man loitering before the display window of a big department store. The man's carriage, a certain roll of the shoulders, touched a memory button. Where had he seen that silhouette before? As Mike looked, the man turned his back, ostensibly to inspect the display window.

Instead of rounding into Ulli's street, Mike walked to the Kleines Joachimsthal, an ancient, moldering passageway that cut through the block, back to Hainstrasse. There he glanced about and, seeing no one, hurried to the number Ten courtyard entrance. The door to the apartment building had been left unlocked. He closed it behind him and heard the lock click. As he mounted the winding stairway, he noticed the beating of his heart. The old steps seemed to creak far more than during his first visit. He rapped softly at apartment 31.

Almost at once the door cracked open a few inches, then swung wide. In the shaft of light Gisela looked as radiant as she had in the Astoria lobby the night he wore the brown turtleneck. They hurried into each other's arms. Gisela closed the door with a flick of her heel. Their kiss had the fever of urgency.

"I missed you, *mi amor*," he said.

"Oh, Miguel, I wanted you so much." She wore a gray skirt and a blouse the color of jonquils.

"Were you questioned by anyone?" He must know at once.

"No. Why do you ask?" She frowned.

He sketched the scene in the currency control room at Checkpoint Charlie with Frau Müller.

"Oh, but I know her. Yes, yes. Lotte Müller and I were schoolmates in Dresden. I saw her last year in Berlin and we talked of old times." She scowled. "But it's very, very bad that they know you and I are acquainted." Taking his hand, she led him to the brocaded chairs by the flimsy coffee table.

"I've tried to guess who reported on us. Perhaps Frau Gotsche at the Astoria desk."

"Or that Culture Ministry woman at dinner. You see now how it is here, Miguel? . . . But tell me your good news. You have good news. I can feel it."

"Yes, but first some bad news, as they say in the jokes." He told her of the man who, he thought, had followed him tonight.

She stood up and switched off the floor lamp. "Are you sure he didn't see you come in here?" At the window she lifted the edge of the fully drawn blind and peered into the dimly lit street.

"I think I ducked him, but I can't be positive."

Several minutes passed before she switched on the light and seated herself again. "We must not be seen together now until we meet on what we over here call the sunny side. . . . We must act fast. I feel there isn't much time left."

"Is Tuesday night fast enough?" he asked.

She brightened at once. "Miguel, tell me. Where? How?"

"They're repairing the fence about a hundred and fifty kilometers southwest of here." He pulled out the topographical map. "Look. It's a little south of a direct line between Meiningen on this side and Fulda on the other."

He spread the map on the floor and they knelt beside it. "The red dot marks the gap," said Mike. He described his nighttime inspection but omitted any mention of Dave.

Gisela used the magnifying glass to study the map. "I'm not sure my pass extends that far," she said. "Kaltennordheim, where my sister, Frauke, lives, is here"—she pointed and measured on the map. "That's a few kilometers. But I'll manage somehow. I can always plead being lost if I'm caught. . . . I hope."

Mike supplied her with details of the operation. She must be in the woods of the sloping ravine a few minutes after seven o'clock Tuesday night. The flashlight across the border would wink twice, precisely at seven fifteen, if nothing appeared to interfere with a crossing. On that signal she should walk down the ravine and begin crawling as soon as she reached flat, unshielded ground. He briefed her on the location of the stream, the tumbledown farmhouse, and the watchtowers and dog runs.

They went over the plan for the ten minutes on Tuesday night until Gisela's mind could recall it like a diagram on a computer screen. "My big problem will be to reach the ravine," she said. "Frauke's husband, Dr. Dieter Augstein, travels a great deal on government missions, and right now he's in Cuba for a month. Maybe Frauke will let me 'steal' their car. . . . Oh, there's so much to figure out."

They talked escape until they were weary. At last Gisela folded the map back into its waterproof cover. She fetched two glasses of vodka from Ulli's closet-size kitchen, and they toasted the venture ahead. They sat on the floor, sipping the strong liquor and listening to the music of Bach. Then, before they knew it, they were talking about themselves.

"I have had you constantly in mind these last few days," she said. "A woman, I think, could live happily with you. But then, perhaps it's my fantasy at work."

"Would you like to know my fantasies about you?"

"Please."

"You're strong and determined. You're lovely. You can charm. And I love the way you smell." He sniffed at her throat. They laughed. "Smart, sensitive, and intelligent too. A taste for elegance. In the West you would wear the latest fashions."

"Oh, my." She glowed. "No negative qualities?"

"Germanic ones. I think you can be demanding, commanding, brusque at times, superorderly."

"And sometimes I lie when I'm afraid the truth would spoil my plans." She looked into his eyes. "And now you."

She said she thought he was a man who had known many women but loved few. He went along smoothly, not wanting to hurt people's feelings, but he had a temper, she guessed. She thought he was about forty-seven years old.

"No," he corrected. "Fifty-three."

She cocked her head, reflecting. "That will be all right."

He leaned over and kissed her forehead. Her remark, for the first time, implied a future. "I have a dark side, Gisela."

"I don't believe it. What could it be?"

"Sometimes I'm terrified at night. I wake up with the shakes." He began hesitantly; he had never confided his night terrors to anyone. Why he now wanted to tell Gisela, he was not sure. At any rate, he talked without restraint, telling her of the childhood punishments and the nightmares with which he had lived ever since, of the fears that ravaged his sleep. "And now you know what none of my friends do," he finished. He felt embarrassed and wary. Women admired strength and shied from weakness. Would Gisela think the less of him now?

"How awful, Miguel." She reached out and stroked his face. "I feel sorry for you. You need your rest, *mi amor*." To his delight, she too was now using the Spanish endearment. He felt easier. Her sympathy carried no overtones of diminished esteem.

Gisela fetched the vodka bottle and refilled their glasses.

"You know I might not make it across, Miguel."

"My expert believes you have a fifty-fifty chance."

"I've got to do it. For Otto Kleist, but for myself too." She reached into a pocket of her skirt and withdrew a bulging envelope. "I've written down much of what I can remember of Otto's calculations. If anything happens to me, you must deliver this to people at this place." She handed him the envelope and a slip of paper. The slip read: "Geophysical Fluid Dynamics Laboratory, Princeton, New Jersey, U.S.A."

"And," she added, "you must make a copy of the contents and deliver that to the ecosystems people at the Marine Biological Laboratory at Woods Hole. In"—she struggled with the old Indian name—"Massachusetts."

He nodded. "You'll get across, Gisela." He shoved the envelope into his pocket. "But if something goes wrong, I'll get this to the right people."

Once more they rehearsed the drill for Tuesday night. Then they talked more of themselves. It was past midnight when he leaned over to her for a good-by kiss. "Until Tuesday night, *mi amor*."

She clung to him. "Yes, *mi amor*. Until Tuesday."

CHAPTER FIVE

DIRTY weather blew in on Tuesday, twirling scraps of paper in dizzy spirals about the streets of Fulda and bringing a chill December drizzle in the afternoon. Lieutenant Dave Simmons welcomed the gusts from the north like old friends. The worse the weather grew, the more buoyant his spirits became. By evening, when he and his father settled down to dinner at an old inn in a small medieval town near the border, Dave fairly rattled with good cheer. With them at the table was Malcolm "Spider" Butler of the British Frontier Service, whom Dave had lured with a veiled telephone call about the night's "adventure." Mike liked Butler the moment they met. Thin, knobby, with rodlike arms and legs, he was a gregarious type, at core a showman.

"You're perhaps thinking they call me Spider because I look like one," he said over steak and beer. "But no. I'm the Spider because I live at the Wall, spinning my web and watching every crack and crevice. I hate the Wall, Michael. But since it provides me with my victuals, I also love it. In admitting that, I am far less hypocritical than our slippery statesmen of the West." He raised a bony finger for emphasis. "Our politicians and businessmen love the Wall, because it keeps the mighty Germans divided. The Jews of the world love it because they think it's at least some small punishment for the gassing of six million Jews by Hitler's

Reich. The West Germans love it because it proves the superiority of their system. And the voters in the Western democracies love it unconsciously because it hides the complexities of international politics and makes everything quite simple. It's a prison wall, and over there are all the bad prisoners and their keepers, and over here are all we good chaps."

The Spider paused for intake of beer. Mike had the impression that Butler delivered his sermon on the Wall to anyone willing to listen. His own thoughts veered to Gisela. Where was she at this moment? Driving with her sister near the border, or sitting in some police station trying to explain what she was doing in the area to skeptical *Vopos*, as the *Volkspolizei*—the people's police—were called.

"Of course, on the other side," the Spider resumed, "the Russians love the Wall because it keeps seventeen million Germans at home working for the glory of dialectical materialism. Several hundred thousand East Germans, the Party nobility, love the Wall for the same reason. In fact, the only people on earth who hate the Wall unreservedly are the poor working types of the DDR who have to live behind it."

Dave saw his opening. "Which brings us, Spider, to tonight's IBC. Our friend will come across, if she comes at all, just"—he studied his wristwatch—"just an hour and fifty minutes from now." Like the Spider, he wore civilian clothes, two sweaters, and a leather jacket to keep him warm inside his rain gear. "Pop," he went on, "Spider thinks the dog-run diversion is a good idea." He bent his head and lowered his voice. "Spider will drive his car to the meadow near the dog run, and then walk about half a mile to the border. He'll start a racket, setting off the dogs, at seven fourteen. Right, Spider?"

"That's it, Davey. Foul night for all of us too, but fine for our lady of the crossing."

Michael wanted to know the distance between Spider Butler's post and the gap in the fence where he and Dave would take their station.

"Just about a mile." Dave sketched a section of the border on the back of a coaster. "We're down here to the south, Pop. That hill near the old farmhouse stands between us and Spider." He ticked off the schedule, made certain all watches jibed to the second, and said they'd meet back at this same inn after Gisela came safely across. Spider would go unarmed, but Dave had an army M-16 in his Opel.

Outside the inn, Dave gave Butler a case enclosing an ambient light scope. "But keep your head down," he reminded. "They've got these things too, you know. . . ."

The two automobiles, each with an easy run to the border, left the inn at six thirty p.m.

Rain pattered on the Opel's roof as Dave headed out of town and onto the winding macadam road. Darkness blanketed the valley and swallowed the hills.

"I let Spider have the old scope," said Dave. "We're going to use the new thermal imagery sight. It'll show people and objects like noontime."

They drove on in silence, and then, before Mike had prepared himself mentally, Dave turned off the highway and switched off his lights. The chill drops fell on their rain gear as they stepped from the car to the muddy road. Mike drew on his gloves. Dave slung the army M-16 across his back, picked up the thermal imagery sight, and the two men set off down the road.

They made their way carefully, trying to avoid puddles and the low, muddy stretches. They could see little, but Mike peered ahead, trying to locate the wooded ravine behind the opening in the frontier fence. He could feel a tightening in his chest and throat. Had Gisela managed to reach the rain-washed gully? Had she been seized by guards?

Dave pulled at his sleeve and they moved off the road, walking through matted weeds and grass and over stretches where mud sucked at their boots. A bulky structure loomed just ahead—the dilapidated farmhouse. When they reached it, Dave pointed to the luminous dial of his wristwatch—7:07. Right on time. The rain fell lightly but steadily, dripping from Mike's chin and funneling off his rain jacket.

Dave took the thermal imagery sight from its case, knelt at the corner of the house, and sighted to the east. Then he handed the

Crossing in Berlin

instrument to his father. Placing the cupped rubber shield against his right eye, Mike sighted across the border, about a hundred yards distant, to the wide, plowed strip where the mines had been exploded a few days ago. He could see the jagged ends of the wire-mesh fence to the left, and to the right some heavy road equipment, a ditch, slanting concrete slabs, and a slope gradually rising to another broken fence beyond. The scene stood out as sharply as if bathed by the ivory light of a full moon.

Mike centered the device on the wooded ravine behind the denuded strip. He gasped. Partially hidden by a tree trunk, low to the ground, was the outline of a crouching human figure. As his eye adjusted to the distance and the eerie light, he could distinguish clothing and the white blur of a face. He was sure it was Gisela, and a wave of tenderness swept over him.

Dave pulled a flashlight from his pocket. He held out his wristwatch so his father could see the dial—7:11. They waited in silence, Mike watching, fascinated, as the greenish second hand swept around the dial—7:14. In the distance a dog barked, and almost at once a great yapping and howling began.

Then, far to their left, they saw a searchlight sweeping back and forth in the direction of the clamoring dogs. The watchtower, Mike knew, was about a mile distant. The area before them, where no fences sealed the border, remained in darkness.

"Now," whispered Dave. He stepped from behind the corner of the farmhouse, aimed his flashlight toward the ground, and blinked it twice. Then he unstrapped his automatic rifle and started walking toward the stream that marked the border. He crouched low, holding the M-16 in both hands as he glided through the rain.

Through the night-sighting instrument Mike again spotted the figure he assumed to be Gisela. She had moved to the base of the wooded gully. As he watched, she flopped to her belly and began squirming toward the border, which lay perhaps a hundred yards ahead of her. On the fringe of Mike's sighting device, bathed in that peculiar ivory light, Dave approached the stream.

Gisela seemed to crawl as slowly as a snail. Her pace exasperated Mike. Hurry, woman. Faster, please, faster, faster. In the distance the dogs howled like a wild pack. Dave reached the stream, dropped prone on the soaked ground.

And then, in the fraction of a second, the world suddenly blazed like noonday. Intense light flooded the entire area of repairs, throwing every rock and furrow, all the road equipment and piles of fencing into bold relief. Searchlights from the concrete watchtower drilled the ground.

Mike dropped the sighting instrument as Gisela reared up like some trapped wild creature. She wore, oddly, a blue stocking cap, and beneath it her features seemed to freeze in a look of panic. In the garish light, she could have been a mime with a face painted white as eggshells.

Her sculpted immobility lasted only an instant. She whipped around and began crawling back to the shelter of the ravine.

"Back!" Mike's needless shout leaped involuntarily from his throat as he jumped up and ran toward the border.

Then came a sound of horror, an efficient, rhythmic clatter of steel. Mud spurted across the width of the strip, scores of miniature geysers erupting from the soaked earth in ragged lines. A lament of bullets whined through the rain.

Had Gisela been hit? Mike could not tell. She reached the protection of the ravine, then struggled to her feet—slowly, Mike thought. She appeared to clutch at her lower leg as she ran, half staggering past rocks and trees. A second figure seemed to materialize from the woods. Had another person joined her? Mike could not be sure. Almost at once Gisela was lost to sight, swallowed by the dark mouth of the night.

To the north, on the paved roadway that ran the length of the frontier, appeared the source of the machine-gun fire: an East German armored troop carrier. As it rolled toward the break in the fence, it sprayed a wide swath of bullets on the East German side, but did not fire across the border.

"Bastards!" Dave Simmons swung his M-16 automatic rifle to the left and pulled off a burst that splattered the armored carrier like a clanging of dishpans.

"No! Dave, don't!" Mike ran to his son.

The firing in the carrier stopped. From a slit in the vehicle a smaller searchlight swept across the border and probed the valley. Father and son dropped to the ground a few yards west of the brook that divided the two Germanys.

Dave began crawling swiftly away. Mike followed. A rifle burst from the carrier chopped at the path near them. Another winged into the furrowed field. By the time the probing light neared the two Americans, they had squirmed behind a mound some fifteen or twenty yards back of the border.

The dazzling illumination continued for perhaps five minutes, which seemed to Mike like an hour. Then all lights went off and the rain-drenched darkness engulfed the frontier once more.

But now a medley of noises filled the night. Far off the angry dogs still barked. Nearer could be heard shouted commands, the grinding of gears, and the hum of wet tires. Close at hand, on this side of the border, Mike heard people running toward them.

"West Germans—the border patrol," Dave said. He sat up and brushed mud from his rain gear. "Did she get away?"

"I think so." But could she possibly elude the DDR guards?

The two-man West German patrol had slowed to a walk. The soldiers were only a few yards away.

"As for us, Pop," said Dave, "we're in trouble."

FEEBLE morning sunlight scratched at the frosty windowpanes of air troop headquarters as Mike Simmons, seated with his son before the tidy desk of Captain Orville McCutcheon, seethed with suppressed anger. This cool, factual review of last night's incident seemed ridiculously divorced from the demonic reality: men employed to track and kill other human beings had fired at an unarmed woman merely because she wanted to move across a few yards of the earth's surface.

"What we want to avoid is a written reprimand going into Dave's record," said Captain McCutcheon. "Your son, Mr. Simmons, is one of our finest young officers."

Mike listened with but one ear. At this moment Gisela might be lying somewhere gravely wounded. Had she escaped the *Grepos* and their raking fire? That question had haunted him since the West Germans had apprehended them last night. The border patrol, after learning of Dave's military status, had "escorted" the Simmonses to Alpha, the American observation post, where they had been interrogated by an S-2 officer.

"Mr. Simmons," asked McCutcheon, "when you visited here last week, were you making plans for your IBC?"

The hated initials lit a fast fuse. "Damn it, Captain, do we have to call her an IBC? She's a human being who put her life on the line last night. She might be dead right now, for all we know."

The explosion shook the captain. McCutcheon shifted uneasily in his chair, a puzzled look on his face. "I know how you must feel. We're all sorry the lady failed to make it across. But unfortunately we must put our feelings aside and deal with the situation as it exists on this side of the border. I'm going to have to report particulars of this IB—pardon—crossing incident to the colonel, and I don't want that report to involve Lieutenant Simmons in an American civilian attempt to bring an East German national across the border." McCutcheon tapped a pencil on his desk blotter.

"Is it against regulations for an officer to help someone defect to our side?" Mike tried to cap his anger.

"It's certainly against policy. The mission of this regiment is to help defend Western Europe's freedom and keep the Warsaw Pact forces on their side of the border. We are decidedly not in the business of spiriting people across the frontier."

Mike wanted to retort that the best way to defend freedom was to encourage it in all places, including frontiers, but a glance at Dave reminded him that his own mission this morning was to help get his son off the army's hook.

McCutcheon fingered a sheet of paper on his desk. "Read one way, this S-2 interrogation report might indicate that an officer plotted with his civilian father to bring an East German national across to West German soil." The captain eyed the pair sitting in front of him. "But I don't think that's the way it happened at all. I think that Lieutenant Simmons escorted his father to the Parrot's Beak sector to show him how the death strip's elaborate weaponry operates at night. While there, they witnessed the attempted shooting of a possible defector. When part of the volley sprayed

Crossing in Berlin

West German territory, Lieutenant Simmons returned the fire with his M-16 rifle, which he'd taken along as a routine precaution." McCutcheon pushed the interrogation report aside. "I take it you don't disagree with any of that, Dave?"

"Thank you, sir," said Dave. "I appreciate it."

"The fact that another West German patrol encountered Spider Butler of the British Frontier Service only a mile away . . ." McCutcheon paused for dramatic effect. "I take it that's just another coincidence in a rather unusual night."

"Thanks again, sir." Dave looked quite solemn.

McCutcheon walked father and son to his office door and laid his hand on Mike's arm. "I'm really sorry, sir. Believe me, if she'd made it, I'd have brought champagne to the celebration."

The Simmonses parted at the gateway guardhouse.

"I don't know what to say, Pop. I know the shooting was an awful thing for you." Dave hesitated. Emotional intimacy was an unmapped battlefield for him. "I hope she gets home safely and that she'll try again someday. . . . I'd like to meet her."

"I must get back to Leipzig. I have to know what happened."

Dave made a fist and struck it lightly against his father's arm. "Take it easy over there, will you?"

They shook hands as they said good-by, and Mike could feel moisture in his eyes as he turned away.

He caught the *Hispania* express to Frankfurt am Main, only an hour from Fulda, and flew from there to West Berlin, arriving in late afternoon. He spent the travel time thinking of ways to get news of Gisela should the Ulli Beitz channel fail. He would have to proceed with great caution. If the authorities held Gisela, if she were wounded or—yes, face it—dead, then her friends were already suspect.

Amid his speculation, he became aware of the strength of his feeling for her. He knew that for the rest of his life he would carry in his mind a painful image of Gisela caught in the brutal glare of searchlights and rearing up, her rain-streaked face frozen in panic, that blue stocking cap looking so poignantly childlike. He could tolerate the memory if Gisela survived uninjured. The sharing of that grotesque scene would bond them in ways that no lovers' interlude could ever match. But if she should die, her look of terror under that sudden flash of searchlights would enter the museum of fears that tormented his nights.

In West Berlin, Mike placed some belongings in the extra suitcase he now kept at his hotel. He also put in papers that he did not wish to take to East Germany—Gisela's letter to the American scientists and a copy of their elevator-parts code; a second copy went in his wallet. Then he called Walter Delaney, ostensibly to let the company's Berlin office know he would give the Leipzig elevators a final inspection, but actually to tell Delaney that once again he would pass behind the Wall. "If I'm not back in a week, send out a search party, will you?"

"No problem. I'll just tell the SSD to watch out for a love-starved American on the prowl for Communist women." Delaney paused, then resumed without banter. "How's your project, Mike? Did you ever contact those professional escape artists whose names I gave you?"

"No. We're trying another route. I'd level with you, but a phone line's not the place."

"No need. I get the picture. If you're not back in seven days, I'll flash the American embassy over there."

MIKE's return to Leipzig was less than auspicious. The Astoria was filled to capacity and the first accommodations would not become available until midnight, when some circus performers from Budapest checked out. Mike would have to remake the bed himself because the chambermaids would have gone home.

He tried to find Sven Alsten, but the Swede was out of town until the next day. Mike dawdled over dinner, then wandered the empty streets. When he finally got to bed, near one o'clock, he dozed fitfully, his night torn by ragged dreams.

In the morning he reached Ulli Beitz's spot at the *Information Zentrum* only a few seconds after the center opened. Mike spoke his code piece about tickets for Herr Simmons, gave his Astoria room number, and added a phrase denoting urgency. All right, Ulli said, she would call as soon as she learned anything.

His room phone rang an hour later. "Herr Simmons?" Ulli's

tone forecast bad news. She was sorry, she said, but the theater would be impossible. The other party had gone on vacation to visit a sister. When would she return? Ulli did not know. When Mike pressed, she pleaded lack of time, many customers in line, you know. But Mike insisted. Please, he begged her, let him come to the Hainstrasse flat this evening. Certainly Gisela could be contacted somehow. Ulli sighed. All right, she said, seven o'clock at the apartment.

At the Interhotel construction site, Mike found Sven Alsten working over a sheaf of papers in the headquarters shack.

"Michael Simmons himself." The Swede shook his head. "Do you know I'm stuck with one of these endless official forms because of you and your elevator doors? Werner Lanz—Herr Brigade Leader—reported your little debate, shall we call it, to his superiors, so now the Ministry of State Security wants a full account of the door-lock assembly situation."

"Why?"

Alsten spread his palms in a gesture of futility. "Who knows? Bureaucratic overkill, the curse of the working classes." He yawned and stretched, then bent over his papers once more.

Mike spent most of the day checking his elevators. When he left the construction site in late afternoon, he felt that he was being followed. He tested his hunch by stepping into the recessed entrance to a bakery. He glanced behind in time to see a man in a clay-colored raincoat halt to study a shopwindow.

Mike walked on to his hotel, noting as he ducked under the great flapping curtain in the doorway that his follower was also heading toward the Astoria. Somehow, he vowed, he would outwit the man and negotiate the few blocks to Ulli's apartment without being followed. He spent the next hour in his room.

Emerging from the hotel at dusk, Mike noted that his tracker paced the sidewalk near the corner. When the man saw Mike, he glanced at his wristwatch, then looked up and down the street, as if searching for someone late for an appointment.

A moment later the stakeout specialist stared in confusion. Clad in a dark blue exercise suit and wearing cushion-soled running shoes and a wide grin, his quarry passed him at a run, crossed the street against the red light, dodged a truck and a Wartburg sedan, and lost himself in a crowd at the Platz der Republik.

When Mike had assured himself that he had lost his tracker, he slowed to a jog and headed up Goethestrasse past a park and small lagoon. Alternating between a jog and a walk, he returned to Leipzig's mid-city area and stopped at a sidewalk stand for a bratwurst on a bun.

He turned into Hainstrasse a few minutes before seven and reached Ulli's courtyard precisely on time. Ulli, apparently having heard his footsteps on the stairs, opened her door before he had a chance to knock. Mike could see that she disliked this visit. She had a strained, apprehensive air, fussed unduly with her great black cloud of hair, and forced a smile. The radio throbbed with a big-band number from a long-ago decade.

They sat down, and Mike accepted a cup of tea with thanks. "I will hurry," he said in his fumbling German. "I know this is inconvenient for you."

"People misunderstand." She turned up the radio's volume.

"I must get in touch with Gisela." He leaned close to Ulli. "And I have to leave soon."

She enunciated slowly in German: "Gisela is at her sister's and will not return until next week."

Gisela alive! The heaviness deep inside him began to dissolve. "She isn't sick, is she?"

"*Nee*. But sad to say, she had an accident that will confine her to her sister's house in Kaltennordheim."

"A bad accident?"

"I don't think so. A bruise, as I understand it. She stumbled and fell while walking."

With a machine gun spitting metal all around her, he added silently. "May I give you a message to read to her?"

"Naturally."

Mike extracted their code from his wallet and constructed a brief message in Spanish on paper provided by Ulli: "Please contact me as soon as possible through Ulli or, if I've returned to the other side, through Sven Alsten."

He slipped the code back in his wallet and handed the message to Ulli. "Lovers' secret talk," he explained. He rose to leave. "Please add my love when you read it to her."

"Naturally." Now, in parting, came a sweet, melancholy smile. Ulli, he saw, was relieved to see him go.

The news about Gisela had given him a powerful lift. In the street, he soon found himself running at a fast clip, the spongy soles buoying his every step. How great to feel the pulse of life and to know that Gisela also lived, apparently outside the clutches of soldiers or agents of the state.

He ran all the way to the Astoria and pulled up at the entrance, panting happily. He reached out to part the woolen drapery that shielded the doorway.

Hands gripped his arms. Two men emerged from the shadows, one on each side of him.

"Herr Simmons, you are required for questioning." The hands on his arms turned him firmly toward the street.

"I must go to my room to change." He tried to draw back.

"That will not be necessary."

"I demand to be allowed to contact the American embassy."

"That will not be possible." The hands on his arms propelled him forward to a waiting limousine, a Russian Zil, which had halted in front of the hotel. A passing couple, arm in arm, gaped for a moment, then hurried away.

CHAPTER SIX

SILENCE, East Germany's dark sleeve of enterprise, wrapped the automobile as the two abductors half lifted, half shoved Mike onto the rear seat. They sandwiched him between them and fitted his eyes with sunglasses, the lenses of which were painted black, allowing him only the narrowest of peripheral vision. The instant he was seated in the center, the limousine rolled away from the curb and accelerated swiftly. It then angled to the right into a main thoroughfare that led to the autobahn to Berlin.

Mike turned to the man on his left. "Where are you taking me?"

"No questions. You will remain silent."

This abduction must mean, of course, that Gisela too had been

or soon would be apprehended. How had agents of the state managed to link them to an escape plan? Retracing his movements of the last ten days, Mike asked himself where he had slipped.

He felt no fear. Instead, indignation simmered, then slowly swelled into anger. "I demand to be allowed to call the American ambassador!" The words exploded from him.

The man on his right turned slightly. "One more word out of you and you'll be gagged," he said dryly.

An eerie hush settled on the car. Mike wondered which state security office or prison in East Berlin awaited him and what kind of inquisitor would question him.

Then he remembered. That code in elevator jargon!

He shoved his right hand into the front pocket of his exercise jacket, found his wallet, explored with his forefinger until he felt the slip of paper, then slowly maneuvered it out. He crumpled the paper into a small ball. Coughing loudly several times, he clapped his hand to his mouth as if to shield his seatmates, and popped in the paper ball. He felt the incriminating code slide down his throat, no more awkwardly than a vitamin pill.

Out of the corners of his eyes Mike saw both men turn toward him. He coughed again and pointed to his throat apologetically. He felt a spurt of confidence at having outwitted the SSD. But later his confidence began to wane as the car rolled through the outlying streets of East Berlin, where streetlamps cast pale yellow pools, and monotonous apartment blocks shouldered the night sky. Via his slit of side vision, Mike noted the city's heavy, brooding mien, and his spirits sank.

They rolled to a stop in the courtyard of a massive stone building, and his two companions bundled him into a dimly lit vestibule. A clerk in a frayed cardigan wrote down Mike's name, occupation, age, nationality, and home address. He was then ordered to turn his pockets inside out. The agents placed the wallet and passport on the counter and motioned to Mike to unstrap his wristwatch. The clerk methodically counted the money in the wallet before logging the three articles in a ledger, and handed Mike a receipt. Not a word had been spoken.

The guards now turned him over in silence to a dour woman

with a complexion the color of ashes. She led Mike down a long corridor that smelled of disinfectant; opened a door, ushered him inside, and then closed the door behind him.

The room was fairly large. It had totally bare walls painted a neutral aging green, and one barred window, the bottom half of which was painted black. An overhead globe gave off a feeble light. A straight-backed wooden chair in the middle of the room faced a kitchen-size metal table on which rested a gooseneck desk lamp. Behind the table stood a worn leather swivel chair. He was in an interrogation room.

Mike seated himself in the wooden chair and waited. And waited. Sharp images fastened on his mind.... A basement room, a stool, four bare walls plastered a dingy white, a five-year-old's dungeon of punishment.... And still he waited. He guessed that he had passed an hour here alone. The silence unnerved him.

He began to tire, and he had just considered the possibility of lying down on the floor when the door opened and in walked a slight, dapper man carrying an armload of what looked like office supplies. He shot a perfunctory smile at Mike, seated himself at the table, and turned on the lamp.

The newcomer was ruddy, sandy-haired, had a trim mustache, and wore a dark blue suit. An SED Party button glinted on his lapel. Without looking up, he began arranging his equipment. He carefully placed three ball-point pens, an inking pad, a rubber stamp, and a watch to his right, lining them up like the knives and spoons of a table setting. In the center he placed a thick pad of lined paper. To the left he stationed a pocket calculator, a small calendar, and a German-English dictionary. Finally, in front of the pad he put down a tape recorder and Mike's passport and wallet.

He switched on the tape recorder. "Well, Herr Simmons, let us begin." He lifted one of the pens.

"I demand my right to call the American ambassador."

"Ah. Wishes to see the U.S.A. ambassador." He jotted down the request. Then he took up Mike's passport. "Well, we have here on this 10 December, Herr Michael Simmons, U.S.A. passport number K 259 1258. Is that correct?"

Mike tried again. "I demand to see the American ambassador."

The official laid down pen and passport and folded his hands neatly on the pad. "It will not be productive to repeat that request, Herr Simmons. I am not authorized to grant any request of yours except to accompany you to the toilet in case of need." He smiled, not unpleasantly. "Well, then, I shall proceed. Please answer my questions."

He opened the passport again. "Born 5 May 1928?"

"Yes."

"Born Omaha, Nebraska, U.S.A.?"

"Yes."

It took the East German interrogator fully two hours to amass required data on Michael Simmons' vital statistics, schooling, career, relatives, religion, as well as his movements within the DDR. At last he placed his palms on the table and leaned back with a proud expression. "Well, I think that completes our assignment." He rose, switched off the desk lamp, bowed to Mike, and gathered up his supplies.

He had reached the door when Mike protested. "Hey, I need to use the toilet."

"That will be taken care of."

The female guard with the ashen complexion made good the promise within a few minutes. She led Mike down the corridor to a closet-size room, which held a toilet. She waited outside, then escorted him silently back to the interrogation chamber.

Again he waited. And waited. Fatigue welled up, demanding surrender. After nodding off several times in the chair, he lay down on the floor and tried to sleep. But he wore only the cotton exercise suit, and a cool draft flowing over the worn carpet disturbed him. He coiled into a fetal position for warmth and finally drifted into a troubled slumber.

"Get up!"

Mike came awake with a start, found himself blinking into a strong beam of light. The gooseneck desk lamp had been twisted so that its bulb shone down on him. He rubbed his eyes, stretched, and slowly raised himself.

"Sit in the chair and face this desk."

When his eyes became accustomed to the light, Mike saw that the owner of the voice was a powerfully built man with heavy shoulders, a bull neck, and brush-cut blond hair.

Like his predecessor, this examiner came equipped with abundant supplies, Mike's passport and wallet among them, which he dumped on the desk like refuse. Then he took a small tape recorder from his pocket and set it up with the microphone adjusted toward Mike. He turned on the machine. "Herr Simmons, I will question you with respect to suspected violation of the laws of the Deutsche Demokratische Republik." He spoke a serviceable if guttural English. "The rules of your interrogation are as follows. One. You will answer all questions. Two. You will not pose questions to the examiner without permission. Three. You will retain an alert posture during interrogation. Do you wish to make a statement before we begin?"

"Yes. I demand my right to call the American ambassador."

"Request denied. You have no such right here."

"Of what am I accused?"

"Not in order. If you ask that again, you will be penalized."

"What kind of penalty?"

"Not in order!" The sudden shout astonished Mike. The interrogator thrust his huge head forward and glared. "You will not ask questions here. I repeat. No questions." Now his shout became a roar. "Is that understood?"

Mike bobbed his head.

"Answer me!"

"Yes." Mike glared back.

"And that kind of belligerent attitude will get you nowhere. Believe me, if you do not cooperate here, you are lost."

Quickly the man rapped out a series of biographical questions that went over ground already covered by his predecessor. Then he stopped. Silence flooded the bare room.

"When did you first go to work for the Central Intelligence Agency?" The question came like a shot from ambush.

"What?" Mike was prepared for almost any opening but this.

"No questions!" Another roar. "Answer me. Now."

"I've never worked for the CIA."

"We'll nail that lie before we finish. . . . Do you know Inge Herschel?"

"No."

"Do not lie. We have information that you met Inge Herschel at dinner in the Astoria dining room in Leipzig the night of Thursday, 26 November."

"Oh. If she works for the Ministry of Culture, yes, I did meet her, but I didn't remember her name."

"Do you know Gisela Steinbrecher?"

"Yes." Oh, God. Now it would start. He felt his heart pounding.

"Where and when did you meet her?"

"At the same gathering at the Astoria."

"What does Frau Steinbrecher do?"

"I understand she's an editor of publications at the Technical University in Dresden."

"Did you ever meet Frau Steinbrecher after that?"

"No." Had he replied too quickly? "Well, I chatted with her the next evening in the lobby. That's all."

"What does Sally Simmons do?"

"I refuse to discuss my daughter."

"How long has she worked for the CIA?"

"Same answer."

"What does David Simmons do?"

"I refuse to discuss my son."

"Is it not true that he is with an offensive strike force stationed in Fulda?"

"I refuse to discuss my son."

"Why did you visit West Berlin twice within the last week?"

"Damages to our elevator installation. I had to get spare parts quickly."

"Do you know Richard Helms?"

"No."

"You do not know Richard Helms, the former head of the U.S. Central Intelligence Agency?" He almost yelled the question.

"Oh, that Helms." Mike throttled his temper. "I've heard of him. I never met or talked to him. You're trying to trap me."

"This office seeks the truth. Do you know Werner Lanz?"

"Yes. He's a brigade leader—the SED representative on the new Interhotel construction job in Leipzig."

"When did the Todd Elevator cover for your CIA activities begin?"

"I've never had any CIA activities." Did the SSD truly suspect that he worked for the CIA? If that was the thrust of this interrogation, Mike felt confident of emerging unscathed. But he assumed that the CIA inquiries merely served to throw him off guard and that the Gisela escape questions would soon begin to pelt him like hail. He mentally braced himself.

His interrogator pressed forward relentlessly, and Mike's string of denials, noes, and nevers grew monotonously long. The minutes dragged into hours, and he felt his strength waning. At last the interrogator flung a final question, sneered at Mike's denial, and swooped up his utensils, pad, and tape recorder.

"Your examination will resume at nine a.m." The powerfully built man stomped to the door.

"What time is it now?" asked Mike.

In answer, the door slammed.

Moments later it opened again, and the dour matron beckoned to him. They marched down the long green corridor. She opened a door, waited until he entered, then locked it.

The room duplicated the one he had just left, in size, color, and dismal aspect, but instead of chairs and a desk, this room had a lidless toilet bowl in one corner, and an iron cot with a mattress and sheet but no blanket. An unshielded bulb in the ceiling threw harsh light that illuminated the bare room as starkly as the frontier under searchlights. Mike looked everywhere for a switch. There was none. At least twelve feet separated the carpetless floor from the ceiling, and even if he stood on the cot, Mike knew he could not reach the bulb.

Now he became aware that the room was unusually cool and growing colder. There was but one window, located near the ceiling. One of those basement-type windows that swing inward and up, it gaped wide open, fixed by a metal arm. The temperature was near freezing, but he could not reach the window to close it.

Crossing in Berlin

Obviously his inquisitors did not want him to sleep in the few remaining hours before they renewed his examination. This fact became doubly evident when an engine of some kind began pounding below his window.

While he could perhaps manage a sleepless night, Mike wondered how long he could survive the cold without falling ill. He had already begun to shiver, and he slapped his arms and legs in an effort to generate some warmth. He had nothing beneath his flimsy exercise suit save a pair of Jockey shorts.

He knocked on the door. When he heard no response, he beat on it until it threatened to crack. At last he heard the rattle of a key in the lock. When the door swung open, the female guard stood facing him.

"Close the window," he said in German. "I am very cold."

"*Ja, ja.*" She unpenned a rush of words, and after she had gone out and locked the door, he persuaded himself that she had promised to fetch someone to close the window.

He paced back and forth near the door, as far from the window as possible. He felt miserable. The air pouring through the opening grew colder. The engine outside pounded, groaned, and gasped. The light overhead continued to throw its merciless glare and his eyes began to itch. He could understand why a prisoner subjected to many nights of this treatment might go mad or tell his interrogators anything they wanted to hear.

He walked. He paced. He jogged. He beat his arms and slapped at his legs. Hours passed, and when he glanced toward the window while slowing from a jog to a walk, he saw the gray smudge of a new day. He guessed the time at six o'clock. Another three hours to go in this insane freezer.

When finally a key scratched the lock and the door opened, Mike was near exhaustion. He had trudged back and forth, fifteen feet to a lap, his legs growing as heavy as lead, for what seemed like an endless winter.

An elderly gray-haired man beckoned him to follow. The instant Mike stepped into the warm air of the corridor, a tremendous shivering convulsed him. Tears welled up in his eyes. Curiously, he felt grateful to his captors for freeing him from the freezer locker, and he realized he must steel himself lest he make some unnecessary concession.

Mike's guide ushered him into last night's examination room. He stood still for a moment, relishing the warmth. Then he saw that the table held a tray of food, and he pulled up the chair and surveyed his breakfast: lukewarm coffee, a hard-boiled egg, two hard rolls, and a pat of butter. He gulped down the food.

His daylight interrogator did not keep him waiting, arriving moments after Mike finished eating. While this official also toted an armful of supplies, he was radically different from the others. A stout, fatherly sort, with a relaxed manner and easy stride, he smiled at Mike and promptly engaged him in small talk.

"Well, Herr Simmons, you enjoyed your breakfast, I hope." He spoke in English with only traces of a German accent.

"Sure did. After that lousy night."

"A bad night? What went wrong?"

"Wrong!" Mike's temper flared. "The room was freezing cold. They refused to close the window. No heat. No blanket. A bright light in my eyes. And some damn motor pounding away outside."

"Oh, I'm terribly sorry." He seemed genuinely distressed. "I can't understand what happened. Somebody failed his duty."

"Come off it. That was all rigged to soften me up for the next round of questioning."

"I beg to differ, Herr Simmons. We have strict rules here. All those detained for questioning must be treated as guests." He frowned sympathetically. "Well, we must begin our work." He switched on the tape recorder. "Are you comfortable, Herr Simmons?"

Mike sneezed, wiped his nose on the sleeve of his exercise jacket. "Hardly. But I guess I'll manage."

"All right, Herr Simmons. Who is Werner Lanz?"

"I told the man last night. Lanz is the SED representative on the Inter construction site in Leipzig where I installed six Todd elevators."

"You had a dispute with Herr Lanz?"

"Yes."

"Would you please describe what happened?" The man tilted

back in his swivel chair and folded his hands behind his head. "Take your time. Just be thorough, please."

Mike recounted the scene with Lanz in the construction shack as accurately as he could recall it. As he spoke of elevators and their parts, his weariness lifted and he felt reasonably normal for a spell. "So, we both took back what we said, but he did post a notice warning workers not to pry open elevator doors."

"Very good. I think I get the picture." The fatherly interrogator nodded amiably. "Now please tell me in detail exactly how those door-lock assemblies work?"

Mike obliged with another lengthy explanation.

"I take it, Herr Simmons, that we come down to a case of your word against Herr Lanz's. Isn't that correct?"

Mike felt fatigue overtaking him again. "Look," he said. "What's this all about? Lanz and I had an argument. What the hell difference does it make?"

The man leaned forward, somewhat stern now. "Beginning with your first days with the Todd concern, describe your various jobs, including your assignments outside the U.S.A."

This time Mike spent perhaps half an hour on his career biography. Amid sneezes and fits of shivering, he covered his foreign tours and his administrative job in New York.

The interrogator questioned him at length on his possible links to U.S. intelligence agencies, then suddenly swerved back to Werner Lanz and the case of the broken door-lock fixtures.

Noon came and slid into gray afternoon, and still they talked about Werner Lanz, door-lock assemblies, Todd's manufacturing procedures, and the prices of materials. The elderly attendant brought cheese, sausage, bread, and water for him, and even while Mike ate his lunch he was quizzed quietly. By midafternoon, in a haze of fatigue, he could no longer tell truth from falsehood. This man's mild questioning and Mike's mumbled, cloudy responses had the texture of fevered dreams.

Yet deep down rested the belief that this whole ridiculous elevator sequence was a diversion designed to lure him into a false sense of security. Any moment now the questions about the aborted escape of Gisela Steinbrecher would begin, shattering his dreamlike trance and driving him toward a lengthy prison sentence. He sensed that he had lost, but he was beyond caring. If he did not sleep soon, he would collapse.

Mike was about to tell him that he had reached the limits of endurance when the interrogator switched off the tape recorder and slowly gathered up his tools. "I'll be back later. Make yourself as comfortable as you can."

The moment the door closed, Mike slipped to the floor and stretched out on the worn carpet. He surrendered to his exhaustion with a feeling of bliss. His muscles yearned for peace, and within a minute he had fallen into a pit of sleep.

A VOICE called, a hand pressed his shoulder. He opened his eyes to see the fatherly official bending over him. "Time to get up." The voice had a soothing quality.

Mike raised himself, straightened up on weakened legs, rubbed his eyes, and looked about. The man seated himself in the swivel chair and motioned Mike to his old seat. "Are you refreshed?"

"Hardly. I could sleep for a week."

"You'll have the chance." The official smiled. He seemed pleased. "You are being released."

Mike blinked. "You mean right now? Just like that?" He had expected anything but this.

"Yes. I'm afraid, Herr Simmons, a mistake has been made."

"But . . ." What had happened to Gisela? Had she not been seized after all? Mike wanted to leave at once, yet his curiosity demanded satisfaction. "Why did your people pick me up, and why these hours and hours of questioning?"

"I'm sorry." The official raised his palms in a gesture of helplessness. "In all societies miscalculations are made."

"I understand." Mike had no grudge against this man. He had behaved decently. "May I leave now?"

"You may." The man stood up and extended his hand. Mike shook it. "We will drive you back to Leipzig."

Leipzig? . . . No, no. He had a sudden, overpowering desire to quit East Germany immediately. "I would rather be taken to Checkpoint Charlie."

Crossing in Berlin

"But your clothes and other belongings are in Leipzig."

"I'll have them sent. I prefer to leave the DDR tonight." He would cross the border and never come back.

The official led him to the registrar's cage to retrieve his wallet, passport, and wristwatch, then to the dimly lit vestibule, where he turned Mike over to two broad-shouldered young men. He gripped Mike's hand in parting.

"A pleasant journey, Herr Simmons."

CHAPTER SEVEN

AFTER the first euphoric hour following what he vowed was his last crossing from East Germany, Mike had slept for fifteen hours. Awakening in midafternoon in his hotel room, he found himself with a cold and a touch of fever. He spent the next three days in bed, nursing his cold and speculating endlessly on the questions that now absorbed his thoughts. Where and in what danger was Gisela? Why had the *Stasi* arrested and quizzed him at such length only to free him abruptly without charges?

He went over his speculations once again when Walter Delaney came to visit on the evening of the third day. By then the worst of the cold had passed, but Mike remained propped in bed, with fruit juices, aspirin, and magazines cluttering the bedside table.

"I told the New York office you had a little brush with the police over there," Mike's fellow Todd executive reported from the room's lone easy chair. "Nothing much, I said, but I told Jacoby you probably wouldn't want to go back. They're sending over a replacement."

Trusting Delaney thoroughly, Mike told him the story of his arrest and interrogation. "How do you figure it, Walt?" Mike asked when he finished. "The heavy questioning and freezer treatment, then suddenly, oops, pardon us, all a big mistake."

Delaney thrust out his legs. "Maybe they honestly suspected you might be CIA. Why not? You have a good job for cover, you hang around Leipzig for a month, then suddenly make a couple of fast trips west. Also your tail reports you taking suspicious walks at night. Looked at from their viewpoint, it makes sense."

"I suppose so. But what a way to check me out."

"That's the system." Delaney lit a cigarette. "My guess is that you were a pawn in some inside Party fight. Suppose a politburo big shot opposed giving an American company a subcontract on a large hotel with high visibility? And somebody else favored it? So Herr Opposed gets you picked up and passes the word to make you look as bad as possible...."

"I figure if they'd connected me to Gisela's escape attempt, they'd have poured it to me."

"Absolutely. You'd have had a grilling that would have rattled your teeth. As of now, they have no idea of your real connection with Frau Steinbrecher. That's my guess."

"And you think that means she's safe?"

"I do. What do you plan to do about her, Mike?"

"I'm wondering whether to get in touch with the commercial escape people." Mike eased out of bed and rummaged in his suitcase for a notebook listing, among other items, the three *Fluchthelfer*—professional escape contacts—Delaney had given him. He read off the names. "Which do you recommend?"

"Wolfgang Dahlem, no question," said Delaney in his raspy, emphatic way. "He's been at the escape business twenty years, ever since the Wall went up. He's so good, the East Germans have tried twice to assassinate him."

"What would I do? Just call this number you gave me?"

"Yeah. And be ready to fork over thirty grand to Dahlem and his crew. He's the deluxe outfit, you know." Delaney stood up. "Well, beat that cold, and let me know how you make out with Dahlem."

"If I go that route. I'm just not sure yet."

The next morning, awakened by streaming sunlight, Mike felt immeasurably better. After breakfast he set off for the huge Ka-De-We department store, pushed through the crowds of Christmas shoppers, and bought himself a topcoat to replace the snug sheepskin left behind in Leipzig. Battling his way past incoming customers toward the exit, he thought how Gisela would love the lavish displays and abundance of luxury goods.

He turned toward Kurfürstendamm, making his way through

throngs of well-dressed Berliners, past the stores, theaters, and glass-enclosed sidewalk restaurants. Today, under the flooding sunshine, brash Berlin crackled and brayed in its defiant isolation.

But Mike soon realized that his mind kept wandering far from the staccato music of the city. He thought of Gisela and the Wall, and before long he found himself on a bus traveling to the Brandenburg Gate. On the way he began wondering how to raise thirty thousand dollars. Should he sell the lot in Omaha? Liquidate his stocks? Close out his savings accounts? Had he indeed decided to spend thirty thousand dollars?

Leaving the bus, he mounted the stairs of a tall wooden observation platform and looked down on the concrete blocks of the Wall. A few yards beyond, in East Berlin, stood the massive Brandenburg Gate, its stone columns framing five passageways for Unter den Linden, once one of Europe's most beautiful boulevards. Now the Wall garroted the graceful old avenue like an executioner's collar, leaving the thoroughfare near the Wall with a seedy, melancholy air.

Mike strolled along the Wall for several hours, realizing that it had a powerful if perplexing attraction for him, taunting him as though it were a living person. In defeating the Wall, outwitting it, he might somehow overcome his private terrors, those shapeless ghouls that haunted his nights.

The bright sunlight had faded into dusk when he took a bus back to the center of the city and then walked the few blocks to his hotel. By then the matter had been settled in his mind. Yes, he would spend what it took to bring Gisela to the West—and to score his own private victory over the Wall. At the hotel reception desk, the ever efficient clerk handed him a message from his box. "Three calls—and all from the same lady."

Mike unfolded the paper in the elevator: "Herr Simmons, please call Ingrid—891-9055. Important."

He called as soon as he reached his room. A woman's voice answered.

"Ingrid? This is Mike Simmons," he said in German.

"Yes, this is Ingrid. I have a message for you." Her tone was guarded. "I think you will recognize the source. The hoist machine has been repaired and operates again in Dresden. Need new counterweight rails and hope you can lend pivot points through this supplier."

Gisela! He felt a surge of joy. In their code, hoist machine was Gisela herself, counterweight rails signified an escape attempt, and pivot points equaled money. To Ingrid he said, "I want to talk to you as soon as possible. Where and when can we meet?"

"The Tano, a bar on Lietzenburger near Meinekestrasse. Come now. I will be in the last booth, wearing dark glasses."

Mike found the Tano after a short walk along Lietzenburger. A small, dark, smoky night spot that, like a hundred others in West Berlin, catered to lonely men with money to spend, the Tano had an intimate three-sided bar tended by a buxom blonde. Photographs of voluptuous nudes, framed in red, covered the walls. Several women in skin-hugging gowns lolled at the bar and scrutinized Mike with quick mercenary glances.

To reach the last booth, Mike turned a corner that separated it from the rest of the establishment. The brown-haired young woman sitting there wore a black dress, sunglasses, and a small, stylish gold wristwatch.

"Ingrid?"

She inclined her head. "Please sit down. A drink?"

"Yes. A vodka on the rocks."

She pressed a buzzer on the wall, and a hostess took the order.

"I suppose you know why I called you," Ingrid said in a low voice. "My group has been contacted by a woman in Dresden who wishes to leave. She gave your name as one able and willing to pay our fee. Is that correct?"

"Yes."

"May I see your passport, please?" Mike handed over the blue booklet. She studied it carefully before returning it.

"Our fees range from fifteen to thirty-five thousand dollars, American, per head," she said. "The exact amount depends on many factors, including the number of people crossing and the difficulty of the job. Can you afford our terms?"

"That depends on the conditions. For instance, how much down payment do you require?"

"We ask five thousand dollars in cash, West German marks, upon agreement, the remainder upon safe arrival of the person on this side. If we fail to deliver, we refund your down payment."

"Before I enter into an agreement with you, I should check with a friend who recommended a service like yours."

"Did he give you a name?"

Mike bobbed his head.

"Was it Wolfgang Dahlem?"

"That's it."

"I represent Herr Dahlem." She smiled broadly. "So, may I tell him you're ready to reach an understanding with us?"

"Please do."

"Wait here, please." She disappeared in the direction of the bar. Mike sipped at his drink and waited while she made a phone call.

"Wolfgang will talk to you now if you're ready." Ingrid stood beside the table. "You walk up Lietzenburger to Fasanenstrasse, turn right to number Seventy. Take the elevator to the second floor. You'll find Wolfgang in apartment two-A."

Mike started to get up, but Ingrid put a hand on his sleeve. "I'll leave now. Wait several minutes before you go."

A whistling wind vied with the roar of traffic as Mike walked along Lietzenburger. Number Seventy Fasanenstrasse was a five-story apartment building with a stone façade. Mike made his way to number 2-A. A stocky man in a turtleneck sweater answered his knock. Admitting Mike to the foyer, he frisked him, then led him into a large, expensively furnished room. The strongman left, and soon the head of the establishment entered. He stood beside a rich brown wall hanging that featured a prowling yellow jaguar.

"Good evening, Mr. Simmons. I'm Wolfgang Dahlem. Sorry we had to greet you the way we did. I'm sure you appreciate the need for precautions." Tall and lean, Dahlem wore a white shirt, green cardigan, and neatly pressed trousers. He appeared to be in his late forties.

They seated themselves on a white corduroy couch, and Mike declined the offer of a cigarette from an ivory box.

"So, to business." Dahlem had not taken his eyes from Mike.

"A woman over there wants to come to the West. She contacted one of us and indicated you would underwrite the journey."

"That's right, subject to our agreement on terms."

"Of course." Dahlem spoke with cool detachment. "Mr. Simmons, I'm going to ask you a lot of questions. I dislike it, but you must understand that the SSD never quits trying to destroy our organization by infiltration, sabotage, and even murder. In this case, since the initial contact came from a Party person who's been honored by the state, we have to be especially careful. It would be entirely possible for both you and Frau X to be *Stasi* agents. That may seem fanciful to you, but not to us, believe me."

"It does strike me as ironic right now. You see, five nights ago the SSD picked me off the street in Leipzig, drove me to East Berlin, and spent about twenty hours grilling me."

"Oh. I want to hear all about that," said Dahlem.

As he had for Walt Delaney, Mike recounted his hours with his East German interrogators, then answered a spate of questions. Dahlem probed at length into Mike's personal and business life. At last, apparently satisfied, he said, "All right, Mr. Simmons, we'll go ahead. Because we're combining several parties, I can reduce your fee. The charge will be twenty-five thousand dollars. That includes both, of course."

"Both?"

"Yes. The girl as well."

"What girl?" Had they, after all, been talking about two different Frau Xs in Dresden?

"Hilde, the daughter."

"Wait a minute, Mr. Dahlem, I'm talking about a woman who edits publications at the Technical University in Dresden."

"So am I." Dahlem smiled faintly. "Frau Gisela Steinbrecher, wife of a Karl Steinbrecher. Correct?"

"Yes, but . . ." Mike faltered. "Gisela has no daughter."

"Oh, but she does." Now Dahlem looked puzzled. "Hilde Steinbrecher, age sixteen."

"You're positive?" Mike was dumbfounded. His mind raced back over discussions with Gisela about family. Had he missed a vital clue somewhere?

"Positive. In cases like this, we insist on talking to the child as well. Should the daughter suddenly decide to stay with the father, well . . . I never force these things. Our business is too delicate. But apparently Hilde is even more determined to escape than her mother is." Dahlem locked his eyes on Mike's once more. "Mr. Simmons, I've assumed an intimate relationship between you and Frau Steinbrecher. Yet you never heard of a daughter?"

"No. Gisela never said a word about a daughter."

Dahlem considered. "If this changes your attitude, you're perfectly at liberty to cancel out."

In a flashing image, Mike could see Gisela's look of terror when the border searchlights exposed her. Had Hilde been crouching in the dark ravine that night, ready to follow her mother across? Again he sensed the strength of the bond fused between Gisela and himself in that harshly brilliant instant. And yet, she had deceived him.

"I'm not sure. I suppose Gisela felt"—he resented her forcing him to equivocate before this cold stranger—"that I might be less inclined to help if a daughter were involved."

"I think that's a fair conclusion. As I say, if you wish to withdraw, you may."

"I have other considerations." Mike had his own secret commitment to breach the Wall and exorcise the demons of the night.

"Perhaps you'd like to think it over until tomorrow?"

"Yes, I would."

Dahlem rose. "So then, Mr. Simmons, I'll expect to hear from you tomorrow." He escorted Mike to the foyer and held the door open. "Time's important now. I'm trying to combine another delivery with the Steinbrechers."

Steinbrechers? The plural form had a curious, unsettling impact. Suddenly any future he might have with Gisela seemed immensely complicated.

That night he could not summon sleep until very late. His thoughts nagged at this new and vexing fact: a pair had become a threesome. Would Hilde reject him, be sullen and withdrawn? Would they live together, all three? He went through a tangle of emotions as he lay sleepless in his hotel bed, but always he came back to Gisela herself. He might respect her courage and rue her distrust of him. But the fact was that he loved her.

In the morning his decision was made. Daughter or no daughter, Gisela was his woman. Together they would beat the Wall.

Wolfgang Dahlem took Mike's signal to go ahead without comment. He awaited only the down payment to put the escape plan into operation. Mike called his New York bank that afternoon.

CHAPTER EIGHT

IN THE evening of the second day of Christmas, Gisela and Hilde walked with special caution along Sidonienstrasse in central Dresden. Mother and daughter walked warily, with that feral tension brought on by the prospect of danger, because at five thirty precisely they were to rendezvous with Herr Dahlem's escape guide, the young man who would try to spirit them out of East Germany. He had instructed them to meet him in front of a building on the southwest corner of Leningrader and Sidonien streets. The building bore a red-and-white sign boasting of the ruling SED Party's program: SERVICE TO THE PEOPLE. "A whim of mine," the young man had explained. He liked to start his escape operations under one of the regime's propaganda banners.

Now, as the minutes clicked toward the appointed time, Gisela thought back over the anxious days since she had fled from the border near Kaltennordheim under the stutter of machine-gun fire. On that cold, rain-swept night nearly three weeks ago, Gisela and her daughter had moved in silence down the ravine near the border. The soft turf, cushioned by pine needles, felt springy under their feet. Fir boughs brushed damply against them.

They had reached the ravine after a soggy trek of somewhat more than a mile. Through the complicity of her sister, Frauke, Gisela had "stolen," then "abandoned" the Augsteins' car, an arrangement made possible by Dr. Augstein's absence in Cuba. After leaving the car concealed in a grove of chestnut trees and birches, Gisela and Hilde had walked along a narrow gravel road, then into the wooded flanks of the Rhön hills.

They came to the foot of the ravine a few minutes before the appointed time and crouched behind two tree trunks, Hilde a few yards behind Gisela. Far away they heard dogs begin to bark.

When Gisela saw the two blinks of light across the way, she immediately flopped to her belly and began to creep forward through the pouring rain. Hilde was to follow after one minute. Gisela wore two old sweaters and a pair of paint-splotched slacks lent her by Frauke. A blue stocking cap protected her head.

When the searchlights lashed her with their brutal light, Gisela whipped around and crawled back toward the ravine just as a burst of machine-gun fire assailed her. In the instant before she rose to her feet at the mouth of the gully, something hit her left leg. It felt like the rap of a stick, followed by a stinging sensation on her lower calf.

Gisela seized her daughter's hand, and together they rushed up the gully. Their clothes snagged on shrubs, and twice they fell and scrambled to their feet. Now Gisela heard the sharp coughs of an automatic rifle, more machine-gun fire, some shouts, and a far-off howling of dogs.

After a frantic, staggering run of half a mile, Gisela and Hilde emerged from the woods. Keeping close to the trees, they hurried along the gravel road, ready to fling themselves to the ground should anyone appear. At last they reached their car, partially hidden by the birches and chestnut trees. Gisela snatched open the door on the driver's side and was about to get in when Hilde called in a stage whisper, "Mother, your leg's bleeding."

Gisela looked down. Blood had soaked through the left leg of her slacks above the ankle. She suddenly became aware of a painful throb. "No time for it now." She swept up a newspaper from the back seat and spread the sheets on the floorboard. Then she started the engine and eased the car backward, careful not to spin the wheels too fast and mire it in the mud.

On the macadam surface, Gisela headed toward Frauke's, pushing the car to its limits. Hilde monitored the road behind as Gisela maneuvered away from gaining headlights and finally turned into the driveway. Frauke appeared the moment the car ground to a halt. She promptly sized up the situation.

"Quick, into the house. Are you all right?"

"Hilde is. I've been shot in the leg. It's not bad, but there's some blood. We must burn these newspapers and slacks before the border guards come by."

Half an hour later not a sign of the escape attempt remained. The bloodstained newspapers and slacks had been consumed in the coal stove, and Frauke had aired the house to rid it of the odor of burning fabric. She had hidden the women's sopping clothes behind the coalbin in the basement. Gisela, in pajamas and with her lower left leg bandaged, had crawled into bed, with hot tea and a book on the table beside her, ostensibly to nurse a cold. Hilde, wearing dry jeans and an old sweater, settled in front of the TV set.

The three women had rehearsed their story while they cleansed Gisela's leg wound. Gisela, they would say, had been in bed with a cold since her arrival in Kaltennordheim two days earlier. Because of the rain, no one had been out since early afternoon.

"I can't shake my feeling of depression," said Gisela. "We were so close; we almost made it, Hilde."

"Please, don't ever try again," said Frauke. "Next time it might be your life."

Hilde looked at her aunt with surprise. "Of course we'll try again." She was a large, awkward girl with close-cropped brown hair. She had just celebrated her sixteenth birthday and she loved all things Western: West German movies and TV, rock and jazz bands, the few contemporary novels that a friend's grandparents managed to bring back from their travels in the West. Someday the girl would outshine her mother's beauty, but the alternate spells of brooding and feverish rebellion that racked her adolescence gave Hilde's features a petulant cast.

"I'm afraid we have no choice but to try again," said Gisela. "They're looking for us now. If we don't escape, they will find us eventually. You know how thorough they are."

Later, while Frauke and Hilde were upstairs undressing for bed, Hilde called from the bathroom. "Look out your window." Her tone was one of wondering delight. "You won't believe it."

Outside, a soft, thick snowfall coated the driveway and covered the car. Lights from the house shimmered on falling flakes.

Crossing in Berlin

In another few minutes no one would be able to tell when the car had last moved out of the driveway.

Too keyed up to sleep, the three women were wide awake when the expected knocking came at the door sometime after midnight.

Frauke threw on a bathrobe and hurried down to open the front door. "*Ach*, Hugo! What a surprise. Do come in." The relief in her voice carried to the women upstairs.

Hugo Noske, of the *Volkspolizei*, the local police, stamped his feet and shook the snow off his cap. He stood diffidently just inside the door as white flakes melted into his green overcoat.

"Please sit down, Hugo. May I offer you coffee? Maybe a swallow of schnapps to warm you on this cold night?" They had known each other for years.

"Nothing, please, Frauke." The *Vopo* squared his shoulders. "I'm here on official business, you understand."

"At this hour? ... What has happened?"

"An incident, no more." He took out pad and pencil. "Who is in residence here now?"

"My sister, Gisela Steinbrecher, and her daughter, Hilde, from Dresden. Gisela has been in bed with a cold ever since they arrived."

"And Dr. Augstein?"

"He's in Cuba on a health mission."

"*Ach, ja.*" Officer Noske made notes. "Now, Frauke, please describe to me your movements since three this afternoon."

"Movements?" She laughed gaily. "We haven't stirred out of the house, any of us, since noon, because of the rain and snow."

"Your neighbors up the road, the Kellers, thought they saw your car drive by a little after eight tonight."

"Must have been somebody else," said Frauke. "My car has not been moved out of the driveway today.... Look at it yourself, Hugo." She led him to the window. Snow had made a smooth white mound of the vehicle and covered the yard and driveway.

The officer smiled at his friend in mock reproof. "Who would know whether any car in Kaltennordheim had been moved before the snow?" He looked inquiringly toward the stairs. "Your sister and niece?"

"They are asleep. But naturally you are welcome to question them. We have nothing to hide here, Hugo."

"I do not suggest that you have." He looked about uncertainly. Noske never forgot Dr. Dieter Augstein's family ties to the chief of state, Heinrich Volpe. "It won't be necessary to disturb them. So good night, Frauke. I regret I had to bother you."

"Always a pleasure to see you, Hugo. Even at this hour."

Officer Noske tramped off through the snow.

Gisela and Hilde did not sleep until the first light of dawn. Instead they planned how to renew their escape efforts as soon as possible.

"We must contact the escape professionals," said Gisela at last. "That's the only way when one is desperate and in a hurry."

"But Mother, the *Fluchthelfer*—they want a fortune."

"I know. But perhaps my American friend could put up the money as a loan to us."

"Oh, I'd work years to pay him back." Hilde studied her mother. "Does he love you?"

Gisela colored. "Perhaps, perhaps not. We've only seen each other a few times."

"He does. I know he does." Hilde beamed. This year she alternately adored and scorned romance.

"Such matters aside, I will ask him for help through the *Fluchthelfer*."

"They say Wolfgang Dahlem is the best," said Hilde, "and I know how to contact his people."

Two days later Frauke drove mother and daughter to Meiningen, where they caught an early morning bus to Dresden. That night Hilde boarded a streetcar and rode downtown. She entered a film theater on Pragerstrasse and went to the counter in the lobby to check her coat. Hilde leaned close to the gray-haired woman attendant.

"I remember the seventeenth of June."

"So." The woman bent her head, examining a metal check. "Who died that day?" Her whisper was husky with age.

"Freedom."

"Where does Goethe live today?"

"On the sunny side."

The old woman peered about to make sure they were still alone. "My child, tomorrow promptly at five thirty, you must go to the Volkspark Grosser Garten. Fifteen meters from the entrance to the *Puppentheater* stand two white benches with a stone receptacle between them. Sit on the right-hand bench. You will be addressed from behind an evergreen bush that grows near it. Answer, but do not look around." She pressed the metal check into Hilde's hand and turned away.

Gisela undertook the next day's mission herself. At five thirty a fine evening mist screened the great park, which lay not far from downtown Dresden and the river Elbe. Gisela entered the broad esplanade and walked along the wide gravel path. Leafless stands of beech and chestnut trees framed the foggy esplanade. In the last glimmer of daylight Gisela found the twin benches and sat down before the clump of evergreens. When she heard the voice, she resisted the temptation to turn around.

"Where does Goethe live today?" A young voice, male, firm, friendly.

"On the sunny side."

"So, you wish to go over there?"

"Yes." She blurted the word, conscious that if this was a trap, agents of the state would seize her.

"How many people?"

"Two. My daughter, who's sixteen, and myself."

"Relax. I have many questions to ask."

The inquiries were routine and predictable. At last the young man seemed satisfied that she and Hilde stood committed to the escape, with no possibility of backing out. "Now to the money," he said. "Many people in this operation take great risks and must be recompensed. For two of you, we need a hundred and sixty thousand East marks, or forty thousand West marks."

"Our payment comes from my friend on the other side." Gisela named Michael Simmons and his address in West Berlin. "But I must give you a message for him in our private code, so he knows it comes from me." She dictated a brief message in the elevator code. "One other thing." She found this difficult to say. "Herr Simmons does not know I have a daughter. Tell him, nicely, please, that two of us will cross. You see, I feared he might . . ."

"I understand. So, we expect word in three days possibly. You must return to this bench at five thirty on the fourteenth."

The next three days went slowly for Gisela. Ulli Beitz called with the coded message Michael had written to find out whether or not she had been seriously injured. How would he react to the news that she had a daughter who would cross with her? Would he abandon her because she had lied by omission? Why, indeed, hadn't she risked the truth with him? On and on went her guilty speculation.

The wound was healing slowly but steadily, the chief complication being Gisela's effort to keep the truth from her husband, Karl. She explained the bandage by saying she had fallen and bruised her leg while ailing with the flu at Frauke's house.

On December 14 she went to the bench. After a few moments the young male voice spoke again. "The operation is on. Your friend agreed to pay."

She hesitated. "For both?" A world hinged on the answer.

"Yes, for Hilde too. We'll contact you when the time comes. Always be ready to leave within a few hours."

The next few days were charged with pain and anxiety. When Gisela returned to work, she removed the bandage from her leg and made every effort not to limp, in order to avoid questions from her associates at the university. She and Hilde passed the time at home by doing English lessons, but even as Gisela struggled to learn the difficult new tongue, the tension was nearly unbearable. At any moment, she knew, agents of the state might knock at her door.

The long-awaited call came on the second day of Christmas when the two women were eating breakfast and Karl still lounged in bed.

"The bench in one hour." Gisela felt an electric charge at the sound of the familiar young voice.

Gisela pulled on her warm winter coat and took a streetcar to the Grosser Garten. The day was damp and chilly, with a gray overcast. This time, as soon as she reached the bench, a young man appeared, sauntering from the direction of the puppet theater. Pale, with delicate features, he wore a turtleneck sweater and a black jacket. Pausing in front of the bench, he bent over to tie his shoelaces.

"We leave tonight," he said without looking up. "You and Hilde must be at the southwest corner of Leningraderstrasse and Sidonienstrasse at five thirty exactly. I drive a black Wartburg. When I stop, get into the car quickly. Bring no belongings except what you can carry in a coat pocket. Your ID, of course. Dress warmly." He straightened up and strolled away.

Gisela and Hilde dressed with care: warm slacks, heavy sweaters, hip-length winter coats, gloves.

They told Karl they were going to an afternoon movie, and they did go to the circular building that housed the plushly appointed cinema. They saw an excellent Hungarian film about slowly ebbing married love, but neither of them could concentrate on it, so they left. They reached the appointed corner early and strolled up and down Sidonienstrasse while darkness fell on the city.

The black Wartburg rolled to the curb on schedule. It pulled away with Hilde in the back seat and Gisela beside the young man, who now wore a fur hat, a thickly padded jacket, and gloves.

"My name's Erich," he said as he accelerated. "I'm going to leave the country myself, and so I'll accompany you all the way. After two years of this work, I'm hot. The *Stasi* might be right behind me." Their escape route, he explained, would take them north on the autobahn some one hundred miles, to the outskirts of East Berlin. If stopped for a police check anywhere, they would say they were headed for the big holiday Lutheran assembly being held in the capital; he drilled them on details.

"If we're stopped," he said with his sardonic smile, "act casual, even a little bored."

They drove through the early winter night with the heat on full blast. In the darkness they saw very little of the countryside, only the lights of the other cars. On the outskirts of Berlin, where open fields gave way to the gardens and toolsheds of city residents who tended vegetable plots in the warm months, Erich turned off the autobahn.

"We're going to a shack where we meet our guide and where we leave the car. After we've gone, the guide will drive the car into the city and abandon it in the street."

Erich drove on with confidence, and Gisela had begun to feel that this time they would make it when a green-and-white car drew alongside, its blue flashing light stroking the night. Police.

Erich stopped. An officer strolled over, asked for their destination and papers. "You say you're going to Strausberger Platz for the Lutheran assembly?"

"That's right, *Herr Wachtmeister*," Erich replied.

"Then why are you way out here in the summer gardens?"

"I'm lost."

The policeman leaned through the open window. "You came from Dresden on the autobahn?"

"Yes."

"Why did you exit so soon?"

"We intended to pick up another passenger."

"What's his name?"

"Rolf Viertel."

"Address?"

"Bukesweg Eighteen. . . . He wasn't home."

"Wait here." The officer strode back to his sedan, unhooked a microphone from a dashboard fixture, and spoke into it.

"Headquarters will confirm the address," said Erich in a low voice, "and we made sure that Viertel would be away. I have more names like that in this area. We plan in detail!"

The officer returned. "All right. Head back the other way."

"*Herr Wachtmeister*, could you please take the time to lead us to a street that heads toward Strausberger Platz? We would appreciate it."

"Follow me." The policeman got back in his car, made a U-turn, and drove down the road.

"Helps build trust in us," said Erich with a smile.

The officer led them to a thoroughfare, pointed the way, and turned his police car south. Two minutes later Erich veered off on a side gravel road and headed back in the same direction they had traveled earlier. "We circle this time," he said.

"No more police, Erich, please," said Gisela.

After a short distance on the graveled surface, Erich turned onto a dirt road and switched off his headlights. The car moved slowly in the dark for several hundred yards. Finally Erich maneuvered the vehicle into a grassy lane and halted. "Follow me."

They all got out and he led them along a path that wound through several fenced gardens, ending at a wooden shack. Erich reached to a rafter of the overhanging roof, brought out a key, and unlocked the door. The windowless interior gave off a medley of garden odors: manure, oil, chemical fertilizer, damp earth.

"We're in the garden hut of a sympathizer," Erich whispered. "Soon our guide comes to lead us to the spot where we leave the DDR. The guide also brings another man who's escaping. You'll follow me, do exactly as I do. If all goes well, we ought to reach West Berlin by midnight."

They waited a full half hour before a rap sounded on the door. Erich opened it and pulled at the women's sleeves, guiding them outside. There they saw two men, their faces indistinct in the moonless night. One of the strangers motioned with his head, and they all fell into line behind him.

They walked silently for a quarter of a mile, passing innumerable small garden plots and shanties. The lights of the city glowed on the horizon. Soon Gisela saw a shimmer ahead. They had reached the banks of a waterway.

The guide dropped to a prone position, and Erich motioned them to do likewise. They lay abreast on hard, stony ground, protected by a slope that hid them from view from the rear.

Erich whispered to Gisela. "Pass the word. We're waiting for a boat to edge up to the bank. When it does, we must board within seconds." Gisela relayed the message.

A patrol boat churned past, and Gisela could imagine marine border guards sweeping the shorelines with searchlights.

Soon the running lights of a boat appeared to the south, then winked off. In a few minutes a dark craft loomed near the shore.

They could see the stubby bow. "Everyone ready," ordered the guide in a low voice. When the vessel brushed the embankment, Erich got to his feet in a low crouch, then straightened up and leaped to the gunwale of the boat.

Gisela and Hilde made the short jump, and the stranger followed. They all stepped down, half falling to the deck from the gunwale. The boat swung back to midstream, and the running lights were switched on once more. Erich ducked into a hatch and led them down a ladder. Gisela's leg ached with pain, and she wondered if the wound had become infected.

Once belowdecks, Erich switched on a flashlight, but cautioned them to silence with a finger at his lips. The shaft of light swept over casks, cartons, coils of rope, a litter of boards.

With the others following, he picked his way forward beneath the low overhead, fingering the woodwork above him. He pressed his hands against one of the panels, and it slid to one side, leaving an opening several feet square.

He handed the flashlight to Gisela. "Shine it up through there." He grasped the edges of the decking and pulled himself up. "Now you get a boost from Hilde." When they had all climbed into the boxlike compartment, Erich slid the panel back into place and fastened it with thumbscrews.

Looking about, Gisela saw that they were jammed together in a storage compartment about six feet high and only a few feet across. The four of them had room to stand or sit, but no space to move around in. A bucket of gravel stood in a corner.

"My name is Werner," said the stranger, blinking in the light. Hilde and Gisela introduced themselves by first names. Werner and Erich apparently already knew each other. They all sank to a sitting position, closely crowded, their knees touching.

"We might as well get used to this," said Erich. "It will take about five hours, barring unforeseen seizure or accident, before we leave the boat in West Berlin."

"Are we on the river Spree?" asked Gisela.

"Right." Erich nodded. "Let me explain. This is a one-shot effort that can't be repeated for other escapers. This old scow is mostly used for short cargo trips inside the city. Tonight we're taking a load of gravel right through the middle of both Berlins to a lock near the Spandau fortress. The gravel is to be used to repair the lock. But instead of dumping the load, we are going to jump ship to freedom."

"The captain too?" Hilde was wide-eyed.

"The skipper especially. He's been planning this with us for weeks, waiting for just the right voyage." Erich pointed overhead. "We've got fifty tons of gravel over us and about two meters deep surrounding us. When the DDR guards board us, they'll hear the sound of gravel everywhere—including right here." With that he dumped the bucket, spreading stones over the panel on which they were sitting.

"Here's our route on the Spree." He pulled a map of the two Berlins from his pocket and opened it wide. "We got aboard here along the Müggelspree."

The river Spree rises in the mountains along East Germany's southern border with Czechoslovakia and joins the broad Havel in West Berlin just below the Spandau lock. The Spree traces a serpentine route of some thirty miles through the heart of the two Berlins. In some areas the river's edge becomes the frontier between East and West, and DDR gunboats bustle about it like snappish hounds.

"We move into West Berlin waters about twenty-five kilometers from where we boarded," said Erich. "The frontier crosses the river where the DDR operates an inspection station on pontoons. Once past that point, we can breathe easier, but we will not try to land anywhere along the West Berlin banks."

"Why not?" Hilde frowned. "I don't understand."

"Because at the inspection station the authorities are putting aboard an engineer who is going to supervise the repairs of the Spandau lock. He'll be in civilian clothes, but actually he's a major in the People's Army. He'll be armed, of course. The boat captain and I can handle him at the lock. That's all planned. But if we nosed into the riverbank somewhere, he might start shooting."

"Do we have any guns?" asked Werner.

Erich patted his jacket pocket. "I've got a revolver. So does the captain."

Hilde smiled nervously at her mother.

"Don't worry about shooting," said Erich. "We've planned carefully to protect you people. Our real danger will come at the inspection station. The border guards always put dogs aboard to sniff out any stowaways like us."

"Dogs!" Gisela had not forgotten the distant, frenzied barking that awful night at the death strip near Kaltennordheim. "How will we ever get through?"

Erich grinned. "Attack dogs are almost invariably male. The captain has a female German shepherd named Andrea, and she's in heat. Those males will go wild. They may try to bust into the captain's cabin, where he's got Andrea tied."

"You mean this whole trip was planned to coincide with the time when the captain's dog would be in heat?" asked Werner.

Again Erich's grin. "Better than that, Werner. The captain's dog comes into heat twice a year, each time for sixteen to twenty-one days. A bitch's heat hits its peak on days ten, eleven, and twelve." Erich cocked a finger. "And this second day of Christmas is day eleven in Andrea's cycle." He beamed at his new friends. "How's that for precise planning!"

"Dogs," mused Werner. "It's nice to learn that faced with a choice between war and love, the dogs choose love."

"I won't try to deceive you," Erich said. "There could still be trouble. If so, the captain will put on full power and try to break through to West Berlin waters."

He refolded his map and they rode in silence as the small freighter slipped downstream, a low, grating sound marking the shifting of the cargo. The vessel slid quietly through the center of East Berlin, past Marx-Engels Platz, and past Unter den Linden. They had been traveling for almost two hours at a good speed when the boat's engine shifted to reduced power and a horn sounded abovedeck.

"The inspection station," said Erich. "From now on, until I give the signal, no more talking and no squirming about." He snapped off his flashlight.

The vessel went dead in the water and bumped against an obstruction of some kind, undoubtedly the heavy pontoons that floated from bank to bank of the Spree, leaving only a narrow, easily controlled passage for river commerce.

Someone threw a line on board. Voices shouted commands, and feet pounded on the decks.

Then came the unmistakable sounds of dogs. Gisela stiffened in the dark. She could hear their panting, their claws. They seemed to be running haphazardly around the deck and over the piles of gravel. Stones slid about with a noise like coal tumbling down a chute. Shivering, Gisela gripped Hilde's hand.

Now she heard the clamor of men's voices. There was laughter, then a shouted command, and the dogs—two? three?—ran across the deck and apparently leaped off the boat to the pontoons. Gisela's breathing returned to normal. Her shivering ceased. She released Hilde's hand.

But now the hatch cover was pulled open with a rasping noise and the sound of shoes clattered down the ladder. "You search the hold," ordered a voice. "I'll test the overhead."

Below them the four fugitives could hear the tester thumping the hold's overhead panels with a pole, each whack rattling the gravel. Gisela hugged her knees, closed her eyes, and waited.

At last the pole struck the panel on which they sat. The gravel rattled about in a satisfying manner, but to Gisela's sensitive ear the sound seemed thinner and looser than that produced elsewhere. Silence. Gisela held her breath.

The banging moved to another panel. She exhaled with relief. The pounding receded and then stopped. Feet in heavy shoes climbed the ladder. The hatch cover slid back in place. The footsteps retreated. Soon the lines were cast off, the engine started again, and the freighter moved ahead.

"We've made it through the inspection station," Erich whispered. "But I'm sure the military engineer's aboard now, so let's keep the talk to a whisper."

"That beautiful Andrea," said Hilde. "I could kiss her to pieces."

"Too bad we can't see the map," said Erich, "but we're passing behind the old Reichstag now. Soon we'll swing due west and loop out to the Spandau lock. Only a couple of hours more."

Now began the final stretch, when the minutes crawled and the little freighter, although rocking gently on its downstream course, seemed mired in molasses. Gisela snuggled into her coat. The air in the compartment grew cold and stale, limbs began to ache, and Gisela could feel a fevered throbbing at her wound.

"We're getting close to Spandau lock," said Erich at last. "This could be either the simplest thing in the world or a shooting match where somebody might get killed."

He kept his voice just above a whisper. "We enter the lock from the south, where the boat will be raised two meters for unloading in the morning. When we arrive, the gunwales will be about even with the pavement. The lockmaster's house and office will be on your right. There is a footbridge that crosses a spillway and leads to the electrically operated gate, the only exit in a chain link fence that runs all around the lock.

"The moment we reach the lock, the captain and I will disarm the army engineer and secure him in the wheelhouse. Then we jump off the starboard side and make for the lockmaster. No trouble expected from him, but if he refuses to push the button that opens the gate, we'll do it. The rest of you must jump off the boat and head for the gate."

"If we're in West Berlin, why all that trouble?" Hilde was baffled. "Why can't we just walk out?"

"Under the Berlin agreements the DDR controls all access to the Western sector," Erich answered. "Although the lock is on West Berlin soil and tended by a West Berliner, he's paid by East Germany. So we're not sure just how he will respond. Anyway, when I give the order, everybody follow me up on deck, fast. Werner first."

They waited. The freighter slowed, idled for a time, then picked up speed again. At last the boat's horn blew once, an anxious plaint on the wintry air.

"All right, here we go." Erich unscrewed the panel and dropped into the hold. Werner followed. The men handed the women down into the cluttered stowage space belowdecks. They heard the captain call out and a muffled reply from the lock tender.

"Now." Erich whipped out his pistol and rushed up the ladder,

Werner behind him. Gisela banged her injured leg cruelly on a step, but Hilde supported her. The lock's floodlamps bathed the decks in light.

"Here!" Werner helped them up to the gunwale, from which they stepped onto pavement. They ran across the top of the lock behind the boat and over the footbridge to the gate. Werner rattled the handle. It did not open.

Gisela, her heart thumping, looked back at the old freighter. On its bridge the garish light spilled over a bizarre scene. A man, apparently the boat's captain, lay sprawled on the deck, a pistol in his hand. Another man, apparently the army engineer, stood a few feet away, his pistol pointed at the prone figure. Andrea, the police dog, raged at the end of her chain in the doorway, barking hysterically at the man, her fangs bared.

Below the bridge, on the main deck of the freighter, Erich slowly raised his revolver, took aim, and fired.

The army officer cried out in pain. His pistol clattered to the deck. The captain, still clutching his own pistol, scrambled to his feet. Erich rushed up the five-rung ladder to the bridge. The major saw his own gun on the deck, and grabbed frantically for the weapon, blood streaming down his hand. Just as he got hold of the gun, Erich smashed the butt of his revolver against the major's head, and he collapsed to the deck like an empty sack.

The captain unfastened Andrea's chain and pulled the dog down the wheelhouse ladder with him. Erich jumped off the bridge. The two men and the dog leaped from the boat and raced to the lockhouse, a stone building with a steeply pitched red tile roof. The lockmaster stood in the building's doorway, bowing deeply with a flourish of his hand that seemed to say, Be my guests, gentlemen. Just don't shoot. The captain quickly found the proper switch. Outside, the gate came alive with buzzing.

Werner threw the gate open for Gisela and Hilde, but they stood transfixed, watching the drama unfold. "Come on!" He grabbed each of them and shoved them through the gate.

Windows in nearby apartments flew open and heads popped out. "Run for it!" someone yelled as the captain, followed by Erich, burst out of the lockhouse.

Werner held the gate open. The two men and the dog ran through. Then Werner walked through himself, while applause broke out from people at the apartment windows. Werner joined the others, and they hugged one another, sobbing and laughing in the brilliant light as Berliners poured into the nearby streets.

"Freedom!" shouted a voice from the window. "Welcome!"

"*Die Sonnenseite!*" Werner opened his arms to his comrades. "My friends, we're safe on the sunny side."

CHAPTER NINE

THE call came shortly after midnight. The telephone rang three times in Mike's hotel room before he fumbled blindly for it. Shards of a shattered nightmare rained about him.

"Michael Simmons?" A woman's voice, vaguely familiar.

"Yes."

"This is Ingrid. The expected delivery has arrived."

"You mean . . . Where?"

"Right here in Berlin."

Now fully awake, he soared on the news. "Where do I go?"

Ingrid laughed softly. "First the money, no? You bring the cash to me at the Tano now. Then we'll go pick up the delivery."

Never had he dressed so swiftly. At the reception desk he withdrew a thick envelope of bills from the hotel safe.

He found Ingrid seated in the rear booth at the Tano, with the bodyguard he had met at Herr Dahlem's apartment. "Good evening, Herr Simmons," said Ingrid. "You remember Hans?"

"Sure." He nodded to the big man, then took the bulky envelope from his pocket. "Frankly, I don't intend to hand this over until I see Gisela and her daughter."

"Oh, you are the suspicious one." Again that soft laugh. "Just count it for us, please. You keep it until we pick them up."

Mike counted through the packet of thousand-mark bills while Ingrid and Hans watched.

"All is in order." Ingrid beamed at him. "So. Let's go."

Hans drove them in a Mercedes-Benz sedan to the Spandau district. They crossed the river Havel, turned north, and stopped on a residential street not far from a brightly lit beer hall, where late revelers sang and caroused. Ingrid led the way to a window that opened on a private room at the rear of the establishment.

There sat Gisela, drinking beer at a round table with two men and a girl. She looked tired, and her clothes looked as if she'd been rolling in dirt, but otherwise she appeared in good health.

"The money before we go in?" Ingrid's smile was urbane. "Less commercial here, no?"

Mike handed over the envelope. She tucked it in her handbag, then guided him through a side door and down a short hallway. Mike stood in the open doorway of the room where Gisela sat.

"Miguel!" A radiant Gisela sprang to her feet.

She came at once into his open arms and he held her close. The magic of their first night in Leipzig enveloped him anew.

"Thank God, you're alive and safe."

"Miguel, I'm so happy." She laughed, then began to weep.

"Easy, baby." But tears welled up in Mike's own eyes.

Gisela pushed away and wiped her eyes. "Here, Miguel, is Hilde." She took her daughter's hand and drew her toward them.

Mike saw a girl with brown, close-cropped hair, blue eyes, and an uncertain smile. He embraced her, felt her stiffen when he kissed her on both cheeks.

"It is a pleasure to meet you," she said in textbook English.

"For me too. I hope we'll become good friends."

Hilde smiled and offered him a stein of beer. "Here, let's drink to it."

Everyone toasted, sharing beers, laughing, joking about how they had outwitted the warders of the Wall.

Ingrid kissed Gisela and Hilde. "Happy sunny side," she said. "So, our job is finished. Erich and I will go now, because he must report to the headman tonight."

"Work, work, work," said Erich with a ragged smile.

Gisela shook his hand. "I'll never forget what you did for us, Erich."

Only after the escape merchants departed did Mike become fully aware of the other man in the room. Suddenly he burst out, "I don't believe it! Herr Brigade Leader—Werner Lanz!"

"The same." Lanz grinned. Then he delivered a small oration, which Hilde translated. "He planned to escape for years," she said, "and would have asked your assistance in Leipzig, but he was already under contract to the *Fluchthelfer*. A brother in Frankfurt financed the trip, so he's going there."

Mike said, "Of all the people I met back there, he seemed least likely to try to get out. . . . Tell me how you three did it."

They exchanged glances. Werner shook his head slowly. Gisela said, "We promised not to talk, to protect those who follow."

"Hey." Mike was surprised. "Your English has improved."

"Hilde has been teaching me." She looked proud of her accomplishment. "And now, Miguel, you learn German, no?" She was buoyant, flushed, feverish with joy.

They finished the beer, congratulated themselves once more on beating the Wall, and went out to find a taxi. As she took his arm, Mike noticed for the first time that Gisela was limping. But when he asked about it, she put him off. "Later," she said.

They dropped Lanz at the Hotel Am Zoo on Kurfürstendamm. He pledged to stay in touch, and they parted like old friends.

Fortunately Mike's hotel had a room for Hilde on his corridor. Or should it be for Hilde and Gisela? Hilde settled the matter. "Mother, I'd like to be alone. You stay with Mr. Simmons."

"It's not Mr. Simmons, Hilde," Mike said. "It's Mike."

In the corridor before her doorway, Hilde kissed her mother good night, then smiled shyly at Mike. "Thanks, Mr. Mike," she said. "I'm going to pay you back every mark I owe."

Alone in their own room, Mike and Gisela came together for a long, hungry kiss that spoke for a tangle of unvoiced emotions.

"*Mi amor*," she said at last. "Look at me. I'm a sight. I want a long, hot bath."

"What about that limp? Were you hurt?"

"A bullet hit my leg that night at the border. But it's not so bad, I think. I get around."

She took off her shoes and Mike peeled back the woolen sock. The wound had festered. "We must get you to a doctor tomorrow," he said.

After her bath Gisela found herself eager to talk. "Forgive me,

Miguel, for not telling you about Hilde. I feared you would not help me and a daughter too. By the last night at Ulli's, I knew you better and I thought you'd welcome us both, but by then I was afraid to correct the lie." She paused before she asked, "What did you think when you learned the truth?"

"Frankly, I resented it. But then I realized how much you'd been through and, well, I felt I didn't have the right to judge."

She told him all that had happened. "To think that was just yesterday and now I'm starting a new life, never to go back."

"We must stay here in Berlin for at least a week, until my replacement arrives to finish up the Leipzig job."

"A whole week!" Gisela was excited. "I have just three duties. First, a doctor for my leg. Then some clothes to buy. Third, I must call the ecology people in your country about Otto Kleist's material. Is that in order?"

"Sounds terrific."

"About the money, Miguel. Hilde and I consider that a loan. We intend to pay you back."

"No money talk," Mike ruled. "There's a lifetime ahead. This week, think extravagantly."

SUNDAY sped by in a swirl of exuberance. After a merry champagne breakfast in Hilde's room, they all went to see a physician, who bandaged Gisela's leg and gave her antibiotic pills.

After lunch at the Delaneys', dressed in borrowed clothing, they joined the crowds on Kurfürstendamm. Fascinated by the wares displayed in windows, the two women stopped before every shop, marveling over the furs, jewels, cosmetics, liquors, books, paintings, antiques, and other luxuries. They spent ten minutes at a window heaped with electrical appliances.

They went to the famous old Kranzler café, at the hub of Berlin, for cakes and chocolate. The weather was unseasonably warm that afternoon and Ku'damm swarmed with life. Hilde was intoxicated by the throngs of young people in jeans, jackets, and flamboyant T-shirts. She looked so hungry for teenage companionship that Mike imagined she might simply spring from the table and dive like a swimmer into the pool of youths.

The next morning Hilde pounded on the door as Mike and Gisela were arising. "Quick," she called. "We're on television."

Mike switched it on, and they watched as a commentator described the escape and shooting at Spandau lock. A camera panned past the lockhouse, chain link fence, and the lock itself, with the old scow still piled high with gravel, riding in the water.

Allgemeiner Deutscher Nachrichtendienst (ADN), the official East German news agency, branded the shooting of the DDR major "attempted murder." The perpetrator and accomplices, when identified, would be charged with treason, criminal border crossing, and conspiracy to commit murder, said the news service, and the DDR would hold West Berlin authorities responsible for harboring "five vicious criminals."

"Do you think the *Stasi* have pinpointed you yet?" Mike asked.

"If they haven't, they will soon," Gisela said.

"Why worry?" asked Hilde. "They can't touch us over here."

"Maybe not," said Gisela, "but I'd just as soon not have our case tossed about on TV and in the newspapers."

After breakfast Mike accompanied the women to Ka-De-We, the nearby department store, to outfit them with presentable clothes. Confronted with apparel of endless sizes, varieties, and modes, mother and daughter at first could do nothing but stare helplessly. When a brisk young salesclerk discovered that they were refugees from "over there," she summoned a manager, who offered them a discount of forty percent on all purchases. As a result, when the Steinbrechers left the store at noon, Gisela wore a stylish purple dress and a fur-trimmed winter coat. Hilde wore new blue jeans, denim jacket, beads, and boots. Mike carried additional packages, and still more were to be delivered to the hotel.

That evening, Mike placed a call to the Geophysical Fluid Dynamics Laboratory in Princeton, New Jersey. After some shuffling he located the proper official, a Benjamin Garraway, the head of the lab's research program.

With Gisela sitting at his elbow to prompt him, Mike sketched the case of Professor Otto Kleist, the suppression of his manuscript, and his ultimate house arrest. Yes, said Garraway, the lab would welcome Frau Steinbrecher's report on the research. The

Princeton group knew of Kleist, but had not heard from him in some time. Garraway also offered to contact Amnesty International, with a hope of applying pressure on East Germany to release Otto Kleist.

Later that night Mike and Gisela arranged to fly to New York in nine days, after Mike's replacement had arrived in Berlin.

Their days now floated by like a honeymoon, yet richer, deeper, more poignant than either of them had experienced before. Richer, because their ordeal in East Germany fused them together in a manner few honeymoon couples experience. Deeper, because they had to delve beneath two radically different cultures to find their common humanity. More poignant, because they were older than most honeymooners and so knew how quickly these precious hours would pass.

Hilde went off by herself one afternoon and came back to the hotel in an ebullient mood. She had met three young East Germans, two brothers and their cousin, a girl, who had come across the previous year in the trunk of a car driven by the boys' father, a chauffeur for the U.S. embassy in East Berlin. In the days that followed, the young émigrés introduced Hilde to a score of their friends, and she was soon leading a hectic life of her own.

Gisela's leg healed nicely, and she and Mike strolled miles of the city's bustling streets, tramped through the winter woodlands, sauntered along the canals and waterways.

Mike was now disconcertingly in love with Gisela, a state he'd not known for at least a decade, since long before his divorce. He showered her with gifts. He found himself touching her constantly and disliked being parted from her for more than a few minutes. He adored her carriage, her stride, the splash of freckles below her eyes, her occasional blushes, the way she ducked her head when she felt especially affectionate.

Gisela became his sum total of existence. Mike found her infinitely absorbing, and as the focus of this adoration, Gisela bloomed like a wild rose. Each day she seemed more beautiful, softer, more poised.

But though their spirits soared, Mike and Gisela both recognized that culturally they were far apart. Mike learned to heed his words lest some offhand remark about East Germany offend Gisela. The DDR was her home turf, and she was quick to counter any statement about it that she considered erroneous or unfair. She in turn found much in the West to criticize.

One day while Gisela was picking her way through the *International Herald Tribune* as part of her daily English lesson, she read a story that quoted an American congressman as saying, "Under the surface the United States is more oppressively racist for black people than apartheid South Africa."

She looked at Mike with a frown. "Is that true?"

"No. That's political exaggeration. We have serious racial conflicts, but we're no South Africa."

"Well, if it's not true, why does a newspaper print it?"

"Newspapers print what people say. They don't necessarily agree with the speaker. That's a free press."

Gisela looked perplexed. "You know that statement will be picked up by the Soviets for propaganda in the Third World."

"I suppose so. That's one of the hazards of democracy."

"So why doesn't your President stop that kind of talk? If it's false, the congressman has no right to hurt his country."

"The President?" Mike was astounded. "How could he possibly monitor what two hundred and twenty million people say?"

"He could appoint people to do it for him."

"And suppose that appointed agency decided that a certain Professor Otto Kleist could not publish or say anything about the increase of carbon dioxide in the atmosphere?"

"Oh, Miguel, you know they'd never do that."

"Censors rule against anybody who displeases them."

"You and I are talking about two entirely different things."

"No, we're not. It's the same issue—freedom of speech."

"There's no absolute freedom." Gisela's jaw was set.

"I agree. Look, Gisela, let's knock this off." He couldn't stand even a few minutes of estrangement. "Soak up the freedoms on this side for a month or so and then we can try again."

They were edgy with each other as they dressed to go out, a bit distant walking along the corridor to the elevator. But then Mike seized and kissed her, and Gisela held him in turn, clinging fiercely. To the lovers, differences in attitude and background seemed trivial when compared with their hunger for each other.

And so the Berlin days rushed to a close. Mike's replacement arrived on Monday, absorbed a three-hour briefing by Mike and Walter Delaney, and passed through Checkpoint Charlie on Tuesday on his way to Leipzig.

That night of early January was the last in Berlin for Mike, Gisela, and Hilde before their flight to New York. Dave Simmons had traveled from Fulda to join them for a farewell dinner.

For this dinner, Mike wanted the women to wear corsages. He would get them at a florist's shop over on Marburgerstrasse.

At the last minute, Gisela decided to go with him. She put on a tailored brown woolen coat and a feathered brown felt hat that Mike had bought her. Then arm in arm the lovers stepped out into the brisk, clear night. Mike noticed how Gisela's shoulder-length hair swung in cadence with her stride, reminding him of the harmonies of music. Yes, she had entered his life like a new, powerful symphony; perhaps transformed that life, for it occurred to him that since her arrival, no wall had loomed in his dreams, nor had a single phantom or ghoul invaded his nights.

"Gisela!" The shout came from a voice they both knew.

It was Ulli Beitz, leaning out the window of a black sedan that had halted opposite them on Augsburgerstrasse. Rays of a streetlamp etched her face and her familiar thundercloud of hair.

"Come on over, Gisela!" Ulli waved gaily.

Gisela ran across the street to greet her. Mike followed at a leisurely pace. Ulli, half out the window, leaned forward to touch her friend. Gisela opened her arms.

At that instant, in a blur of movement, a door flew open and arms from within the car seized Gisela, whose feet flew off the pavement as she was pulled inside. The door slammed shut and the black sedan vaulted forward with a clash of gears. Mike lunged at a rear door handle, but missed and went sprawling on the pavement. He tried to read the rear license plate, but the automobile was already veering right into Rankestrasse, its tires screeching.

Mike scrambled to his feet, then sprinted toward the florist's shop at the corner of Marburgerstrasse. He must phone the police. He tried to think as he ran. What make was the car? A Volga? Yes, a Soviet Volga with diplomatic plates.

AT NOON on Wednesday, January 6, Rolf von Staufen, press officer to the mayor, faced a dozen reporters in West Berlin's city hall and read a statement:

> "The mayor today lodged a strenuous protest with the government of the DDR against a gross violation of the 1971 four-power agreements covering operation of this city.
>
> "The mayor referred to the brazen kidnapping on Augsburgerstrasse last night, under cover of diplomatic immunity, of a recent refugee from the Deutsche Demokratische Republik. A respected professional, a doctor of chemistry, this woman was apparently concealed on the floor of a Soviet Volga sedan and taken across at the Friedrichstrasse transit point under cover of diplomatic immunity. Known officers of the DDR Ministry of State Security were identified riding in the kidnap vehicle.
>
> "It is with a heavy heart that the mayor files this protest. Kidnapping of an innocent civilian stains the good record of cooperation and détente that has prevailed between the two halves of the divided city in recent years.
>
> "The mayor calls upon East Berlin officials to release Frau Dr. Gisela Steinbrecher at once and to permit her to travel in peace where she pleases."

A reporter for *Die Welt* asked if Frau Dr. Steinbrecher was one of the five persons who escaped through Spandau lock on the second night of Christmas. Yes, replied the press officer.

A correspondent for the Associated Press asked what happened to Frau Steinbrecher after she was taken across the frontier. The press officer said it "was understood" that the SSD had detained her for interrogation.

"What does the mayor propose to do if the DDR ignores his demand?" asked another reporter.

"If and when that occurs," replied von Staufen, "appropriate measures will be considered."

They sat disconsolately in Walter Delaney's living room in the pale afternoon sunlight, like the bereaved just returned from graveside rites. Mike Simmons stirred his fourth cup of coffee. Hilde Steinbrecher, dry-eyed at last, leafed through a copy of *Stern*. Dave Simmons stretched his long legs and gazed at the fireplace with its crackling birch logs.

When the wall phone rang, Walter Delaney answered, then gestured to Mike. "For you. The police."

"You take it, Walt. You know my German's not good enough."

Mike felt drained, interested in little but sleep. Last night had been an emotional roller coaster. First came the shock, then a burst of frantic activity, alerting the police, Delaney, and the U.S. mission. He went through an outpouring of rage against the East German regime, then comforted Hilde in her tears only to find himself sobbing as well.

"Bad news." Delaney replaced the phone in its wall bracket. "The East German army engineer who got slugged at the lockhouse died this morning of a fractured skull."

The news hit Mike like a blow to the stomach. The implication took immediate shape: Gisela's chances of ever leaving the DDR had suddenly plunged toward zero.

"The guy was named Horst Ludendorff." Delaney took a seat on the sofa beside Hilde. "Unfortunately for us, he'd been a very popular East German bike champion back in the 1950s."

There was a long silence. At last Hilde said, "That means they'll put Mother on trial?"

"It means a trial, so called," said Delaney, "certain conviction, and probably a long term in prison."

"So what's our next step?" Dave wanted action.

"I think the wisest course right now is to do nothing," said Delaney. "Relations between the two Berlins and the two Germanys are very complex; there are many interlocking services. The two sides talk like enemies, but they know they need each other. So I'd advise watchful waiting to see what the governments do."

They talked for some time. Fearful that Hilde too might be kidnapped, they arranged for her to stay with the family whose teenage children had befriended her. Then Dave reserved a seat

Crossing in Berlin

on an afternoon flight to return to Fulda. As they waited at the airport for his plane, Dave, in a rare gesture, threw an arm around his father's shoulders. "I wish I'd met her, Pop. I guess you know what I feel for you."

"It's as if we'd just buried her." Mike felt his throat tighten. "I love her, Dave."

"I know." He gripped Mike's shoulder. "You going to stay here or go back to the States?"

"I couldn't bear to leave now. She's just a couple of miles away, you know." He motioned to the east. "I'll stay put. I'll tell the company I need a rest and take a leave of absence. How long, I don't know."

Dave picked up his bag. "I'm being transferred, but I'll be in Fulda for a while. If you feel low, call me. That's an order."

"Okay, commander."

Back at his hotel, Mike switched on the television and watched the evening news. It led off with the usual quota of international misery, Arabs and Jews fighting in Jerusalem, a jumbo-jet crash in Kenya; then came news from East Berlin.

"The public prosecutor of East Berlin," said the West German announcer, "states that Gisela Steinbrecher of Dresden will be tried on a charge of being an accessory to the murder of Horst Ludendorff, according to ADN, the official East German news agency. Ludendorff, who the prosecutor contended was shot and brutally beaten by the Steinbrecher woman and four other alleged criminals, died today in a hospital here."

Like TV commentators the world over, this one offered his dread tidings in a pleasant conversational tone. "In another aspect of the case, ADN quotes DDR Minister of Justice Anton Zumpe, rejecting as totally absurd the charge by the mayor of West Berlin that Frau Steinbrecher was kidnapped by DDR security agents riding in a Soviet Volga with diplomatic plates. The minister said that on the contrary, Frau Steinbrecher returned to DDR territory of her own volition and confessed her crime to the authorities. Zumpe will therefore recommend, in event of the Steinbrecher woman's conviction, that the judge take her change of heart into consideration when sentencing the offender."

The phrase "returned to DDR territory of her own volition" echoed long after Mike had turned off the TV. Ordinarily he would have flared angrily at the official lies. But tonight he lacked the will to dispute such a brazen perversion of the truth. The minister had turned the kidnapping inside out like a reversible jacket, so that rough dark leather became a cheerful plaid.

THE chancellor of West Germany worked late that night. A bright moon etched the city of Bonn and bathed the Rhine and the majestic poplars that bordered the swiftly flowing river just below the chancellery.

Chancellor Kurt Rauschnig had grappled all day with the kidnapping of Gisela Steinbrecher, the death of a wounded officer, and the DDR's charge of murder. What did this explosive event portend for the beleaguered city?

Early that morning he had marshaled a crisis committee, which pondered that question throughout the day and submitted its report to him early that evening. He dined at his desk and threshed out all aspects of the case. Now, as the hour neared midnight, Rauschnig asked a secretary to put through a call on the scrambled secure channel to West Berlin's mayor, Peter Leonhard, at his home.

He hoped this talk would not prove difficult. He expected a protest, but on the other hand, Peter owed him more than one favor. He had never faltered when Leonhard pressed him for more federal funds for the always fiscally embarrassed city.

"Peter!" the chancellor boomed. "Anything new on this kidnapping matter?"

"Not unless it's the American. Did I tell you that there was an American businessman mixed up in the Steinbrecher escape?"

"*Ja, ja.* I saw that in the intelligence report. What's your next move, Peter?"

"Tomorrow I plan to expose the lie of the DDR minister of justice. Zumpe has the gall to say that Frau Steinbrecher returned over there of her own free will." Mayor Leonhard laughed. "Such audacity! The poor woman was dragged headfirst into that car in view of a dozen people. We have their names."

The chancellor let silence rule the line. He was noted for his long and ambiguous pauses. "Ordinarily I would applaud that plan of attack, Peter, but I've been gathering advice from many sources, and I've come up with quite a different approach. May I give you a bit of my thinking?"

"Naturally."

"We're not at all sure what this kidnapping portends for our current viable accommodations with the other side. We have a hint that the abduction may have stemmed from a feud between two SSD officials. We just don't know. In these circumstances, I believe the wisest course may be to say nothing for a few days."

"But I'm responsible for the safety of our city's streets. If I fail to nail the lie, Berliners will hold me in contempt."

Rauschnig lowered his voice. "There's a chance that if the other side also says nothing, the incident may be forgotten as the days and weeks go by."

"Too many people know of this, Herr Chancellor."

"True. I appreciate your point. Yet it would be irresponsible to let this escalate into a crisis that we might have prevented." Again Rauschnig let silence hover on the line. "Especially with the Weimar meeting coming up."

Mayor Leonhard belonged to the high-level political team that would brief the chancellor before his summit conference with the DDR chairman, Heinrich Volpe, in the city of Weimar.

"Naturally. That would be most unfortunate." The mayor was feeling the pressure. "What would you advise me to do?"

"If at all possible, Peter, I wish that you would say nothing tomorrow and see if this incident will fade away, as so many others have. After all, when we weigh the interests of one person against the well-being of sixty-two million people in the Federal Republic..."

"Of course." Leonhard thought the exact phrase should be *freedom* of one person, but he did not quibble. "Sometimes here in Berlin, up against the Wall, we lose perspective."

"Your perspective's a good one, Peter. If it weren't for the Weimar meeting..."

"I'll do my best, Herr Chancellor, to defuse the issue."

CHAPTER TEN

Because of the need to economize, Mike had moved from his hotel to an old two-room apartment on Bleibstreustrasse, between Ku'damm and the main railroad line. At the home office, Mark Jacoby had approved a three-month leave of absence from Todd Elevator, and Mike's last paycheck had arrived ten days ago. Now he would have to draw on his savings for an indefinite period.

After those first fevered days following Gisela's kidnapping, Mike had entered a void; spokesmen for the two opposing Berlins had lapsed into a puzzling and, to Mike, deafening silence. Not another word had been heard from any official, East or West. The press appeared to have joined in the fraternity of silence.

Winter settled in, and as the cold strengthened its grip, Mike's vigil in Berlin assumed the shapeless aspect of futility. What indeed could he accomplish here? Yet he could not bring himself to leave. Whenever the urge surfaced, he thought of Gisela huddled in a cell somewhere in East Berlin, only a few miles away. He loved her and he could not tear himself away from this divided city while she remained in either half. So he hung on, battling depression and hopelessness by such tactics as daily runs in the crackling air, taking German lessons, and dining twice a week with Hilde, with whom he felt a warm rapport.

Day after day dragged by without news of any kind. Then late one afternoon he received a phone call from Ingrid, who said that she had news and would wait for him at the Tano.

In the isolated rear booth, Ingrid greeted him like an old ally, and indeed he had come to trust her as he would a friend.

"What's the news?" he asked. He had no hope.

"Bad, I'm afraid, Herr Simmons." She studied him through a veil of smoke. "Frau Steinbrecher was tried in secret in East Berlin three days ago. Her lawyer, appointed by the court, presented no evidence on her behalf, merely petitioned for leniency because, he said, she had returned of her own volition."

"And?" Already he could feel the hurt.

"She was convicted on three counts: treason, criminal border crossing, and conspiracy to commit murder. The judge sentenced her"—she touched his arm—"to twenty years in prison."

A dull gray weariness settled over him. He had expected the worst and the worst had come. He felt only numb despair.

"She began serving time yesterday." Ingrid's voice seemed to echo in some distant cave. "We're not sure where."

"Twenty years." A generation of prison life. Gray hair, the sad shuffle of an elderly inmate.

"We all sympathize with you. None of us were prepared for a kidnapping." Ingrid sounded somewhat petulant.

"I feel so damn hopeless, Ingrid." The weariness pressed like a heavy weight.

She questioned him about his life, his finances, his plans; and Mike, glad to have a listener, poured out his frustrations.

When he finished she said, "If you're short of funds, Herr Dahlem can lend you a few thousand at no interest."

"No, I'll manage. But thanks."

"We can get a message to Frau Steinbrecher. It might take weeks, but if you have some word you wish to pass . . ."

"Yes, tell her that I love her always." His voice seemed to belong to some melancholy stranger. "And not to lose hope."

Back at the apartment, he telephoned Hilde. The girl took it bravely at first, but then she broke into tears, and for a long time her sobs were the only sound between them. "We will figure out some way," he said when Hilde's weeping subsided. But he could not mask his feeling of doom.

He broke the news to Delaney and then wrote to Dave, who was now in the States under detached-duty orders for specialized helicopter training. He had just addressed and sealed the letter to Dave when it happened: the rage blew up as suddenly as a tornado, ripping his melancholy to shreds.

He paced the kitchen where he'd been writing on the creaky wooden table. He smashed his fist against the swinging kitchen door and sent it banging back on its hinges. And as he raged, great tides of energy swept through him. To hell with Delaney's watchful waiting. Somehow he would find a way to help Gisela.

He was still pacing, his mind steaming, when the telephone

rang. "It's been weeks, Michael." A British accent. "I tracked you through your hotel. Dave forgot to tell me you'd moved."

"Spider!" Strange, he'd just been thinking, Call Spider Butler in Helmstedt. He knows the politics of the Wall, he hates the Wall, and he's a shrewd operator. "I got awful news today, Spider. They've sentenced Gisela to twenty years."

"I know. That's why I rang you as soon as I got word."

"Spider, I'm stymied. I need help. Could I come over tomorrow and see you?"

"Better I come there. I have a few errands in Berlin anyway. I'll take the morning train and be there for lunch."

Mike met Spider Butler in the grimy rail station near the Bahnhof Zoo. They walked to the Italian restaurant on Marburgerstrasse where Mike had dined with Walt Delaney.

In a side booth, they ordered wine and lasagna. Mike brought Butler up to date on himself and Gisela since that rainy night at the border. "But now," he concluded, "I don't know where to turn. Everybody seems to have forgotten the kidnapping already."

Butler nodded. "These governments usually follow the same script. If it's a simple escape, neither side says a word. If it's something unusual, they bluster a bit, but then close down like clams. Remember what I said that night at the border, Michael. Except for the East German people, almost everyone is secretly happy with the Wall."

"Yeah, I'm learning that firsthand."

Butler leveled his fork at him. "But what you haven't learned is that you, Michael Simmons, have a powerful weapon that could blast a nice big hole in that Wall."

"I do?" Mike's smile was a faint one. "What is it?"

"Publicity! The power of the press! You have one of the great stories of today's Wall. The escapes, shootings, seizures—they happen every week. People are hardened to them. But your story adds romance, the ancient bond between man and woman."

"Suppose Gisela's story were featured," said Mike. "You think that would build up enough pressure to force her release?"

"It could if you do it right, Michael. It might build into something big. Is there any part of this thing you haven't told me?"

"Do you know about Otto Kleist?"

"Kleist?" Butler frowned. "No. Who's he?"

Mike told of the chemist's research on carbon dioxide in the atmosphere and of Kleist's house arrest.

"Wizard." Butler beamed. "Romance and science."

Together they planned approaches to the press. Butler would tip off newsmen to hidden aspects of the escape and kidnapping. Mike would make himself available for interviews and would encourage Hilde to do likewise.

They parted in midafternoon. "Let's stay in touch," said the Spider. "If we're smart, this just might work."

The first call came from Hester McKinnon, a feature writer for the *International Herald Tribune*. She made a date to interview both Mike and Hilde, and she arrived punctually at four thirty the same afternoon with a photographer.

Under a two-column headline several days later, the story began on the front page and covered considerable space inside. McKinnon covered all angles of the case, including Dr. Kleist, the border ordeal of mother and daughter, the kidnapping, and Gisela's secret conviction. Hilde cut out the story and put it into a folder.

After that, the phone in the kitchen of the gloomy apartment rang a dozen times a day. *Bild* of Hamburg, *The New York Times*, the Frankfurter *Allgemeine Zeitung*, *The Wall Street Journal*, CBS, and *Le Monde* of Paris—all sought interviews.

These first splatters of publicity turned into a downpour. The Washington *Post* and the Los Angeles *Times* interviewed Mike and Hilde, as did the Sydney *Daily Telegraph* in Australia and Rio de Janeiro's *Jornal do Brasil*. Almost every major television network in Europe, the United States, and South America devoted time to the story.

The first direct response to this deluge of publicity came not from a government but from Todd Elevator, Inc. Mike answered the phone one evening to hear the voice of Mark Jacoby, his chief, calling from New York.

"You're all over the damn tube and the feature sections," Jacoby said. "Pretty clever, that elevator code, old buddy."

"I thought you'd like that."

"But they weren't very happy up on the twelfth floor." Jacoby's tone became confidential. "They didn't like bringing Todd into the picture. Frankly, the East-bloc business has become quite a thing for Todd. We did seventeen million gross last year in Lenin country, and we figure to do better this year."

"Terrific, Mark. But what are you leading up to?"

"I'm afraid it's not the best news, Mike. The twelfth floor has canceled your leave. You'll have to make other arrangements."

"You mean I'm fired?"

"Listen, old buddy, any company trying to do business with the Russians or their friends just can't afford to have Michael Simmons on the payroll. As one of Todd's old international hands, you must realize that as much as we do."

"Yep. An old hand for twenty-five years—and no gold watch." Mike was steaming now. "Look, Mark, you tell the twelfth floor for me that I understand Todd's position completely. And I'm sure Todd will likewise understand the steps I'm forced to take."

"Meaning what exactly?"

"A woman I love is being held in prison, sentenced for a fifth of a century. I intend to do everything and anything possible to get her out. When you report back to the twelfth floor, please quote me on that—old buddy."

When the Associated Press called for its nightly check on the story that was catching the fancy of news editors around the world, Mike told of his dismissal because his company coveted Communist business so much. The next morning the New York *Daily News* carried the headline: WALL FIGHTER FIRED.

BY MID-FEBRUARY the Wall-severed romance of Gisela Steinbrecher and Michael Simmons had captured the emotions of millions of people around the world. The stormier the winds and the deeper the snow, the more people took refuge indoors— and the more they read, saw, and heard of the luckless lovers. Their thirst for news and gossip about the couple seemed unquenchable. Hilde's folder of clippings grew.

Mail poured in from almost every continent, some addressed

merely "Michael Simmons, West Berlin." One day alone brought Mike more than a hundred letters, including a brochure advertising a resort in the Bahamas, with the manager's invitation "to stay as our guests when Gisela wins her release."

Initially, public interest focused exclusively on Mike, Hilde, and Gisela, but as weeks passed, the predicament of Otto Kleist attracted more and more attention, and the pressure for official action mounted steadily. Amnesty International placed Dr. Kleist on its ten-most-wanted list—those political prisoners whom the human rights society wanted released most. More than a thousand chemists, from many countries, signed a petition beseeching the East German government to permit Kleist to publish his findings and to travel wherever he wished.

Mike was almost never alone now. If journalists and electronics crews were not tramping about his apartment, he was off dining with reporters, officials, and new acquaintances. People recognized him on the street, and much as he fought against it, Mike found himself developing a public personality, a kind of hollow shell in which often used phrases echoed like political bromides. Only his nights remained unaltered. Demons, marauders, and misshapen brutes terrorized the shadowed hours.

Mike learned that his ready access to the media gave him a kind of power he had never known before. He had told the Associated Press the reason he'd been fired, and a week later a subdued Mark Jacoby telephoned him from New York.

Jacoby complained, "I had no idea you'd repeat our conversation to the media, Mike. They always distort accounts."

"You didn't listen, Mark. I told you I intended to do everything and anything I could to get Gisela Steinbrecher out of prison. And the press, incidentally, quoted me accurately."

"I think you acted out of a spirit of revenge." Jacoby sounded put upon. "Airing your dismissal can't possibly help your woman."

"I disagree. It shows everybody just how far and how insidiously the Wall's influence goes."

"Well, in any case, I'm authorized to offer you a deal."

"Careful, Mark. Remember I'll use anything you say if it'll help the cause."

Jacoby cleared his throat. "Before I relay our proposition, I'll need your promise that you won't mention it to anyone."

"Okay." Mike's curiosity won out. "You have my word."

"If you agree not to mention Todd again to the media, we'll mail you a check for six months' salary today."

"Some people would call that a bribe." The lure of money was surprisingly pale. "No thanks, Mark."

"We can make that a year's salary."

"Say, you guys must be hurting. No, not for any amount. That's it, old buddy."

Another surprising result of Mike's publicity campaign was a phone call from Werner Lanz, who had been living with his brother in Frankfurt. Lanz, the former brigade leader, confided that he had information of vital concern to Mike and offered to fly to Berlin the next day for a confidential talk.

Mike and Hilde met Lanz the next afternoon at Tegel airport. The stocky Leipziger refused all but small talk on the bus ride into the city's center. He declined to talk in Mike's apartment or anywhere else indoors, insisting despite the freezing weather that they talk outside. So, bundled against the cold, they stomped along Budapesterstrasse in the crisp night air. Hilde translated for Mike as Lanz told his story.

Two nights ago an old friend from Leipzig, on a business trip to Frankfurt, had quietly defected and sought refuge in the home of Lanz's brother. Werner had long known that his friend served as a secret agent of the SSD in Leipzig. He had not been prepared, however, for some of the revelations that poured forth when the dam of secrecy broke.

"Right off you should know," said Lanz, "that Wolfgang Dahlem and the core of his group are informers for the DDR."

"Come on, Werner. That's impossible." Mike had expected anything but this.

"I thought so too, until I heard all the particulars."

"If that's true, how could you and Hilde and the rest have gotten out?"

"Dahlem has a cozy arrangement with the *Stasi*. He's allowed to bring out twenty people a year without interference. In return, he reports on anybody and anything over here that the SSD orders."

"That's awfully hard to believe, Werner."

"Ingrid's code name as a DDR informer is Sparrow," Lanz went on. "Dahlem is Lark, and Hans is Hawk."

"How about Erich, who guided us out?" asked Hilde.

"No. He had no connection with the *Stasi*. None of the people working for Dahlem in the DDR are informers. Only the three here in West Berlin—Dahlem, Ingrid, and Hans. Everyone else is clean. That's why the outfit functions so smoothly. As for Gisela," Lanz continued, "my friend says there is no question that Dahlem had her under constant watch. On the night of her seizure, Hans was stationed across from your hotel. He used a walkie-talkie to alert the kidnap car. The operation had its own code name—Sundown."

"Ironic." Mike felt the bitterness rising. "One thing bugs me, Werner. I can't understand why the DDR wheels resorted to kidnapping. That seems like tremendous overkill. Gisela had no secrets that I know of."

"My friend speculated that the seizure arose from rivalry between two SSD department heads—Heinz Lungwitz, chief of computer intelligence, and Gerhard Ehrengruber, chief of interrogation. When Ehrengruber's people questioned you, Mike, they failed to discover your part in Gisela's escape attempt. That was pieced together by one of Lungwitz's computer specialists. Ehrengruber apparently felt so outwitted that he vowed to get Frau Steinbrecher back somehow. So he prevailed upon the head of the SSD to have her snatched out of West Berlin."

"A rash act."

Lanz agreed. "It's rumored inside the SSD that Chairman Volpe didn't like it, especially because he is soon to meet with the West German chancellor. My friend looks for a shake-up in the SSD."

"That gives me some hope, Werner. I'm indebted to you."

The biting cold at last forced them indoors. They dined before an open fire at a favorite restaurant, where they confined themselves to small talk. Later Mike and Hilde accompanied Lanz to the Hotel Am Zoo, then took a taxi to Hilde's apartment. During the drive, Mike said, "I've decided to face Dahlem and Ingrid right away—tonight. If you haven't heard from me by midnight, I want you to call Walt Delaney and have him take you to the police. Then you tell them everything we heard from Lanz. Here's Dahlem's address." He jotted it down.

Back at his apartment, Mike called Ingrid. "I must see you and Herr Dahlem together tonight," he said.

"I'm not sure that can be arranged so quickly." Ingrid's tone was guarded. "What's this about?"

"I'm sorry I can't say over the phone—except that it's of vital concern to your business."

"Let me see what I can do, Herr Simmons. I'll call you back."

Curiosity surmounts formidable obstacles. Dahlem and Ingrid, it turned out, could see him on short notice after all.

A few minutes later Mike faced Hans in apartment 2-A in the building on Fasanenstrasse, and again the big man passed his hands rapidly over Mike's jacket and trousers.

Wolfgang Dahlem and Ingrid awaited him on the corduroy couch. Ingrid, as usual, wore sunglasses. Dahlem gave the same impression of discretion and class that Mike had noticed on their previous meeting. Hans prepared to leave the room.

"Please, I'd prefer that Hans stay with us," said Mike.

Dahlem shrugged. "As you wish." He motioned Mike to a chair. "And so, Mr. Simmons?"

"I have some information of value to you." Mike assumed a troubled look. "But first, Herr Dahlem, I want to take you up on your generous offer, as relayed by Ingrid, to lend me some money. Frankly, I'm in a financial jam and I need funds tonight." He drew out savings passbooks from two New York banks. "I have thirty-five thousand dollars on deposit, but it will take time to get the money from the States, and I need it now."

"Just how much do you need?" Dahlem was wary.

"Forty thousand marks."

"That's a formidable amount to be asking for in the middle of the night, Mr. Simmons. What is this information so valuable to my business?"

"I need to clear up this money thing first. I'm in a fix. If I don't produce tonight, they'll beat the hell out of me." Mike put on a mask of anguish. Was he carrying this off?

Dahlem studied him in silence. "I haven't got that kind of money here. I only keep a sum for emergencies."

"How much? If I could just make a decent down payment tonight . . ."

"Fourteen thousand marks is all I have."

"Then let me have it, please. I'll sign an IOU and put up these two bank accounts for collateral."

"That won't be necessary. Hans is our insurance." Hans beamed like a child and flexed his enormous hands. Dahlem turned to Ingrid. "Fetch that cash from the safe." He spoke as casually as a man ordering a drink.

Ingrid walked into the adjoining bedroom and closed the door. The three men waited wordlessly. Returning, Ingrid handed Dahlem an envelope and he counted out ten bills of a thousand marks each and slightly more than four thousand in smaller denominations. He handed the currency to Mike.

"And now. This vital concern?" Dahlem's smile was cool, self-assured, even a bit condescending.

Mike got up. "I'm here to lay some ugly facts on the line, Herr Dahlem, but first you should know that any effort to harm me or take back the money will be useless." He spoke with a confidence he did not feel. "Two bodyguards are waiting outside. They'll come up here in half an hour if I'm not out by then."

Dahlem fixed Mike with his deep blue eyes. "That's an ominous opening, Mr. Simmons."

"I have solid information that you helped the SSD kidnap Gisela Steinbrecher."

No one made a sound. Ingrid, still standing, fingered her sunglasses. Dahlem sat motionless. Finally he broke the silence. "That's the most outrageous statement ever made in this room, Mr. Simmons. It is also, of course, completely false."

"So I thought when I first heard it." Mike kept his eyes on Dahlem. "But not after I learned the facts. You and Ingrid and Hans have been secret informers for the SSD for many years."

"You're a liar," said Dahlem without heat. "Do you realize that I could sue you in our courts for—what's the word, calumny?"

"You could, but you won't, because you'd stand exposed as a spy for the East Germans."

"That's all, Simmons." Dahlem rose to his feet. Like a huge robot, Hans took a step forward. "You will leave at once. If you don't, we'll throw you out."

"If that happens, I'll call a press conference tomorrow morning." Mike paused for effect. He relished this. "To describe your work for the DDR—including operation Sundown."

Dahlem stood very still.

Mike pressed his advantage. "For Sundown, we can thank those three clever birds, Lark, Sparrow, and Hawk."

Dahlem slowly settled back onto the couch. His blue eyes held Mike in a steady gaze. "Perhaps you'd better tell us exactly what you want," he said at last.

"You have the gall to ask me what I want!" Mike felt the swift, pumping rhythm of his anger. "You helped kidnap the woman I love and send her up for twenty years. . . . Twenty years! And then you send the little Sparrow to break the news. 'We have means to get a message to Frau Steinbrecher,' she says. I'll bet you do. I want the rest of the twenty-five thousand dollars I paid you, and I want it by tomorrow noon."

"Is that all?" Dahlem's low tone betrayed no emotion.

"No. I demand that you go to work at once to spring Gisela from prison. If she's not out in six weeks, the press gets the full story on Lark, Sparrow, and Hawk."

"And if she's released, what prevents you, then, from making these false allegations public?"

"You think I want to be knocked off?" Mike nodded toward the big man.

"For that matter, Hans could do a fair job on you right now."

Mike forced a laugh. "Do you think I'm stupid? My hired men are waiting across the street." He glanced at his wristwatch. "If I'm not out in—let's see, another ten minutes—they'll be up here to find out why."

Dahlem stared at Mike as if trying to assess his degree of

determination. "I'll have the rest of the money for you by noon," he said flatly.

"What about Gisela?"

"I'll make some preliminary calls first thing in the morning."

Mike started toward the foyer. "I'll be back at noon tomorrow," he said at the door. Dahlem nodded.

Mike returned the next day, and he was not surprised when the building superintendent, scratching at his bald head, said that the three people in number 2-A had left shortly before six that morning for a long vacation.

That afternoon Mike disclosed at a press conference that Wolfgang Dahlem, the most reputable of the professional escape merchants, had for years been a secret informer of the SSD, along with his top assistants.

CHAPTER ELEVEN

PRESIDENT McCullough ceased his nervous pacing about the Oval Office and leveled a finger at his friend. "You know the joke of it? The Todd Elevator people never gave me a single dime for my campaign." He frowned as he continued his walking monologue. "But because some philandering Todd executive had the hots for one of those East German blondes, I get creamed by the press. They made me look like a fool this morning, Sam."

"Oh, Mr. President, that's going too far." Sam Wertheimer knew the signs. Time to rein in his old friend. He continued soothingly. "You said that eventually the Wall must come down because freemen will not tolerate it forever. That's true enough."

"Then came Porter's question and the others that followed, all about whether I would use force to demolish the Wall. I had to dodge and equivocate and fall back on platitudes."

President McCullough dropped into a leather armchair and gazed out moodily as winter twilight veiled the South Lawn of the White House. He and the presidential counsel, Sam Wertheimer, met almost every evening to assess the events of the day.

"Strange how this romance of a businessman and a lady editor has caught the people's fancy," McCullough mused.

"It's made people over here think about the Wall again, and that's all to the good."

"Good for them, but not for me. The Wall forces me to be a hypocrite. Publicly I have to view it as an abomination, but privately, well, you know we're not exactly unhappy it's there."

"Yeah. Can you imagine competing economically against a united Germany?"

McCullough drummed on the arm of his leather chair. "I just wish this man and his girl would vanish somehow. No way can I get the Soviets to put pressure on the East Germans without their coming back at us with exorbitant demands."

"We can't make the Steinbrecher woman vanish, or get her out of prison, but maybe there's a way to cut her down to size so she'll fade out of the evening news."

"How, Sam?" McCullough looked up eagerly.

"Best you don't know, Mr. President. Then you won't have to deny or affirm. Just trust me. There's an angle I can plant with the press. Something about the lady's background, let's say."

MIKE heard the news from Hester McKinnon of the *International Herald Tribune*. When she called from Paris, Mike was mulling over the optimistic conjectures of Spider Butler and Walt Delaney, with whom he had just had lunch. Both men thought that Mike's publicity push had generated terrific pressure and that sooner or later East Germany would have to release Gisela. Delaney had predicted she'd get out before the end of the year. Butler had wanted to bet ten pounds that she'd come across by early June. Now, as he took the call from Paris, Mike felt more confident than he had in days. If he persevered, held steady, he and Hilde would win Gisela's freedom.

"McKinnon of the *Herald Tribune*," Hester began abruptly. "We have a wire story out of Washington quoting reliable intelligence sources as stating that Frau Steinbrecher is actually an East German secret agent in the employ of the SSD."

"What? That's ridiculous." Mike was stunned. "It was the *Stasi* who kidnapped her."

McKinnon went on. "We also have a story out of Moscow.

Premier Nikolai Varentsov says that Frau Steinbrecher is a spy for West Germany."

"Why, that's just as crazy!"

"The American intelligence people say that Gisela's kidnapping was faked. After holding her a few months, they say, the DDR will let her return to the West, where she can move about the world with you, working for the SSD wherever she goes."

"I tell you that's insane."

"But, of course, you've only known Gisela Steinbrecher for, let's see . . . about two weeks altogether. Isn't that right?"

"Yes, but—"

McKinnon interrupted. "You don't have any proof that she isn't an agent, do you?"

"No, but how could anyone . . . Could you prove you're not a spy for the Soviets? Anybody can make charges of espionage."

Hester McKinnon turned out to be the advance scout of an invading horde. Newsmen and newswomen phoned from papers, TV networks, and press agencies from as far away as Johannesburg, Hong Kong, and Buenos Aires. In late afternoon Mike squeezed in a call to Hilde. She came over and handled many of the interviews, in a voice brimming with indignation.

The news fraternity wanted proof of innocence—dates, times, places, character references—that neither Mike nor Hilde could provide. Whatever arguments they marshaled in Gisela's behalf were dismissed as the expected defenses of a loyal friend and a daughter. And as the hours rolled by, Mike came to realize that his revelation two days earlier of the perfidy of the Dahlem trio had been ill timed, to say the least. Dahlem's link to the SSD only served to confuse a picture already laced with suspicions.

In the evening, during a lull, Mike and Hilde sat in the kitchen sipping coffee and eating honey-and-almond cakes. Hilde had become a fond companion. Week by week she was maturing, with less of the brooding and giggles of adolescence and more of her mother's outer grace and inner strength.

"This makes it awfully rough for getting your mother out," said Mike. "The press has made up its mind that Gisela is somebody's secret agent, just whose they're not sure."

Hilde scowled. "They're horrible. I think they don't believe a word I say."

Near midnight Mike took Hilde back to her friends' apartment. They were both weary and dispirited. The prospect of Gisela's release, which at noonday had appeared promising, now looked shadowed and remote. As the taxi moved slowly through the icy streets, a light snowfall lay clean and white on the city, a shroud for dying hopes.

GISELA heard the allegations almost as soon as Mike did. Her informant was a paunchy, middle-aged guard named Gerhard Zweig, who made a practice of relaying news items to Gisela.

On this particular afternoon Zweig leaned against the narrow, barred door of Gisela's cell. "I have news for you, Frau Steinbrecher," he said in a low voice. "You're being called a spy in Washington and in Moscow. Some people claim you're a double agent, working for both sides. I heard it on the radio."

"Not so fast, Herr Zweig. Tell me what has happened, *bitte*."

Delighted to oblige, the guard told her of the Russian and American claims.

"That's frightful news, Herr Zweig. If you can, please let me know any other developments."

"It will be my pleasure." He continued on his rounds, his keys jangling at his belt.

Depressed, Gisela slowly seated herself in a straight-backed wooden chair. She knew this latest news crippled her chances for gaining release, and the thought evoked bitter frustration. But she could not blame people for believing the allegations any more than she could blame Ulli Beitz for beckoning her into the arms of the *Stasi* kidnappers. At first she had hated her best friend for allowing herself to be pressed into the role of traitor, but as the long prison days and nights faded into one another, she realized that Ulli had acted from an instinct for survival.

Now she consciously tried to regain her equilibrium. Sitting on the hard chair in her gray prison smock, she looked about the room where she had lived for thirty-seven days. It was small but not cramped. She could walk five steps on a side. The cell had a washstand, a cot, the chair, and a small wooden table. The four walls, painted a heavy, institutional green, had only two openings: the narrow, barred door and one small window, which had not been washed in weeks.

Prison life had proved less harsh than Gisela had expected, but the dreariness surpassed anything she had imagined. The corridors, dining hall, kitchen, offices, and visitors center were the same dull green as her cell. And the noise, until she learned to tune it out, was maddening. Steel doors clanged; commands, groans, and curses echoed in the corridors; steam pipes rattled, keys jangled, and feet tramped; the kitchen and dining hall sounded like boiler rooms.

In this drab, noisy, lonely world, Gisela found some comfort in the steady disciplined routine of prison life. She also resumed her former practice of praying. In recent years she had been only an intermittent churchgoer. Now she prayed daily. She also sensed that if she were to make this lengthy journey inside these walls without losing her sanity, she must avoid emotional extremes. No peaks, no valleys, just day-by-day living in the psychic lowlands. She planned several intellectual projects: reading the complete works of Goethe and Shakespeare, both available in the prison library; working chemical equations in her head; and writing poetry. She knew her salvation lay within herself, in the honing of mental discipline, questing into the unknown reaches of the spirit, banishing self-pity, searching quietly for serenity.

And so the morning after Gerhard Zweig, the gossipy guard, informed her that both Washington and Moscow reported her as a spy, Gisela awoke without anger. What would be, would be. She stretched, yawned, and deducted another day from her sentence. Thirty-eight gone; seven thousand two hundred and sixty-seven more to go.

On a blustery night in early March, two months after Gisela's kidnapping, Mike Simmons reached a reluctant conclusion. He could do no more. He had lost. They—he, Gisela, and Hilde—had lost. His publicity campaign to free Gisela had sputtered and died, destroyed by those curious accusations from Washington and Moscow. Since then, East Berlin had denied that Gisela Steinbrecher was an East German spy, as "intelligence sources" in Washington alleged; Bonn had denied that she served as a secret agent for West Germany, as Nikolai Varentsov charged in Moscow; and Wolfgang Dahlem had further roiled the waters of suspicion by turning up in Paraguay and claiming that Michael Simmons had been on his *Fluchthelfer* payroll.

Now it had been many days since any reporter had called Mike. Editors had lost interest. The affair was tainted.

It was not as if he had given up without a fight, Mike told himself. He had called a political officer at the American embassy in East Berlin and implored him to intercede on Gisela's behalf, despite the charges from Washington. He had flown to Frankfurt and prevailed on Werner Lanz to contact some of his influential old Party friends. He had also imposed on Walt Delaney to contact a friend of his, a Deutsche Bank official named Rudolf Lerchbacher, who handled all of Todd Elevator's financing in Germany and who also floated loans to East Germany's Finance Ministry. Later Delaney had reported that Lerchbacher had agreed to call the minister of finance and apply pressure.

"But frankly, Mike, Rudi's not at all hopeful," said Delaney. "The finance minister knows the West will continue to extend credit no matter what happens to Frau Steinbrecher. No credit, no trade. And both sides want the trade."

So, in the end, nothing had worked. Day after day passed without word of any kind from East Germany. Now, on this bitter March night, Mike concluded that he could do no more for Gisela. He called Hilde at her friends' apartment to tell her.

"I understand, Mr. Mike," Hilde said when he finished. "I guess trying to do anything more would be a waste of time and energy. So, now? Will you stay here?"

"No. My money will run out soon. It's time I get back to the States and rustle up a new job."

"Don't forget that Mother and I owe you about forty thousand marks—well, twenty-six thousand with what you got back from Dahlem. When I get out of school, I intend to pay it all back."

He was touched. "I didn't lend that money, Hilde. I gave it."

"Oh, I want to pay it back." Her resolute tone reminded him of Gisela. "When do you think you'll go to America?"

"Next Monday. That'll give me time to clear up things here."

"I'll miss you, Mr. Mike," said Hilde. "A lot."

"I wish you'd come with me, Hilde. I think you'd like America."

"No, I've had enough changes for one year. I'm beginning to feel at home here now. But I'd love to visit during vacation."

"We'll put it on the calendar. . . . And Hilde, even if we failed, we did our best."

"Mr. Mike, we didn't fail completely. We did a lot for Dr. Kleist. I'll bet he gets out sometime."

Hilde was right, of course. In his absorption with Gisela, Mike tended to ignore the growing movement in the non-Communist world to force East Germany to terminate the house arrest of Otto Kleist and permit him to travel to the West. Only the day before, Mike had heard a rumor that "the two lawyers" had opened negotiations on Kleist. The lawyers, Joachim Mertz in West Berlin and Max Reschke in the Eastern half of the city, had arranged the exchange of hundreds of political prisoners in East Germany for millions of West German marks. While many denounced the practice as Communist blackmail and the sale of human flesh, the strange brokerage continued for the simple reason that each German state wanted what the other had.

Affluent West Germany wanted to obtain the freedom of political prisoners for a variety of reasons: to forge a reputation as a friend of humanity, to reunite families, to appease voters, and to provide a source of hope for those East Germans who loathed their government's repressive measures. East Germany, well supplied with political prisoners but short on foreign currency, hungered for the Federal Republic's marks.

As for Gisela, someday when the political climate had altered, Mike might return and do battle once more. But for now, and for long months of the future, he must learn to live without her.

ON A bright, frosty morning, the day after Mike had made his decision to return home, his British friend Spider Butler sat in the reception room outside of Kurt Rauschnig's office in Bonn, wondering why he had been summoned by the West German chancellor. A buzzer sounded on the desk of one of the chancellor's secretaries, and she led Butler to the inner office.

Kurt Rauschnig advanced from his wide desk with hand extended. "Ah, how nice of you to come on such short notice," he said, in measured English with a trace of British accent.

"*Guten Morgen.*" Butler shook hands with the chancellor, then continued in German. "I appreciate your kindness, but let's speak German. In this office, German becomes us."

Rauschnig laughed, waved Butler to a seat, and settled behind his desk in a swivel chair. "May I call you Spider?" Rauschnig began. "The name has a ring to it."

"By all means. I'd take offense if you didn't."

"Then to come to the point, Spider. I need your advice, and I trust you to hold everything said here in strict confidence."

"You have my word. In my business, we're used to security."

"Fine. Last night I had a telephoned report from Joachim Mertz in Berlin. You've heard of him?"

Butler nodded. "Many times. The lawyer who negotiates for the release of prisoners over there."

"Exactly." Rauschnig leaned forward on his desk with folded arms. "Several days ago Herr Mertz opened talks with the East German attorney, Max Reschke, on the possible release of Otto Kleist. Late yesterday they reached agreement. Kleist will come across in return for our payment of a hundred and twenty thousand marks. A high price, but his is an unusual case. Kleist will cross Friday night."

"That's good news. But how is our service involved?"

"Here's the point for you. After the deal was concluded, Reschke asked, 'How much would you pay for the woman?'"

"Frau Steinbrecher?"

"Right. Of course, Reschke would never initiate such an inquiry on his own without orders from Chairman Volpe. My guess is that Volpe is just as anxious as I am to come to our Weimar meeting next week with no irritating minor disputes."

The chancellor paused, apparently ordering his thoughts. "I also think Rudolf Lerchbacher of the Deutsche Bank may have had some impact. He has told me that at his request the DDR finance minister had urged Volpe to release Frau Steinbrecher. One never knows for sure when dealing with East Berlin, but the ball now seems to be in our court. How much will we pay for Frau Steinbrecher? Indeed, will we pay anything at all?" Rauschnig leaned back in his chair. "That's where I need your help, Spider. I understand you're acquainted with this American, Michael Simmons. What can you tell me about him?"

"Mike Simmons is a fine human being. I like and trust the man," said Butler. "He is a businessman with a certain touch of innocence I often see in Americans. He says what he thinks. And he's terribly in love with Gisela Steinbrecher."

Rauschnig pressed his fingers together and studied them as if looking for a clue. "And Gisela Steinbrecher. What about her?"

"While I haven't met the woman, I've heard a lot about her from Mike," said Butler. "I don't think she's an agent for anyone. Mike had his suspicions at the start, but she proved herself to him. Personally, I don't believe a word of those charges out of Moscow and Washington."

Rauschnig's knowing smile appeared to be one of assent. "Frau Steinbrecher has never been our agent. As for the Washington charges that she's a DDR spy . . ." He shrugged. "Our intelligence people have not a shred of evidence that she's anything but what she claims to be."

The chancellor talked with Spider for another half hour before he rose and escorted him to the door. "I'd like to do something for Frau Steinbrecher," he said. "But first I must think of the Federal Republic. We'll see."

"You might want to talk to Walter Delaney," said Butler. "He's known Simmons for a long time."

"I intend to. I already have his number from Herr Lerchbacher." Rauschnig put out his hand. "Thank you for your help."

"My pleasure, Herr Chancellor," said Butler.

ON A raw afternoon two days later, the two lawyers, Joachim Mertz and Max Reschke, sat in Reschke's smoky, disordered office on Rosa Luxemburgstrasse in East Berlin.

Crossing in Berlin

Meeting both men for the first time, a stranger would most certainly have mistaken their political loyalties. Mertz, from the capitalist West, was harried and lean. He had a nervous cough and spoke in jerky, unfinished sentences. Reschke, from the Communist East, with its recurrent food shortages, was good-humored and heavy. The two men had become friends despite their differing loyalties. They reveled in the gamesmanship of negotiation, haggling as stubbornly as tradesmen at a bazaar. Yet each knew the other had limits beyond which his government would not permit him to go.

Both men were nicotine addicts, Mertz with his cigars and Reschke with his cigarettes. "As I told you on the phone, Herr Reschke," said Mertz after they had chatted and smoked awhile, "I have the green light to go ahead on the woman."

"A pity. I'm afraid you made the trip for nothing." The East Berlin attorney shook his head. "I regret to say, Herr Mertz, that the signals have changed on this side. I can no longer offer you the woman at any price."

"So I've wasted my—"

"Only an hour or two. Why not relax, Herr Mertz?" Reschke held out a box. "Try my Cuban cigars."

"Thank you." Mertz bit off an end of the cigar. "Too bad about the woman. I wonder what you would have asked for her?"

"We would have needed a hundred thousand marks, Herr Mertz."

"Absurd." He coughed, punctuating his disdain. "We would have offered only ten thousand, you know."

"A joke, my esteemed negotiator, not a serious offer."

"That fellow who tried to make it to Denmark in his homemade submarine . . . You sold him for ten."

"He wasn't a celebrity." Reschke held out a lighted match for the West Berliner's cigar. "We might have been persuaded to drop to ninety."

"She's not a major general, but we might have gone to fifteen."

"I must remind you. The woman's not for sale, so it's futile to talk price. Tell me, how is Frau Mertz's health?"

"The usual. Another cold. She stays in bed and takes nose

drops." Mertz glanced down. "This ashtray's smoldering. One stray spark . . . They'd hold me for arson."

Reschke tamped out the fire with a pencil and dumped the ashes into a wastebasket. "As long as we're here, Herr Mertz, why not try to reach a figure that might guide us to a quick settlement at a later date, in case the climate . . . Subject always, of course, to the wear and tear of inflation."

"Naturally."

"As I said, we might have taken ninety."

"Ninety!" Mertz laughed in mock disgust. "My people might go to twenty-five—if, of course, you ever let the poor woman go."

"You're not in our range, Herr Mertz. She was guilty of conspiring to murder an innocent civil engineer."

"You mean an armed major in the People's Army. Let's not be loose with the facts. And she didn't conspire to murder. She was at least fifty meters away when Ludendorff was slugged in a fight." Mertz propped his feet on the wastebasket. "Now, when are you going to name a sensible price for the woman?"

"If this had been real bargaining, I would have required seventy, as recompense for the woman's skills, which would be lost to the nation. We are dealing here with an editor who has a Ph.D., schooled and trained at great expense to the state."

"Thirty."

Reschke waved off a billow of smoke. "An onlooker, you know, might note that if we split the difference, we'd arrive at fifty."

"Nonsense. I would, however, have gone to thirty-five . . . possibly forty." Mertz held out his hand.

"Done." Reschke shook it. "Forty thousand marks when and if my government changes its mind."

"Too bad your people decided not to deal for the woman. It would have made a neat, tidy . . ."

"Yes, it would." Reschke looked sad.

"You've forgotten, Herr Reschke. We've struck a deal, even if our clients haven't."

Reschke brightened, swung out of his chair, went to a shelf, and took down a bottle of Scotch. He poured liquor into two shot glasses, a ritual of many years' standing.

"What time did we say for Kleist?" he asked.
"Eleven o'clock Friday night."
"I regret it's not a package crossing."
"Yes. I wonder what happened with your people?"
"I have no idea." Reschke smiled at his old adversary. "But if I did, I wouldn't tell you."

CHAPTER TWELVE

THREE days before his scheduled departure for New York, Mike returned to his apartment from a neighborhood restaurant feeling oddly restless. In the kitchen, he opened the refrigerator, peered about, closed the door again. He raised the room's small window, looked out at the night. Icy cold, clear skies, a splash of stars, not much wind.

What was bothering him? Perhaps that phone call yesterday from Delaney's wife. Walt, she had said, had received a call from some high official in Bonn, but he refused to discuss the nature of the conversation with her. Just a hunch, she said, but there might be some development in Mike's situation. So maybe he should not leave the apartment for long periods.

The telephone rang, an unnerving sound, perhaps because it rang so seldom these days. Mike lifted the receiver.

"Herr Simmons?"

"Yes."

"My name is Joachim Mertz. I don't know if—"

"Of course." Mike was alert at once. "Everyone knows you."

"Would you be available for a meeting at eleven tonight?"

"Yes. Eleven's fine." Hope shot upward. Gisela? "Where, Herr Mertz?" he asked eagerly.

"You know Friedrichstrasse at Kochstrasse?"

"Checkpoint Charlie? Sure."

"Good. This must remain confidential for another few hours, you understand, but the DDR is releasing someone you—"

"Frau Steinbrecher!"

"No, no." Mertz coughed, a ragged, nervous clearing of the throat. "It is Professor Kleist who is coming across."

"Oh." Mike's disappointment saturated the line.

"I'm calling on you because of your connections with the laboratories in the U.S.A. that await Otto Kleist and his data."

"Of course, I'll be glad to help." Mike tried to pump some vitality into his voice.

"If you could assist me while I get the professor settled..."

"No problem. I'd like to help in any way I can."

"My government will be in your debt, Herr Simmons. So, I'll meet you in front of the Haus Am Checkpoint Charlie at eleven. I'll be wearing a black overcoat with fur collar and a blue cap."

It took a force of will for Mike to part from his own deep disappointment and turn toward the good news of Otto Kleist's coming release. Slowly adjusting to the prospect of meeting the famous professor, he set about preparing himself. With two hours to go, he settled down to peruse the thick file folder that he and Hilde had filled with news clippings about Kleist. The professor would surely want some of these.

Some minutes after ten he bundled up the clippings, put on his overcoat, gloves, and fur hat, and walked down to the street. He hailed a cab and rode through the center of Berlin out to the drab commercial area near Checkpoint Charlie.

The night seemed to crackle as he stepped from the cab at Friedrichstrasse and Kochstrasse. A light snow had fallen in the afternoon, dusting cars, trees, and pavement. Though moonless, the night was clear. Hundreds of stars etched the velvet sky.

At the control point, overhead floodlights burned through the night, lighting the area like a movie set. In front of the Haus Am Checkpoint Charlie, the museum that chronicled the Wall's brutal history, a lone man paced up and down. He wore a black overcoat with fur-trimmed collar and a blue cap, and, like Mike, he carried a folder under his arm.

"Herr Mertz?"

"Herr Simmons." His breath climbed in the night like smoke.

Mike nodded. They shook hands.

Since Joachim Mertz continued to pace, Mike fell into stride beside him. They walked several minutes in silence, up to a stand of white birches near the East-West dividing line and back again toward the blue glow of the subway station across Kochstrasse. Save for the military men inside the control huts and the West Berlin police at their post, no one was to be seen.

"You've been in contact with the other side, Herr Mertz?"

"With my counterpart in East Berlin. We reached agreement on the professor. The Federal Republic is buying his freedom."

"How much?"

"One hundred and twenty thousand marks. They gouge us."

"Was there any news of Frau Steinbrecher?"

"Yes. At first they hinted they might sell her too, but when I started to bargain for her, Volpe's people . . ."

"Any chance she may be released soon?"

"Oh, I would think not." Mertz coughed nervously. "They seldom reverse themselves twice. Point of pride."

A police officer stepped outside his command post. "A phone call for you, Herr Mertz." He held the door open. "Herr Reschke."

"*Ach.*" Mertz hurried into the station.

Mike continued to walk, his breath misting in the cold. Ahead of him, on the East Berlin side, the garish light spilled over a gray concrete watchtower, where two soldiers looked out through binoculars, apparently at Mike. Minutes passed. Mike walked as far as the white dividing line, turned, and tramped back to Kochstrasse. He made two full turns, a matter of ten minutes or so, before Joachim Mertz came out of the police station.

"False alarm. Kleist is not coming across tonight," he said. "He has had the flu and he told my counterpart that he wishes to wait until tomorrow for the crossing."

"Do you believe that?"

"From anyone else over there, I might not. But Herr Reschke I believe. We never lie to each other."

"Well, I want out of this cold. Let's grab one of those cabs." Mike motioned with his head. "I'll buy you a drink."

"Another night, perhaps," said Mertz with a sudden, broad smile. "Right now you have more important business. The comrades have done what I said they wouldn't. They've reversed themselves again. The lady doctor of chemistry is being—"

"Gisela!" Mike seized Mertz by the arms.

Mertz was still grinning. "She's going through the controls this minute on the other side with Herr Reschke."

Mike felt a rush of joy, a wild urge to laugh, shout, and cry all at once. "But why? What happened to make them change their minds?"

"Thank the good professor," said Mertz. He stamped his feet on the icy sidewalk. "In his final interview today with the *Stasi*, Kleist warned that the minute he crossed to this side he would launch his own campaign to free Gisela."

"Bless him. . . . But why didn't they just put him back under house arrest and keep 'em both?"

"They couldn't. I turned over the one hundred and twenty thousand marks for him this morning. Reschke and I have an ironclad agreement. Once the money passes, no changes can be made by either side." Mertz consulted his watch. "She's due to cross in just three—"

Mike broke away from the lawyer and ran toward the white line that separated the two Berlins. He raced up the steps of the nearby observation platform and peered over the railing toward the DDR border compound. He focused his sight on the iron gate, last exit from East German controls.

He caught his breath. Just beyond the glare of the floodlights stood three figures—a civilian, it seemed, flanked by two officers in gray uniforms. The military men moved aside and the third person stepped forward. A pause. Then the gate creaked open.

Yes, yes. It was Gisela, walking into the bizarre ivory light. She wore a tailored brown coat and a felt hat with a jaunty feather, the same outfit in which she had been kidnapped. Mike brushed tears from his eyes.

"Gisela!" He shouted it from the platform.

She looked up. "Miguel!" She began to run. He rushed down the steps and ran toward her.

They met on West Berlin terrain, just a few feet inside the line. They held each other tightly. He found her lips. And the love that he had suppressed came surging up in a great, rich flood.

"Ahmm." Lawyer Mertz cleared his throat. "There will be some papers to . . ."

Crossing in Berlin

They separated and Mike introduced the attorney to Gisela. She had no prison pallor; the cold had put roses in her cheeks.

"Welcome to the sunny side once more." Mertz handed her the folder. "This time you must be processed in the regular manner. You're expensive cargo, you know." He smiled thinly.

"How much was paid for me?"

"We haven't paid yet, but we will. Forty thousand marks."

"Forty!" She beamed at Mike and her eyes glistened. "So, *mi amor*, you see how valuable I am?"

"The word is priceless," Mike said.

Mertz escorted them to the intersection. He motioned them to a taxi, but Gisela demurred.

"Not just yet, Herr Mertz. There is something I must do."

Hooking her arm in Mike's, she walked back through the Allied control area and guided him to the observation platform. They mounted the steps and stood by the railing, gazing down at the Wall and its lethal paraphernalia to thwart escape: mines, spikes, slabs, and barbed wire. They faced it without speaking. From the East German watchtower, a guard surveyed them through binoculars. Mike shivered. The cold was piercing, and he wondered about the demons and those other walls that plagued his nights. Would they vanish for good, now that he and Gisela had triumphed over the Wall of Berlin?

"That's enough." She tugged at his arm. "I had to see it one last time. Now I must put all that out of my life forever."

Mike took off his glove to hold her chilled hand, which began to warm in his grasp. Hand in hand they left the platform and walked to the waiting taxi.

The Human Side of the Story
by Laura Bergquist Knebel

Long before we married fifteen years ago, I knew Fletcher Knebel as a rarity in the fiercely competitive Washington press corps. We both covered the White House for *Look* magazine in the electric days of the Kennedy administration, and Fletch generously shared his political expertise and contacts. So when he plunged into novel writing with *Seven Days in May* (co-authored with Charles W. Bailey), I sent him a fan note. Since then, I've watched him spin ten novels.

The idea for *Crossing in Berlin* was sparked by a visit to Germany and his first chilling glimpse of the Wall. "It seemed huge, sinister, sullen," he said, "and a symbol of the psychological barriers we humans build between ourselves." He decided to write a new thriller, different from most novels of espionage and intrigue—about "how that Wall reflects our dark, subterranean urge to shrink away from life and the world, just as a whole state, East Germany, has withdrawn behind its concrete and steel-mesh barriers."

Fletcher Knebel

Fletch's life changes radically when a novel is in progress. While writing *Crossing in Berlin* he still lived bodily in our house in Princeton, New Jersey, but in spirit he had moved to Germany. His study was cluttered with books on the divided nation. And back he went, with the old reportorial passion for authenticity, making three more trips to explore, to probe, and to check out names, streets, slang, and attitudes.

As *Crossing* took shape, his typewriter began rattling at nine a.m., weekends included. His ideas, he tells me, "strike clearly and cleanly, like a sudden stroke of lightning, or sunshine."

I always read Fletch's manuscripts, furiously scribbling my notes and questions in the margins. So I know *Crossing*'s two central characters well, the American Mike and the East German Gisela. Still, I wonder: How did such very real people ever come out of that rattling typewriter in the study?

PHOTO BY MARY CROSS

Acknowledgments

Page 94, line 18; 99, lines 11-12: from the song "Careless Hands," words and music by Bob Hilliard and Carl Sigman. Copyright 1949 by Edwin H. Morris & Company, A Division of MPL Communications, Inc., © renewed 1976 by Better-Half Music Co., © renewed 1977 by Edwin H. Morris & Company, A Division of MPL Communications, Inc. International copyright secured. All rights reserved. Used by permission.

Page 95, lines 1-2: from the song "(Ghost) Riders in the Sky," words and music by Stan Jones, copyright 1949 by Edwin H. Morris & Company, A Division of MPL Communications, Inc., © renewed 1977 by Edwin H. Morris & Company, A Division of MPL Communications, Inc. International copyright secured. All rights reserved. Used by permission.

Page 126: portrait of Louisa Catherine Adams, oil by Charles Bird King, c. 1824, courtesy of the Smithsonian Institution, National Collection of Fine Arts. Gift of Mary Louisa Adams Clement in memory of her mother, Louisa Catherine Adams Clement.

Page 126: portrait of John Quincy Adams, oil by John Singleton Copley, 1796, courtesy of the Museum of Fine Arts, Boston. Gift of Mrs. Charles Francis Adams.

Pages 276, 332: maps by George Buctel.